D0648288

THE ALKALOIDS

Chemistry and Physiology

VOLUME IV

THE ALKALOIDS
Chemistry and Physiology

Edited by

R. H. F. Manske
Dominion Rubber Research Laboratory
Guelph, Ontario

H. L. Holmes
Cambridge, Massachusetts

VOLUME IV

1954
ACADEMIC PRESS INC., PUBLISHERS
NEW YORK

ACADEMIC PRESS INC.
111 Fifth Avenue, New York, New York 10003

United Kingdom Edition published by
ACADEMIC PRESS INC. (LONDON) LTD.
Berkeley Square House, London W.1

LIBRARY OF CONGRESS CATALOG CARD NUMBER: 50-5522

Second Printing, 1968

PRINTED IN THE UNITED STATES OF AMERICA

PREFACE

The present volume contains an account of the chemistry and biosynthesis of the various classes of isoquinolines in ten separate chapters; we hope that it will serve as a textbook in this field of chemistry.

The two additional chapters on two classes of alkaloids whose structures are as yet unknown are designed to provide an up-to-date critical summary.

This completes the chemistry portion of our series, except for a chapter on miscellaneous alkaloids which will appear in Volume V along with the chapters on pharmacology.

Once more we are pleased to thank not only our fellow chemists for their generous reception of our past volumes but also our very conscientious and patient contributors. We also thank the many authors who have sent us reprints of their recent work to aid us in the compilation of a supplement.

R. H. F. M.
H. L. H.

March, 1954

CONTENTS

Preface v

The Biosynthesis of Isoquinolines 1

By R. H. F. MANSKE, *Dominion Rubber Research Laboratory, Guelph, Ontario*

Simple Isoquinoline Alkaloids

By L. RETI, *Buenos Aires, Argentina*

I. Introduction 7
II. The Anhalonium Alkaloids 8
III. Extraction and Separation of the Anhalonium Alkaloids 9
IV. The Anhalonium Isoquinolines 10
V. Structure and Synthesis of the Anhalonium Alkaloids 13
VI. Other Natural Simple Isoquinolines 15
VII. Pharmacology 19
VIII. References 20

Cactus Alkaloids

By L. RETI, *Buenos Aires, Argentina*

I. Introduction 23
II. Constitution and Occurrence 23
III. Location of the Alkaloids in Tissues of the Cacti 25
IV. Extraction of Cactus Alkaloids 25
V. References 26

The Benzylisoquinoline Alkaloids

By ALFRED BURGER, *University of Virginia, Charlottesville, Virginia*

I. Introduction 29
II. Papaverine 30
III. Laudanosine 48
IV. Monophenolic Bases of the Laudanosine Type 57
V. Biogenesis of the Benzylisoquinoline Alkaloids 69
VI. References 71

The Protoberberine Alkaloids

By R. H. F. MANSKE, *Dominion Rubber Research Laboratory, Guelph, Ontario*, and WALTER R. ASHFORD, *Merck & Co., Ltd., Montreal, Quebec*

I. Introduction 78
II. Occurrence 78
III. Berberine 78
IV. Canadine 91
V. Palmatine 92
VI. Shobakunine 93
VII. Tetrahydropalmatine 93
VIII. Jatrorrhizine and Columbamine 95
IX. Corypalmine and Isocorypalmine 95

X. Scoulerine . . . 97
XI. Sinactine . . . 98
XII. Cheilanthifoline . . . 98
XIII. Ophiocarpine . . . 99
XIV. Capaurine and Capauridine . . . 100
XV. Capaurimine . . . 102
XVI. Stylopine and Coptisine . . . 102
XVII. Corydaline . . . 103
XVIII. Corybulbine . . . 107
XIX. Isocorybulbine . . . 108
XX. Thalictrifoline . . . 108
XXI. Thalictricavine . . . 108
XXII. Nandinine . . . 109
XXIII. Worenine . . . 110
XXIV. Umbellatine . . . 111
XXV. Neprotine . . . 111
XXVI. Thalictrine . . . 112
XXVII. Coreximine . . . 112
XXVIII. References . . . 113

The Aporphine Alkaloids

By R. H. F. MANSKE, *The Dominion Rubber Research Laboratory, Guelph, Ontario*

I. Introduction . . . 119
II. Glaucine . . . 120
III. Glaucentrine . . . 122
IV. Boldine . . . 123
V. Laurotetanine . . . 125
VI. N-Methyllaurotetanine . . . 126
VII. Dicentrine . . . 126
VIII. Actinodaphnine . . . 127
IX. Domesticine . . . 128
X. Nantenine . . . 128
XI. Phanostenine . . . 129
XII. Crebanine . . . 129
XIII. Corydine . . . 129
XIV. Isocorydine . . . 130
XV. Corytuberine . . . 130
XVI. Suaveoline . . . 132
XVII. Bulbocapnine . . . 132
XVIII. Laurepukine . . . 134
XIX. Isothebaine . . . 135
XX. Tuduranine . . . 136
XXI. Laureline . . . 137
XXII. Pukateine . . . 138
XXIII. Anolobine . . . 139
XXIV. Stephanine . . . 141
XXV. Roemerine . . . 141
XXVI. Anonaine . . . 142
XXVII. Other Aporphines . . . 142
XXVIII. References . . . 143

The Protopine Alkaloids

By R. H. F. MANSKE, *Dominion Rubber Research Laboratory, Guelph, Ontario*

I. Introduction . . . 147
II. Occurrence . . . 148
III. Cryptopine . . . 149
IV. Cryptocavine . . . 155
V. Protopine . . . 157
VI. Allocryptopine . . . 159
VII. Hunnemanine . . . 160
VIII. Cryptopalmatine . . . 161
IX. Corycavine . . . 162
X. Corycavamine . . . 163
XI. Corycavidine . . . 163
XII. References . . . 164

Phthalideisoquinoline Alkaloids

By JAROSLAV STANEK, *Charles University, Praha, Czechoslovakia,*
and R. H. F. MANSKE, *Dominion Rubber Research Laboratory, Guelph, Ontario*

I. Introduction . . . 168
II. Constitution . . . 169
III. Syntheses . . . 180
IV. Discovery, Isolation, and Properties . . . 183
V. Physiology and Pharmacology . . . 189
VI. References . . . 190

Bisbenzylisoquinoline Alkaloids

By MARSHALL KULKA, *Dominion Rubber Research Laboratory, Guelph, Ontario*

I. Introduction . . . 199
II. Alkaloids Containing One Diphenyl Ether Linkage . . . 203
III. Alkaloids Containing Two Diphenyl Ether Linkages . . . 211
IV. Alkaloids Containing Three Diphenyl Ether Linkages . . . 237
V. References . . . 243

The Cularine Alkaloids

By R. H. F. MANSKE, *Dominion Rubber Research Laboratory, Guelph, Ontario*

I. Introduction . . . 249
II. Cularine . . . 249
III. Cularimine . . . 251
IV. Cularidine . . . 252
V. References . . . 252

α-Naphthaphenanthridine Alkaloids

By R. H. F. MANSKE, *Dominion Rubber Research Laboratory, Guelph, Ontario*

I. Introduction . . . 253
II. Occurrence . . . 253
III. Structure . . . 256
IV. Pharmacology . . . 261
V. References . . . 262

The Erythrophleum Alkaloids

By G. Dalma, *Research Laboratory, ATANOR S.A.M., Buenos Aires, Argentina*

I. Isolation 265
II. Properties of the Alkaloids 266
III. Pharmacology 271
IV. References 272

The Aconitum and Delphinium Alkaloids

By E. S. Stern, *J. F. Macfarlan and Co. Ltd., Edinburgh, Scotland*

I. Introduction 275
II. The Chemistry of the Atisines 278
III. The Chemistry of the Aconitines 292
IV. The Monoester Alkaloids Derived from Methoxyl-rich Amino Alcohols Analogous to the Aconines 320
V. "Miscellaneous" Alkaloids Isolated from Aconitum and Delphinium Species 328
VI. References 330
Author Index 335
Subject Index 350

CHAPTER 25

The Biosynthesis of Isoquinolines

R. H. F. MANSKE

Dominion Rubber Research Laboratory, Guelph, Ontario

It can be said that the exact mechanism by which a plant cell elaborates an isoquinoline alkaloid is not yet known. Nevertheless the cumulative circumstantial evidence which has been amassed is so complete that a series of biosynthetic reactions can be written which leave only detail for further research. It was Pictet (1) in 1906 who first drew attention to some similarities of and possible synthetic routes to a number of alkaloids. The following four decades witnessed a gradual realization that alkaloids are derivable from the naturally occurring common precursors such as amino acids. Biological oxidations and reductions as well as carboxylations came to light particularly in studies with animals. For example it was demonstrated that phenylalanine is convertible into tyrosine (2) in the normal rat, thus lending strong support to the supposition that dioxyphenylalanine (dopa) (3, 4) is in fact derived or derivable from tyrosine and that the trihydroxy compound may also be so derived. Having available 3,4-dihydroxyphenylalanine it is only necessary to assume that the plant cell can effect the changes of decarboxylation, deamination, and oxidation to arrive at the two intermediates, 3,4-dihydroxyphenethylamine (I) and 3,4-dihydroxyphenacetaldehyde (II), necessary for the synthesis of norlaudanosine (III) (5). The combination of a β-arylethylamine and

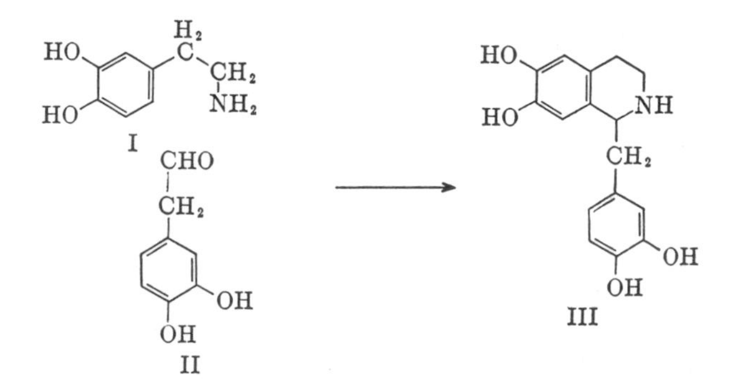

a carbonyl compound to yield isoquinolines has been the subject of a series of researches by Schöpf and by Hahn and their associates (6, 7, 8, 9). The free aldehydes as well as the corresponding pyruvic acids condense with the amines under conditions which might prevail in the plant cell, although the participation of enzymes is not excluded (10, 11) because of the fact that practically all 1-substituted isoquinolines occur in an optically active form. Those isoquinolines in which there is no substituent in position 1 are theoretically derivable from formaldehyde as second component. It is very doubtful whether formaldehyde ever occurs in plant cells even in very low concentrations, so that some equivalent must be looked for. Supplying plants with possible labeled precursors may help in solving this problem although it should be borne in mind that the anabolic facilities of plants are very considerable. Consequently a large number of compounds which may be regarded as formaldehyde equivalents are easily suggested, the more obvious being glyoxylic acid and formic acid, the former having the merit that it is known to be widely distributed in vegetable matter and that decarboxylation may take place during or after condensation. In the following discussion the term "formaldehyde" will be understood to mean any compound which, after a series of events, will produce the same result that might be anticipated with the use of formaldehyde. The subsequent changes involving methylation of nitrogen or of oxygen, and methylenation of oxygen require only those reactions which have become so well known (12).

It is reasonable to assume that the benzylisoquinolines are the intermediates which a plant must synthesize before it can elaborate most of the other isoquinolines.

The aporphines are derivable from III by the removal of two hydrogen atoms, one from each of the benzene nuclei, and III can yield two different

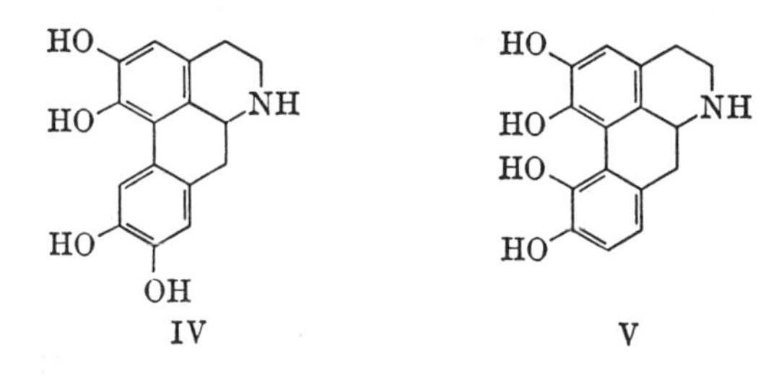

aporphines (IV or V) depending upon whether ring closure takes place ortho or para to a hydroxyl (13). In general a particular plant elaborates aporphines of either one or the other type, but a number are now known which elaborate representatives of both types (14, 15, 16), and it is more reasonable to assume a common precursor than to envision two separate sets of precursors. It should be noted that the final oxidative ring closure (i.e., dehydrogenation between the benzene nuclei of III) requires positions activated by an ortho or a para hydroxyl, and the natural occurrence of both laureline (VI) and pukateine (VII) (17) can best be explained by assuming

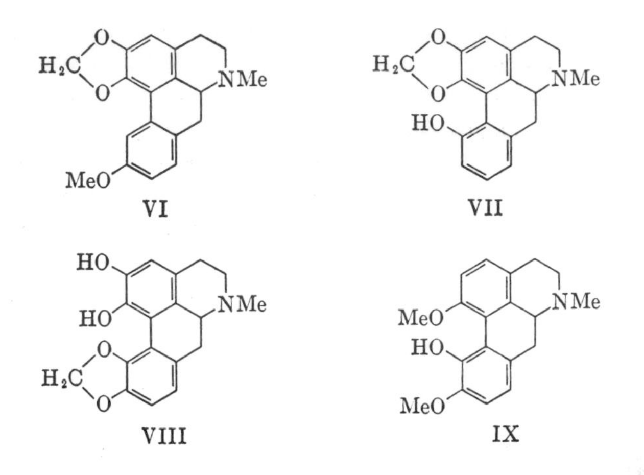

the ultimate elimination of a hydroxyl from the intermediate tetrahydroxy compound formed from III. Convincing credence is lent to this view because of the copresence of laurepukine (VIII) in the same plant. It is very probable that the biosynthesis of isothebaine (IX) (18) is also via a tetrahydroxy compound because the original ring closure to a benzylisoquinoline (hetero ring formation) meta to a hydroxyl is not possible (19).

Until recently, the hetero ring closure of a benzylisoquinoline ortho to a hydroxyl was not known, but the formation of cularine (XI) from X by the removal of two hydrogens offers a satisfactory biosynthesis of this alka-

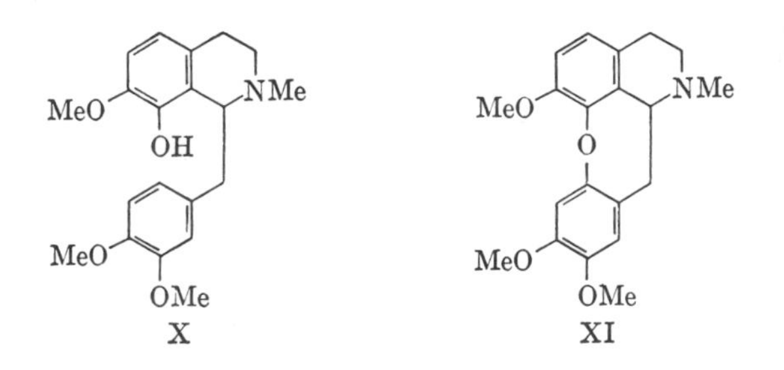

loid (20). This is the first known example in which diphenyl ether formation in alkaloids has proceeded by the abstraction of a hydrogen para to a hydroxyl. In the bisbenzylisoquinolines such ether formation usually takes place ortho to a hydroxyl whether the ultimate alkaloid is of the double

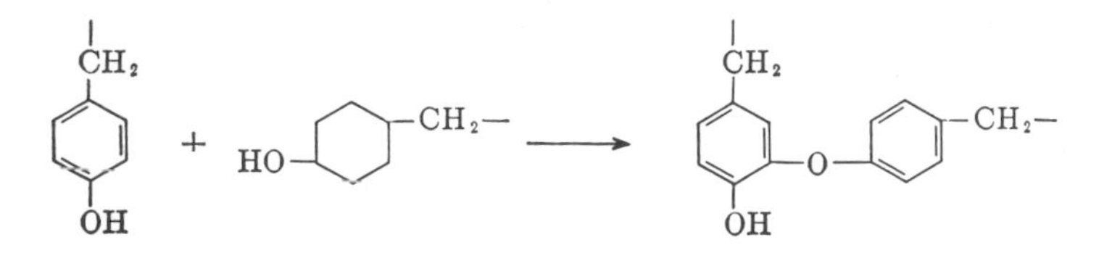

diphenyl ether type with the large rings or of the single diphenyl ether open type. The alkaloid magnolamine has recently been shown to be an example in which diphenyl ether formation is the result of the abstraction of a hydrogen para to a hydroxyl (21, 22).

The protoberberines are examples of the formation of a second isoquinoline ring by a reaction which must be strictly analogous to the first step although only "formaldehyde" is thus far known as the condensing agent. Here, however, the ring closure, with one known exception, takes place in a position ortho to the hydroxyl (III → XII). The attempted condensation

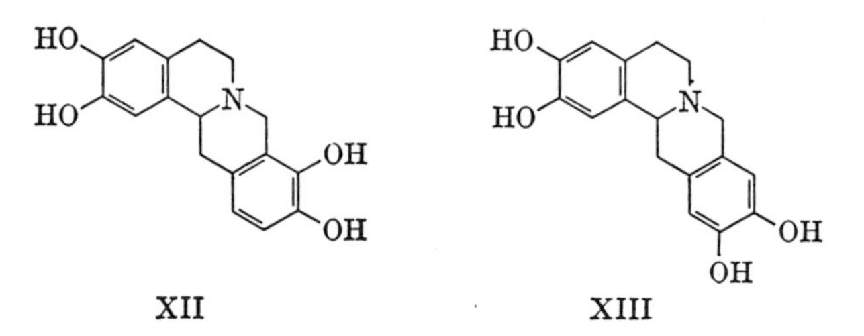

in vitro always yields the isomer XIII when the hydroxyls are methylated, and the recent observation that coreximine (16, 23) has the oxygens in the positions shown in XIII lends strong support to the supposition that the benzylisoquinolines are also the precursors here. A still more convincing observation is the isolation of corpaverine (XIV) from a plant which elaborates protoberberines almost exclusively (24). It is quite evident that this

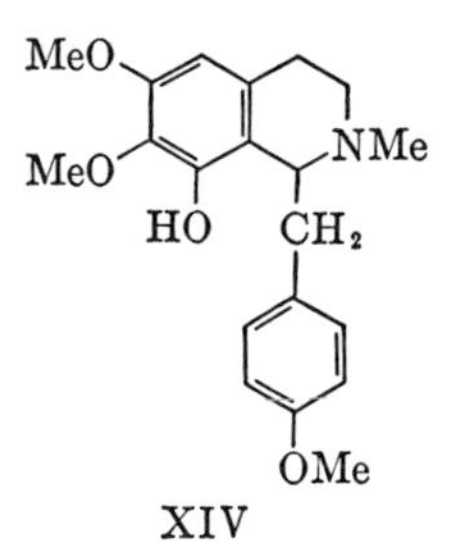

alkaloid survives as the ultimate product because there is no activating hydroxy ortho or para to the position at which condensation could take place (benzyl nucleus).

The presence of a methyl group in position 13 (the position of the hydroxyl in XV) in the protoberberines and in the protopine bases is readily explicable. It may be assumed that the aldehyde II on condensation with "formaldehye" can give rise either to a hydroxymethyl derivative or to a methylene compound, which upon hydrogenolysis or reduction, respectively, ould generate the *C*-methyl drivative of II and consequently the methyl group would ultimately appear at position 13. There is the closest possible analogy for the above-mentioned hydroxymethyl derivative in the well-known tropic acid, $C_6H_5 \cdot CH(CH_2OH)COOH$.

The protoberberines, however, are not in themselves necessarily end products in all plants. They are very susceptible to oxidation, and the two most likely points of attack are those which would give rise to XV and XVI. The former (XV) is ophiocarpine, an alkaloid accompanying other protoberberines (25) as well as phthalideisoquinolines, and the further oxidation of a methylene to a carboxyl and *N*-methylation complete the syn-

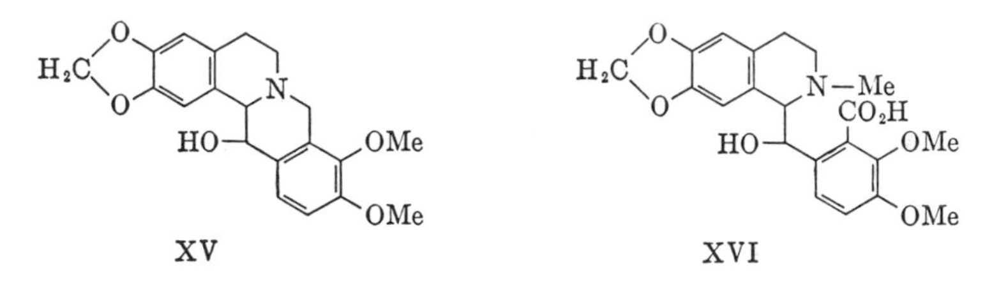

thesis of these lactonic alkaloids. However, the 1-position of the isoquinoline is also vulnerable to chemical attack, and if XV is hydrated in the appropriate manner the product may be XVII, which on *N*-methylation

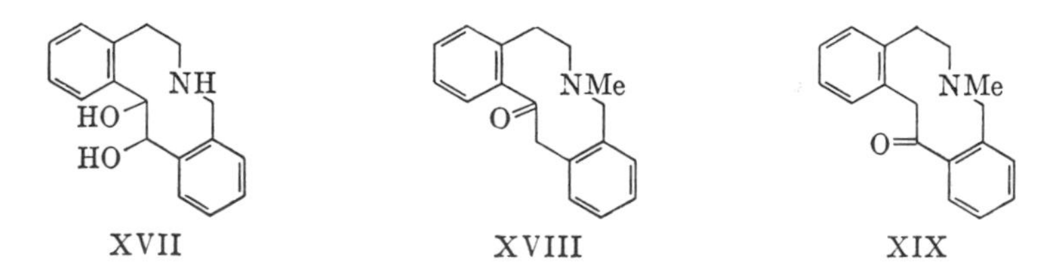

and loss of water can give rise to either XVIII or XIX, that is, either the protopine type or the cryptocavine type. It is, of course, possible to arrive at XVIII by oxidation at only one carbon followed by *N*-methylation, and such a mechanism would account for the genesis of the protopine group but another kind of mechanism would be required for XIX. It is simpler to assume that XVII is the intermediate for both forms.

The chelidonine group of alkaloids cannot conveniently be looked upon as derived from benzylisoquinolines. In view, however, of the copresence of chelidonine with those already mentioned, it is to be expected that the ultimate precursors are the same. It can be assumed that the dihydroxyphenylalanine is converted to a substituted phenylacetaldehyde, and two molecules of this can give rise to the aldol XX, which could conceivably ring-close to XXI, in strict analogy with the mechanism which must be involved in the well-known formation of β-phenylnaphthalene from phenyl-

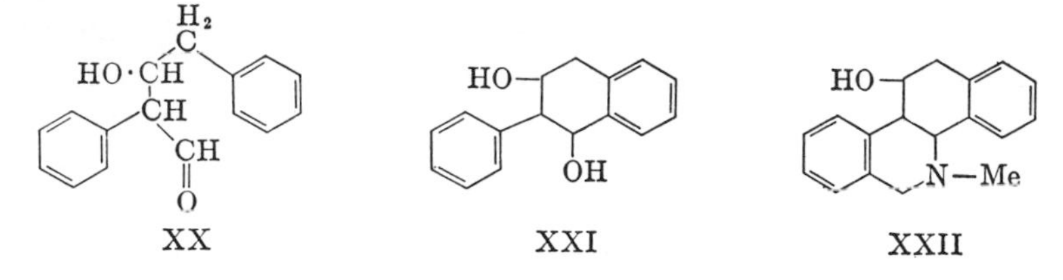

acetaldehyde. Replacement of the thus formed hydroxyl by amino or methylamino followed by ring closure with "formaldehyde" is sufficient to form the nucleus (XXII) of chelidonine and related alkaloids. Turner and Woodward (26) have suggested a biosynthetic route to the benzophenanthridenes from the berberines, but the position of the secondary hydroxyl would not by this mechanism be unambiguously fixed.

In conclusion it is admitted that the biosynthetic route of no alkaloid is known with certainty. The main routes are nevertheless known with a reasonable degree of assurance, and it is confidently expected that much of the detail will be revealed when the tools of labeled carbon and nitrogen compounds are brought to bear on the problem.

References

1. A. Pictet, *Arch. Pharm.*, **244**, 389 (1906).
2. A. R. Moss and R. Schoenheimer, *J. Biol. Chem.*, **135**, 415 (1940).
3. T. Torquati, *Arch. farmacol. sper.*, **15**, 308 (1913).
4. M. Guggenheim. *Z. physiol. Chem.*, **88**, 279 (1913).
5. E. Winterstein and G. Trier, Die Alkaloide, Gebr. Bornträger, Berlin, 1910.
6. G. Hahn and F. Rumpf, *Ber.*, **71**, 2141 (1938).
7. G. Hahn and O. Schales, *Ber.*, **68**, 24 (1935).
8. G. Hahn and H. Wassmuth, *Ber.*, **67**, 696 (1934).
9. C. Schöpf and H. Bayerle, *Ann.*, **513**, 190 (1934).
10. E. Späth and F. Kesztler, *Ber.*, **68**, 1663 (1935).
11. L. Reti, in L. Zechmeister, Progress in the Chemistry of Organic Natural Products, Springer, Vienna, 1950. Vol. VI, p. 268.
12. E. Leete and L. Marion, *Can. J. Chem.*, **31**, 126 (1953).
13. R. Robinson, *J. Chem. Soc.*, **111**, 876 (1917).
14. M. Freund and W. Josephi, *Ber.*, **25**, 2411 (1892).
15. J. Gadamer, *Arch. Pharm.*, **249**, 224 (1911).
16. R. H. F. Manske, *Can. J. Research*, **8**, 592 (1933).
17. G. Barger and A. Girardet, *Helv. Chim. Acta*, **14**, 481 (1931).
18. W. Klee, *Arch. Pharm.*, **252**, 211 (1914).
19. E. Schlittler and J. Müller, *Helv. Chim. Acta*, **31**, 1119 (1948).
20. R. H. F. Manske, *J. Am. Chem. Soc.*, **72**, 55 (1950).
21. N. F. Proskurnina, *J. Gen. Chem.* (*U.S.S.R.*), **16**, 129 (1946).
22. M. Tomita, E. Fujita, and T. Nakamura, *J. Pharm. Soc. Japan*, **71**, 1075 (1951).
23. R. H. F. Manske, *J. Am. Chem. Soc.*, **72**, 4796 (1950).
24. R. H. F. Manske, *J. Am. Chem. Soc.*, **74**, 2864 (1952).
25. R. H. F. Manske, *Can. J. Research*, **B17**, 51 (1939).
26. R. B. Turner, and R. B. Woodward, in The Alkaloids, Academic Press, New York, 1953, Vol. III, p. 57.

CHAPTER 26

Simple Isoquinoline Alkaloids

L. RETI

Buenos Aires, Argentina

		Page
I.	Introduction	7
II.	The Anhalonium Alkaloids	8
III.	Extraction and Separation of the Anhalonium Alkaloids	9
IV.	The Anhalonium Isoquinolines	10
	1. Anhalamine	10
	2. Anhalinine	10
	3. Anhalidine	10
	4. Anhalonidine	10
	5. Pellotine	10
	6. *O*-Methyl-*d*-anhalonidine	12
	7. Anhalonine	12
	8. Lophophorine	12
V.	Structure and Synthesis of the Anhalonium Alkaloids	13
	1. Anhalonidine and Pellotine	13
	2. Anhalamine, Anhalidine, and Anhalinine	14
	3. Anhalonine and Lophophorine	14
VI.	Other Natural Simple Isoquinolines	15
	1. Carnegine	15
	2. Salsoline and Salsolidine	16
	3. Corypalline	18
	4. Hydrohydrastinine	18
	5. Hydrocotarnine	18
VII.	Pharmacology	19
	1. Anhalonine	19
	2. Anhalonidine	19
	3. Pellotine	19
	4. Lophophorine	19
	5. Carnegine	20
	6. Salsoline	20
VIII.	References	20

I. Introduction

The large group of alkaloids of the isoquinoline type ranges in complexity from the simple isoquinolines, more exactly defined as simple tetrahydroisoquinolines, with only one aromatic nucleus, to the complicated structures of the bisbenzylisoquinolines.

According to suggestions first made by Pictet and Spengler (1) and later by Späth (2), the substituted β-phenethylamines may be considered as the precursors of the simple isoquinolines. For example, mescaline and formaldehyde would yield anhalinine:

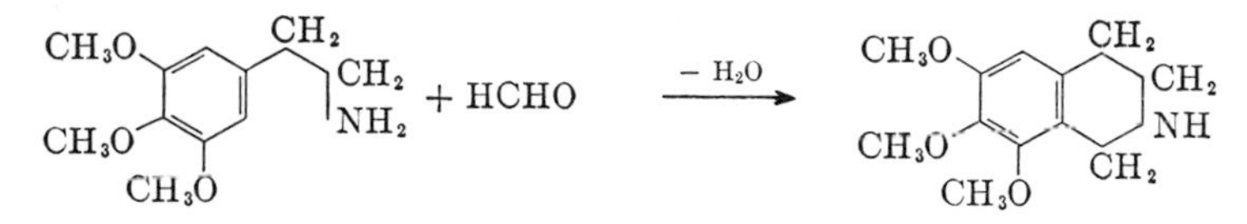

The simultaneous occurrence of substituted phenethylamines and isoquinoline derivatives in the same species (*Anhalonium lewinii* Hennings) and the facility with which similar ring closures are performed *in vitro*, under conditions which can be considered as being comparable to physiological ones, make the above hypothesis seem reasonable.

Comparatively few simple isoquinoline alkaloids have been found to occur naturally. Until now such compounds have been encountered in three or four species of the Cactaceae, in a Chenopodiaceae [*Salsola arbuscula* Pall. (*S. richteri* Karel)], in three species belonging to the family of the Fumariaceae [*Corydalis pallida* (Thunb.) Pers., *C. aurea* Willd., *C. tuberosa* DC.] and in one Papaveraceae (*Papaver somniferum* L.). While no doubt exists as to the native occurrence of the anhalonium and salsola isoquinolines, hydrohydrastinine and hydrocotarnine may have been artifacts from the benzylisoquinoline alkaloids of *Corydalis tuberosa* and *Papaver somniferum*.

II. The Anhalonium Alkaloids

In chemical literature *Anhalonium lewinii*, *A. williamsii* Lem. and *A. jourdanianum* Lewin are mentioned as different species. However, botanists definitely recognize only one species (*Anhalonium williamsii* Britton and Rose; *Lophophora williamsii* (Lemaire) Coulter). It would be worth while to investigate, using fresh and well-identified material, whether only pellotine is present in *A. williamsii*, as stated by Heffter. Such findings may give support to a revision of the taxonomy of these cacti.

These small cacti grow from central Mexico to southern Texas and are the material of an illicit commerce, carried out by some Indian tribes. The globular plants are sliced into three or four sections and then dried in the sun; these dried pieces are the "mescal buttons" of the trade. The plant is also known as pellote, peyote, and peyotl; it is called challote in Starr County, Texas. Interest in the cactus alkaloids arose when the remarkable use by the Indian tribes and the strange pharmacological properties of this little cactus became known. (See Mescaline, Vol. III, pp. 331–334, and Cactus Alkaloids, Vol. IV, chap. 27).

Eleven bases have been isolated from *Anhalonium lewinii*; three phenethylamines: mescaline, *N*-methylmescaline, and *N*-acetylmescaline (see β-Phenethylamines Vol. III, chap. 22); and eight simple isoquinolines: anhalamine, anhalidine, anhalinine, anhalonidine, pellotine, *O*-methyl-*d*-

anhalonidine, anhalonine, and lophophorine. An extensive study on various varieties of pellote and their alkaloidal contents was published by Beccari (3).

The clarification of the structure and the syntheses of all of the *Anhalonium* alkaloids must be credited to Späth and his coworkers. The accomplishment is all the more remarkable since Späth had to contend with a scarcity of material; several fundamental structures were determined on very small samples, left over from Heffter's and Heyl's experiments.

III. Extraction and Separation of the Anhalonium Alkaloids

Extraction of the drug and isolation of the alkaloids from *A. lewinii* have been described by Heffter (4), Kauder (5), Tomaso (6), and Späth and Becke (7), as well as by Steiner-Bernier (8).

The total alkaloidal content and the relative amount of the individual alkaloids varies widely; Heffter's figures (%) are: mescaline 6.3; anhalonidine 5.3; anhalonine 3.0; lophophorine 0.5; anhalamine 0.1. Späth's yields, working with old material, are much lower. The other bases occur in very small quantities: anhalamine 0.1 %; anhalinine 0.01 %; anhalidine 0.001 %.

In Heffter's opinion (9), *A. lewinii* does not contain pellotine, the main alkaloid of *A. williamsii*. Kauder found pellotine in the "mescal buttons," but Heffter attributes this to contamination by *A. williamsii*. This opinion is shared by Lewin (10). Morphologically, these species are difficult to separate. Späth and Becke's extraction and isolation process is as follows:

The drug is extracted with cold alcohol, and water is added to the sirup obtained by evaporating the extract *in vacuo*. The insoluble residue is treated with dilute hydrochloric acid. The solutions are united and filtered, and the filtrate is made alkaline with strong potassium hydroxide and extracted with ether. At this point the ether solution (*a*) contains the non-phenolic bases, while the aqueous solution (*b*) contains the phenolic alkaloids.

(*a*) After evaporation of the solvent, the free bases are distilled *in vacuo* and the mescaline recovered as its crystalline sulfate. The regenerated bases from the mother liquor are redistilled *in vacuo* and treated with dilute hydrochloric acid when anhalonine hydrochloride crystallizes. The filtrate, after concentration, yields anhalinine hydrochloride. By a complicated treatment of the mother liquors, a further quantity of mescaline and a little lophophorine can be obtained.

(*b*) The solution is acidified with hydrochloric acid, made alkaline again with excess potassium carbonate, and extracted exhaustively with ether. The residue from the extract is dissolved in dilute hydrochloric acid and anhalamine hydrochloride recovered. From the mother liquors anhalonidine hydrochloride is obtained by concentrating and adding alcohol. Pellotine may be recovered as picrate from the filtrate.

IV. The Anhalonium Isoquinolines

Table 1 includes all of the tetrahydroisoquinoline bases found in *Anhalonium lewinii*, and shows their structures and interrelations.

1. Anhalamine, $C_{11}H_{15}O_3N$

Anhalamine was first isolated by Kauder (5). According to Heffter (11) the drug contains 0.1 % anhalamine. The base crystallizes in microscopic needles, m.p. 189–191°; hydrochloride, from water with 2 H_2O, m.p. 258°; from alcohol with 1 H_2O; sulfate, colorless prisms, very soluble in water, less in alcohol; well-crystallized platinichloride and aurichloride; picrate, m.p. 237–240°; monobenzoyl derivative, m.p. 167.5°; dibenzoyl derivative, m.p. 128–129°; *N-m*-nitrobenzoyl derivative, m.p. 174–175°; *O,N*-dimethylanhalamine methiodide, m.p. 211.5–212.5°.

O-Methylanhalamine is termed anhalinine, and *N*-methylanhalamine is anhalidine.

2. Anhalinine, $C_{12}H_{17}O_3N$

Anhalinine was isolated by Späth and Becke (12) (yield, 0.01 %). Free base, m.p. 61–63°; hydrochloride, white crystals, m.p. 248–250°; picrate, m.p. 184–185°; aurichloride, m.p. 139–140°; platinichloride, m.p. 207–208°; *m*-nitrobenzoyl derivative, m.p. 147–148°; methiodide, m.p. 211.5–212.5°. *N*-methylanhalinine (= *O*-methylanhalidine) was prepared by Castrillon (63) by condensation of mescaline with formaldehyde by the Eschweiler-Clarke reaction. Hydrochloride, from abs. alcohol, m.p. 215–216°.

3. Anhalidine, $C_{12}H_{17}O_3N$

Anhalidine was found by Späth and Becke (13) (yield, 0.001 %). Free base, m.p. 131–133°; sublimes in high vacuum at 85–95°; *O*-methylanhalidine methiodide, m.p. 211.5–212.5°.

4. Anhalonidine, $C_{12}H_{17}O_3N$

Anhalonidine was discovered by Heffter (4). According to this author pellote contains as much as 5 % of the alkaloid. The free base crystallizes in small octahedra, m.p. 160–161°; picrate, m.p. 201–208°; *N*-benzoyl derivative, m.p. 189°; dibenzoyl derivative, m.p. 125–126°; *N-m*-nitrobenzoyl derivative, m.p. 207–208°; *N*-methylanhalonidine hydroiodide (pellotine hydroiodide), m.p. 125–130°; *N*-methylanhalonidine methiodide (pellotine methiodide), m.p. 199°.

5. Pellotine (*N*-Methylanhalonidine), $C_{13}H_{19}O_3N$

Pellotine was isolated by Heffter (9) from *Anhalonium williamsii* (0.74 % of the fresh plant) and was found later by Kauder (5) in *A. lewinii*. The

TABLE 1

TETRAHYDROISOQUINOLINE ALKALOIDS ISOLATED FROM ANHALONIUM LEWINII

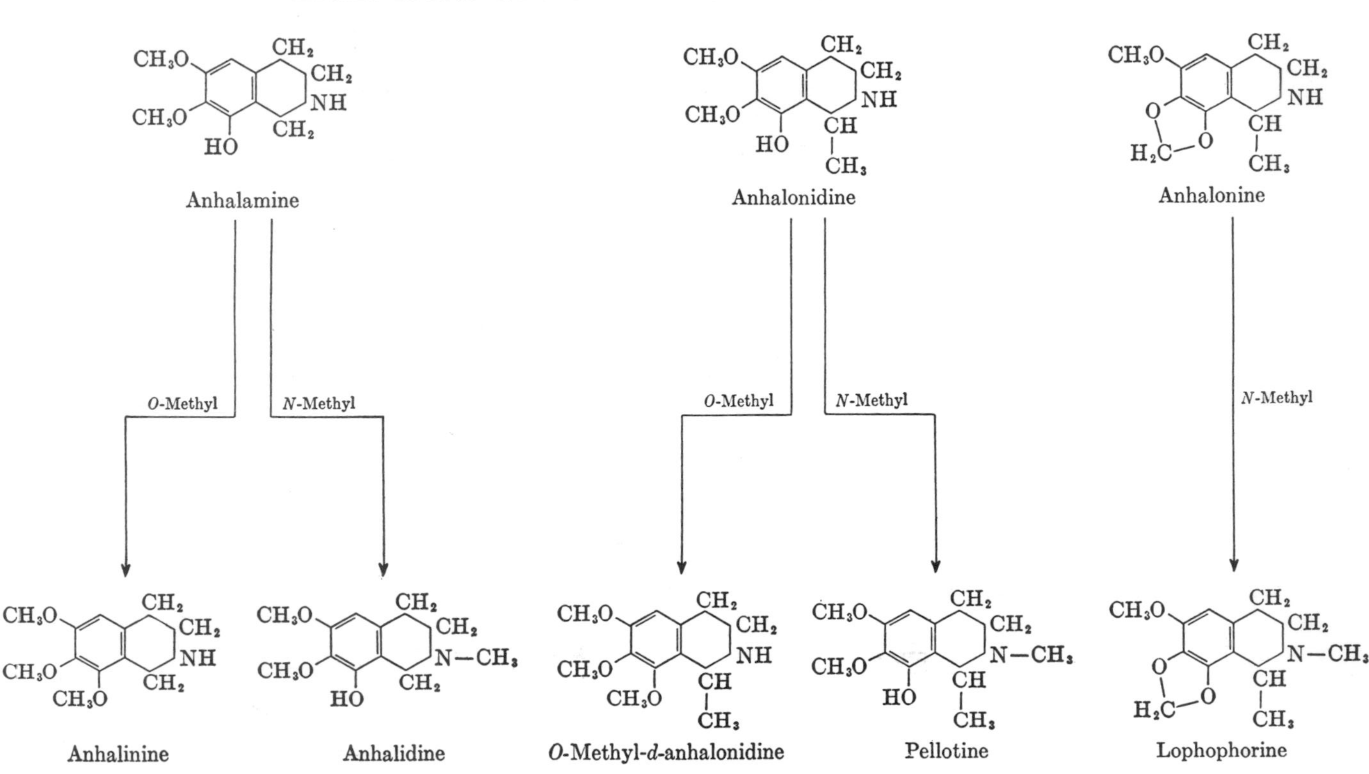

base is only slightly soluble in water; crystallizes from alcohol, m.p. 111–112°; the salts have a bitter taste; hydriodide, m.p. 125–130°; picrate, m.p. 167–169°; aurichloride, m.p. 147–148°; methiodide, m.p. 199°; *O*-methylpellotine methiodide, m.p. 226–227°.

Späth and Kesztler (14) prepared the optically active forms of pellotine and studied their racemization to determine whether the compound is present in the plant in the inactive form or is racemized when manipulated or during the aging of the drugs. By means of *d*-tartaric acid a fraction with $[\alpha]_D^{17}$ $-15.2°$ was obtained from racemic pellotine. Considering the ease with which this base undergoes racemization, the authors suppose that optically active pellotine is present in the plant. Nakada and Nishihara (51) prepared 6,7,8-trimethoxy-1-methyl-3,4-dihydro-isoquinoline, from which the methyl ether of pellotine was obtained.

6. *O*-Methyl-*d*-anhalonidine, $C_{13}H_{19}O_3N$

Späth and Bruck (15) found very small quantities of a new isoquinoline alkaloid in the mother liquors from the crystallization of the non-phenolic bases of *A. lewinii*. Its structure was established by analytical and synthetic methods. It is an oil, b.p. 140° (0.05 mm.); optically active, $[\alpha]_D^{16}$ $+20.7°$ (methanol). It yields a characteristic 2,4,6-trinitrobenzoyl derivative, m.p. 259–260°, $[\alpha]_D^{14}$ $+39.7°$ (methanol). The *dl*-form had been synthesized by Späth (2) as early as 1921.

7. Anhalonine, $C_{12}H_{15}O_3N$

Anhalonine was discovered by Lewin (16, 17, 10). According to Heffter (4) the drug contains about 3% anhalonine. The base crystallizes from light petroleum in needles, m.p. 85.5°, $[\alpha]_D$ $-56.3°$ (chloroform); hydrochloride, $[\alpha]_D^{17}$ $-41.9°$; *N*-methylanhalonine methiodide (lophophorine methiodide), m.p. 223°. Heated to its melting point the quaternary iodide is racemized and then melts at 242–243°.

Späth and Kesztler (18) prepared optically active forms of synthetic anhalonine base, with the following properties: *l*-anhalonine, m.p. 85–86°, $[\alpha]_D^{25}$ $-56.3°$ (chloroform); *d*-anhalonine, m.p. 84.5–85.5°, $[\alpha]_D^{25}$ $+56.7°$. The synthetic *l*-form, when methylated with formaldehyde and formic acid, gave an *N*-methyl derivative, $[\alpha]_D^{25}$ $-47.3°$ (chloroform), identical with natural lophophorine; picrate, m.p. 162–163°.

8. Lophophorine (*N*-Methyl-*l*-anhalonine), $C_{13}H_{17}O_3N$

Lophophorine was detected by Heffter (4) (yield 0.5%). It is an oily base, $[\alpha]_D$ $-47°$ (chloroform); hydrochloride, $[\alpha]_D^{17}$ $-9.47°$; picrate, m.p. 162–163°; methiodide, m.p. 223°; trinitro-*m*-cresolate of the quaternary compound, m.p. 171–172°; picrate of the quaternary compound, m.p. 211–212°.

V. Structure and Synthesis of the Anhalonium Alkaloids

1. Anhalonidine and Pellotine

Degradation experiments disproved Späth's first assumption that the other bases in "mescal buttons," were structurally similar to the then known mescaline. Späth, therefore, gathered experimental evidence for their structure, mainly of synthetic nature, working on the hypothesis that their structures were of the isoquinolinic pattern (2). Starting from *N*-acetylmescaline the following route was followed:

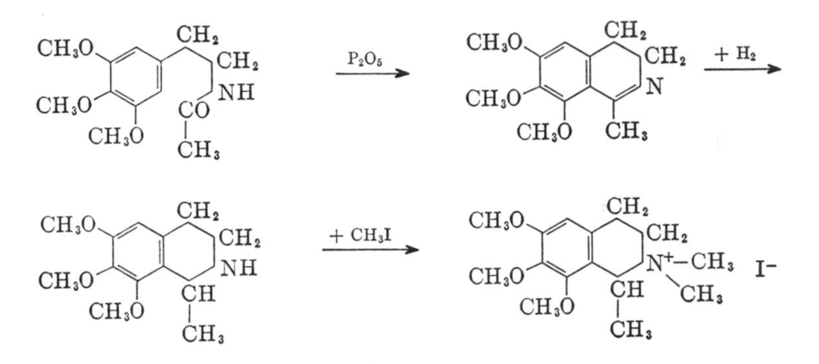

The quaternary iodide obtained was shown to be identical with *O*-methylpellotine methiodide. Pellotine and anhalonidine yield, on complete methylation, the same product, and, since anhalonidine is a secondary base, pellotine must be *N*-methylanhalonidine.

In a further study Späth (19) described the synthesis of anhalonidine and pellotine. Treatment of the *O*,*N*-diacetyl derivative of the 5-hydroxy-3,4-dimethyoxyphenethylamine with phosphorus pentoxide, and reduction of the resultant dihydroisoquinoline followed by hydrolysis of the *O*-acetyl group afforded anhalonidine. However, the position of the free hydroxyl group in anhalonidine (and pellotine) had still to be determined; two different structures were possible, since the ring closure might have taken place either in the ortho (I) or para position (II) to the hydroxy group:

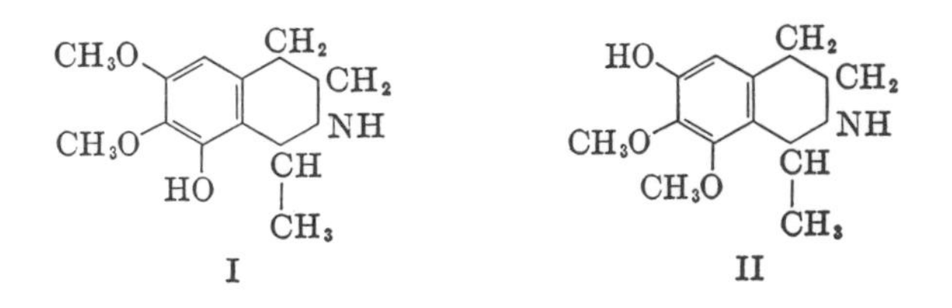

The correct anhalonidine structure (I) was proved by Späth and Passl

(20) as follows: Pellotine was converted into its *O*-ethyl ether, which on oxidation with permanganate yielded known 4,5-dimethoxy-3-ethoxyphthalic acid (III). This was confirmed using a different analytical method by Späth and Boschan (21), and by a new synthesis of pellotine (22).

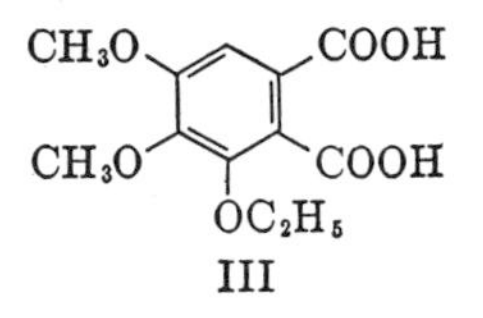

III

2. Anhalamine, Anhalidine, and Anhalinine

Anhalamine differs from anhalonidine by containing a —CH_2 less; Späth (2) therefore inferred that the former was a simple isoquinoline. *O*-methylanhalamine, later found to be a natural constituent of "mescal buttons" and called anhalinine (12), was obtained *in vitro* by condensing mescaline with formaldehyde. Späth and Röder (23) synthesized anhalamine by condensation of 5-benzyloxy-3,4-dimethoxyphenethylamine with formaldehyde, and further operations. The position of the free hydroxyl, however, still remained uncertain. The decision was made by Späth and Becke (24) who showed that *O,N*-diethylanhalamine, upon oxidation with permanganate, yielded the same 4,5-dimethoxy-3-ethoxyphthalic acid as was obtained by Späth and Passl (20) in the case of pellotine. All known phenolic tetrahydroisoquinolines which occur in the "mescal buttons" contain, therefore, the free hydroxyl in the 8-position.

Anhalidine is *N*-methylanhalamine (13).

3. Anhalonine and Lophophorine

It was demonstrated by Späth and Gangl (25) that, contrary to the belief of Heffter, lophophorine is *N*-methylanhalonine. They showed that both alkaloids contain a methylenedioxy group, and starting from the assumption of a methylisoquinoline structure and considering a biochemical relationship with the other *Anhalonium* bases of known constitution, the structures IV and V were considered for anhalonine:

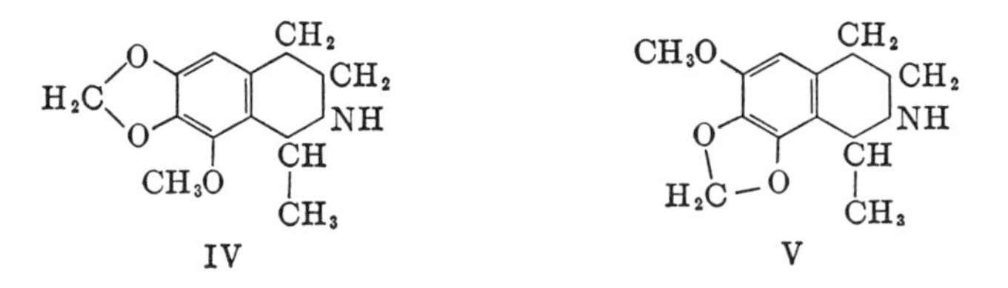

Compound IV was then prepared by the action of methyl magnesium iodide on cotarnine iodide by Freund and Reitz's method (26). The quaternary iodide of this tetrahydroisoquinoline base was found to be different from lophophorine methiodide. Compound V was similarly synthesized by condensing (in the presence of phosphorus pentoxide) acetylhomomyristicylamine to a dihydroisoquinoline, which was then reduced to the tetrahydro derivative. The quaternary iodide of V proved to be identical with inactive lophophorine methiodide. Eventually, structure V for lophophorine was confirmed by Späth and Becke (12) by the isolation of isocotarnic acid (3,4-methylenedioxy-5-methoxyphthalic acid) from the oxidation products of the quaternary base corresponding to anhalonine.

Späth and Kesztler (18) achieved the synthesis of anhalonine and lophophorine. Synthetic *dl*-anhalonine (25) was resolved into its optical antipodes by fractional crystallization of the *l*-tartrate. The *l*-form obtained proved to be identical with natural anhalonidine, and lophophorine was obtained by methylation of this substance with formaldehyde and formic acid.

VI. Other Natural Simple Isoquinolines

1. Carnegine, $C_{13}H_{19}O_2N$

Heyl (27) in 1901 isolated from the Mexican cactus *Cereus pecten-aborigi-num* Engelm. an alkaloid as its crystalline hydrochloride (yield, 0.65%) and termed it pectenine. The same author (28) found (1928) in the American cactus *Carnegiea gigantea* Britton and Rose a base with the composition $C_{13}H_{19}O_2N$. This alkaloid was named carnegine, and several of its crystalline derivatives were characterized. In 1929 Späth (29) established the structure of carnegine and described its synthesis. Finally, a few months later, Späth and Kuffner (30) reported that carnegine and pectenine were identical.

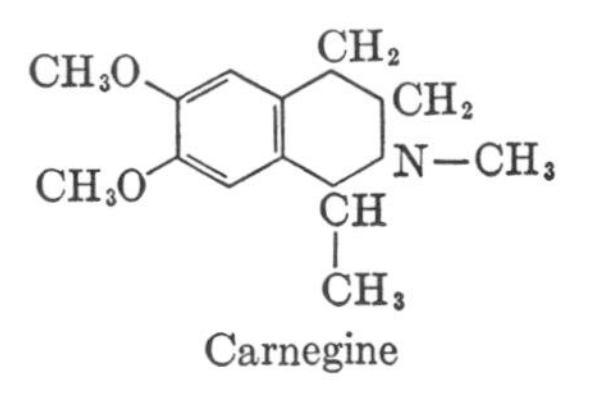

Carnegine

Carnegine is an optically inactive colorless sirup, b.p. 170° (1 mm.). The salts are crystalline: hydrochloride, m.p. 210–211°; hydrobromide, m.p. 228°; picrate, m.p. 212–213°; methiodide, m.p. 210-211°; and trinitro-*m*-cresolate, m.p. 169–170°.

Späth synthesized carnegine, without having carried out cleavage experiments, making use only of the empirical formula as well as the presence of two methoxyl groups, and being guided by the evident structural relationships with the *Anhalonium* bases. Starting from *N*-acetylhomoveratrylamine, the following route was followed:

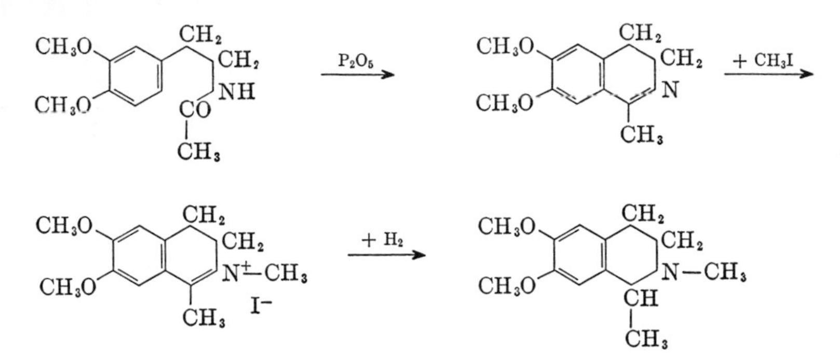

The derivatives of the synthetic oily base were identical with those of naturally occurring carnegine and pectenine. Furthermore, the possible alternate structure (the product of ring closure in *o*-position to one of the methoxy groups) was excluded by the observation that permanganate oxidation of the dihydro compound gave *m*-hemipinic and not hemipinic acid.

Schöpf and Bayerle (31) obtained "norcarnegine" under mild ("physiological") conditions (pH 5, at 25°) by condensing hydroxytyramine with acetaldehyde.

Nakada and Nishihara (51) synthesized carnegine by suspending veratrylacetoxime in toluene and treating with $POCl_3$, obtaining 1-methyl-6,7-dimethoxy-3,4-dihydro-isoquinoline. Catalytic reduction of the methyl methosulfate of this compound yielded carnegine.

2. Salsoline, $C_{11}H_{15}O_2N$ and Salsolidine, $C_{12}H_{17}O_2N$

These alkaloids are not cactus alkaloids, but their structure reveals a surprising analogy with carnegine. Actually, carnegine is *O,N*-dimethylsalsoline.

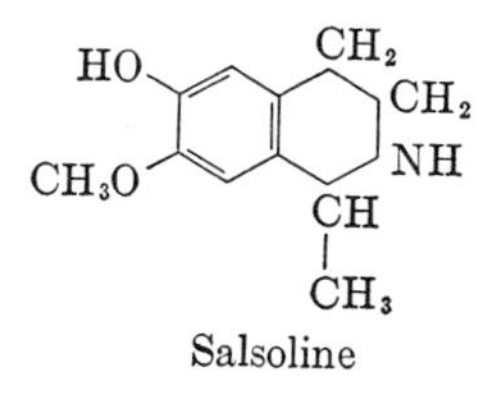

Salsoline

Salsoline and salsolidine (*O*-methylsalsoline) have been found by Orekhov and Proskurnina (32–35, 36, 37) in the desert plant *Salsola arbuscula* (*S. richteri*) belonging to the family Chenopodiaceae. A third alkaloid, of unknown constitution (salsamine), occurs in traces in the drug.

The plant yields by extraction with dichloroethane 0.32% of salsoline. The alkaloid isolated from old plants is optically inactive, but, if a recent crop is extracted, a mixture of *dl*- and *d*-salsoline results. Salsolidine occurs in the plant likewise as a mixture of the *dl*- and *l*-forms (37). The properties of these natural alkaloids are, therefore, somewhat different from those of the synthetic forms. The optically active bases are stable with respect to racemizing agents, and thus racemization must have taken place in the plant tissue itself and not in the course of extraction and isolation. According to Proskurnina and Merlis (52), *d*-salsoline is extremely resistant to racemization by alcoholic KOH.

Konovalova, Platonova and Konovalova (53), isolated salsoline and salsolidine from infusions of *Salsola arbuscula* (*S. richteri*) by adsorption on bentonite.

Natural salsoline melts at 218–221°; hydrochloride, 1.5 H_2O, m.p. 141–152°; *O*,*N*-dibenzoyl derivative, m.p. 166–168°; *N*-benzoyl derivative, m.p. 172–174°. Resolution of salsoline through its bitartrate (36) yields the pure *d*-form, m.p. 215–216°; hydrochloride, m.p. 171–172°, $[\alpha]_D$ +40.1°, and the pure *l*-form, m.p. 215–216°; hydrochloride, m.p. 171–173°, $[\alpha]_D$ −39.2°.

Natural salsolidine (*O*-methyl-*l*-salsoline) (36), m.p. 69–70°, $[\alpha]_D$ −53°; hydrochloride, m.p. 229–231°, $[\alpha]_D$ −26.2°; picrate, m.p. 194–195°; picrolonate, m.p. 220–221°.

Synthetic salsolidine (Späth and Dengel, 38): *dl*-base, m.p. 53–53.5°; hydrochloride, m.p. 196–197°; picrate, m.p. 201–201.5°; picrolonate 241°. Free *l*-base, m.p. 47.5–48.5° $[\alpha]_D^{16}$ −59.7° (alcohol); hydrochloride, m.p. 235–236°, $[\alpha]_D^{18}$ −24.8°. Free *d*-base, m.p. 47.5–48.5°; $[\alpha]_D^{16}$ +59.90° (alcohol); hydrochloride, m.p. 235–236°, $[\alpha]_D^{17}$ +25.3°. The optically active picrates, m.p. 193–194°; picrolonates, m.p. 235–236°.

Proskurnina and Orekhov (37) explained these differences by showing that *d*- and *l*-salsolidine occur in two forms (m.p. 41–45° and 71–73°), produced, respectively, by distillation in vacuum and crystallization from water; both forms gave identical HCl salts, m.p. 233–235°.

The third alkaloid, salsamine, is not found in all samples; base, m.p. 155–157°; picrate, m.p. 213–214°; picrolonate, m.p. 220–221°.

Methods applicable to the determination of salsoline include a colorimetric method introduced by Bezuglyĭ (54), volumetric titration with diazotized *p*-nitraniline, salsolidine not interfering, as proposed by Konovalova and Zaĭtseva (55), and electrolytic separation of the alkaloid, according to Babich (56).

Salsoline, when methylated with diazomethane, yields *O*-methylsalsoline, the *l*-form of which is salsolidine. *O*,*N*-dimethylsalsoline is carnegine. *O*-Methylsalsoline, oxidized with permanganate, yields *m*-hemipinic acid. The position of the hydroxyl group was established by Späth, Orekhov and Kuffner (39) by synthesis, starting from isovanillin. Salsolidine was synthesized by Späth and Dengel (38).

A synthesis of salsoline, under "physiological conditions" was achieved by Kovàcs and Fodor (57) by condensing 3-hydroxy-4-methoxy-phenethylamine with acetaldehyde, following Schöpf and Bayerle's (31) method.

3. Corypalline, $C_{11}H_{15}O_2N$

Corypalline was found by Manske (40) in *Corydalis pallida* and in the seeds of *C. aurea*. The base melts at 168°; picrate, m.p. 178°.

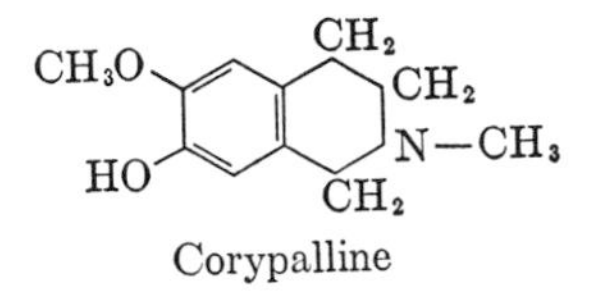

Corypalline

On methylation it yields 2-methyl-6,7-dimethoxytetrahydroisoquinoline (m.p. 82°), and upon ethylation, 2-methyl-6-methoxy-7-ethoxytetrahydroisoquinoline (m.p. 65°). The synthesis of corypalline was accomplished by a route parallel to that used by Späth, Orekhov, and Kuffner (39) in their synthesis of salsoline.

4. Hydrohydrastinine, $C_{11}H_{13}O_2N$

Hydrohydrastinine, m.p. 66°, is a degradation product of hydrastine or of cotarnine, but, according to Späth and Julian (41), it also occurs in *Corydalis tuberosa*.

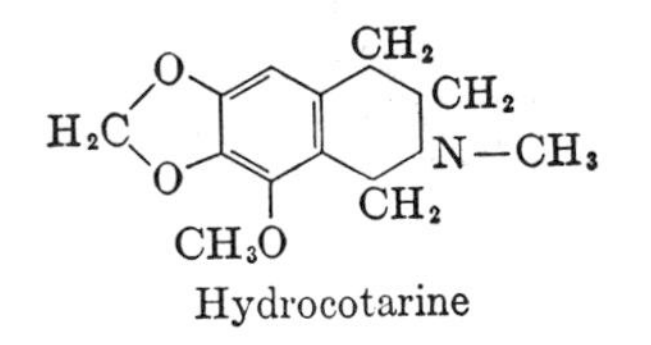

Hydrocotarine

5. Hydrocotarnine, $C_{12}H_{15}O_3N$

Hydrocotarnine is a well-known hydrolytic product of narcotinc. Hesse (42) found it in opium, both as a free base and in the form of salts; color-

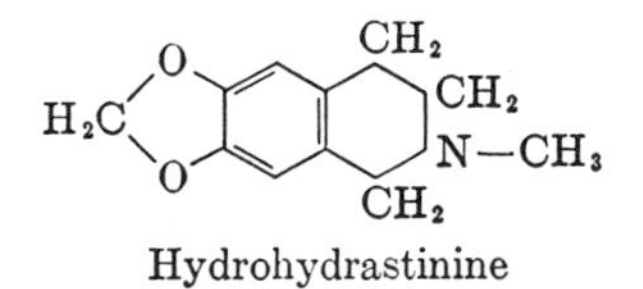

Hydrohydrastinine

less plates, from light petroleum, m.p. 55.5–56.5°; hydrobromide, m.p. 236–237°, sparingly soluble in water.

Hydrohydrastinine and hydrocotarnine may be obtained from cotarnine by reduction, according to Clayson (58).

Rodionov and Chentsova (59) mention the formation of hydrocotarnine and hydrohydrastinine by reaction of cotarnine and hydrastinine with caustic alkali, either *per se* or in a crossed Cannizzaro reaction with formaldehyde.

Several derivatives of hydrocotarnine have been prepared by Semonsky (60).

The preparation of hydrastinine, hydrohydrastinine and hydrocotarnine, starting from narcotine and cotarnine has been described by Pyman and Remfry (43), Tanaka, Midzuno and Okami (44) and Topchiev (45). See Narcotine and Cotarnine under Phthalideisoquinoline Alkaloids, Vol. IV, chap. 32.

VII. Pharmacology

A chapter on the pharmacology of the cactus alkaloids has been written by Joachimoglu and Keeser (46) in Heffter's pharmacological handbook.

1. Anhalonine

Anhalonine was examined by Heffter (47); 5–10 mg., when injected in the frog, produced an increase in the reflex excitability after a phase of paresis. In the rabbit similar symptoms are observed but general hyperexcitability predominantes.

2. Anhalonidine

Doses of 20–25 mg. of the hydrochloride produced narcosis in the frog followed by increased excitability. Doses of 30–50 mg. provoked a curarizing effect. Large doses caused complete paralysis. No significant symptoms have been observed in mammals (47).

3. Pellotine

In doses of 5–10 mg. pellotine caused temporary convulsions in frogs, and the same effects were observed in dogs and cats (47). Several authors, cited by Joachimoglu and Keeser (46), believe that pellotine could be used in man as a relatively safe narcotic.

4. Lophophorine

Lophophorine is the most toxic of the bases obtained from *Anhalonium lewinii* (47); 0.25–1 mg. of injected hydrochloride provokes a long-lasting tetany in the frog. Although the animal recovers, the increased excitability may last for several days. There is no action on the isolated frog's heart. In rabbits 7 mg. of lophophorine per kilogram of body weight produced hyperexcitability and accelerated respiration; 12.5 mg. per kilogram provoke tetany; and 15–20 mg. per kilogram is the lethal dose. Intravenous injection of 2.5 mg. caused an increase in blood pressure; larger doses, a fall. There is no effect on the heart.

5. Carnegine

Its pharmacological action is very similar to that of the isoquinoline bases obtained from *Anhalonium lewinii* (27, 48). The lethal dose in the frog is 3–4 mg.; the injection of 2–3 mg. of hydrochloride produces increased reflex excitability and convulsions; larger doses cause paresis. Carnegine provokes convulsions also in warm-blooded animals.

6. Salsoline

According to Gvishiani (49), salsoline resembles papaverine in its effects on blood circulation, and hydrastinine in its action on smooth muscles. Its use in the treatment of hypertension has been reported by Wastl (50).

Several *N*-derivatives of salsoline and salsolidine were prepared by Proskurnina and Merlis (52, 61) and found to lack the pharmacologic action of the parent substances.

Like other blood pressure reducing substances, salsoline has been found to display antihistaminic activity (62).

VIII. References

1. A. Pictet and T. Spengler, *Ber.*, **44,** 2030 (1911).
2. E. Späth, *Monatsh.*, **42,** 97 (1921).
3. E. Beccari, *Arch. farmacol. sper.*, **61,** 161 (1936).
4. A. Heffter, *Ber.*, **29,** 216 (1896).
5. E. Kauder, *Arch. Pharm.*, **237,** 190 (1899).
6. C. Tomaso, *La Chimica*, **10,** 408 (1934); *Chimie & Industrie*, **34,** 138 (1935).
7. E. Späth and F. Becke, *Monatsh.*, **66,** 327 (1935).
8. M. Steiner-Bernier, Thèse Doct. Pharm., Paris, 1936.
9. A. Heffter, *Ber.*, **27,** 2975 (1894).
10. L. Lewin, *Ber. deut. botan. Ges.*, **12,** 283 (1894).
11. A Heffter, *Ber.*, **34,** 3004 (1901).
12. E. Späth and F. Becke, *Ber.*, **68,** 501 (1935).
13. E. Späth and F. Becke, *Ber.*, **68,** 944 (1935).
14. E. Späth and F. Kesztler, *Ber.*, **69,** 755 (1936).
15. E. Späth and J. Bruck, *Ber.*, **72,** 334 (1939).
16. L. Lewin, *Arch. exptl. Pathol. Pharmakol.*, **24,** 401 (1888).
17. L. Lewin, *Arch. exptl. Pathol. Pharmakol.*, **34,** 374 (1894).
18. E. Späth and F. Kesztler, *Ber.*, **68,** 1663 (1935).
19. E. Späth, *Monatsh.*, **43,** 477 (1922).
20. E. Späth and J. Passl, *Ber.*, **65,** 1778 (1932).
21. E. Späth and F. Boschan, *Monatsh.*, **63,** 141 (1933).
22. E. Späth and F. Becke, *Ber.*, **67,** 266 (1934).
23. E. Späth and H. Röder, *Monatsh.*, **43,** 93 (1922).
24. E. Späth and F. Becke, *Ber.*, **67,** 2100 (1934).
25. E. Späth and J. Gangl, *Monatsh.*, **44,** 103 (1923).

26. M. Freund and H. H. Reitz, *Ber.*, **39**, 2219 (1906).
27. G. Heyl, *Arch. Pharm.*, **239**, 451 (1901).
28. G. Heyl, *Arch. Pharm.*, **266**, 668 (1928).
29. E. Späth, *Ber.*, **62**, 1021 (1929).
30. E. Späth and F. Kuffner, *Ber.*, **62**, 2242 (1929).
31. C. Schöpf and H. Bayerle, *Ann.*, **513**, 190 (1934).
32. A. Orekhov and N. Proskurnina, *Ber.*, **66**, 841 (1933).
33. A. Orekhov and N. Proskurnina, *Ber.*, **67**, 878 (1934).
34. A. Orekhov and N. Proskurnina, *Khim. Farm. Prom.*, **1934**, No. 2, 8–10; *Chem. Abstr.*, **28**, 5460 (1934).
35. A. Orekhov and N. Proskurnina, *Bull. acad. sci. U.R.S.S., Sér. chim.*, **1936**, 957; *Chem. Abstr.*, **31**, 5365 (1937).
36. N. Proskurnina and A. Orekhov, *Bull. soc. chim. France*, [5]**4**, 1265 (1937).
37. N. Proskurnina and A. Orekhov, *Bull. Soc. chim. France*, **6**, 144 (1939).
38. E. Späth and F. Dengel, *Ber.*, **71**, 113 (1938).
39. E. Späth, A. Orekhov and F. Kuffner, *Ber.*, **67**, 1214 (1934).
40. R. H. F. Manske, *Can. J. Research*, **B15**, 159 (1937).
41. E. Späth and P. L. Julian, *Ber.*, **64**, 1131 (1931).
42. O. Hesse, *Ann.* (*Suppl.*), **8**, 261 (1872).
43. F. L. Pyman and F. G. P. Remfry, *J. Chem. Soc.*, **101**, 1595 (1912).
44. Y. Tanaka, T. Midzuno and T. Okami, *J. Pharm. Soc. Japan*, **50**, 559 (1930).
45. K. Topchiev, *J. Applied Chem.* (*U.S.S.R.*), **6**, 529 (1933).
46. G. Joachimoglu and E. Keeser, "Kakteenalkaloide," in A. Heffter, Handbuch der Experimentellen Pharmakologie, Springer-Verlag, Berlin, 1924, Vol. II, p. 1104.
47. A. Heffter, *Arch. exptl. Pathol. Pharmakol.*, **40**, 385 (1898).
48. A. Mogilewa, *Arch. exptl. Pathol. Pharmakol.*, **49**, 137 (1903).
49. G. J. Gvishiani, *J. Physiol. U.S.S.R.*, **24**, 1174 (1938); *Chem. Zentr.*, **1939, I**, 463.
50. N. Wastl, *Hahnemannian Monthly*, **81**, 243 (1946).
51. T. Nakada and K. Nishihara, *J. Pharm. Soc. Japan*, **64**, 74 (1944).
52. N. F. Proskurnina and V. M. Merlis, *J. Gen. Chem., U.S.S.R.*, **21**, 740 (1951).
53. A. A. Konovalova, T. F. Platonova, and R. A. Konovalova, *J. Appl. Chem.* (*U.S.S.R.*), **23**, 927 (1950).
54. D. V. Bezuglyı, *Med. Prom. S.S.S.R.*, **1949**[4], 33.
55. A. A. Konovalova and O. A. Zaĭtseva, *Med. Prom. S.S.S.R.*, **1949**[4], 31.
56. S. Kh. Babich, *Zhur. Anal. Khim.*, **6**, 234 (1951).
57. Ö. Kovàcs and G. Fodor, *Chem. Ber.*, **84**, 795 (1951).
58. D. B. Clayson, *J. Chem. Soc.*, **1949**, 2016.
59. V. M. Rodionov and M. G. Chentsova, *Zhur. Obshcheĭ Khim.*, **21**, 321 (1951).
60. M. Semonsky, *Collection Czechoslov. Chem. Communs.*, **15**, 1024 (1951).
61. N. F. Proskurnina and V. M. Merlis, *Zhur. Obshcheĭ Khim.*, **19**, 1571 (1949).
62. S. D. Balakhovskiĭ and N. A. Troitskaya, *Doklady Akad. Nauk S.S.S.R.*, **67**, 691 (1949).
63. J. A. Castrillón, *J. Am. Chem. Soc.*, **74**, 558 (1952).

CHAPTER 27

Cactus Alkaloids

L. RETI

Buenos Aires, Argentina

		Page
I.	Introduction	23
II.	Constitution and Occurrence	23
III.	Location of the Alkaloids in Tissues of the Cacti	25
IV.	Extraction of Cactus Alkaloids	25
V.	References	26

I. Introduction

General surveys on cactus alkaloids have been published previously by Späth and Becke (1) and Reti (2, 3, 4). An exhaustive survey on cactus alkaloids and some related compounds has been published recently by Reti (5); see also the book of Hobschette (6) and the chapter on alkaloids of the Cactaceae in Henry's monograph (7); for peyote cf. Ewell (8), Safford (9), Reutter (10), and Amorosa (11).

II. Constitution and Occurrence

The presently known cactus alkaloids are of simple chemical constitution. They are either substituted β-phenethylamines, evidently related to and probably derived from the naturally occurring aromatic amino acids (tyrosine, dihydroxyphenylalanine, *N*-methyltyrosine, etc.), or they are simple tetrahydroisoquinolines that could originate from these bases by condensation and cyclization through the action of organic compounds containing one or two carbon atoms (formaldehyde and acetaldehyde "equivalents").

Obviously, under these conditions, it will be quite possible to find bases of the same type in plants of widely separated botanical families or even in products of animal metabolism. The individual cactus alkaloids will be found, therefore, under the headings β-Phenethylamines (see Vol. III, chap. 22) and Simple Isoquinoline Alkaloids (see Vol. IV, chap. 26), where are also included all other natural bases of similar structure but different origin.

The data in the literature on the alkaloidal composition of cacti are meager and incomplete. Alkaloids have been noted in some thirty species, but in many instances the examined material has been scanty and not well defined. The chemical constitution of the bases is known only with reference to nine species of the 1235 recorded by Britton and Rose (12).

However, the early investigations of Lewin (13–16), Heffter (17–23), and Heyl (24, 25), and the more recent ones of Herrero-Ducloux (26–30), Reti (2–4, 31–36), and others, seem to indicate that the faculty of producing and storing alkaloidal substances should be considered one of the characteristics of this botanical family.

Alkaloids of known structure have been isolated from the following cacti:

1. *Anhalonium lewinii* Hennings, syn. *Lophophora williamsii* (Lemaire) Coulter; Britton and Rose, known as pellote, peyote, peyotl, and challote. The dried slices are called "mescal buttons." Contains: mescaline, *N*-methylmescaline, *N*-acetylmescaline, anhalamine, anhalidine, anhalinine, anhalonidine, pellotine, *O*-methylanhalonidine, anhalonine, and lophophorine (1, 37–59).

2. *Anhalonium fissuratum* Engelmann, syn. *Ariocarpus fissuratus* (Engelmann) Schumann, contains hordenine (anhaline) (17).

3. *Cereus pecten-aboriginum* Engelmann, syn. *Pachycereus pecten-aboriginum* (Engelmann) Britton and Rose, contains pectenine (identical with carnegine) (24).

4. *Carnegiea gigantea* (Engelmann) Britton and Rose, contains carnegine (25).

5. *Trichocereus candicans* (Gillies) Britton and Rose, contains hordenine and candicine (31, 60, 61).

6. *Trichocereus lamprochlorus* (Lemaire) Britton and Rose, contains hordenine and candicine (34).

7. *Trichocereus terscheckii* (Parmentier) Britton and Rose, contains mescaline and trichocereine (32, 36).

8. *Trichocereus spachianus* (Lemaire) Riccobono, contains candicine (62).

9. *Stetsonia coryne* (Salm-Dyck) Britton and Rose, contains coryneine (35).

The presence of alkaloids of undetermined structure has been recorded for the following cacti:

1. *Opuntia vulgaris* Miller (63, 64).
2. *Selenicereus grandiflorus* (L.) Britton and Rose. Sultan (65) isolated from the plant 2% of an alkaloid and called it cactine.
3. *Neomamillaria magnimamma* (Haworth) Britton and Rose (20).
4. *Epiphyllum ackermannii* (Haworth) Britton and Rose (20).
5. *Schlummbergera russeliana* (Gardner) Britton and Rose (20).
6. *Astrophytum myriostigma* Lemaire (20).
7. *Cereus peruvianus* (L.) Miller (20).
8. *Echinocereus mamillosus* Rümpler (20).
9. *Echinocactus visnaga* Hooker (20).
10. *Ariocarpus retusus* Scheidweiler (17).
11. *Dolichotele uberiformis* (Zuccarini) Britton and Rose (15).
12. *Rhipsalis teres* (Vellozo) Steudel (15).

13. *Lophocereus schottii* (Engelmann) Britton and Rose. Heyl (24) found in this cactus considerable amounts of an amorphous base, m.p. 82–86°, called pilocereine, $C_{30}H_{44}N_2O_4$. Amorphous salts; 13.48 % methoxyl. *Pilocereine*—The amorphous alkaloid found by Heyl (24) in *Lophocereus schottii*—has been recently obtained in crystalline form and investigated by Djerassi, Frick and Geller (72). The major part of the alkaloids resides in the green epidermis, a minor part in the cortex, while the central core is practically devoid of alkaloids. From the crude and complex alkaloid fraction (*ca.* 3.7 % on the dry plant) pure crystalline pilocereine can be separated in an over-all yield, based on dry plant, of 0.5 %.

Pilocereine, $C_{30}H_{42}O_4N_2$, recrystallized from ethyl acetate and from methanol is optically inactive, m.p. 176.5–177°. Pilocereine dihydrochloride, $C_{30}H_{42}O_4N_2 \cdot 2HCl \cdot 2H_2O$, m.p. 228–232° (dec.); diperchlorate, m.p. 214–217° (dec.); dioxalate, forms a dihydrate. The dimethiodide dihydrate decomposes at 230–240°. Acetyl pilocerine, $C_{32}H_{44}O_5N_2$, m.p. 186–186.5°. (All melting points corr.). The pilocereine molecule contains two tertiary nitrogen atoms, one forming part of a heterocyclic ring, while of the four oxygen atoms, two are present as methoxyl groups, one as a phenolic hydroxyl group and the fourth appears to be present in an ether linkage.

14. *Pachycereus marginatus* (DC.) Britton and Rose (66).
15. *Gymnocalycium gibbosum* (Haworth) Pfeiffer (27).
16. *Gymnocalycium multiflorum* (Hook.) Britton and Rose (29).
17. *Echinopsis eyriesii* (Turpin) Zuccarini (26).
18. *Trichocereus* sp. aff. *T. terscheckii* (30).
19. *Trichocereus thelegonoides* (Spegazzini) Britton and Rose (62).
20. *Trichocereus thelegonus* (Weber) Britton and Rose (62).
21. *Trichocereus huascha* (Weber) Britton and Rose (62).

III. Location of the Alkaloids in Tissues of the Cacti

Few observations only are available on this subject. Janot and Bernier (67) found that in pellote the alkaloids are almost exclusively located in the internal cells of the cortical parenchyma at the top of the plant. In *Trichocereus candicans* Niedfeld (60), utilizing microchemical methods, observed that the alkaloids are mostly situated in the chlorophyllaceous cortical parenchyma.

Reti and Castrillón (36) found 0.29 % total alkaloids in the green epidermis of *Trichocereus terscheckii*, while the central parts, including cortical parenchyma, contain 0.45 %.

IV. Extraction of Cactus Alkaloids

Fresh cacti, with a water content of 90–95 %, are difficult to handle; the juice is not easily separated from the fibers, and the presence of mucilaginous substances causes trouble during extraction. Thus, it is preferable to dry the plants immediately after they are collected, in order to avoid losses and deterioration. The plants should be cleaned, the spines extracted with nippers, and the remaining material cut in thin slices and dried in the sun or better in a low-temperature dryer (40–60°). The dried substance is easy to grind, and the powder can be stored if necessary.

The powdered material is extracted following the usual procedure. Extractions of the drug and isolation of the alkaloids from *Anhalonium lewinii* have been described by Heffter (19), Kauder (68), Tomaso (69), and Späth and Becke (1), as well as by Steiner-Bernier (70); and the extraction of alkaloids from *Pilocereus sargentianus* and *Cereus pecten-aboriginum*, by Heyl (24, 25).

The extraction and isolation of the alkaloids of *Trichocereus candicans* (71) will serve as an example of general applicability:

Five hundred grams of dried and powdered material was extracted exhaustively with 95% ethanol acidified with 0.3% of acetic acid. The solvent was removed *in vacuo* and water was added and evaporated again until 500 cc. of ethanol-free solution remained. The solution, decanted from chlorophyll, waxes, etc., was extracted several times with ether in order to eliminate impurities; it was then filtered, made alkaline with excess solid sodium carbonate, the soluble bases extracted exhaustively with ether, and the aqueous solution (A) put aside. The concentrated ether extracts were shaken with strong potassium hydroxide solution, and the ether layer, after washing, was evaporated to dryness thus yielding very small quantities of non-phenolic bases. The alkaline solution was acidified with hydrochloric acid, made alkaline with sodium carbonate, and again extracted with ether. The ether extracts were dried over anhydrous sodium sulfate and after concentration the hordenine (anhaline) crystallized. The mother liquors yielded more, less pure, hordenine. Total yield: 2.5 g. hordenine; 0.5% on the dry plant.

The aqueous solution (A) contained the non-extractable quaternary bases. It was acidified with hydrochloric acid, filtered and precipitated with concentrated Mayer's reagent (50 g. of mercuric chloride, 200 g. of potassium iodide, 400 cc. of water), added with constant stirring. The precipitate was filtered, suspended in hot water, and hydrogen sulfide was bubbled through the suspension until all the mercury was precipitated as sulfide. The hot filtered solution on cooling yielded candicine iodide (hordenine methiodide) in straw-colored needles. The salt was recrystallized from hot water with the aid of charcoal and yielded colorless crystals, which melted at 234°. The mother liquors contained only small amounts of candicine. Total yield: 16.4 g. of candicine iodide; 2% of candicine on the dry plant.

V. References

1. E. Späth and F. Becke, *Monatsh.*, **66**, 327 (1935).
2. L. Reti, *Anales asoc. quím. argentina*, **23**, 26 (1935).
3. L. Reti, *Ciencia e invest. (Buenos Aires)*, **3**, 405 (1947).
4. L. Reti, *Proc. Conf. Cultivation of Drug and Assoc. Econ. Plants in Calif.*, *Los Angeles, 3rd. Conf.*, **1947**, 110.
5. L. Reti, *Fortschr. Chem. org. Naturstoffe*, **6**, 242 (1950).
6. A. Hobschette, Les Cactacées Medicinales, Doin, Paris, 1929.

7. T. A. Henry, The Plant Alkaloids, 4th ed., Blakiston, Philadelphia-Toronto, 1949.
8. E. E. Ewell, *J. Am. Chem. Soc.*, **18,** 624 (1896).
9. W. E. Safford, *J. Am. Med. Assoc.*, **77,** 1278 (1921).
10. L. Reutter, *Schweiz. Apoth. Zts.*, **62,** 441 (1924).
11. M. Amorosa, *Ann. chim. farm.* (Suppl. *Farm. ital.*), Aug., **1938,** 77; *Chem. Abstr.*, **32,** 9092 (1938).
12. N. L. Britton and J. N. Rose, The Cactaceae, The Carnegie Institution of Washington, 1919–1923.
13. L. Lewin, *Arch. exptl. Pathol. Pharmakol*, **24,** 401 (1888).
14. L. Lewin, *Arch. exptl. Pathol. Pharmakol.*, **34,** 374 (1894).
15. L. Lewin, *Ber. deut. botan. Ges.*, **12,** 283 (1894).
16. L. Lewin, Phantastica, Dutton, New York, 1931.
17. A. Heffter, *Arch. exptl. Pathol. Pharmakol.*, **34,** 65 (1894).
18. A. Heffter, *Ber.*, **27,** 2975 (1894).
19. A. Heffter, *Ber.*, **29,** 216 (1896).
20. A. Heffter, *Arch. exptl. Pathol. Pharmakol.*, **40,** 385 (1898).
21. A. Heffter, *Ber.* **31,** 1193 (1898).
22. A. Heffter, *Ber.*, **34,** 3004 (1901).
23. A. Heffter and R. Capellmann, *Ber.*, **38,** 3634 (1905).
24. G. Heyl, *Ber. deut. pharm. Ges.*, **239,** 451 (1901).
25. G. Heyl, *Arch. Pharm.*, **266,** 668 (1928).
26. E. Herrero Ducloux, *Rev. fac. cienc. quím. Univ. nacl. La Plata*, **6,** II, 43 (1930).
27. E. Herrero Ducloux, *Rev. fac. cienc. quím. Univ. nacl. La Plata*, **6,** 75 (1930).
28. E. Herrero Ducloux, *Rev. farm. (Buenos Aires)*, **74,** 87 (1931).
29. E. Herrero Ducloux, *Rev. farm. (Buenos Aires)*, **74,** 251 (1932).
30. E. Herrero Ducloux, *Rev. farm. (Buenos Aires)*, **74,** 375 (1932).
31. L. Reti, *Compt. rend. soc. biol.*, **114,** 811 (1933); *Rev. soc. argentina biol.*, **9,** 344 (1933).
32. L. Reti, *Atti. congr. intern. chim., 10th Congr., Rome, 1938*, **5,** 396 (1939).
33. L. Reti, *Atti congr. nazl. chim. ind., Milan, 1924.*
34. L. Reti and R. I. Arnolt, *Actas y trabajos V°congr. nacl. med., Rosario*, **3,** 39 (1935).
35. L. Reti, R. I. Arnolt, and F. P. Ludueña, *Compt. rend. soc. biol.* **118,** 591 (1935); *Rev. soc. argentina biol.*, **10,** 437 (1934).
36. L. Reti and J. Castrillón, *J. Am. Chem. Soc.* **73,** 767–9 (1951).
37. E. Späth, *Monatsh.*, **40,** 129 (1919).
38. E. Späth, *Monatsh.*, **42,** 97 (1921).
39. E. Späth, *Monatsh.*, **42,** 263 (1921).
40. E. Späth, *Monatsh.*, **43,** 477 (1922).
41. E. Späth, *Ber.*, **62,** 1021 (1929).
42. E. Späth and F. Becke, *Ber.*, **67,** 266 (1934).
43. E. Späth and F. Becke, *Ber.*, **67,** 2100 (1934).
44. E. Späth and F. Becke, *Ber.*, **68,** 501 (1935).
45. E. Späth and F. Becke, *Ber.*, **68,** 944 (1935).
46. E. Späth and F. Boschan, *Monatsh.*, **63,** 141 (1933).
47. E. Späth and J. Bruck, *Ber.*, **70,** 2446 (1937).
48. E. Späth and J. Bruck, *Ber.*, **71,** 1275 (1938).
49. E. Späth and J. Bruck, *Ber.*, **72,** 334 (1939).
50. E. Späth and F. Dengel, *Ber.*, **71,** 113 (1938).
51. E. Späth and J. Gangl, *Monatsh.*, **44,** 103 (1923).
52. E. Späth and P. L. Julian, *Ber.*, **64,** 1131 (1931).

53. E. Späth and F. Kesztler, *Ber.*, **68**, 1663 (1935).
54. E. Späth and F. Kesztler, *Ber.*, **69**, 755 (1936).
55. E. Späth and F. Kuffner, *Ber.*, **62**, 2242 (1929).
56. E. Späth, A. Orekhov, and F. Kuffner, *Ber.*, **67**, 1214 (1934).
57. E. Späth and J. Passl, *Ber.*, **65**, 1778 (1932).
58. E. Späth and H. Röder, *Monatsh.*, **43**, 93 (1922).
59. E. Späth and P. Sobel, *Monatsh.*, **41**, 77 (1920).
60. H. A. Niedfeld, Tesis del profesorado suplente, Universidad del Litoral, Rosario, 1931.
61. J. T. Lewis and F. P. Ludueña, *Compt. rend. soc. biol.*, **114**, 814 (1933); *Rev. soc. argentina biol.*, **9**, 352 (1933).
62. A. J. Haagen-Smit and M. Olivier, private communication.
63. J. Faiveley, Thèse Doct. Méd., Paris, 1920.
64. F. Falco and S. Hilburg, *Rev. fac. quím. ind. y agr., Univ. nacl. litoral. Santa Fé, Arg.*, **15/16.**, No. 26, 71 (1946/47).
65. F. W. Sultan, *N. Y. Med. J.*, 681 (1891).
66. J. Roca, *Anales inst. biol., Univ. nacl. Méx.*, **7**, 97 (1936).
67. M. M. Janot and M. Bernier, *Bull. sci. pharmacol.*, **40**, 145 (1933).
68. E. Kauder, *Arch. Pharm.*, **237**, 190 (1899).
69. C. Tomaso, *La Chimica*, **10**, 408 (1934); *Chimie & industrie*, **34**, 138 (1935).
70. M. Steiner-Bernier, Thèse Doct. Pharm., Paris, 1936.
71. J. Castrillón, Thesis, Buenos Aires University, 1950.
72. C. Djerassi, N. Frick and L. E. Geller, *J. Am. Chem. Soc.*, **75**, 3632 (1953).

CHAPTER 28

The Benzylisoquinoline Alkaloids

ALFRED BURGER

University of Virginia, Charlottesville, Virginia

Page

I. Introduction 29
II. Papaverine 30
  1. Occurrence, Separation, and Properties 30
  2. Chemical Structure 32
  3. Reduction 34
  4. Quaternary Papaverinium Salts 36
  5. Substitution Reactions of Papaverine 38
  6. Syntheses of Papaverine 39
  7. Pharmacology 44
  8. Papaverine-like Compounds 45
III. Laudanosine 48
  1. Occurrence and Properties 48
  2. Chemical Structure and Reactions 51
  3. Syntheses of Laudanosine 55
  4. Steric Configuration 56
  5. Pharmacology 57
IV. Monophenolic Bases of the Laudanosine Type 57
  1. Laudanine 57
    a. Occurrence and Properties 57
    b. Structure and Chemical Reactions 58
    c. Syntheses of Laudanine 58
  2. Laudanidine (Tritopine) 59
  3. Codamine 60
    a. Occurrence, Properties, and Reactions 60
    b. Synthesis of Codamine 61
  4. Pseudolaudanine and Pseudocodamine 62
    a. Pseudolaudanine 62
    b. Pseudocodamine 63
  5. Neprotine 63
  6. Coclaurine 65
  7. Armepavine 68
  8. Corpaverine 68
V. Biogenesis of the Benzylisoquinoline Alkaloids 69
VI. References 71

I. Introduction

Alkaloids containing the 1-benzylisoquinoline system have attracted the attention of organic chemists and phytochemists, pharmacologists, and clinicians because of their interesting reactions, their traceable derivation from proteins, their relation to natural products of similar constitution, and their often pronounced, and in some cases beneficial, physiological action.

From a chemical structural viewpoint, they may be divided into several groups. The alkaloids in which the aliphatic carbon atom of the benzyl group is connected only to positions 1 and 1′ comprise the opium bases papaverine, xanthaline, laudanosine, and various phenolic derivatives of these tetramethoxy compounds, as well as the *Cocculus* base coclaurine, the *Papaver* alkaloid armepavine, the *Mahonia* base neprotine, and a constituent of *Corydalis*, corpaverine. This chapter is devoted to a discussion of this group.

Among other alkaloids containing the benzylisoquinoline structure are bases in whose molecules the extranuclear carbon atom of the benzyl group is part of a lactone ring, as in narcotine and hydrastine. If one additional carbon atom connecting position 2′ with the cyclic nitrogen establishes a new six-membered ring, a third group of alkaloids might be considered, of which berberine and corydaline are well-known examples. Finally, connecting the 8- and 6′-positions leads to the alkaloids of the aporphine group.

Most of the alkaloids in the simple benzylisoquinoline series differ from each other mainly by the degree of hydrogenation of the heterocyclic ring, and the number and character of nuclear substituents, especially hydroxyl or alkoxyl groups, but variations in the methylene bridge are also encountered.

If the ether linkages are more complex, relationships with other groups of alkaloids may well be mentioned. Thus, curine, oxyacanthine, and tubocurarine, as well as several other not closely related bases having widely different types of physiological activity, such as the mycobacteriostatic alkaloid cepharanthine, may be interpreted as derivatives of benzylisoquinoline.

Compared to its companion alkaloids, papaverine has attained a dominant place in the benzylisoquinoline group, partly because more of it occurs in opium and its routine isolation is not too difficult, but chiefly because of its use in medicine. It is one of the few alkaloids manufactured synthetically, and its reactions have been explored with uncommon thoroughness. Because of the close connections between papaverine and the other members of this groups, the way for many of the reactions and syntheses of the minor alkaloids will be paved on the pages devoted to papaverine.

II. Papaverine

1. Occurrence, Separation, and Properties

Papaverine usually occurs to the extent of 0.5 to 1% in opium (1) and was isolated from the mother liquors of the morphine extraction in 1848 (2). It is found in all parts of *Papaver somniferum* L. (var. *album*), especially in the unripe capsules. The alkaloid is precipitated from the mixed hydrochlorides of the opium bases by sodium acetate together with narcotine, and separated from the latter by precipitation with potassium ferricyanide and decomposition of the precipitate with dilute sodium hydroxide solution (3). Conversion to papaverine acid oxalate is especially suitable to complete this separation (4, 5), but, although this salt crystallizes in a state of great purity, the last traces of cryptopine are hard to remove (6a) and interfere with most qualitative tests for papaverine. Pure papaverine gives no color reaction with cold concentrated sulfuric acid (6b).

Chromatographic separation of papaverine has been studied in recent years (7), and the increasing importance of the compound as a spasmolytic drug has led to renewed efforts to simplify its purification procedure (8).

Papaverine crystallizes from ethanol as rhombic prisms or small white needles melting at 147–148°C. It is readily soluble in hot benzene, glacial acetic acid, ethanol, or petroleum ether, sparingly soluble in ether and carbon tetrachloride, and almost insoluble in water. It is a weakly monoacidic base and forms many salts with common acids, and metallic double salts. With alkyl halides, sulfates, etc., papaverine yields quaternary salts; a number of addition products with acyl halides have also been described.

TABLE 1

SOME CHARACTERISTIC SALTS OF PAPAVERINE[a]

Name	Formula, P = $C_{20}H_{21}NO_4$	Appearance	M.p.,°C.
Hydrochloride	$P \cdot HCl$	Monoclinic	220–221 (dec.)
Hydrobromide	$P \cdot HBr$	Pale yellow prisms	213–214 (dec.)
Hydriodide	$P \cdot HI$	Monoclinic, dimorphous	196–200 (dec.)
Acid oxalate	$P \cdot (COOH)_2$	Colorless	201–202
Picrate	$P \cdot C_6H_3N_3O_7$	Plates	186
Picrolonate	$P \cdot C_{10}H_8N_4O_5$	Fine crystals	220
Thiocyanate	$P \cdot HSCN$	Colorless needles	152
Platinichloride	$2P \cdot HCl \cdot PtCl_4$	Orange, rhombic	212–213
Cadmium chloride	$2P \cdot HCl \cdot CdCl_2$	Tetragonal	176
Methiodide	$P \cdot CH_3I$	Nearly white	195
Methosulfate	$P \cdot (CH_3)_2SO_4$	Hygroscopic	about 110
Ethiodide	$P \cdot C_2H_5I$	Yellow	216 (dec.)
Ethobromide	$P \cdot C_2H_5Br$	Pale yellow	206–207
Butobromide	$P \cdot C_4H_9Br$		217 (dec.)
Phenacyl bromide	$P \cdot C_6H_5COCH_2Br$	Yellow	190–194
Phenacyl nitrate	$P \cdot C_6H_5COCH_2ONO_2$	Yellow needles	173 (dec.)
N-Methyl *p*-toluene sulfonate	$P \cdot CH_3C_6H_4SO_3H$		171

[a] A complete list may be found in the monograph by L. F. Small and R. E. Lutz: The Chemistry of Opium Alkaloids, Supplement No. 103 to the Public Health Reports, U. S. Government Printing Office, Washington, D. C., 1932.

The formula of papaverine is $C_{20}H_{21}NO_4$. It is 1-(3,4-dimethoxybenzyl)-6,7-dimethoxyisoquinoline (I).

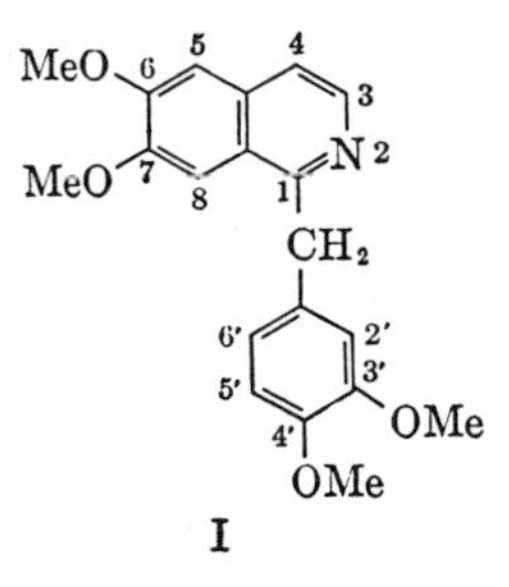

I

2. Chemical Structure

The four oxygen atoms of papaverine are present in methoxyl groups since boiling hydriodic acid cleaves the compound into four moles of methyl iodide and a new base, papaveroline (I with four hydroxyls instead of methoxyls), which contains four phenolic hydroxyl goups, is easily oxidized, and is stable only in the form of its salts.

The main structural features of papaverine were elucidated by oxidative degradation, largely through the work of Goldschmiedt and his school (9).

Oxidation with sodium bichromate in boiling acetic acid followed by extraction with chloroform gives a nearly quantitative yield of papaveraldine (II) (10). The same ketone may also be obtained by oxidation with potassium permanganate in acid solution, with selenium dioxide (11), or by photooxidation (12). It exhibits halochromism (13), and may be oxidized further to 6,7-dimethoxyisoquinoline-1-carboxylic acid (III), which was at first misinterpreted as a dimethoxycinchoninic acid. Among the evidence

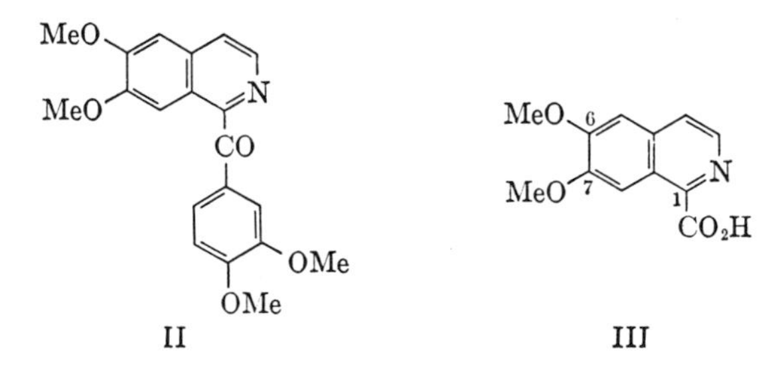

II III

which decided in favor of the true structure of III was the formation of *N*-ethyl-*m*-hemipinimide (IV) in the oxidation of ethylpapaverinium bromide, which could only be explained by assuming the presence of an isoquinoline nucleus in papaverine.

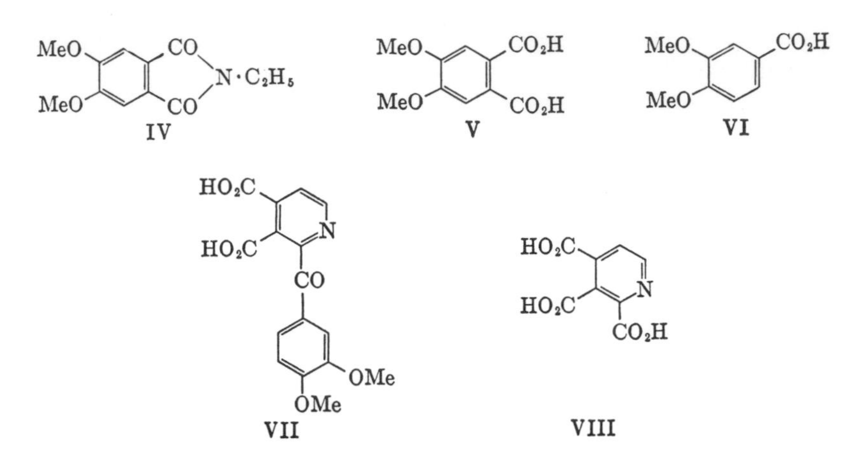

Permanganate oxidation of papaverine in neutral medium furnishes *m*-hemipinic acid (V), veratric acid (VI), papaverinic acid (α-veratroylcinchomeronic acid) (VII), and pyridine-2,3,4-tricarboxylic acid (VIII). The last-named product (VIII) may serve as evidence for the point of attachment of the nitrogen-free portion of the isoquinoline system. Dimethoxyisoquinolines are oxidized to pyridine-3,4-dicarboxylic (cinchomeronic) acid, but papaverine yields VIII under analogous conditions, thus marking position 1 as the connecting point.

Since fusion with alkali splits papaverine to 6,7-dimethoxyisoquinoline and 3,4-dimethoxytoluene (dimethylhomocatechol), it is likely that the latter is linked to the 1-position of the isoquinoline by way of the methyl group. The structure of the isoquinoline follows from its oxidation to *m*-hemipinic acid (V) and that of the dimethoxytoluene from its conversion to veratric acid (VI).

Careful oxidation of papaverine with mercuric acetate in dilute acetic acid solution (14) leads to papaverinol (IX), which is also obtained by reduction of papaveraldine (II). The secondary alcohol itself may be reduced to papaverine (13).

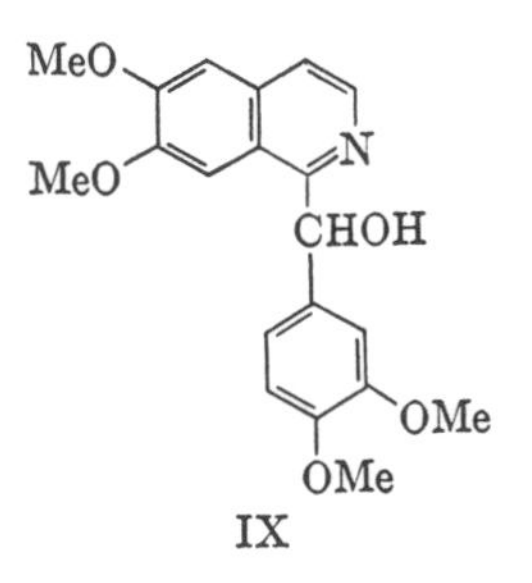

The structure of papaverine, deduced from these reactions, is obviously that represented by I. It was that of the first opium alkaloid to which the correct structure was assigned (1888).

3. Reduction

Reduction of papaverine with tin and hydrochloric acid yields two products, 1,2,3,4-tetrahydropapaverine (X) (15) and pavine (9, 15, 16, 17). Tetrahydropapaverine may also be obtained by electrolytic reduction of papaveraldine or papaverine, or by catalytic hydrogenation of papaverine or 3,4-dihydropapaverine (18); it can be dehydrogenated to papaverine by means of palladium (19).

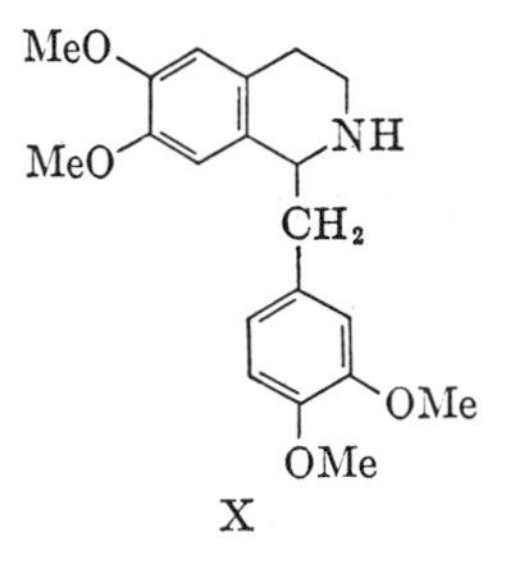

X

Pavine is a secondary amine and contains asymmetric carbon atoms; it has been resolved into optical isomers through the α-halogenocamphorsulfonates (20). Its resistance to further reduction and to oxidation (21a) exclude its formulation as 1,2-dihydropapaverine; it is especially noteworthy that veratric acid (VI) has never been obtained from the oxidation of pavine or any of its derivatives. Pyman proposed formula XIa for pavine in spite of this observation, and in spite of the fact that *N*-methylpavine can be demethylated smoothly with hydrobromic or hydriodic acid, which undoubtedly would cleave the ethylenimine ring. The remethylation of the phenolic compound from the ether cleavage to *N*-methylpavine methiodide proves that the pavine ring skeleton has been preserved in these reactions. Pyman based his formulation largely on a product from the exhaustive methylation of pavine which contained a double bond in a ring, and whose oxidation yielded a dicarboxylic acid containing the same number of carbon atoms; he believed the degradation product could be represented as the dimethylaminobenzylindene (XIb).

The demethylation of *N*-methyl-1,2-dihydropapaverine (XV) (see below) with boiling hydrobromic acid has pointed the way to revise the improbable formula XIa of pavine. The double bond of XV disappears in this reaction, and *N*-methylnorpavine hydrobromide is formed. This can be remethylated quantitatively to N-methylpavine methohalide.

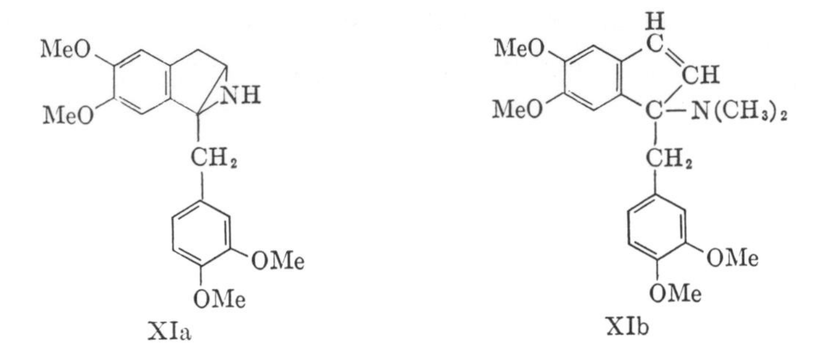

The disappearance of the double bond in the 3,4-position of *N*-methyldihydropapaverine must be caused by an addition process of the unsaturated linkage to another portion of the molecule. Sterical considerations led Schöpf (21b) to propose formulas XIIa or XIIb for pavine. The corresponding des-bases from the exhaustive methylation would thus have formulas XIIc, or XIId, respectively, instead of XIb as postulated at an earlier date.

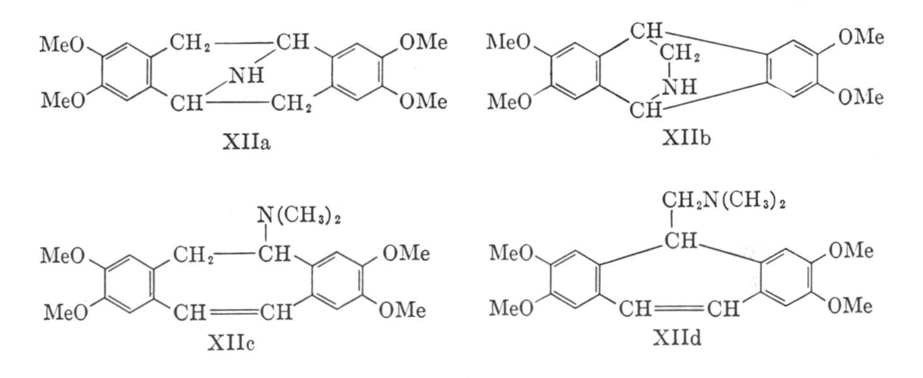

These structural derivations make it appear likely that the slow reduction of papaverine with pure tin and hydrochloric acid leads first to the hitherto unknown 1,2-dihydropapaverine, which, under the influence of the acid, is stabilized to the non-reducible pavine. In accordance with this view, no pavine is formed when tin activated by 1.6% of antimony is used in the reduction, tetrahydropapaverine being the only reaction product.

3,4-Dihydropapaverine (XXXIV) has not been observed among the reduction products of the parent alkaloid but has been prepared by synthetic methods (13b, 22, 23, 24). It may be converted to papaverine by dehydrogenation (19, 25, 26), to tetrahydropapaverine by catalytic hydrogenation, and to papaveraldine by oxidation (13a).

4. Quaternary Papaverinium Salts

Alkylpapaverinium salts, often called papaverine methochloride, ethosulfate, etc., are prepared readily from the base and alkyl halides, sulfates, etc., by standard methods. Their reduction furnishes *N*-alkyltetrahydropapaverines (21, 27, 28). For example, *N*-methylpapaverinium sulfate yields DL-laudanosine (XIII) on cathodic reduction (29); another publication records an almost quantitative yield of XIII by reduction of methylpapaverinium chloride with zinc-cadmium alloy and acetic–formic acid (28).

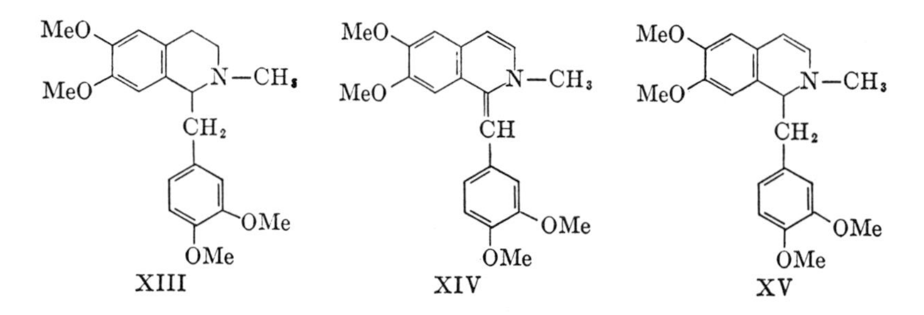

Schöpf and Thierfelder (30) isolated two intermediates when this reaction was modified in the following manner. Addition of one mole of sodium ethoxide to an ethanolic solution of methylpapaverinium iodide gave a deep yellow color. This was interpreted as a rearrangement to the benzal derivative XIV. The yellow solution absorbed one mole of hydrogen in the presence of platinum catalysts, and *N*-methyl-1,2-dihydroisopapaverine (XV) (see below) could be isolated (21b). This compound was hydrogenated to DL-laudanosine (XIII) in alcoholic acetic acid solution.

The alkylpapaverinium halides and hydroxides undergo a series of interesting reactions with alkalis. In dilute solution, *N*-alkyl phenolbetaines (31) are formed. Methylpapaverinium iodide for example yields *N*-methylnorpapaverinium betaine (XVI), which may be reconverted to the starting material by methyl iodide, and to methyl-"homopapaverinium" iodide when boiled with ethyl iodide. Proof that the derived phenolbetaine in-

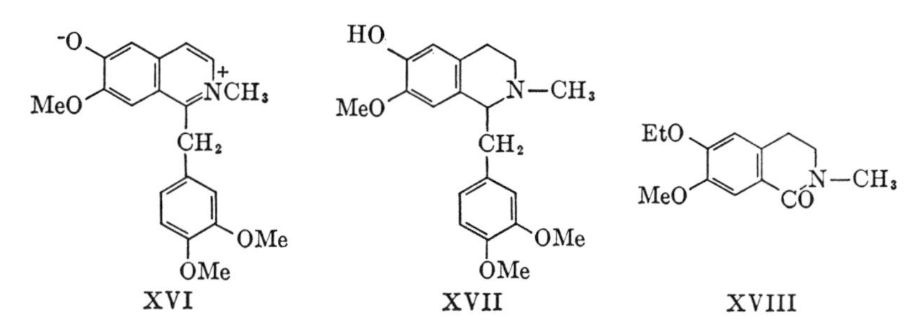

volves the O_6 oxygen lies in the fact that reduction of the latter results in pseudolaudanine (XVII) (31, 32); the ethyl ether of this compound furnishes 1-keto-2-methyl-6-ethoxy-7-methoxy-1,2,3,4-tetrahydroisoquinoline (XVIII) on gentle oxidation (33).

Such a conclusion cannot be reached when methylpapaverolinium chloride is converted to a phenolbetaine by dehydrochlorination with pyridine. This betaine is probably an anhydronium base (34) and may be an intermediate between resonance hybrids, such as a phenolbetaine (XIXa) and a quinone (XIXb) (35). Concentrated alkalis convert alkylpapaverinium salts to *N*-alkylisopapaverines (36, 37, 38, 39) which may be reconverted to alkylpapaverinium halides in acid solution. Potassium permanganate oxidizes the isopapaverines to 1-keto-2-alkyl-5,6-dimethoxy-1,2-dihydroisoquinolines, thus pointing to the presence of a saturated linkage between C_1 and nitrogen.

Gadamer and Knoch (40) treated papaverine with ethyl chlorocarbonate and obtained a compound which they regarded as *N*-carbethoxyisopapaverine (XX), formed by dehydrochlorination of an intermediate quaternary product. However, on the basis of their studies on the action of ethyl

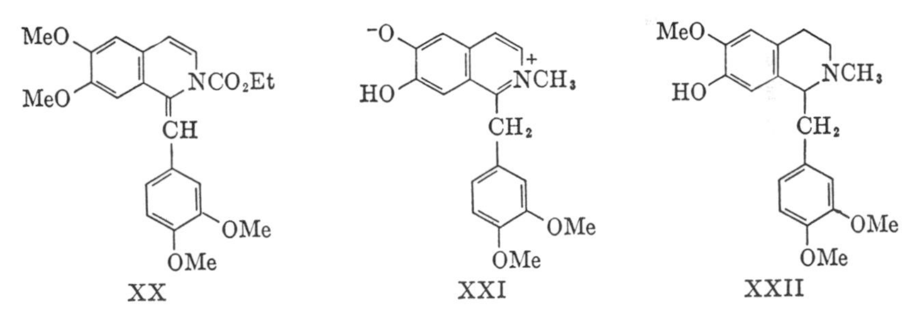

chlorocarbonate on pyridine, Arens and van Dorp (41) believe that the product cannot be represented by XX but by a bimolecular formula.

Papaverine hydrochloride decomposes on melting with the loss of methyl chloride, the methyl group being furnished by the methoxyl group in position 7. The resulting compound, protopapaverine (XXI), may be regarded as a phenolbetaine of trimethylpapaveroline since, on methylation and subsequent reduction, it gives DL-codamine (XXII) (42) (p. 61). When this order of reactions is reversed, DL-laudanosine (XIII) is formed. Methylation with diazomethane closes up the 7-hydroxyl group and yields *N*-methylpapaverinium betaine.

5. Substitution Reactions of Papaverine

The methylene group of the dimethoxybenzyl moiety is the most easily condensed position of the papaverine molecule. Formaldehyde reacts at this point to give methylenepapaverine (XXIII) (43), which may be hydrogenated to a saturated derivative (44). However, in the presence of sul-

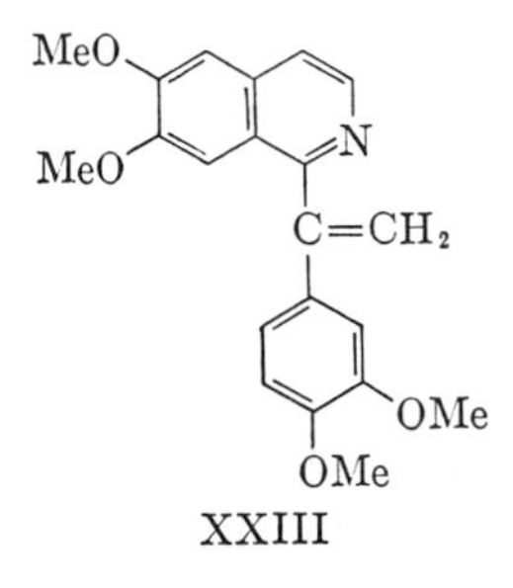

XXIII

furic acid, formaldehyde and other aldehydes with a pronounced tendency for hemiacetal formation, such as opianic acid, are said to condense at the 5-position, the latter furnishing 5-opianylpapaverine (45).

Like other alkaloids having a free position para to a hydroxyl or methoxyl in an aromatic ring, papaverine can be sulfonated with cold sulfuric acid. The interpretation of the position of the sulfonic acid group in papaverine-6′-sulfonic acid is supported by the inability of the compound to couple with diazonium salts. The compound probably has an inner salt structure (46).

Nitration of papaverine yields 6′-nitropapaverine (47, 27), the structure of which follows from the reduction of its methochloride to DL-aminolaudanosine (XXIV) (27, 30, 48), whose diazonium salt, when subjected to a Pschorr reaction with copper powder, closes a new ring to form a phenanthrene (XXV) which is identical with DL-glaucine (48), the racemate of an alkaloid of the aporphine group. In the stannous chloride reduction of

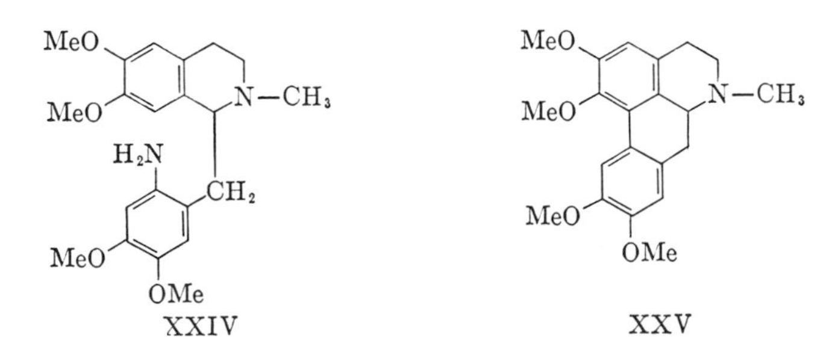

XXIV XXV

6′-nitropapaverine, a by-product is formed (27b) which has been called

anthranilopapaverine and has been formulated without proof as 5,6-dimethoxy-3-[1-(6,7-dimethoxy)isoquinolyl)]-anthranil (XXVI). This compound can be sulfonated to the so-called anthranilopapaverinesulfonic acid.

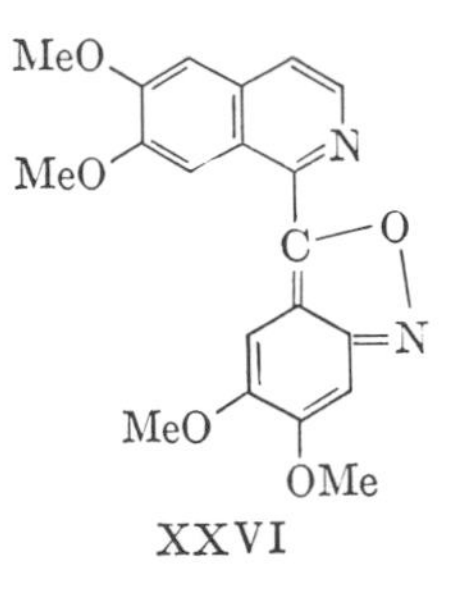

XXVI

Under the influence of sulfuric acid, acetic anhydride introduces an acetyl group into the 6′-position of papaverine (49). The reaction product, 6′-acetylpapaverine (XXVII), is a neutral pseudobase, which rearranges slowly in aqueous alcoholic solution to the alkaline quaternary base coralyn (XXVIII) related to dehydrocorydaline. An isomer of the natural alka-

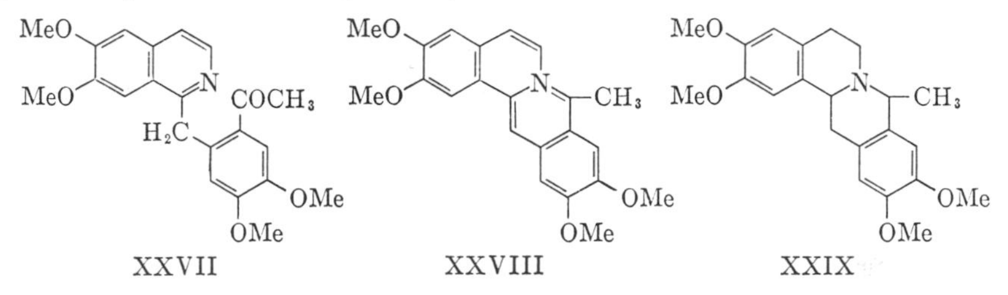

loid corydaline, α-coralydine (XXIX), is formed by condensing tetrahydropapaverine with acetal (50), in a reaction analogous to the erroneous Pictet and Gams synthesis of tetrahydroberberine (51a). Condensation with formaldehyde leads to norcoralydine, which lacks the methyl group in the central ring (52, 53). Papaveroline has been iodinated in hydriodic acid solution and found to give a monoiodo compound which according to Kitasato and Robinson (35) is 6′-iodopapaveroline.

6. Synthesis of Papaverine

Pictet and Gams (51) carried out the first complete synthesis of the alkaloid in 1909. Veratrol was acetylated in a Friedel-Crafts reaction, the acetoveratrone (XXX) was treated with nitrous acid, and the corresponding isonitroso derivative reduced to aminoacetoveratrone (XXXI) with tin and hydrochloric acid. The hydrochloride of this α-amino ketone was condensed with homoveratroyl chloride, and the resulting homoveratramidoacetoveratrone (XXXII) reduced to the corresponding secondary alcohol. The latter yielded the heterocyclic ring of papaverine under the influence of phosphorus pentoxide with the loss of two molecules of water.

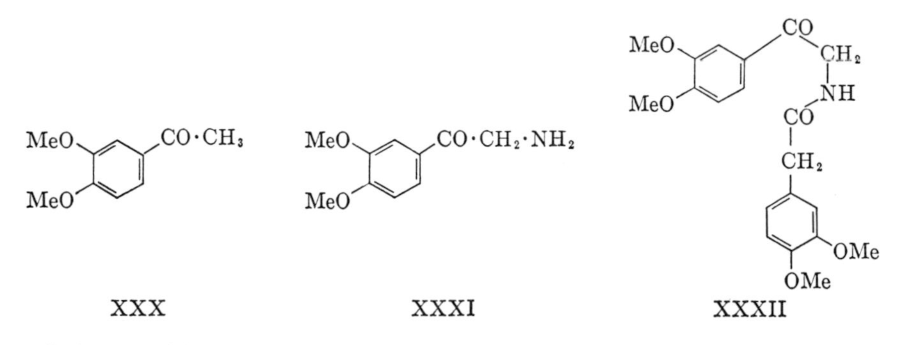

Prior to this synthesis, Pictet and Finkelstein (22) had attempted a synthesis of the alkaloid by way of its 3,4-dihydro derivative but were unable to remove the two extra hydrogen atoms from its pyridine ring. Späth and Burger (19) completed this synthesis by dehydrogenating 3,4-dihydropapaverine with palladized asbestos at 200°. Homoveratrylamine and homoveratroyl chloride were condensed, and the amide (XXXIII) converted to 3,4-dihydropapaverine (XXXIV) by a Bischler-Napieralski iso-

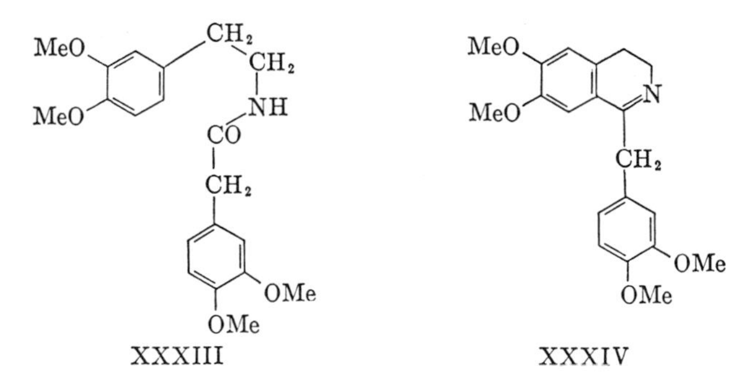

quinoline ring closure. Air oxidation of 3,4-dihydropapaverine yields 3,4-dihydropapaveraldine, which may be dehydrogenated by the action of potassium hydroxide (13b).

Since papaveraldine (II) is reduced to papaverine (p. 33), this constitutes another synthesis of the parent alkaloid. It should be mentioned that the alkaloid xanthaline, first isolated from opium mother liquors by T. and H. Smith Co. (54), has been identified with papaveraldine by Dobson and Perkin (55).

3,4-Dihydropapaverine is also obtained in a somewhat unexpected series of reactions (23, 24), initiated when homoveratramidoacetoveratrone

(XXXII) is treated with phosphorus oxychloride. An oxazole derivative (XXXV) is formed first which can be hydrogenated to homoveratrylhomoveratramide(XXXIII).

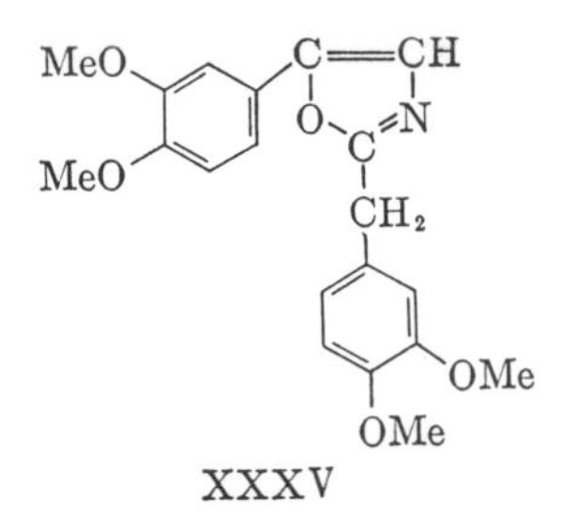

XXXV

The dehydrogenation of 3,4-dihydropapaverine may be carried out most suitably by the procedure of Kindler and Peschke (25). The dihydro compound is heated with palladium black in a hydrogen-acceptor medium, such as dihydrophellandrene, and good yields of papaverine are obtained in larger batch operations. Kindler and Peschke also improved a number of intermediate steps, such as the preparation of homoveratric acid from acetoveratrone by a Willgerodt reaction and formation of the amide by heating the acid and homoveratrylamine in tetralin solution.

The ease with which the dehydrogenation occurs in hydrogen-accepting media or high-boiling solvents, and which has been confirmed by many investigators, contrasts with the observation of Dobrowsky (73), who could not dehydrogenate other 3,4-dihydroisoquinoline derivatives under comparable conditions in a long series of systematically altered experiments. The dehydrogenation was studied particularly extensively by Harlay (56a), who used selenium, sulfur, nickel, silver, and palladium oxide in boiling carophyllene and obtained yields of papaverine ranging up to 85%. The use of an inert atmosphere has also been recommended (18).

Definite improvements over the older directions were also achieved in two almost identical syntheses published independently by Rosenmund, Nothnagel, and Riesenfeldt (56), and by Mannich and Walther (57) in 1927. Based on the observation (58) that β-nitrostyrenes add the elements of methanol when treated with sodium methoxide, these authors prepared 1-methoxy-1-(3,4-dimethoxyphenyl)-2-nitroethane (XXXVI) from 3,4-dimethoxy-β-nitrostyrene, reduced the nitro group, and cyclized the homoveratroyl derivative (XXXVII) of the resulting β-methoxy-β-(3,4-dimethoxyphenyl)ethylamine with phosphorus oxychloride. The ether base loses both water and methanol in this process and yields papaverine directly in yields up to 40%. This synthesis has also been applied to compounds differing from papaverine in the nuclear substituents.

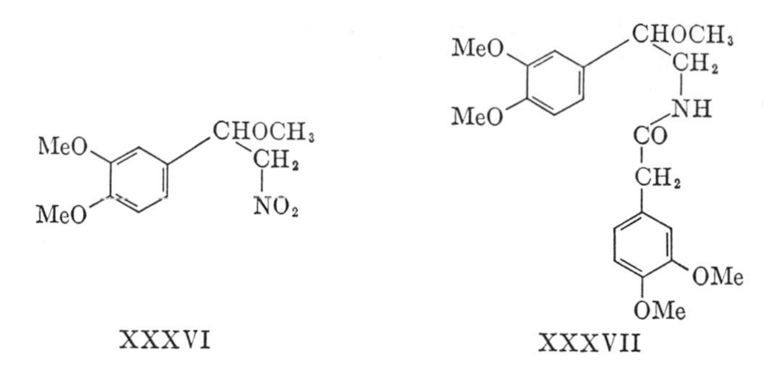

A synthesis of tetrahydropapaverine under such mild conditions that they may well serve as a model for analogous hypothetical reactions in phytochemistry has been reported by Späth and Berger (59). Homoveratrylamine was condensed with homoveratraldehyde in ether solution at room temperature; the resulting product, perhaps an aldimine, yielded 8 % of tetrahydropapaverine (X) on treatment with 19 % hydrochloric acid, apparently by hydration of the double bond and subsequent elimination of water.

In all of the syntheses discussed, alkoxy derivatives of α-aminoacetophenone or of β-phenethylamine were employed to supply the main structural outline of the isoquinoline system. Some of these amines are hard to obtain, especially if the resistant aromatic methoxyl groups are replaced by more sensitive substituents which may serve in the preparation of partly demethylated derivatives of papaverine or laudanosine. A significant innovation (60) which avoids the preparation of such unstable amines is the degradation of β-phenylpropionic acid azides (hydrocinnamic acid azides) to the corresponding isocyanates, which add to the required phenylacetic acids probably with the intermediate formation of four-membered cyclic hemiacetals. The latter are transformed to *N*-carboxylic acids, which lose carbon dioxide and yield amides needed in the isoquinoline syntheses. In practice, the azide is heated with the phenylacetic acid in benzene solution for several hours, and the amide is isolated from the reaction mixture without difficulty.

Conversely, if the substituted phenylacetic acid or its chloride are not readily accessible, the diazo ketone obtained from the corresponding aromatic acid chloride and diazomethane may be treated directly with the substituted phenethylamine. An Arndt-Eistert type rearrangement occurs which leads directly to the phenethylamide of the respective homo acid. An example for this type of reaction may be found in the synthesis of 1-benzylhydrohydrastinine (61).

Commercial syntheses of papaverine have been used for about fifteen years, but reports that certain laboratory procedures could not be stepped up to plant scale have appeared from time to time. Nevertheless, it could be expected that some of the best methods published in the scientific literature would form the basis of industrial syntheses. Indeed, the first commercial procedure ever published was an industrial extension and simplification of the method of Kindler and Peschke (25). Milliken, Shaw, Ferguson, and Waldo of Eli Lilly and Company (26) found it possible to dispense with the isolation of the 3,4-dihydropapaverine (XXXIV) from the condensation of the amide XXXIII with phosphorus oxychloride in thiophene-free benzene. The purification of XXXIV needs to consist only of an anhydrous caustic wash of the original acid reaction mixture followed by a water wash. The latter removes water-soluble solids which otherwise are found to precipitate on and inactivate the catalyst used in the next step. The intermediate is dried finally by azeotropic distillation.

In place of the dihydrophellandrene recommended by Kindler and Peschke, decahydronaphthalene (decalin) is the solvent of choice in the dehydrogenation. A 5% palladized carbon catalyst is preferable to other catalysts but necessitates reagents containing less than 0.005% sulfur. The benzene is removed from the dihydropapaverine and displaced by decalin until the temperature reaches 165°. The catalyst is slurried in, and the mixture is refluxed for five hours. Filtration of the catalyst from the hot solution, crystallization of papaverine from the filtrate, slurrying of the product with ether, and recrystallization from hot aqueous alcohol complete the procedure.

A second commercial synthesis of papaverine was performed by Wahl (62) in 1947 but not published until three years later. 3,4-Dimethoxyphenylpyruvic acid (XXXVIII), prepared from veratraldehyde and hippuric acid, was treated with ammonium hydroxide at 100° under pressure, and the resultant diamide (XXXIX) was hydrolyzed to the corresponding β-(3,4-dimethoxyphenyl)-α-(3,4-dimethoxyphenylacetamido) propionic acid. The methyl ester of this compound was cyclized readily with phosphorus oxychloride, and the resulting ester was saponified to 3,4-dihydropapaverine-3-carboxylic acid (XL). The latter was decarboxylated at 140° in tetralin solution to 3,4-dihydropapaverine, and addition of palladium-on-carbon catalyst to the reaction mixture furnished papaverine, four parts of vanillin leading to one part of the alkaloid in over-all yield.

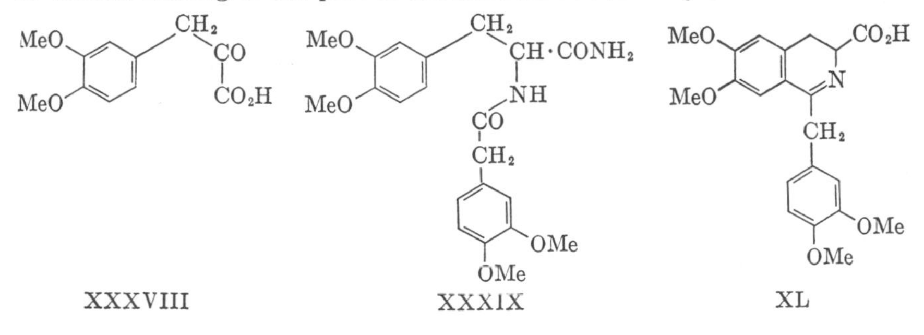

An almost identical method has been proposed by Galat (63), who prepared thc acid corresponding to the amide XXXIX, preferably by the action of ammonia on α-(*N*-benzamido)-3,4-dimethoxycinnamic acid. 3,4-Dihydropapaverine was isolated when the decarboxylation of XL was conducted in an atmosphere of hydrogen.

The decarboxylation and dehydrogenation of ethyl dihydropapaverine-3-carboxylate by means of sulfur or selenium at temperatures not exceeding 180° had also been disclosed previously in a patent (64).

7. Pharmacology

Although the pharmacological effects of papaverine have been investigated by many workers, no clear-cut picture of its activity can be drawn from their reports. This may be due to personal differences between the observers in choosing the phenomena to be emphasized, and to the effect of different doses. Therefore, only a bare outline of this phase will be presented in this chapter. The reader is referred to the excellent monograph by Krueger, Eddy, and Sumwalt (65), which offers a complete survey up to 1941 and includes a comprehensive bibliography. A few selected references to important publications up to 1951 have been included in the following paragraphs.

Papaverine does not cause deep narcosis or marked analgesia. It may produce convulsions, and cause the Straub tail reaction. The excitability of isolated nerves and muscles is abolished. Respiration is not profoundly affected. A single injection in rabbits causes an increase in blood sugar which is cancelled out by adrenalectomy or by a repetition of the injection over a period of days. Hyperglycemia follows withdrawal.

The blood pressure falls after administration of papaverine but may rise subsequently perhaps owing to liberation of epinephrine. Amplitude and rate of heart beat increase in the intact animal, but the latter diminishes in perfused hearts. Blood vessels are relaxed; however, actual use of papaverine in acute arterial occlusions does not seem to have been very successful. Since papaverine usually decreases the cholesterolytic power of blood, and always its cholesterol content, and causes increased elimination of bile acids in the stools, it has been postulated that it aids in the transformation of cholesterol into bile acids.

The muscles of the gastrointestinal tract are usually relaxed, and their motility is decreased; however, papaverine is not strongly constipating. Emesis is rare. Smooth muscles other than vascular or gastrointestinal show a decrease in tone and motility. In isolated eserinized strips of leech muscle, the contractions caused by acetylcholine are not inhibited by papaverine.

The toxic dose of papaverine has not been determined conclusively for any animal. Values reported range from 25 to 500 mg. per kilogram for various species, the average values from 100 to 200 mg. per kilogram. Sulfonamides increase the toxicity of the alkaloid, but this potentiation is abolished by certain amino acids, especially, *p*-aminobenzoic acid (66a). In this connection it may be noted that papaverine hydrochloride causes a marked decrease in ascorbic acid (66b). Like that of many other aromatic heterocyclic compounds, the toxicity of papaverine is increased by hydrogenation and conversion to quaternary salts.

The only definite tolerance to papaverine has been observed in rabbits, which develop tolerance to its hyperglycemic effect. The fate of papaverine in the body of dogs or rabbits seems determined largely by its enzymatic destruction, perhaps a demethylation, which takes place most rapidly in the liver (67).

Clinically, papaverine is used as an antispasmodic, and is given by mouth or by vein in doses of 30 to 80 mg. It has been found useful in the treatment of spastic conditions of the stomach and intestines caused by hyperacidity and duodenal ulcers. Other applications, such as in the treatment of biliary colic, asthma, vascular spasms, including angina pectoris, spasm secondary to embolic phenomena, and peripheral vascular diseases, have been more or less abandoned, and several synthetic antispasmodics have made inroads on the fields formerly reserved for papaverine. However, a shortage of papaverine developed when its usefulness was at a peak, and several methods were developed for the industrial synthetic production of the alkaloid to take care of this condition (see p. 43). A brief selected bibliography may serve as a guide to the literature concerning the clinical application of papaverine (68).

Since spasms may be the result of disorders of the central nervous system, papaverine is administered frequently in the form of salts of acidic drugs, which, on their own, exert a sedative or analgesic action. Examples of such molecular combinations are papaverine diethyl barbiturate (m.p. 138°), papaverine dipropyl barbiturate, papaverine phenobarbiturate (Pavemal, m.p. 145–146°), and papaverine coumarin-3-carboxylate (m.p. 129°).

8. Papaverine-like Compounds

Out of the desire to improve upon the therapeutic properties of papaverine by cutting down toxic effects and broadening its field of application in the relief of spasms, a number of structurally related compounds have been synthesized and tested. Of these Eupaverine, 1-(3,4-methylenedioxybenzyl)-3-methyl-6,7-methylenedioxyisoquinoline (XLI) (69), and Perparine, 1-(3,4-diethoxybenzyl)-6,7-diethoxyisoquinoline, the tetraethoxy analogue (70) of papaverine, have been used widely in medicine.

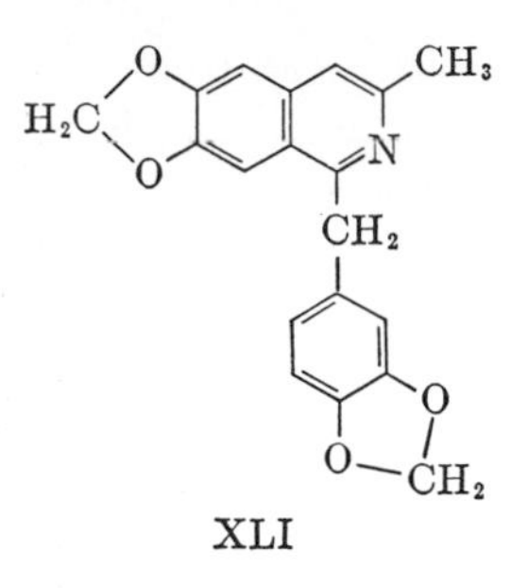

XLI

Eupaverine has been studied mostly in Europe. It has been administered by mouth, intravenously, and even intra-arterially, in doses of 0.12 to 0.3 g., with a total daily dosage as high as 2 g. Its use has been concerned with spastic conditions, usually those associated with embolic phenomena (70). A total of about forty compounds has been tested in this series. They differ from papaverine mostly in their substituents in the aromatic and isoquinoline rings, such as, methyl in position 3, methylenedioxyl, various alkoxyl, or phenyl groups in 6, 7, 3′, and 4′, and in alterations of the connecting methylene group (—CHOH, =CO, etc.) (71). While no definite conclusions concerning the relations of chemical structure and physiological action in this class of compounds can be drawn, tests of compounds derived from 1-phenylisoquinoline have demonstrated that the omission of the methylene group does not abolish antispasmodic activity, and that variation of nuclear substituents may produce compounds superior to papaverine in therapeutic value.

Table 2 shows most of the papaverine analogues tested as antispasmodics, together with any reported results of the tests.

Additional pharmacological data taken from the comprehensive report of Dobrowsky (22b) are shown in Tables 3 and 4. One compound mentioned in this work, 1-(3-pyridyl)-3-methyl-6,7-methylenedioxyisoquinoline (XLII) should be mentioned separately; it is about as toxic although more irritating than papaverine, but exhibits about 20 times the antispasmodic activity of the alkaloid on the isolated strip of rabbit intestine. This is in contrast to the much lower activity (2 to 5 times papaverine) observed for the isomeric 3-picolyl derivative (XLIII) (72b).

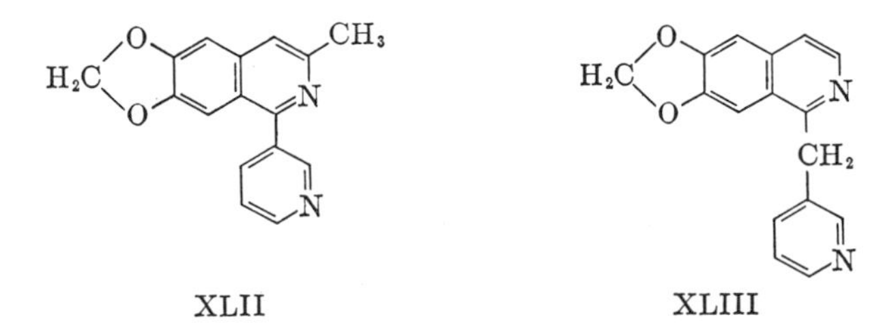

XLII XLIII

TABLE 2

No.	Derivative of 1-substituted isoquinoline	Antispasmodic activity	References
1	Papaverine	Maximum effective dilution, 100,000	72a, b
2	1-(3,4-Dimethoxybenzyl)-6,7-diethoxy-		72a
3	1-(3,4-Diethoxybenzyl)-6,7-dimethoxy-		72a
4	1-(3,4-Diethoxybenzyl-6,7-diethoxy- (Perparine)	3× papaverine	69, 72a
5	1-(3,4,5-Triethoxybenzyl)-6,7-dimethoxy- (Octaverine)		72a
6	1-(3,4-Methylenedioxybenzyl)-3-methyl-6,7-methylenedioxy- (Eupaverine)	Maximum effective dilution, 250,000	70, 72b
7	1-(3,4-Methylenedioxyphenyl)-6,7-methylenedioxy- (Neupapaverin)	Maximum effective dilution, 250,000	72b
8	1-Benzyl-6,7-methylenedioxy-	Maximum effective dilution, 250,000	72b
9	1-Phenyl-6,7-methylenedioxy-	Maximum effective dilution, 2,500,000	72b
10	1-(3-Pyridyl)-6,7-methylenedioxy-	Maximum effective dilution, 2,000,000	72b
11	1-Phenyl-3-methyl-	Maximum effective dilution, 1,250,000	72b
12	1-Phenethyl-3,4-dihydro-3-methyl-6,7-methylenedioxy-	Causes increase in muscle tone	72b
13	1-Benzyl-3-methyl-6,7-dimethoxy-		72c
14	1-(3,4-Dimethoxyphenethyl)-3-methyl-6,7-dimethoxy-		72c
15	1-(3,4-Methylenedioxyphenethyl)-3-methyl-6,7-dimethoxy-		72c
16	3-Methylpapaverine	Most active of compounds No. 13–19	72c
17	1-(3,4-Methylenedioxybenzyl)-3-methyl-6,7-dimethoxy-		72c
18	1-(3,4,5-Trimethoxybenzyl)-3-methyl-6,7-dimethoxy-		72c
19	1-(3,4,5-Triethoxybenzyl)-3-methyl-6,7-dimethoxy-		72c
20	1-Phenyl-3-methyl-6,7-dimethoxy-		72d
21	1-*p*-Methoxyphenyl-3-methyl-6,7-dimethoxy-		72d
22	1-(3,4-Dimethoxyphenyl)-3-methyl-6,7-dimethoxy-		72d

TABLE 2—*Continued*

No.	Derivative of 1-substituted isoquinoline	Antispasmodic activity	References
23	1-(3,4-Methylenedioxyphenyl)-3-methyl-6,7-dimethoxy-		72d
24	1-(3,4,5-Trimethoxyphenyl)-3-methyl-6,7-dimethoxy-		72d
25	1-(3,4,5-Triethoxyphenyl)-3-methyl-6,7-dimethoxy-		72d
26	1-(4-Methoxyphenyl)-3-methyl-6,7-methylenedioxy-		72d
27	1-(3,4-Dimethoxyphenyl)-3-methyl-6,7-methylenedioxy-		72d
28	1-(3,4,5-Trimethoxyphenyl)-3-methyl-6,7-methylenedioxy-		72d
29	1,3-Dimethyl-6-methoxy-7-hydroxy-		72e
30	1,3-Dimethyl-6,7-dimethoxy-		72e
31	1,3-Dimethyl-6-methoxy-7-benzyloxy-		72e
32	1,3-Dimethyl-6-methoxy-7-(3,4-dimethoxybenzyl)-		72e
33	1,3-Dimethyl-3,4-dihydro-	Five of the compounds (Nos. 33–40) relaxed spasms induced by acetylcholine or barium chloride and were much less toxic in mice than papaverine	72f
34	1,3-Dimethyltetrahydro-		72f
35	1-Phenyl-3-methyl-3,4-dihydro-		72f
36	1-Phenyl-3-methyltetrahydro-		72f
37	1-Benzyl-3-methyl-3,4-dihydro-		72f
38	1-Benzyl-3-methyltetrahydro-		72f
39	1-Phenethyl-3-methyl-3,4-dihydro-		72f
40	1-Phenethyl-3-methyltetrahydro-		72f

Papaverine and several of its homologues and derivatives exhibit a distinct local anesthetic activity which reaches a maximum in dihydrobromoperparine hydrochloride (73a). The values listed in Table 5 refer to tests on the rabbit cornea with acidic solutions (pH 2.9–4.1).

III. Laudanosine

1. Occurrence and Properties

The last alkaloid to separate from the mother liquors of the morphine extraction, laudanosine was isolated from opium in small amounts by Hesse (4, 74) in 1871. Opium contains less than 0.1% of this compound.

Laudanosine crystallizes from alcohol in prisms, or from ligroin in needles. It is soluble in alcohol, chloroform, ether, and hot petroleum ether, slightly soluble in ammonium hydroxide, and insoluble in water or alkalis. Its

TABLE 3

ANTISPASMODIC ACTIVITY AND TOXICITY OF SOME 1-BENZYLISOQUINOLINE DERIVATIVES (22b)

CUT 28-IT

R_6	R_7	$R_{3'}$	$R_{4'}$	Activity (isolated rabbit gut)	Toxicity	Therap. ratio
OCH_3 (Papaverine)	OCH_3	OCH_3	OCH_3	1	1	1
OC_2H_5 (Perparine)	OC_2H_5	OC_2H_5	OC_2H_5	2	1	2
OCH_2O		OCH_3	OCH_3	1½	½	3
OCH_2O		OCH_2O		1	3	⅓
OCH_3	OCH_3	OCH_2O		1	⅓	3
OCH_3	OCH_3	—	—	2	>1	>2
OC_2H_5	OCH_3	—	—	2	>1	>2
i-$C_5H_{11}O$	OCH_3	—	—	>1	<1	<1
OCH_2CH_2O		—	—	2	>1	>2
OCH_3	OCH_3	OCH_3	OCH_3 $R_3 = CH_3$	1	<1	>1
OCH_3	OCH_3	OCH_2O $R_3 = CH_3$		1½	½	3
OCH_2O		OCH_3	OCH_3 $R_3 = CH_3$	⅓	⅓	1
OCH_2O (Eupaverine)		OCH_2O $R_3 = CH_3$		2	½	4
OCH_3	OCH_3	$R_3 = CH_3$		2[a]	1	2
OCH_2O		$R_3 = CH_3$		2	1	2

[a] Possesses local anesthetic properties.

TABLE 4

PHARMACOLOGICAL PROPERTIES OF SOME 1-SUBSTITUTED ISOQUINOLINE DERIVATIVES (73)

Derivative of 1-substituted isoquinoline	Pharmacological property
1-Benzyl-3,4-dihydro-6,7,8-trimethoxy-	Causes spasms; toxicity 20× papaverine
3',4',6,7-Tetramethoxy-α-hydroxy- (Papaverinol)	Narcotic, not anesthetic
1-(3,4-Diethoxyphenyl)-6,7-diethoxy-	Activity 2×, toxicity ½× papaverine
1-Phenyl-	More active and toxic than papaverine
Tetrahydroeupaverine	Toxic, acts like strychnine
N-Acetonyltetrahydroeupaverine	Toxic, papaverine-like
1-(α-Ethylbenzyl)-3-methyl-6, 7-methylenedioxy-	Less active and toxic than papaverine
1-(α-Phenylbenzyl)-3-methyl-6,7-methylenedioxy-	Less active and toxic than papaverine
1-Piperonyl-3-methyl-6,7-methylene-dioxy-	2× papaverine activity, much less toxic
1-(3,4-Diethoxyphenyl)-3-methyl-6,7-methylenedioxy-	Activity and toxicity like Eupaverine
1-(3,4-Diethoxyphenyl)-3-methyl-6,7-diethoxy-	Less active than papaverine
1-Phenyl-3-methyl-6,7-methylenedioxy-	Less toxic than Eupaverine, twice as active
1-Phenyl-3-methyl-6,7-methylenedioxy-1,2,3,4-tetrahydro-	Spasmogenic
1-Phenyl-2,3-dimethyl-6,7-methylene-dioxy-1,2,3,4-tetrahydro-	Weakly musculotropic
1-Piperonyl-2,3-dimethyl-6,7-methylene-dioxy-1,2,3,4-tetrahydro-	Activity 2× papaverine, toxicity 2× papaverine
1-Phenyl-2-allyl-3-methyl-6,7-methylene-dioxy-, bromide	Toxicity 250× papaverine, irritating
1-Phenyl-3-methyl-6,7-diethoxy-	Activity like papaverine, toxicity 3× papaverine
1-Phenyl-3-methyl-	More active and toxic than Eupaverine
1,3-Diphenyl-6,7-methylenedioxy-	Activity 2× papaverine, toxicity 4× papaverine
1-Isoamyl-3-methyl-6,7-methylenedioxy-	As active, and 6× as toxic as Eupaverine
1-β-Styryl-3-methyl-6,7-methylenedioxy-	Activity 2× papaverine, toxic
1-Phenethyl-3-methyl-6,7-methylene-dioxy-3,4-dihydro-	Local anesthetic, not mydriatic
1-(9-Fluorenyl)-3-methyl-6,7-methylene-dioxy-3,4-dihydro-	Less active and toxic than papaverine

solution reacts alkaline and tastes bitter. This optically active base from opium melts at 89° and does not sublime. Its absorption spectrum has been studied by Dobbie and Lauder (75). Color tests with concentrated sulfuric acid demonstrate a rose coloration which disappears on warming,

TABLE 5

TOXICITY, ANTISPASMODIC ACTIVITY, AND LOCAL ANESTHETIC ACTIVITY OF SOME PAPAVERINE DERIVATIVES

Hydrochloride of	LD_{50} in mice subcut., g./kg.	Antispasmodic activity	Local anesthetic activity
Papaverine	0.22	1	0.5
Dihydropapaverine	0.32	1	0.25
Dihydrobromopapaverine	0.28	2	0.6
Perparine	0.66	7	7.2
Dihydroperparine	0.12	10	9.1
Dihydrobromoperparine	1.23	7	9.8
Cocaine	—	—	1

but turns to greenish-gray and violet at 130°. Alkaloid reagents give a number of colors, e.g., Mandelin's reagent, red-brown; Fröhde's reagent, pink-violet; and Lafon's reagent, purple-red to brown (76).

The hydrochloride, hydrobromide, and acid oxalate of (+)-laudanosine are amorphous; the quinate of (−)-laudanosine, formed in the optical resolution of the racemic mixture, melts at 120° and shows $[\alpha]_D$ −96.74°. DL-Laudanosine furnishes a number of crystalline salts, for instance, a hydrochloride, hydriodide, auri-, platini- and mercurichloride, picrate, (m.p. 174–175°), methiodide (m.p. 215–217°), and ethiodide (m.p. 202–203°).

2. Chemical Structure and Reactions

Laudanosine (XIII) has the formula $C_{21}H_{27}NO_4$ and contains four methoxyl groups. Its nitrogen atom is tertiary. Only few degradations have been carried out with the natural alkaloid. Exhaustive methylation leads through a normal methine step (XLIV) to a stilbene derivative called laudanosene (XLV).

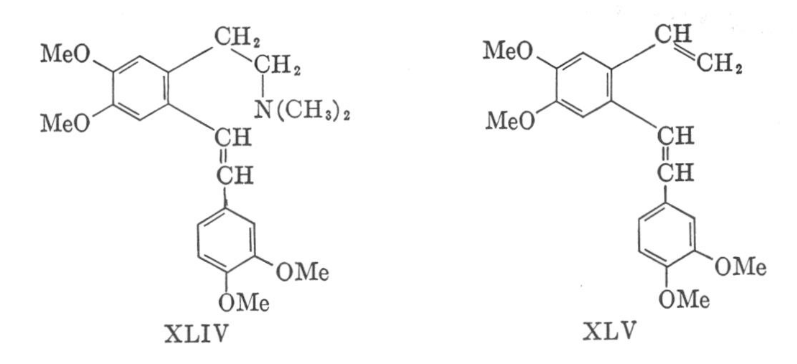

Oxidation of laudanosine furnishes veratraldehyde (77) while oxidative degradation of methyllaudanosine methine (XLIV) gives veratric acid (VI), trimethylamine, and 2-vinyl-4,5-dimethoxybenzoic acid; the latter was identified by hydrogenation to the known 2-ethyl-4,5-dimethoxybenzoic acid (78).

Most of the reactions of laudanosine have been carried out with the racemic mixture obtainable by reduction of quaternary papaverinium salts (p. 36). For instance, Gadamer and Kondo (79) obtained by oxidation with mercuric acetate, veratraldehyde and 4,5-dimethoxy-2-(β-methylaminoethyl) benzaldehyde (XLVI) (or its ring-chain tautomer, laudaline), which resembles cotarnine in its properties. The same products are formed when manganese dioxide is chosen as the oxidizing agent (80). In both

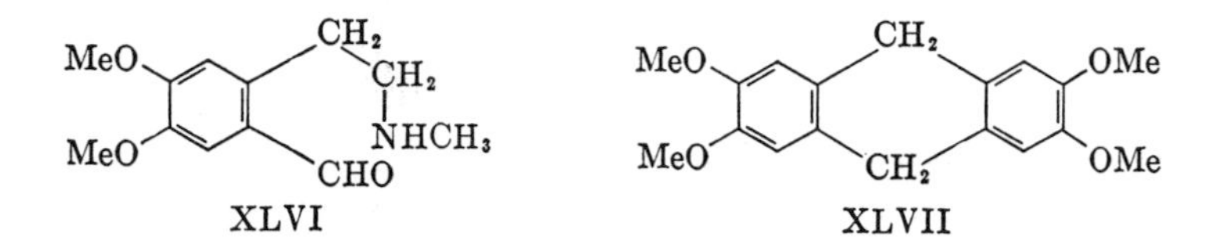

procedures another nitrogen-free product of the formula $C_{14}H_8(OCH_3)_4$ was isolated. A reinvestigation of the oxidation with manganese dioxide in sulfuric acid (81) revealed that the mechanism of the reaction involved a split of laudanosine into laudaline sulfate and veratryl alcohol; the latter either appears as veratraldehyde, or can condense further to 2,3,6,7-tetramethoxy-9,10-dihydroanthracene (XLVII), now recognized as the other "oxidation product."

In contrast to papaverine (I), which can be oxidized gently to papaverinol (IX) (p. 33), it has not been possible to isolate the corresponding hydroxylaudanosine (XLVIII) from analogous oxidation experiments with laudanosine. Nevertheless, two compounds of this formula (XLVIII), apparently diastereoisomers, are obtained when methylpapaverinolium chloride is hydrogenated in 70% alcohol solution in the presence of Adams' catalyst. They were given the names α- and β-hydroxylaudanosine, respectively (82). The Hofmann degradation of these secondary alcohols takes an unusual turn. When hydroxylaudanosine methochloride is heated with sodium or silver hydroxide in aqueous medium, not the expected ketonic amine (XLIX), but *N*,*N*-dimethyl-2-vinyl-4,5-dimethoxybenzylamine (L) and veratraldehyde are formed. The veratryl nucleus is detached from the rest of the molecule in the initial step of the reaction. The structure of L was corroborated by hydrogenation to *N*,*N*-dimethyl-2-ethyl-4,5-dimethoxybenzylamine (LI), and Emde degradation of this derivative to 4-methyl-5-ethylveratrol and trimethylamine. Moreover, LI was also synthesized for comparison.

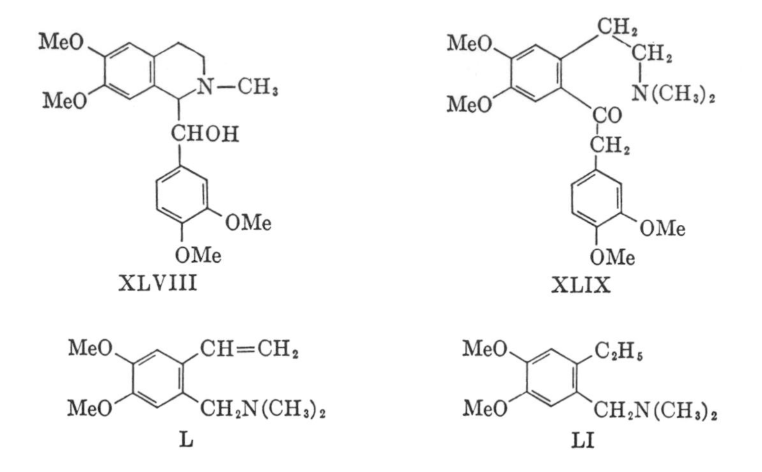

Demethylation of racemic laudanosine with 48% hydrobromic acid (30) or anhydrous aluminum chloride (82) splits all four methoxyl groups and furnishes laudanosoline, but two or three methoxyl groups may be preserved if other reagents and milder conditions are chosen. When heated with 35% hydrochloric acid at 100° for twenty minutes, all four possible monophenolic isomers are formed and may be isolated from the reaction mixture by fractional extraction and crystallization (83). They are laudanine (LII) (m.p. 166–167°), pseudolaudanine (LIII) (m.p. 120–121°), DL-codamine (XXII) (oily), and pseudocodamine (LIV) (m.p. 129-130°). A discussion of their structure may be found on pages 57–63.

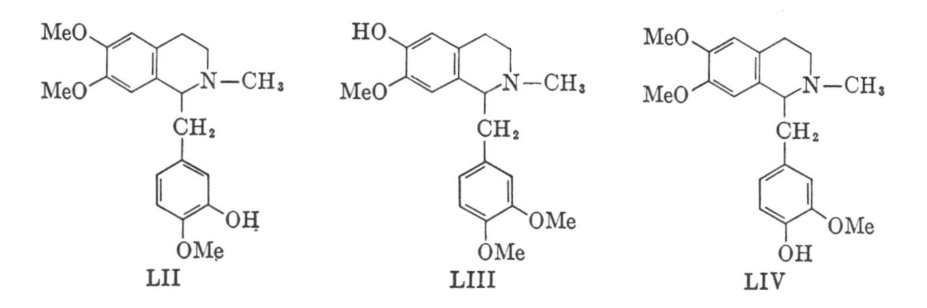

The same treatment with hydrochloric acid when applied to (−)-laudanosine gave again mixtures of phenolic bases from which a product identical with the opium alkaloid laudanidine [(−)-laudanine, LII] could be isolated. (+)-Laudanosine furnished the optical isomer of the natural alkaloid under analogous conditions (29).

Laudanine is also formed in low yields by heating DL-laudanosine with

4.5 moles of anhydrous aluminum chloride in nitrobenzene solution at 80°. With six moles of the same reagent, a 50% yield of laudanosoline 3′,7-dimethyl ether (LV) is obtained (84). The structure of this substance was proved by ethylating both phenolic hydroxyl groups and the tertiary nitrogen atom, and treating the ethosulfate with alkali. The resulting des-base was ozonized to vanillin ethyl ether and 2-(β-methylethylaminoethyl)-4-ethoxy-5-methoxybenzaldehyde (LVI); this compound was identical with the basic aldehyde obtained by a similar treatment of pseudolaudanine (LIII). Since the position of the phenolic hydroxyl in pseudolaudanine had been ascertained previously (33), its degradation product (LVI) could serve as a reference compound in this series of reactions.

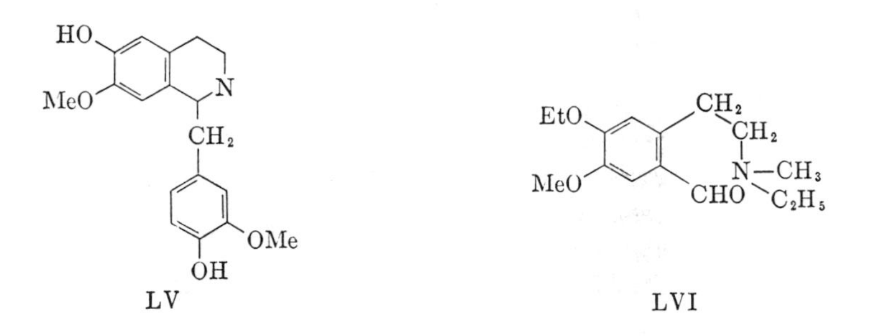

By a similar scheme, DL-laudanosoline 3′,4′-dimethyl ether (LVII), obtained by reduction of protopapaverine (XXI) (p. 37), can be degraded to the amino aldehyde LVIII and veratraldehyde.

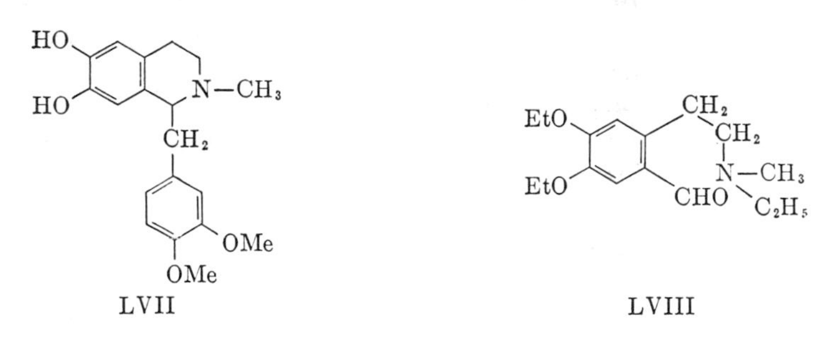

Laudanosoline shows an interesting behavior on careful oxidation. In an effort to follow the biogenesis of isoquinoline alkaloids, Robinson and Sugasawa (82) and Schöpf and Thierfelder (84) dehydrogenated laudanosoline with a possible ring closure to an aporphine system in mind. Using chloranil (tetrachloroquinone) or tetrabromoquinone, platinum and oxygen, or potassium ferricyanide as dehydrogenating agents, both groups of workers obtained the same unexpected material, 2,3,9,10-tetrahydroxy-7-methyl-dibenzo[*b*, *g*]tetrahydropyrrocolinium halide (LIX).

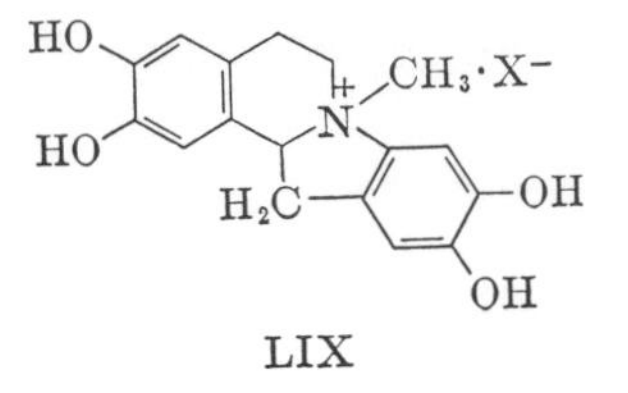

LIX

An analogous ring closure takes place when DL-norlaudanosine (tetrahydropapaverine) (X) hydrochloride is heated with formaldehyde, 2,3,10,11-tetramethoxy-5,6,13,13a-tetrahydro-8-dibenzo[*a*,*g*]quinolizine (LX) being formed (18). This (norcoralydine) was subsequently shown to be the DL-form of the dimethyl ether of coreximine.

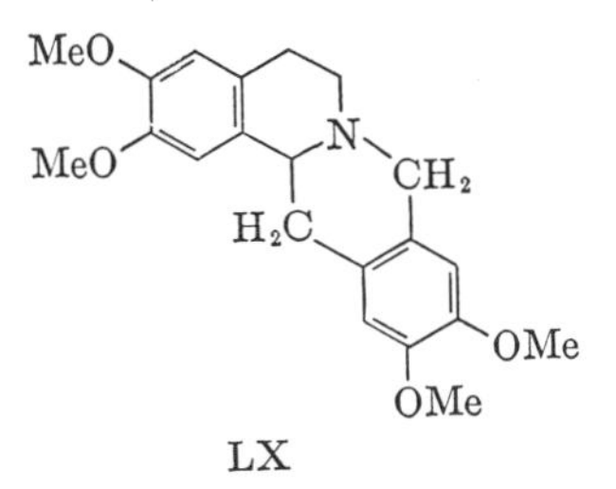

LX

Bromination of DL-laudanosine with bromine in glacial acetic acid furnished 6′-bromo-DL-laudanosine. A chlorine atom could be introduced into the same position by treatment with sulfuryl chloride and pyridine, or phenyl iodide chloride. The position of the bromine atom was determined by degradation to 6-bromoveratraldehyde and an amino aldehyde which also results from DL-laudanosine by the same series of steps.

3. Syntheses of Laudanosine

As mentioned above, quaternary papaverinium salts were reduced to DL-laudanosine (XIII) under a variety of conditions (17, 28, 29, 30, 76). Alternatively, tetrahydropapaverine may be treated with methyl iodide to give DL-laudanosine hydriodide (85). The route from papaverine via protopapaverine and DL-laudanosoline 3′,4-dimethyl ether (LVII) has already been mentioned. Methylprotopapaverinium iodide can be reduced to DL-codamine (XXII), which can be methylated to DL-laudanosine. Not only DL-codamine but its three phenolic isomers (p. 53) can be converted to DL-laudanosine by the action of diazomethane (33, 83, 86).

Since papaverine has been synthesized by different methods, these reactions constitute syntheses of DL-laudanosine. Pictet and Athanasescu (76) completed the synthesis of the optically active opium alkaloid by resolution of the racemic mixture with quinic acid.

The first complete synthesis of DL-laudanosine was achieved by Pictet and Finkelstein (22) by way of 3,4-dihydropapaverine (XXXIV), conversion to its methochloride, and subsequent reduction.

4. Steric Configuration

Early descriptions of natural laudanosine recorded it as a dextrorotatory base, $[\alpha]^{15}$ +103.23°, $[\alpha]^{22.5}$ +105°, in 97% alcohol (74b). However, observations in other solvents revealed that the medium has a profound effect on the direction of the rotation of the alkaloid (87). A few of these values are recorded in Table 6. They demonstrate that polar solvents cause laudanosine on the whole to rotate to the right, while non-polar solvents have the opposite effect.

A similar influence of solvent action and salt formation on the rotation of related bases has been observed for (−)-1-benzyl-2-methyl-1,2,3,4-tetrahydroisoquinoline (protolaudanosine) (LXI) and L(−)-α-phenylethylamine (LXII).

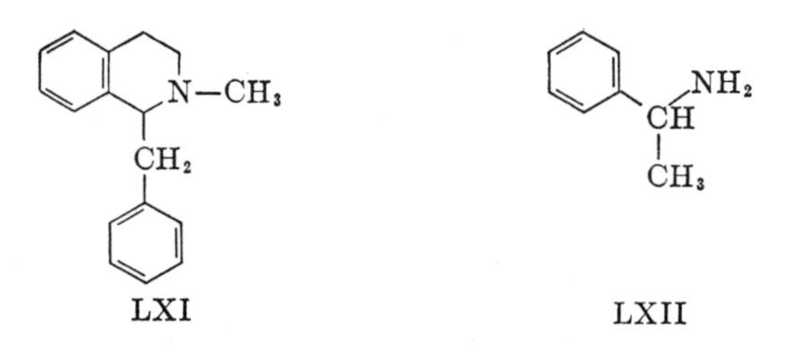

Assuming that this striking analogy in behavior may be taken as a basis for assigning a similar configuration to these compounds, an absolute configurational determination of one of them would suffice for the correct interpretation of the other members of this group. Such a determination has been carried out by Leithe (87) who degraded the benzoyl derivative of

TABLE 6

OPTICAL ROTATION OF NATURAL LAUDANOSINE

Solvent	Concentration	$[\alpha]^{17}_D$
Carbon bisulfide	3.15	−8.0°
Ether	0.61	−0.5°
Benzene	2.25	+2.2°
Pyridine	1.80	+8.3°
Chloroform	1.67	+52°
Absolute ethanol	1.42	+90°
97% Ethanol	1.53	+100°
1 *N* Hydrochloric acid	1.36	+102°

LXII to the accepted reference compound L(+)-benzoylalanine. The configuration of the related opium alkaloids laudanosine, codamine, and laudanidine may therefore be written as follows:

L(+ in chloroform)-laudanosine
L(+)-codamine
D(−)-laudanidine

In a steric formula, the substituted benzyl group of these products can be thought to have the same configuration as the carboxyl group in L-alanine.

5. Pharmacology

DL-Laudanosine causes central motor paralysis and exaggerated spinal reflexes in winter frogs and mice (71). Given intravenously, it produces convulsions by acting on the spinal nerve centers in chloralosed dogs, even if the spinal cord is cut just below the medulla. Intraspinal anesthetics prevent the convulsions (88).

On the heart, respiration, and smooth muscles, laudanosine has an action quite similar to that of papaverine, but when injected into the canal of the medulla laudanosine produces convulsions while papaverine acts as an anesthetic (89). A polymethylene bis-quaternary salt of laudanosine showed considerably more curare activity than *d*-tubocurarine but less than dimethyltubocurarine (90).

IV. Monophenolic Bases of the Laudanosine Type

1. Laudanine

a. Occurrence and Properties. The name laudanine is derived from laudanum (opium) from which Hesse (4b, 74a) isolated it from the alkaline mother liquors of the extraction of morphine in amounts corresponding to about 0.005% of the opium used. The alkaloid crystallizes from chloroform as colorless rhombohedra melting at 166–167°. It is soluble in chloroform, benzene, and hot alcohol, and very slightly soluble in ether (1:647 at 18°) (4a). In the writer's experience it can be precipitated under a layer of ether from the water solution of its salts by means of sodium bicarbonate, and extracted rapidly into smaller volumes of ether while still amorphous, but it crystallizes from the solvent on standing (83). The absorption spectrum (75) and the density (1.256) (91) of the alkaloid have been determined.

Laudanine has the formula $C_{20}H_{25}NO_4$. It reacts basic but goes into solution in excess alkali. This behavior, as well as its color reaction with ferric chloride, suggests the presence of a phenolic hydroxyl group. In concentrated sulfuric acid the compound turns red, the color changing to violet on heating to 150°.

Laudanine is optically inactive in spite of the presence of an asymmetric carbon atom in its formula (LII). Not many asymmetric compounds occur in living cells as raccmates (92); apparently laudanine has not been formed by racemization of its naturally occurring *levo*-form (laudanidine) during the extraction from opium since Späth and Burger have been unable to effect the racemization of laudanidine (29).

The following salts of laudanine have been described: hydrochloride, sulfate, oxalate, tartrate, platinichloride, aurichloride, picrate (m.p. 176–177°), and the sodium salt.

b. Structure and Chemical Reactions. Laudanine contains one phenolic hydroxyl group and three methoxyl groups. Its nitrogen atom is tertiary. Oxidation with alkaline permanganate solution destroys the phenolic ring and yields *m*-hemipinic acid (V). This proves that the phenolic hydroxyl is not located in the isoquinoline system.

Methylation with methyl iodide (93) or diazomethane (86) yields DL-laudanosine (XIII). Likewise, ethylations with ethyl iodide, ethyl sulfate (84), or diazoethane furnish 3′-ethyllaudanine. Oxidation of this ethyl ether ruptures the molecule, and Späth (86) was able to isolate 3-ethoxy-4-methoxybenzoic acid from the reaction mixture, thus locating the position of the hydroxyl group in laudanine.

Protection of the phenolic hydroxyl group during the oxidation can also be effected by carbethoxylation.

The Hofmann degradation of ethyllaudanine ethosulfate leads to a desbase which, on ozonization, is split into isovanillin ethyl ether and the amino aldehyde LXIII. This may be accepted as additional proof of the structure of laudanine.

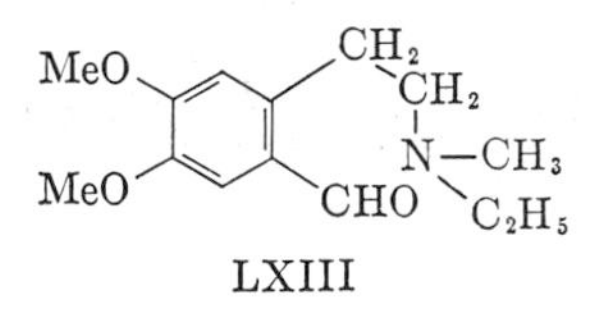

LXIII

c. Syntheses of Laudanine. The synthesis of laudanine was accomplished by Späth and Lang (94) who used the Bischler-Napieralski isoquinoline synthesis in their task. On the whole, their procedures were patterned upon the synthesis of DL-laudanosine (22). The main difficulty was to start with the proper derivative of homoprotocatechuic acid in which the phenolic hydroxyl, later to appear in laudanine, was protected during the various synthetic steps. Carbethoxyhomoisovanillyl chloride (LXIV) was condensed with homoveratrylamine and the resulting amide was cyclized in toluene solution with phosphorus pentoxide to 1-(carbethoxyisovanillyl) -6,7-dimethoxy-3,4-dihydroisoquinoline (LXV). The methochloride of this base was reduced with tin and hydrochloric acid, simultaneously hydrolyzing the carbethoxy group and yielding a product identical with laudanine from opium.

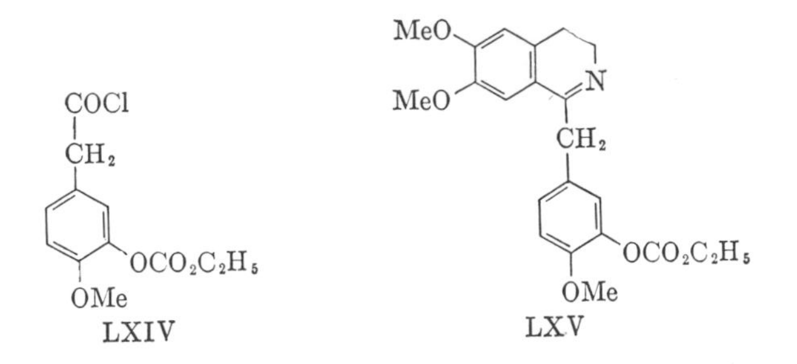

Laudanine was also obtained by Späth and Burger (29) by heating DL-laudanosine with concentrated hydrochloric acid at 100° for twenty minutes. It was the first substance to separate from the mixture of phenolic bases thus obtained. Heating of DL-laudanosine with a nitrobenzene solution of 4.5 moles of anhydrous aluminum chloride (84) gave an 8% yield of laudanine.

2. Laudanidine (Tritopine)

When laudanine is isolated from opium extraction liquors, it is frequently contaminated by an optically active companion-alkaloid which Hesse (95) separated through its more soluble hydrochloride, and which he named laudanidine. Analysis of the compound established the formula $C_{20}H_{25}NO_4$ and demonstrated the presence of three methoxyl groups. Its solubility in alkali, and a color reaction with ferric chloride suggested the presence of a phenolic hydroxyl. It resembles laudanine in crystal form and its colorations with concentrated sulfuric acid; however, the alkaloid is strongly levorotatory, $[\alpha]_D^{15}$ −87.8°, $[\alpha]_D^{17}$ −90.6°, $[\alpha]_D^{18}$ −100.6° (in chloroform) being reported. The few salts of laudanidine described include the hydriodide, acid oxalate, and platinichloride, and resemble closely those of laudanine. The similarities between laudanidine and laudanine prompted Hesse to regard the former as an optically active form of laudanine.

This prediction was borne out by later structural studies (96). Methylation of laudanidine (LII) with diazomethane gave *levo*-laudanosine (XIII); this relationship accounted for the ring system and all functional groups but left the position of the phenolic hydroxyl group in doubt. This question was settled by ethylation to *levo*-ethyllaudanidine and oxidation to the same 3-ethoxy-4-methoxybenzoic acid obtained from the racemic mixture.

The synthesis of laudanidine by Späth and Burger (29) followed the pattern used by them in their synthesis of laudanine. *levo*-Laudanosine, prepared by the resolution of the racemic mixture with quinic acid (76), was heated with concentrated hydrochloric acid under controlled conditions. A mixture of phenolic bases was obtained from which a base identical with natural laudanidine was isolated.

Under analogous conditions, (+)-laudanosine was cleaved to the enantiomer of natural laudanidine. When the two optical isomers were mixed in solution, laudanine crystallized out, thus confirming the relationship of these three forms.

While dextrorotatory laudanidine has not yet been discovered in opium, its occurrence in this material is in the realm of possibility.

In 1890, Kauder (93b) worked up the mother liquors of protopine oxalate and isolated an alkaloid which he named tritopine. It was soluble in alkali, and its analysis and color reactions made likely its relation to the monophenolic laudanosine derivatives. Späth and Seka (97) obtained a sample of tritopine, probably from Kauder's original collection, and determined its correct formula, $C_{20}H_{25}NO_4$. It melted at 184° (evac. tube) and exhibited $[\alpha]_D^{18}$ −85.7° (in chloroform). A comparison of tritopine and its salts with (−)-laudanidine and its corresponding salts established the identity of the two samples.

For a study of the true configuration of laudanidine, recognized as D(−)-laudanine, see page 57 (87).

3. Codamine

a. Occurrence, Properties, and Reactions. Like most of the other phenolic opium alkaloids of this group, codamine was isolated by Hesse (4) from morphine mother liquors. It is separated from laudanine and two other bases by fractional crystallization. According to Hesse, it occurs in Turkish opium to the extent of 0.0033%.

The large colorless rhombohedra of the alkaloid crystallize from ether. They melt at 126–127° and are very soluble in ethanol, chloroform, or ligroin, and slightly soluble in boiling water. The solutions of codamine react alkaline; its salts reported by its discoverer are mostly amorphous, but the platinichloride and acid tartrate are crystalline.

Codamine is tasteless while its salts taste bitter; ferric chloride and concentrated nitric acid give a dark-green color while the solution in concentrated sulfuric acid turns green, and then violet on heating. Its optical rotation has never been determined, but since it can be methylated to L(+)-laudanosine, its configuration must be L(+)-codamine (87). This was corroborated by mixing L(+)-laudanosine from the methylation just mentioned with a sample of levorotatory laudanosine; from the solution of this mixture DL-laudanosine crystallized on cooling (33).

This lead, together with analytical evidence (formula, $C_{20}H_{25}NO_4$; three methoxyl groups by Zeisel-Pregl determination) suggested that codamine is a monophenolic derivative of laudanosine, and thus an isomer of laudanine and laudanidine.

The proof of the structure of codamine by Späth and Epstein (33) is an elegant example of microtechnique in alkaloid chemistry. Working with a total of 0.2 g. of the natural base, these investigators studied its methylation with diazomethane using 0.01 g., and its ethylation with ethyl iodide and potassium hydroxide, and subsequent oxidation of an 0.0085-g. sample.

Oxidation of codamine ethyl ether (LXVI) cleaved the benzylisoquinoline system to 4-methoxy-5-ethoxyphthalic acid (LXVII) and veratric acid (VI). While the formation of these two acids precluded the location of the phenolic hydroxyl in the benzyl residue, LXVII could have arisen from either a 6- or 7-ethoxy-substituted isoquinoline system. This question was settled by repeating the potassium permanganate oxidation of 0.0085 g. of codamine ethyl ether (LXVI) under gentle conditions. This time, 1-keto-2-methyl-6-methoxy-7-ethoxy-1,2,3,4-tetrahydroisoquinoline (LXVIII) was isolated; its structure was confirmed by synthesis, and therefore codamine is XXII.

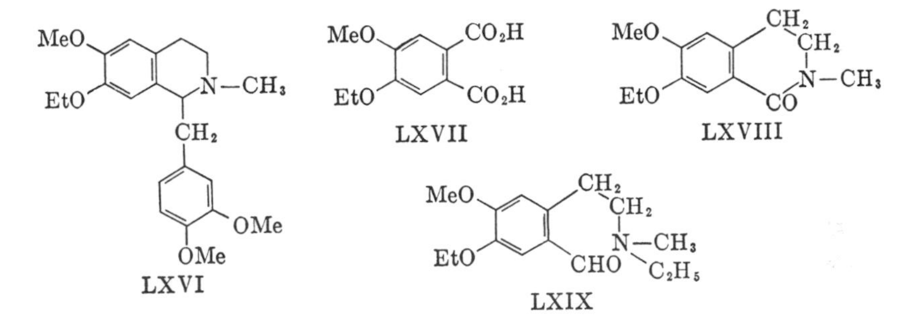

Further evidence for the structure of codamine was furnished by Hofmann degradation of its racemic ethyl ether (84) and subsequent ozonization. In a series of steps analogous to those in related series, two aldehydes, the amino aldehyde (LXIX) and veratraldehyde, were obtained.

b. Synthesis of Codamine. A synthesis of DL-codamine (42) starts from protopapaverine (XXI), which is converted to its quaternary chloride and then reduced with tin and hydrochloric acid. A preparative improvement (84) consists in the catalytic hydrogenation of the quaternary salt.

A total synthesis of DL-codamine (83) started from vanillin benzyl ether, which was condensed with nitromethane; the resulting 3-methoxy-4-benzyloxy-β-nitrostyrene of m.p. 122–123° was reduced to 3-methoxy-4-benzyloxyphenethylamine (LXX) (98), m.p. 67–69°. The homoveratramide of this compound was cyclized by phosphorus pentoxide in xylene in a yield of 15%, and the resultant 3′,4′,6-trimethoxy-7-benzyloxy-3,4-dihydroisoquinoline (LXXI) was converted to the methochloride and reduced with tin and hydrochloric acid. The readily hydrolyzable benzyl ether group, which had provided protection of the phenolic hydroxyl during this synthesis, was removed by action of hydrochloric acid. The oily DL-codamine was identified by its picrate (m.p. 182–184°, 187–189°) (42), which was identical with a sample of DL-codamine picrate obtained by partial hydrolysis of DL-laudanosine with hydrochloric acid (83). Racemic codamine has not yet been resolved.

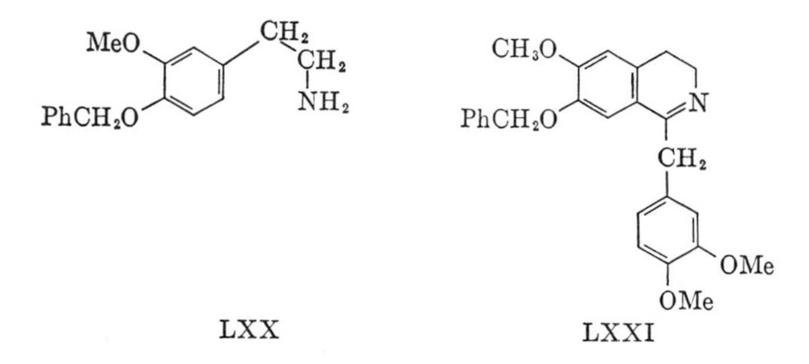

4. Pseudolaudanine and Pseudocodamine

The two bases described in this section have not been found in plant materials, but are formed by certain chemical reactions from papaverine or laudanosine.

a. Pseudolaudanine. Pseudolaudanine or 1-(3,4-dimethoxybenzyl)-2-methyl-6-hydroxy-7-methoxy-1,2,3,4-tetrahydroisoquinoline (LIII) was prepared first by Decker and Eichler (31, 32) by reduction of *N*-methylnorpapaverinium betaine (XVI), which, in turn, results from the action of dilute alkalis on methylpapaverinium iodide. A purer product (m.p. 120–121°) may be obtained in better yields by hydrogenation of the phenolbetaine in the presence of Adams' catalyst (84) or by electrolytic reduction (83).

The base LIII was also found by Burger (83) in the mother liquors of laudanine obtained by partial demethylation of DL-laudanosine (29). Vice versa, pseudolaudanine can be methylated to laudanosine (33, 42).

The structure of pseudolaudanine was ascertained further by oxidation of its ethyl ether. Controlled oxidation yielded 1-keto-2-methyl-6-ethoxy-7-methoxy-1,2,3,4-tetrahydroisoquinoline (LXXII) (83) while more vigorous oxidative cleavage furnished 4-ethoxy-5-methoxyphthalic acid (LXVII) and veratric acid. The ethyl ether has also been degraded to an amino aldehyde of the cotarnine type (LXXIII), and veratraldehyde (84).

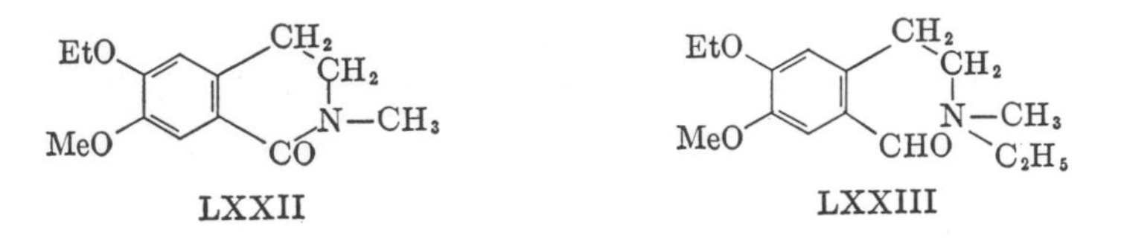

LXXII LXXIII

b. Pseudocodamine. When DL-laudanosine is heated with concentrated hydrochloric acid at 100° for twenty minutes, and the resulting mixture of phenolic bases is separated by fractional extraction with insufficient amounts of hydrochloric acid and then by fractional crystallization from ether, laudanine, a second base melting at 129–130°, and later pseudolaudanine crystallize out (83), while DL-codamine remains in the final mother liquors as an oil. The base melting at 129–130° gives a characteristic color reaction. Its colorless solution in concentrated sulfuric acid turns violet on addition of potassium bichromate.

Since no short name has been proposed for this iosmer, and the name isolaudanine has been given an unidentified substance of m.p. 76° obtained by reduction of "trimethylpapaveroline" methochloride (98a), the name pseudocodamine is proposed for the new phenolic base.

Pseudocodamine (LIV) was found to be 1-(3-methoxy-4-hydroxybenzyl)-2-methyl-6,7-dimethoxy-1,2,3,4-tetrahydroisoquinoline. Ethylation with diazoethane led to an ethyl ether (m.p. 176–180°) which could be oxidized to *N*-methylcorydaldine and 3-methoxy-4-ethoxybenzoic acid (LXXIV).

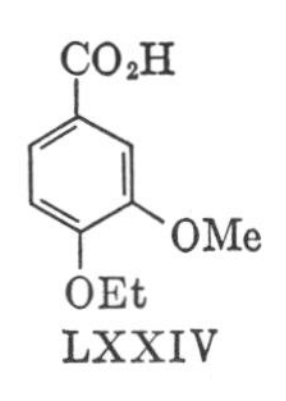

LXXIV

5. NEPROTINE

The optically inactive base neprotine, $C_{19}H_{23}NO_6$, was discovered by Chatterjee (99) in *Berberis nepalensis* Spreng. and was subsequently found to occur in several species of *Mahonia*, growing in different parts of India. The amount of base appeared to vary with the species, as shown in Table 7. Except for *M. simonsii*, the various species contain much larger amounts of berberine than neprotine (102).

Neprotine is a secondary amine and possesses two phenolic hydroxyl and two methoxyl groups (103). When treated with methylmagnesium iodide in anisole (104), neprotine yields five equivalents of methane, whereas

TABLE 7

PER CENT OF NEPROTINE IN MAHONIA SPECIES (99, 100, 101)

Species	Parts examined	Neprotine, %
Berberis nepalensis Spreng.	Root	0.020
B. nepalensis (*M. acanthifolia* Wall. ex G. Don)	Root	0.007
Mahonia griffithii Takeda	Bark	0.001
M. borealis Takeda	Root	0.311
M. simonsii Takeda	Root	0.270
M. leschenaultii Takeda	Root	0.011
M. sikkimensis Takeda	Bark	0.001
M. manipurensis Takeda	Root	Traces

neprotine dimethyl ether produces only two equivalents of methane under the same conditions. Since neprotine is converted to a trimethyl derivative with dimethyl sulfate—the two phenolic hydroxyls and the imino group being methylated—the two other active hydrogen atoms must be part of alcoholic hydroxyl groups. Zinc-dust distillation of neprotine (LXXV) furnished isoquinoline, and from the comparison of ultraviolet absorption spectra of neprotine and the accompanying berberine the presence of a tetrahydroisoquinoline nucleus in neprotine was anticipated. Oxidation of neprotine with potassium permanganate formed hemipinic acid (LXXVI), while with manganese dioxide and sulfuric acid opianic acid (LXXVII) was obtained. Both products of oxidation show that the two methoxyl groups are present in the same benzene nucleus, and in adjacent positions, and the aldehyde group in opianic acid must be derived from a primary alcohol group in the same nucleus; the production of the carboxyl group indicates the fission of the link of the benzene ring to the tetrahydroisoquinoline system, and makes likely the existence in neprotine of a 1-(*o*-dimethoxy-hydroxymethylbenzyl) isoquinoline structure. Moreover, the two phenolic hydroxyl groups of neprotine must be located in the isoquinoline portion of the molecule since oxidation destroys the latter and does not permit isolation of identifiable fragments. When, however, neprotine dimethyl ether is oxidized, both hemipinic acid—from the substituted benzyl group—and *m*-hemipinic acid (V) were obtained. The *m*-isomer must have originated in the aromatic portion of the tetrahydroisoquinoline system, and places the two phenolic hydroxyl groups in positions 6 and 7.

Of the two alcoholic hydroxyl groups, one must be primary, since it appears as an aldehyde group in opianic acid. It must be located ortho to the benzyl carbon atom, and since one of the two methoxyl groups of neprotine occupies one ortho position, only the other ortho position is available for the —CH_2OH group. From analogies with other alkaloids in the benzylisoquinoline series, the benzyl bridge appears as the most likely place for the other—secondary—alcohol group. It is quite likely that it would be inert to usual reagents for hydroxyl groups. A related base, (LXXVIII), could not be methylated or acetylated (105).

Although neprotine contains one asymmetric carbon atom, it is optically inactive. Optically active forms of the alkaloid have not yet been isolated.

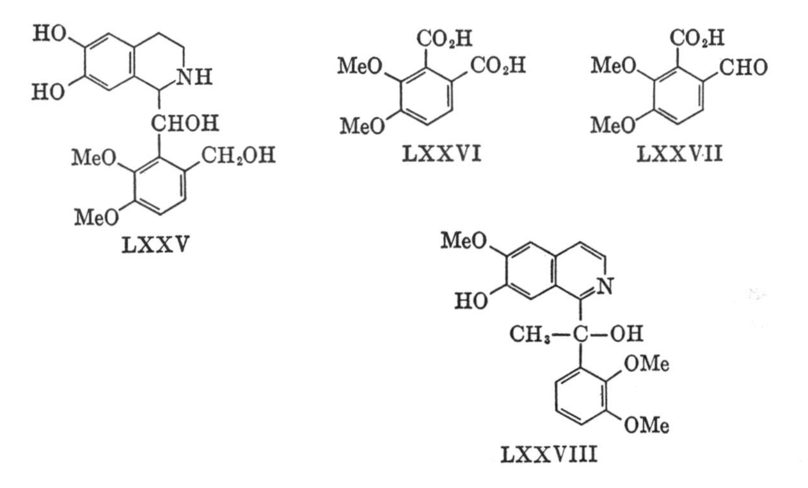

6. Coclaurine

The alkaloid (+)-coclaurine is found in the evergreen menispermaceous shrub *Cocculus laurifolius* DC., which occurs principally in India, southern China, and Japan. The Chinese drug *Koshiu-wyaku* consists of the dried root of this tree. An alkaloid probably identical with coclaurine was isolated from the bark and leaves by Greshoff but the pure base was described first by H. and T. Kondo (106). It shows m.p. 221°, $[\alpha]_D^{21}$ +0.9° (in methanol), and it is soluble in alkali. Its hydrochloride melts at 264°.

The structure of coclaurine was established by zinc-dust distillation, which gave *p*-cresol, methylamine, and other products, and by exhaustive methylation followed by oxidation. Hofmann degradation of the fully methylated alkaloid (LXXIX) led first to methine (LXXX) and then to the diene (LXXXI). The methine was oxidized to anisic (LXXXII), and *m*-hemipinic (V) acids.

DL-Dimethylcoclaurine was synthesized by the Bischler-Napieralski method starting with homoveratrylamine and *p*-methoxyphenylacetyl chloride. The 3,4-dihydroisoquinoline derivative first obtained was hydrogenated in the presence of palladium. The necessary comparison with material from the optically active alkaloid was achieved by subjecting the synthetic dimethylcoclaurine to exhaustive methylation, which robs C_1 of the tetrahydroisoquinoline system of its asymmetric character. The methine base (LXXX) thus obtained was identical with that from (natural) coclaurine dimethyl ether.

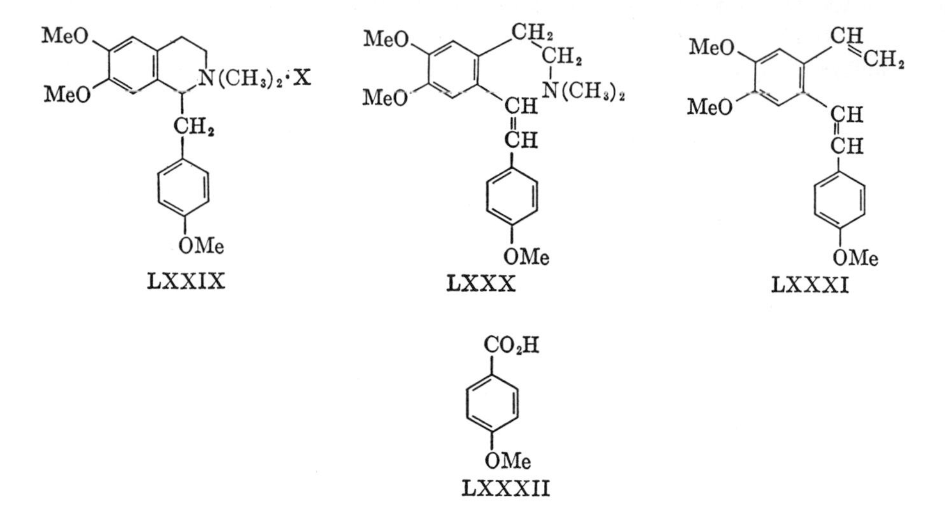

The positions of the phenolic hydroxyl groups were ascertained by exhaustive methylation of coclaurine diethyl ether followed by oxidation whereby 3-ethoxy-4-methoxy-6-ethylbenzoic acid (from the isoquinoline portion), and *p*-ethoxybenzoic acid (from the hydroxybenzyl moiety) were obtained.

These degradation reactions thus established the chemical constitution of the alkaloid as 1-(4-hydroxybenzyl)-6-methoxy-7-hydroxy-1,2,3,4-tetrahydroisoquinoline (LXXXIII). It is of interest that this formula, if quaternized, expresses closely one-half of the structure of the curare alkaloid *d*-tubocurarine chloride. A suitably bisected formula of this drug is shown in LXXXIV.

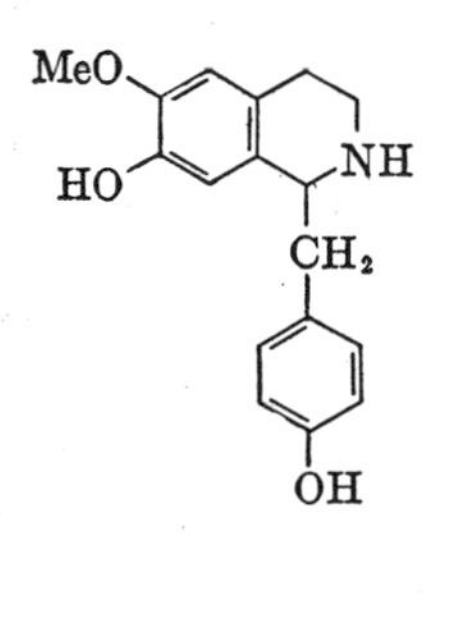

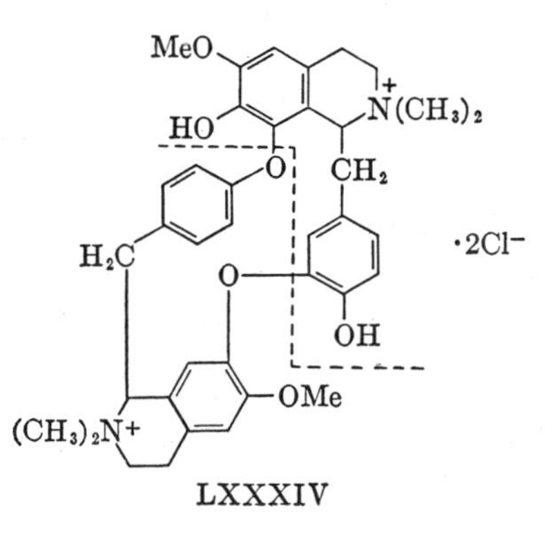

LXXXIII LXXXIV

Additional contemporary interest in coclaurine as a potentially active fragment of the *d*-tubocurarine structure was furnished by a report of Plugge (107), who tested extracts of the source of this alkaloid and found them to possess a weak and definite curare-like activity. The extracts exerted a general paralyzing activity, principally at the neuromuscular junction of the motor nerves as shown by experiments in frogs. Since coclaurine thus presented one of the rare cases of curariform activity in a non-quaternary compound, and since the frog method is no longer considered adequate for screening tubocurarine-like activity, synthetic DL-coclaurine (see below) was tested (108), but neither this compound nor its methochloride exhibited any effect up to a dose of 1 mg. on neuromuscular transmission in dogs.

The synthesis of DL-coclaurine was announced almost simultaneously by Finkelstein (108) and by Kratzl and Billek (109). In Finkelstein's method, vanillin benzyl ether was condensed with nitromethane, and the resulting β-nitrostyrene derivative was reduced to 3-methoxy-4-benzyloxyphenethylamine by means of lithium aluminum hydride. Condensation with 4-carbethoxyhydroxyphenylacetyl chloride yielded *N*-(3-methoxy-4-benzyloxyphenethyl)-4-carbethoxyhydroxyphenylacetamide, which was cyclized with phosphorus oxychloride to 1-(4-carbethoxyhydroxybenzyl)-6-methoxy-7-benzyloxy-3,4-dihydroisoquinoline (LXXXV). This base was hydrogenated in the presence of Adams' catalyst, and the resulting tetrahydro base was freed from protecting groups by treatment with warm hydrochloric acid.

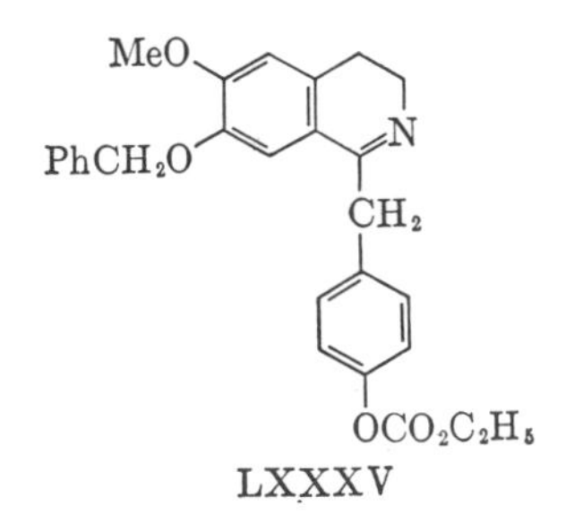

LXXXV

The method of Kratzl and Billek (109) made use of the condensation of 3-methoxy-4-hydroxyphenethylamine with 4-benzyloxyphenylacetyl chloride; the free phenolic hydroxyl group of the resulting amide was now benzylated, and this operation was followed by ring closure, hydrogenation, and acid removal of the groups protecting the phenolic hydroxyls as described above.

7. Armepavine

Armepavine was isolated from *Papaver caucasicum* Bieb. (110, 111) (*P. armeniacum* Lam. and *P. floribundum* Desf.). It forms a hydrate which melts at around 100° while the anhydrous base melts at 148–149° and shows $[\alpha]_D$ −118.7° (in chloroform).

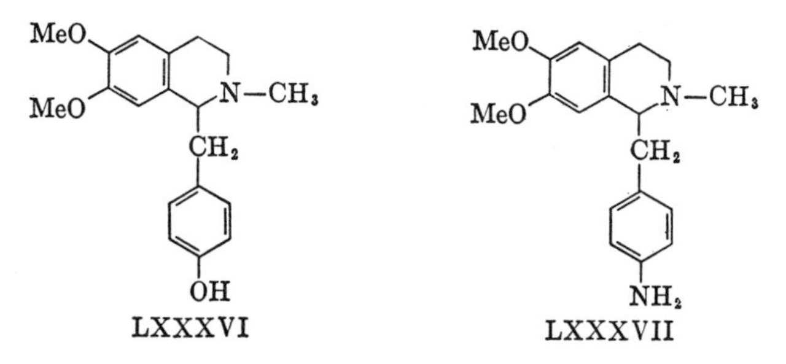

Chemically, armepavine may be regarded as the 7-methyl ether of *N*-methylcoclaurine. It is 1-(4-hydroxybenzyl)-2-methyl-6,7-dimethoxy-1,2,3,4-tetrahydroisoquinoline (LXXXVI) (110). Its structure follows from its methylation to a non-phenolic base which can be oxidized to anisic acid. The methiodide of this methylated base can be degraded to trimethylamine and 2-(β-styryl)-4,4′,5-trimethoxystilbene. This diene is oxidizable to anisic and meta-hemipinic acid. Armepavine ethyl ether, obtained by treatment of the alkaloid with diethyl sulfate and alkali, has been oxidized to *p*-ethoxybenzoic acid, thereby fixing the phenolic hydroxyl group of the alkaloid in the benzyl portion. Moreover, armepavine can be oxidized to *p*-hydroxybenzoic acid and 1-keto-2-methyl-6,7-dimethoxy-1,2,3,4-tetrahydroisoquinoline.

A recent synthesis of armepavine is of special interest because of the means by which the phenolic hydroxyl was introduced. *p*-Nitrophenylacetyl chloride was condensed with 3,4-dimethoxyphenethylamine and the resulting amide cyclized in the usual way by treatment with phosphorus oxychloride in chloroform. The methiodide of the generated dihydroisoquinoline on reduction yielded the amino compound LXXXVII, which was diazotized and boiled with dilute sulfuric acid. The DL-armepavine thus obtained (m.p. 166°) yielded an *O*-methyl ether (m.p. 92°), which on Hofmann degradation gave rise to a methine (m.p. 87°) and a vinylstilbene (m.p. 79°). Their properties were the same as those of the compounds obtained from the natural base (111a).

8. Corpaverine

Corydalis aurea Willd. contains several alkaloids, from which a protoberberine-type base, capaurine (112), as well as a benzylisoquinoline derivative, corpaverine (previously labeled F24), have been isolated (113). Corpaverine has the empirical formula $C_{20}H_{25}NO_4$ and is optically active, $[\alpha]_D^{20}$ $-154.2°$ (2.63 in chloroform). It is phenolic, and yields *p*-anisic acid on oxidation with permanganate ion. Its phenolic hydroxyl group is located in the isoquinoline moiety of the molecule since the aromatic ring of this system is destroyed in the oxidation. Corpaverine ethyl ether, on the other hand, could be degraded to the corresponding methine, and the latter on exhaustive methylation followed by oxidation yielded both *p*-anisic (LXXXII) and 3-ethoxy-3,4-dimethoxyphthalic acid (LXXXVIII). Corpaverine, which is a tertiary amine and contains three methoxyl groups, must therefore have the formula LXXXIX.

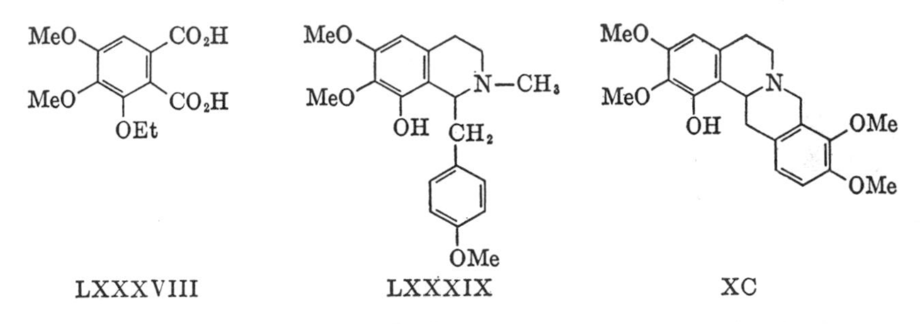

The position of the phenolic hydroxyl group in corpaverine is the same as in the alkaloid capaurine (XC) which accompanies it in the plant. This plant is chiefly noted for the almost exclusive elaboration of protoberberines (type XC), and the assumption that benzylisoquinolines are intermediates in their synthesis is quite likely. Such a last step, however, requires another ring closure, and for this purpose a point of attack must be activated by a hydroxyl or methoxyl in the ortho or para position. This activation is lacking in corpaverine, and in consequence this alkaloid is the end-product in the plant. It would be difficult to devise an experiment which would give clearer evidence of the nature of the ultimate intermediate in the biogenesis of the protoberberines.

V. Biogenesis of the Benzylisoquinoline Alkaloids

The question how plants synthesize alkaloids of the benzylisoquinoline group has motivated the performance of several experiments designed to imitate such syntheses with products, and under conditions a plant could command.

Phenethylamine and its derivatives are the most likely precursors of the isoquinoline system. Their sources are undoubtedly β-phenylalanine and its nuclear substituted derivatives, from which they can arise by carboxylase-catalyzed decarboxylation.

Ring closure to isoquinoline derivatives could be brought about by condensation with aldehydes. This view was proposed first in the book by

Wintersteiner and Trier (114), who pointed out that the papaverine or laudanosine-type alkaloids may be formed from β-3,4-dimethoxyphenylalanine via homoveratrylamine and its condensation product with 3,4-dimethoxyphenylacetaldehyde.

3,4-Dimethoxyphenylacetaldehyde should be formed in the normal process of deamination of β-3,4-dimethoxyphenylalanine to 3,4-dimethoxyphenyl pyruvic acid and decarboxylation of this keto acid. This series of hypothetical steps would explain the synthesis of tetrahydropapaverine (X) from one known amino acid.

Robinson (115) took a different view in proposing a derivation of the corresponding phenolic aldehyde and amine from α-hydroxy-β-ketobutyraldehyde and acetone.

These speculations remained unsupported by experiments until about 1930 when several groups of workers turned their attention to this problem. One of the first model experiments was the synthesis of DL-tetrahydropapaverine from homoveratrylamine and homoveratraldehyde by Späth and Berger (59), but this could barely be called a synthesis "under physiological conditions" since cyclization of the intermediate aldimine required treatment with 19% hydrochloric acid. Later, Hahn and Schales (116) announced they had obtained 1-(3,4-methylenedioxybenzyl)-6,7-methylenedioxy-1,2,3,4-tetrahydroisoquinoline (XCI) from homopiperonylamine hydrochloride and homopiperonal at pH 5 and 25°, but their results were shown to be erroneous by Späth, Kuffner, and Kesztler (117a), who proved that the end-product of their reaction did not have the structure assigned to it by Hahn and Schales; they also pointed out that condensation of phenethylamines with phenylacetaldehydes under mild conditions meets with considerable difficulties, while other aldehydes, such as formaldehyde or acetaldehyde, undergo the reaction readily. However, when they repeated the reaction of homopiperonal with homopiperonylamine under more drastic conditions (117b), using 17% hydrochloric acid at 90° for one hour for the cyclization of the intermediate condensation product, they could isolate compound XCI and identify it with an authentic (13a) sample.

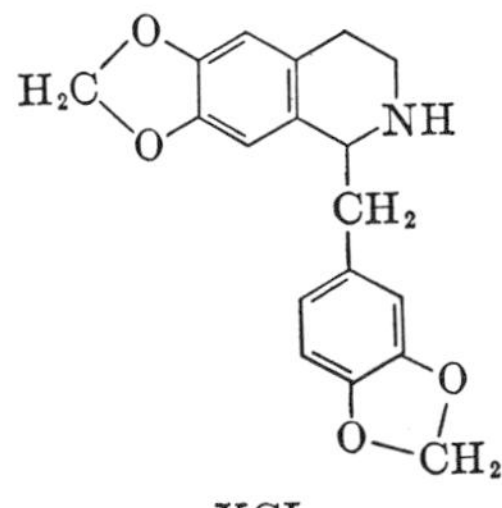

XCI

In support of the hypothetical phytochemical formation of tetrahydroisoquinoline derivatives from phenethylamine derivatives and aldehydes, Schöpf and Bayerle (118) examined the condensation of acetaldehyde with 3,4-dihydroxyphenethylamine and its *N*-methyl derivative (epinine). Four hundredth molar solutions of the hydrobromides of these bases were allowed to stand with 0.08 molar concentrations of acetaldehyde for three days at pH 3–5 and 25.0°. On evaporation of the solutions salts of XCII and XCIII, respectively, were obtained in excellent yields. These bases

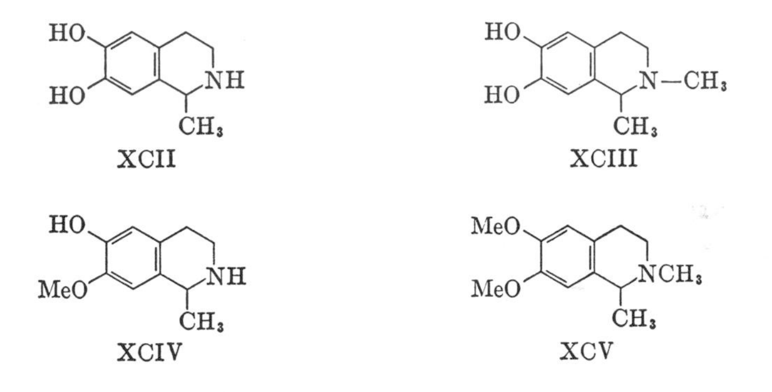

are related to the alkaloids salsoline (XCIV) and carnegine (XCV) which, although they contain asymmetric centers, occur in the optically inactive state in the plant. This may be explained on the basis of the synthesis just described which proceeds under strictly physiological conditions without the influence of enzymes. If this mode of formation holds for other tetrahydroisoquinoline alkaloids which are asymmetric at C_1, the occurence of the optically inactive laudanine would not require any special conjecture. Salsoline has been obtained by condensing homoisovanillylamine with acetaldehyde under conditions possible in the cell (119). That activation of the nuclear position for isoquinoline ring closure by a suitable group is necessary is shown by the failure of acetaldehyde to condense with tyramine, homoveratrylamine, and homovanillylamine under similar conditions.

VI. References

1. (a) G. Dragendorff, Die Heilpflanzen, Enke, Stuttgart, 1898, p. 249.
   (b) E. Machiguchi, *J. Pharm. Soc. Japan*, No. **529,** 185 (1926); *Chem. Abstr.*, **20,** 2725 (1926).
2. G. Merck, *Ann.*, **66,** 125 (1848); **73,** 50 (1850).
3. P. C. Plugge, *Arch. Pharm.* [3]**25,** 343 (1887); *Analyst,* **12,** 197 (1887); *Z. anal. Chem.*, **30,** 385 (1891); *Rec. trav. chim.*, **6,** 167 (1887).
4. (a) O. Hesse, *Ann.* (*Suppl.*), **8,** 261 (1872).
   (b) O. Hesse, *Ann.*, **153,** 47 (1870).
5. A. H. Allen, Commercial Organic Analysis, Blakiston, New York, 1912, Vol. VI, p. 372.

6. (a) A. Pictet and G. H. Kramers, *Ber.*, **43**, 1329 (1910).
(b) G. E. Foster, *Analyst*, **71**, 139 (1946).
7. R. Levi and F. Castelli, *Gazz. chim. ital.*, **68**, 459 (1938); *Arquiv. biol.* (*São Paulo*), **23**, 263 (1939); *Anales farm. bioquím.* (*Buenos Aires*), **11**, 6 (1940); *Chem. Abstr.*, **34**, 7532 (1940). H. Willstaedt, Swedish Patent 98873 (May 14, 1940); *Chem. Abstr.*, **40**, 990 (1946).
8. L. A. Alyavdina, Russian Patent 39109 (Oct. 31, 1934); *Chem. Abstr.*, **30**, 3591[4] (1936); S. and V. Busse, *Khim. Farm. Prom.*, **1933**, 127; *Chem. Abstr.*, **28**, 478 (1934).
9. G. Goldschmiedt, *Monatsh.*, **4**, 704 (1883); **6**, 372, 667, 954 (1885); **7**, 485, 504 (1886); **8**, 510 (1887); **9**, 42, 327, 762, 778 (1888); **10**, 673 (1889); **19**, 321 (1898); G. Goldschmiedt and H. Strache, *ibid.*, **10**, 156, 692 (1889); G. Goldschmiedt and F. Schranzhofer, *ibid.*, **13**, 697 (1892); G. Goldschmiedt and A. Kirpal, *ibid.*, **17**, 491 (1896); G. Goldschmiedt and O. Hönigschmidt, *ibid.*, **24**, 681 (1903); *Ber.*, **36**, 1850 (1903); A. Hirsch, *Monatsh.*, **12**, 486 (1891); L. Stuchlik, *ibid.*, **21**, 813 (1900); F. Schranzhofer, *ibid.*, **14**, 521, 597 (1893); H. Wegscheider, *ibid.*, **18**, 418 (1897); **23**, 387 (1902).
10. M. I. Kabachnik and A. I. Zitser. *J. Gen. Chem.* (*U.S.S.R.*), **7**, 162 (1937).
11. K. N. Menon, *Proc. Indian Acad. Sci.*, **A19**, 21 (1944).
12. A. Müller and M. Dorfman, *J. Am. Chem. Soc.*, **56**, 2787 (1934); J. Büchi and H. Welti, *Pharm. Acta Helv.*, **16**, 67 (1941).
13. (a) J. S. Buck, W. H. Perkin, Jr., and T. S. Stevens, *J. Chem. Soc.*, **127**, 1462 (1925).
(b) J. S. Buck, R. D. Haworth, and W. H. Perkin, Jr., *J. Chem. Soc.*, **125**, 2176 (1924).
14. J. Gadamer and W. Schulemann, *Arch. Pharm.*, **253**, 284 (1915).
15. F. L. Pyman, *J. Chem. Soc.*, **95**, 1610 (1909).
16. F. L. Pyman, *J. Chem. Soc.*, **107**, 176 (1915).
17. F. L. Pyman and W. C. Reynolds, *J. Chem. Soc.*, **97**, 1320 (1910).
18. L. E. Craig and D. S. Tarbell, *J. Am. Chem. Soc.*, **70**, 2783 (1948).
19. E. Späth and A. Burger, *Ber.*, **60**, 704 (1927).
20. W. J. Pope and S. J. Peachy, *J. Chem. Soc.*, **73**, 893 (1898).
21. (a) F. L. Pyman, *J. Chem. Soc.*, **95**, 1738 (1909).
(b) C. Schöpf, *Experientia*, **5**, 201 (1949).
22. (a) A. Pictet and Marie Finkelstein, *Ber.*, **42**, 1979 (1909).
(b) A. Dobrowsky, *Monatsh.*, **82**, 122 (1951).
(c) E. Kaufman, E. E. Eliel, and J. Rosenkranz, *Ciencia* (*Mex.*), **7**, 136 (1946).
23. J. S. Buck, *J. Am. Chem. Soc.*, **52**, 3610 (1930); *J. Chem. Soc.*, **1933**, 740.
24. P. C. Young and R. Robinson, *J. Chem. Soc.*, **1933**, 275.
25. K. Kindler and W. Peschke, *Arch. Pharm.*, **272**, 236 (1934).
26. W. Milliken, G. L. Shaw, J. W. Ferguson, and J. H. Waldo, Div. of Medicinal Chem., Abstracts 111th Meeting A.C.S., Atlantic City, N. J., April 14, 1947.
27. (a) R. Pschorr, *Ber.*, **37**, 1926 (1904).
(b) R. Pschorr, *Ber.*, **37**, 1937 (1904).
28. W. Awe and H. Unger, *Ber.*, **70**, 472 (1937).
29. E. Späth and A. Burger, *Monatsh.*, **47**, 733 (1926).
30. C. Schöpf and K. Thierfelder, *Ann.*, **497**, 22 (1932).
31. H. Decker and G. Dunant, *Ann.*, **358**, 288 (1908).
32. H. Decker and T. Eichler, *Ann.*, **395**, 377 (1913).
33. E. Späth and H. Epstein, *Ber.*, **59**, 2791 (1926).

34. J. W. Armit and R. Robinson, *J. Chem. Soc.*, **127,** 1604 (1927).
35. Z. Kitasato and R. Robinson, *J. Chem. Soc.*, **1932,** 785.
36. A. Claus and E. Hüetlin, *Ber.*, **18,** 1576 (1885).
37. H. Decker and O. Klauser, *Ber.*, **37,** 520 (1904).
38. A. Claus and A. Edinger, *J. prakt. Chem.* [2]**38,** 491 (1888).
39. A. Claus and O. Kassner, *J. prakt. Chem.*, [2]**56,** 321 (1897).
40. J. Gadamer and F. Knoch, *Arch. Pharm.*, **259,** 135 (1921).
41. J. F. Arens and D. A. van Dorp, *Rec. trav. chim.*, **65,** 722 (1946).
42. E. Späth and H. Epstein, *Ber.*, **61,** 334 (1928).
43. W. Koenigs, *Ber.*, **32,** 3599 (1899).
44. E. Späth and N. Polgar, *Ber.*, **59,** 2787 (1926).
45. M. Freund and K. Fleischer, *Ber.*, **48,** 406 (1915).
46. Z. Kitasato and K. Goto, *Ber.*, **63,** 2696 (1930); K. Goto and Z. Kitasato, *J. Chem. Soc. Japan*, **52,** 162 (1931).
47. (a) T. Anderson, *Ann.*, **94,** 235 (1855).
    (b) O. Hesse, *Ber.* **4,** 693 (1871).
    (c) O. Hesse, ref. 4a.
    (d) H. Decker, *Ber.*, **38,** 1275 (1905).
48. J. Gadamer, *Arch. Pharm.*, **249,** 680 (1911).
49. W. Schneider and K. Schröter, *Ber.*, **53,** 1459 (1920).
50. A. Pictet and S. Malinowski, *Ber.*, **46,** 2688 (1913).
51. (a) A. Pictet and A. Gams, *Ber.*, **44,** 2480 (1911).
    (b) A. Pictet and A. Gams, *Compt. rend.*, **149,** 210 (1909).
52. G. Hahn and W. Kley, *Ber.*, **70,** 685 (1937).
53. E. Späth and W. Gruber, *Ber.*, **70,** 1538 (1937).
54. T. and H. Smith Co., *Pharm. J. and Trans.*, [3]**23,** 793 (1893).
55. Bessie Dobson and W. H. Perkin, Jr., *J. Chem. Soc.*, **99,** 135 (1911).
56. K. W. Rosenmund, M. Nothnagel, and H. Riesenfeldt, *Ber.*, **60,** 392 (1927).
56a. V. Harlay, *Compt. rend.*, **224,** 568 (1937).
57. C. Mannich and O. Walther, *Arch. Pharm.*, **265,** 1 (1927).
58. K. W. Rosenmund, *Ber.*, **46,** 1034 (1913).
59. E. Späth and F. Berger, *Ber.*, **63,** 2098 (1930).
60. C. Schöpf, H. Perrey, and I. Jäckh, *Ann.*, **497,** 47 (1932).
61. M. Tomita and M. Satomi, *J. Pharm. Soc. Japan*, **58,** 165 (1938); *Chem. Zentr.*, **1938, II,** 3396.
62. H. Wahl, *Bull. soc. chim. France*, **17,** 680 (1950); **18,** D1 (1951).
63. A. Galat, *J. Am. Chem. Soc.*, **72,** 4436 (1950); **73,** 3654 (1951).
64. F. Boedecker and A. Heymans, German Patent 674,400 (1937).
65. H. Krueger, N. B. Eddy, and Margaret Sumwalt, The Pharmacology of Opium Alkaloids, Part 2. Supplement No. 165 to the Public Health Reports, U. S. Government Printing Office, Washington, D. C., 1943.
66. (a) S. Markees and V. Demole, *Helv. Physiol. Pharmacol. Acta*, **1,** 241 (1943); *Chem. Abstr.*, **38,** 2388[8] (1944).
    (b) E. Frommel, J. Piquet, C. L. Cuénod, M. Loufti, and J. Aron, *ibid.*, **3,** 83 (1945); *Chem. Abstr.*, **40,** 402[8] (1946).
67. J. Levy, *Bull. soc. chim. biol.*, **27,** 578 (1945).
68. S. R. Elek and L. N. Katz, *J. Am. Med. Assoc.*, **120,** 434 (1942); F. D. Murphy, H. H. Cole, and E. M. Stevenson, *Illinois Med. J.*, **85,** 119 (1944); A. C. Pfohl, *J. Iowa State Med. Soc.*, **33,** 464 (1943); G. de Takats, *War Med.*, **3,** 291 (1943); G. de Takats, W. C. Beck, and G. K. Fenn, *Surgery*, **6,** 339 (1939); D. C. Col-

lins, *Calif. and Western Med.*, **51**, 307 (1939); H. S. Diehl, *Lancet*, **56**, 533 (1936); M. L. McCall, T. B. Fitch, and H. W. Taylor, *Am. J. Obstet.-Gynecol.*, **61**, 393 (1951).
69. J. Weijlard, E. F. Swanezy, and E. Tashijan, *J. Am. Chem. Soc.*, **71**, 1889 (1949).
70. A. Dobrowsky, *Monatsh.*, **82**, 122, 140 (1951); H. H. Bradshaw and R. J. Chodoff, *Surg. Gynecol. Obstet.*, **70**, 768, 772 (1940); W. Denk, *Zentr. Chir.*, **1936**, 2; H. Kohlmayer, *ibid.*, **60**, 1698 (1933); O. Dopffel and H. Kutschera-Aichbergen, *Z. klin. Med.*, **137**, 341 (1940); H. Karstendieck, *Münch. med. Wochschr.*, **85**, 794 (1938); A. Tamches, *Presse méd.*, **1938**, 1376; B. Tsopelas, *Klin. Monatsbl. Augenheilk.*, **101**, 830 (1938); G. Leiner, *Klin. Wochschr.*, **16**, 639 (1937).
71. (a) ref. 65, p. 1039.
(b) S. Sugasawa and S. Sakurai, *J. Pharm. Soc. Japan*, **56**, 563 (1936).
(c) S. Sugasawa and H. Yoshikawa, *ibid.*, **54**, 305 (1934).
(d) S. Sugasawa, *ibid.*, **55**, 224 (1935).
(e) S. Sugasawa and K. Kakemi, *ibid.*, **55**, 1283 (1935).
(f) E. Merck, British Patent, 348956 (1930).
(g) O. Wolfes, German Patent 550122 (1929).
72. (a) K. V. Issekutz, M. Leinzinger, and Z. Dirner, *Arch. exptl. Pathol. Pharmakol.*, **164**, 158 (1932); *Chem. Abstr.*, **26**, 3836 (1932).
(b) H. Kreitmair, *ibid.*, **164**, 509 (1932); *Chem. Abstr.*, **26**, 3297 (1932).
(c) G. Fodor, *Chem. Abstr.*, **32**, 2124 (1938).
(d) V. Bruckner and G. von Fodor, *Ber.*, **71**, 541 (1938).
(e) G. von Fodor, *Ber.*, **76**, 1216 (1943).
(f) R. W. Cunningham and E. J. Fellows, *Federation Proc.*, **1**, 148 (1942).
73. A. Dobrowsky, *Monatsh.*, **82**, 140 (1951).
73a. A. Quevauviller and S. Garcet, *Compt. rend. soc. biol.*, **144**, 165 (1950).
74. (a) O. Hesse, *Ber.*, **4**, 693 (1871).
(b) O. Hesse, *Ann.*, **176**, 189 (1875).
75. J. J. Dobbie and A. Lauder, *J. Chem. Soc.*, **83**, 626 (1903).
76. A. Pictet and B. Athanasescu, *Ber.*, **33**, 2346 (1900).
77. H. Decker and L. Galatty, *Ber.*, **42**, 1179 (1909).
78. T. Kondo and N. Mori, *J. Pharm. Soc. Japan*, **51**, 615 (1931).
79. J. Gadamer and R. Kondo, *Arch. Pharm.*, **253**, 281 (1915).
80. F. L. Pyman, *J. Chem. Soc.*, **95**, 1266 (1909); V. K. Baghwat, D. K. Moore, and F. L. Pyman, *ibid.*, **1931**, 443.
81. (a) F. E. King, P. L'Ecuyer, and F. L. Pyman, *J. Chem. Soc.*, **1936**, 731.
(b) F. E. King and P. L'Ecuyer, *ibid.*, **1937**, 427.
82. R. Robinson and S. Sugasawa, *J. Chem. Soc.*, **1932**, 789.
83. A. Burger, Dissertation, Vienna, 1927.
84. C. Schöpf and K. Thierfelder, *Ann.*, **537**, 143 (1939).
85. F. L. Pyman, *J. Chem. Soc.*, **95**, 1610 (1909).
86. E. Späth, *Monatsh.*, **41**, 297 (1920).
87. W. Leithe, *Ber.*, **63**, 1498 (1930); **64**, 2827 (1931).
88. F. Mercier and J. Delphaut, *Compt. rend. soc. biol.*, **118**, 168 (1935); *Chem. Abstr.*, **29**, 3034[7] (1935).
89. J. Delphaut and J. Paret, *Compt. rend. soc. biol.*, **118**, 107 (1935); *Chem. Abstr.*, **29**, 5185[5] (1935).
90. E. P. Taylor and H. O. Collier, *Nature*, **167**, 692 (1951).
91. H. Schröder, *Ber.*, **13**, 1074 (1880).
92. K. Hess, *Ber.*, **53**, 1375 (1920); K. Hess and W. Weltzien, *ibid.*, **53**, 119 (1920); F. Pringsheim, *ibid.*, **53**, 1372 (1920).

93. (a) O. Hesse, *J. prakt. Chem.*, **65**, 42 (1902).
(b) E. Kauder, *Arch. Pharm.*, **228**, 419 (1890).
94. E. Späth and N. Lang, *Monatsh.*, **42**, 273 (1921).
95. O. Hesse, *Ann.*, **282**, 208 (1894).
96. E. Späth and E. Bernhauser, *Ber.*, **58**, 200 (1925).
97. E. Späth and R. Seka, *Ber.*, **58**, 1272 (1925).
98. S. Kobayashi, *Sci. Papers Inst. Phys. Chem. Research (Tokyo)*, **6**, 149 (1927); *Chem. Zentr.*, **1928, I**, 1027.
98a. A. Pictet and G. H. Kramers, *Arch. sci. phys. et nat.*, [4]**15**, 121 (1903).
99. R. Chatterjee, *J. Am. Pharm. Assoc., Sci. Ed.*, **33**, 210 (1944).
100. R. Chatterjee and M. P. Guha, *J. Am. Pharm. Assoc., Sci. Ed.*, **39**, 181, 577 (1950).
101. R. Chatterjee, M. P. Guha, and S. K. Sen, *J. Am. Pharm. Assoc., Sci. Ed.*, **40**, 36 (1951).
102. R. Chatterjee and M. P. Guha, *J. Am. Pharm. Assoc., Sci. Ed.*, **40**, 229 (1951).
103. R. Chatterjee and M. P. Guha, *J. Am. Pharm. Assoc., Sci. Ed.*, **40**, 233 (1951).
104. T. Zerewitinoff, *Ber.*, **45**, 2384 (1912).
105. R. D. Haworth and W. H. Perkin, *J. Chem. Soc.*, **127**, 1453 (1927).
106. H. Kondo and T. Kondo, *J. Pharm. Soc. Japan*, No. **524**, 876 (1925); No. **538**, 1029 (1926); No. **554**, 324 (1928); No. **562**, 1156, 1163 (1928); *J. prakt. Chem.*, **126**, 24 (1930).
107. P. C. Plugge, *Arch. exptl. Pathol. Pharmakol.*, **32**, 266 (1893); cf. H. King, *J. Chem. Soc.*, **1935**, 1381.
108. J. Finkelstein, *J. Am. Chem. Soc.*, **73**, 550 (1951).
109. K. Kratzl and G. Billek, *Monatsh.*, **82**, 568 (1951).
110. R. Konovalova, S. Yunusoff, and A. Orechoff, *Ber.*, **68**, 2158 (1935); *J. Gen. Chem. (U.S.S.R.)*, **10**, 641 (1940).
111. R. Konovalova, S. Yunusoff, and A. Orechoff, *Ber.*, **68**, 2277 (1935).
111a. L. Marion, L. Lemay, and V. Portelance, *J. Org. Chem.*, **15**, 216 (1950).
112. R. H. F. Manske and H. L. Holmes, *J. Am. Chem. Soc.*, **67**, 95 (1945).
113. R. H. F. Manske, *Can. J. Research*, **16**, 81 (1938); *J. Am. Chem. Soc.*, **74**, 2864 (1952).
114. E. Wintersteiner and G. Trier, Die Alkaloide, Bornträger, Berlin, 1910, p. 307. cf. A. Pictet and T. Spengler, *Ber.*, **44**, 2030 (1911).
115. R. Robinson, *J. Chem. Soc.*, **111**, 876 (1917).
116. G. Hahn and O. Schales, *Ber.*, **68**, 24 (1935).
117. (a) E. Späth, F. Kuffner, and Friedericke Kesztler, *Ber.*, **69**, 378 (1936).
(b) E. Späth, F. Kuffner and Friedericke Kesztler, *Ber.*, **70**, 1017 (1937).
118. C. Schöpf and H. Bayerle, *Ann.*, **513**, 190 (1934).
119. O. Kovacs and G. Fodor, *Chem. Ber.*, **84**, 795 (1951).

CHAPTER 29

The Protoberberine Alkaloids

R. H. F. MANSKE

Dominion Rubber Research Laboratory, Guelph, Ontario, and

WALTER R. ASHFORD

Merck & Co. Ltd., Montreal, Quebec

		Page
I.	Introduction	78
II.	Occurrence	78
	Tables 1 and 2	79
III.	Berberine	78
	1. Occurrence	78
	2. Isolation, Detection, Determination	84
	3. Structure of Berberine	87
	4. Other Degradation Products and Synthesis of Berberine	90
IV.	Canadine	91
V.	Palmatine	92
VI.	Shobakunine	93
VII.	Tetrahydropalmatine	93
VIII.	Jatrorrhizine and Columbamine	95
IX.	Corypalmine and Isocorypalmine	95
X.	Scoulerine	97
XI.	Sinactine	98
XII.	Cheilanthifoline	98
XIII.	Ophiocarpine	99
XIV.	Capaurine and Capauridine	100
XV.	Capaurimine	102
XVI.	Stylopine and Coptisine	102
XVII.	Corydaline	103
XVIII.	Corybulbine	107
XIX.	Isocorybulbine	108
XX.	Thalictrifoline	108
XXI.	Thalictricavine	108
XXII.	Nandinine	109
XXIII.	Worenine	110
XXIV.	Umbellatine	111
XXV.	Neprotine	111
XXVI.	Thalictrine	112
XXVII.	Coreximine	112
XXVIII.	References	113

I. Introduction

The protoberberines (II and III) are a group of alkaloids which can theoretically be derived from the benzylisoquinolines (I) by condensation with formaldehyde. In vitro, this condensation yields a mixture of II

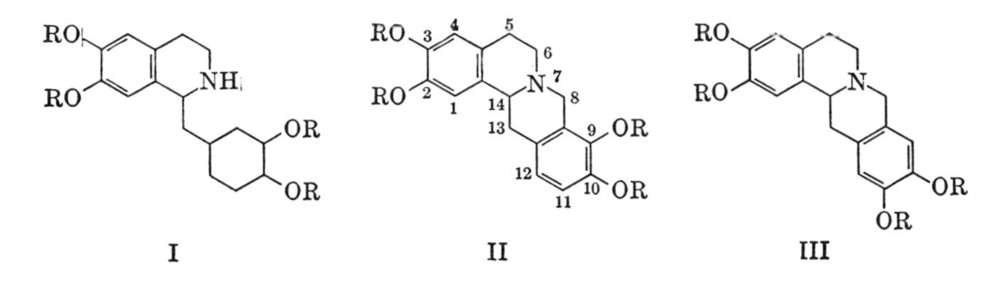

and III when the substituents in the benzyl group are hydroxyls (1, 2) but only III when the hydroxyls are fully alkylated. There are no known naturally occurring protoberberines with less than four *O*-substituents, but some have been discovered recently which have an additional phenolic hydroxyl at position 1 (3, 4, 5) or an aliphatic hydroxyl at 13 (6).

In the following chapter the tetrahydro and the dehydro bases will be discussed together, and the numbering will be that shown in II.

II. Occurrence

The protoberberines occur in a wide variety of botanical families. They are distributed in many genera of the Papaveraceae, generally as the tetrahydro bases, while in the Berberidaceae, Menispermaceae, Ranunculaceae, Rutaceae, and Anonaceae they occur mostly in the quaternary dehydro form.

Tables 1 and 2 show the distribution of alkaloids in families and genera which are known to elaborate mostly isoquinolines. The protoberberines are included in a separate column in the Papaveraceae.

III. Berberine

1. Occurrence

Since canadine is easily oxidized by atmospheric oxygen to berberine there is little doubt that berberine is a constituent of all plants which contain canadine. However, there are many occurrences of berberine unaccompanied by canadine, particularly in plants of the Berberidaceae and Menispermaceae, and it would seem that there is present in these plants a specific oxidative system which converts the presumably intermediate tetrahydro bases into the quaternary compounds.

Many of the older records of the occurrence of berberine are of doubtful

TABLE 1

PAPAVERACEAE

Plant	Aporphines and others	Protoberberines	Protopines
Adlumia cirrhosa Rafin.	Adlumine (7)		Protopine (7, 8)
(*A. fungosa* (Ait.) Greene)	Bicuculline (7)		Allocryptopine (8)
	Adlumidine (7)		
Argemone alba Lestib.		Berberine (9)	
A. hispida A. Gray	$C_{17}H_{13(15)}OH(OMe)_3N$, m.p. 238°, $[\alpha]_D$ −77° $C_{17}H_{13}$- $(OMe)_4N$, m.p. 153°, $[\alpha]_D$ −214°	(Could be partly racemic isocorypalmine (10))	
A. mexicana L.		Berberine (11)	Propotine (11)
Bocconia arborea Wats.	Chelerythrine (12) Neutral compounds (12): $C_{20}H_{15}O_4N$, m.p. 191° $C_{31}H_{33}O_5N$, m.p. 332° $C_{20}H_{17}O_4N$, m.p. 302°		Allocryptopine (12) Prototine (12)
B. cordata Willd.	Chelerythrine (13, 14)		Allocryptopine (13, 14) Protopine (13, 14)
B. frutescens L.			Allocryptopine (15) Protopine (15)
B. pearcei Hutchinson	Chelerythrine (16)		Protopine (17) Allocryptopine (unpublished) (17)
Chelidonium majus L.	Chelidonine (18) Homochelidonine (18) Chelerythrine (18) Sanguinarine (19) Methoxychelidonine (20) Sparteine (21) Base, $C_{19}H_{24}ON_2$, m.p. 198–199°, $[\alpha]_D$ −40.7° (20)	Coptisine (22) Berberine (23)	Protopine (18) Allocryptopine (15)
Corydalis ambigua Cham. and Schlecht.		Corybulbine (24) *l*-Corypalmine (25) Corydaline (24) Dehydrocorydaline (24) Coptisine (24, 26) Stylopine (26) *dl*-Tetrahydropalmatine (25, 26) *dl*-Tetrahydrocoptisine (25, 26) *l*-Tetrahydrocoptisine (25, 26)	Protopine (24) Allocryptopine (?) (25)
C. aurea Willd.	Bicucine (5) Bicuculline (5) Cordrastine (5) Corypalline (5) Corpaverine (5, 27) F24, $C_{19}H_{23}O_4N$, m.p. 138° (5)	Aurotensine (Scoulerine (5, 28) Capaurine (5) Capauridine (5) Corydaline (28) *l*-Tetrahydropalmatine (5, 28) *dl*-Tetrahydropalmatine (5, 28) Dehydrocorydaline (29)	Allocryptopine (5, 28) Protopine (5)
C. bulbosa DC. (*C. solida* Sw.)	Bulbocapnine (30) Base (*a*), m. p. 145° (30) Base (*b*), m.p. 132° (30)		Protopine (31)

TABLE 1—(*Continued*)

Plant	Aporphines and others	Protoberberines	Protopines
C. caseana A. Gray	Bicuculline (32) F33, $C_{19}H_{21}O_4N$, m.p. 257° (32) F35, $C_{20}H_{23}O_4N$, m.p. 145° (32)	Corypalmine (32) *l*-Isocorypalmine (32) *dl*-Isocorpyalmine (32) *l*-Scoulerine (32) *l*-Tetrahydropalmatine (32)	Allocryptopine (32) Protopine (32)
C. cheilantheifolia Hemsl.	Neutral compound, $C_{21}H_{18}O_8N_2$, m.p. >360° (33)	Berberine (33) *l*-Canadine (33) *l*-Cheilanthifoline (33, 34) *l*-Corypalmine (33) *l*- and *dl*-Stylopine (33)	Allocryptopine (33) Protopine (33)
C. claviculata DC.	Cularine (35) F52, yields cularine on methylation (35)	*l*- and *dl*-Stylopine (35)	Protopine (35)
C. cornuta Royle	Acetylornithine (36)	*d*-Stylopine (36)	Protopine (36)
C. crystallina Engelm.	Bicuculline (37) Capnoidine (37)		Protopine (37)
C. decumbens Pers.	Bulbocapnine (38)	Dehydrocorydaline (38) *d*-Tetrahydropalmatine (38)	Protopine (38, 39)
C. lutea (L.) DC.	Isocorydine (40) Ochrobirine (40)	*l*-Stylopine (40) *l*-Tetrahydropalmatine (40) *l*-Isocorypalmine (40)	Protopine (40)
C. micrantha (Engelm.) Gray	F41, m.p. 177° (37) F42, m. p.239° (37) F43, $C_{20}H_{23}O_4N$, m.p. 230° (37) (all phenolic)	Capauridine (37) Capaurine (37) Scoulerine (37) *l*-Tetrahydropalmatine (37)	Protopine (37)
C. montana (Engelm.) Britton	F56, $C_{23}H_{27}O_6N$, m.p. 207° (29)	Capaurine (29) Capauridine (29) Capaurimine (29) Corydaline (29) Scoulerine (29) *dl*-Tetrahydropalmatine (29) Dehydrocorydaline (29)	Protopine (29)
C. nobilis Pers.	Bicuculline (41) Corlumine (41) Corytuberine (41) F53, $C_{21}H_{21}O_5N$, m.p. 183° (41) F54, $C_{19}H_{23}O_5N$, m.p. 143° (41) F55, m.p. 209° (41)	Stylopine (41) *d*- and *dl*-Tetrahydropalmatine (41) Corydaline (41) *d*-Isocorypalmine (41)	Protopine (41) Cryptopine (41)
C. ochotensis Turcz.	Ochotensine (42) Ochotensimine (42) F49, $C_{20}H_{23}O_4N$, m.p. 228° (42) Acetylornithine (42)	Aurotensine (42)	Cryptocavine (42) Protopine (42)
C. ochroleuca Koch	Bicuculline (43) Ochrobirine (43) F45, $C_{20}H_{19}O_8N$, m.p. 268° (43) F46, $C_{11}H_9O_2N \cdot \frac{1}{2}H_2O$, m.p. 227° (43)	*l*-Corypalmine (43) *l*-Isocoryplamine (43) *l*-Tetrahydropalmatine 43)	Protopine (43)
C. ophiocarpa Hook. f. and Thoms.	*l*-Adlumine (6) F40 m.p. 196° (6)	Berberine (6) *l*-Canadine (6) *l*-Corypalmine (6) Ophiocarpine (6)	Cryptocavine (6) Allocryptopine (6) Protopine (6)

TABLE 1—(*Continued*)

Plant	Aporphines and others	Protoberberines	Protopines
C. pallida (Thunb.) Pers.	Corypalline (44)	Capauridine (45) Capaurimine (45) Capaurine (45) Scoulerine (45) *d*-Tetrahydropalmatine (45) *dl*-Tetrahydropalmatine (45) F51, $C_{20}H_{23}O_4N$, m.p. 171° (45), yields *dl*-tetrahydropalmatine on methylation	Protopine (45)
C. platycarpa Makino	Isocorydine (46) Bicuculline (46) Neutral compound, C_6H_9ON, m.p. 172° (46)	*d*- and *dl*-Scoulerine (46) Corybulbine (46) Corydaline (46) *l*-Isocorypalmine (46) *dl*-Stylopine (46) *l*-Tetrahydropalmatine (46)	Protopine (46)
C. scouleri Hook.	*l*-Adlumine (47) Bicuculline (47) Capnoidine (47) Corlumidine (47) Corlumine (47)	Cheilanthifoline (34, 47) *l*-Scoulerine (47)	Cryptopine (47) Allocryptopine (47) Protopine (47)
C. sempervirens (L.) Pers.	*l*-Adlumine (28) Bicuculline (48) Capnoidine (48)		Cryptopine (48) Protopine (48)
C. sibirica (L.) Pers.	Ochrobirine (49) Bicuculline (49) Corlumine (49) Ochotensine (49) F15, $C_{19}H_{19}O_5N$, m.p. 212° (49) F16, $C_{18}H_{17}O_5N$, m.p. 236° (49) Acetylornithine (49)	Cheilanthifoline (49) Scoulerine (49)	Cryptopine (49) Protopine (49)
C. ternata Nakai	*l*-Corydine (50) Isocorydine (50) *l*-Glaucine (50)	*l*-Canadine (50) Tetrahydrocoptisine (50) Stylopine (50)	Allocryptopine (50) Protopine (50)
C. thalictrifolia Franch.	Adlumidine (51) F59, $C_{19}H_{20}O_3N(OMe)$, m.p.176° (51)	*l*-Corypalmine (51) *d*-Stylopine (51) *d*-Thalictrifoline (51) Dehydrothalictrifoline (51)	Protopine (51)
C. tuberosa DC.	Bulbocapnine (52) Corydine (53) Corytuberine (54) Glaucine (55) Hydrohydrastinine (56) (*a*) $C_{21}H_{23}O_5N$, m.p. 121° (30) (*b*) $C_{21}H_{21}O_8N$, m.p. 230°, $[\alpha]_D$ −112.8° (30) (*c*) $C_{18}H_{14(16)}O_5NMe(OMe)_2$, m.p. 137.5°, $[\alpha]_D$ +96.8° (30)	*d*-Canadine (56) Corybulbine (53) Isocorybulbine (53) Corydaline (52) Dehydrocorydaline (57) *d*-Corypalmine (58) Scoulerine (59) *d*-Isocorypalmine (59) Tetrahydrocoptisine (56) *d*-Tetrahydropalmatine (58) Thalictricavine (unpublished) (60)	Corycavamine (53) Corycavidine (61) Corycavine (53) Protopine (55)
Dactylicapnos macrocapnos Hutchinson		*l*- and *dl*-Stylopine (62)	Allocryptopine (62) Protopine (62)
Dendromecon rigidum Benth.			Protopine (63) Allocryptopine (63)

TABLE 1—(*Continued*)

Plant	Aporphines and others	Protoberberines	Protopines
Dicentra canadensis (Goldie) Walp.	Bulbocapnine (64) Corydine (64) Isocorydine (64) F22, $C_{37}H_{40}O_{10}N_2$(?) (28)		Protopine (64)
D. chrysantha Walp.	Bicuculline (65) Chrycentrine (65) F25, $C_{18}H_{14}O_6$(NMe), m.p. 230° (28)		Cryptocavine (65) Cryptopine (65) Protopine (65)
D. cucullaria (L.) Bernh.	Bicuculline (66) Corlumine (28) Cularine (28) Cularidine (28) Ochotensine,(28)		Cryptopine (66) Allocryptopine (28) Protopine (66)
D. eximia (Ker) Torr.	Corydine (67) Dicentrine (67) Eximidine (67) Glaucentrine (28, 67) *d*-Glaucine (67) F21, $C_{16}H_{13}ON(OMe)_4$, m.p. 80° (28) Cularimine (28) Cularine (28)	Coreximine (28)	Protopine (67)
D. formosa Walp.	Corydine (68) Corytuberine (68) Dicentrine (68) Glaucentrine (68) Glaucine (68) Cularine (68)		Protopine (68)
D. ochroleuca Engelm.	Bicuculline (65)		Cryptopine (65) Protopine (65)
D. oregana Eastwood	Corydine (69) Dicentrine (69) Glaucentrine (69) Glaucine (69) Cularine (28)	*l*-Corypalmine (69)	Allocryptopine (69) Protopine (69)
D. pusilla Sieb. and Zucc.	Dicentrine (70)		Protopine (70)
D. spectabilis Lem.	Base, m.p. 142–145° (?) (71)		Protopine (65, 71)
Dicranostigma franchetianum (Prain) Fedde	Chelidonine (72)	*dl*-Stylopine (72)	Protopine (72)
D. lactucoides Hook. f. and Thoms.	Chelerythrine (73) Sanguinarine (73) Isocorydine (73)		Protopine (73)
Eschscholtzia californica Cham.	Chelerythrine (74) Eschscholtzine (74) $C_{21}H_{19}O_5N$ (amorphous), cryst. oxalate (74) (*a*) m.p. 242–243° (75) (*b*) m.p. 217° (75)		Allocryptopine (76) Protopine (76) Cryptocavine (74)
Fumaria officinalis L.	F37, $C_{19}H_{17}O_3N(OMe)_2$, m.p. 177° (77) F38, $C_{19}H_{16}O_5N(OMe)$, m.p. 255° (77)	{Scoulerine (77) {Aurotensine (77) *l*- and *dl*-Sinactine (77) {*dl*-Tetrahydrocoptisine (77) {Stylopine (77)	Cryptocavine (77) Protopine (77)

TABLE 1—(*Continued*)

Plant	Aporphines and others	Protoberberines	Protopines
Glaucium fimbrilligerum Boiss.	Corydine (78) Chelerythrine (78) Sanguinarine (78)		Allocryptopine (78) Protopine (78)
G. flavum Crantz	Isocorydine (79) Glaucine (80)	Aurotensine (79)	Protopine (80)
G. serpieri Heldr.	Isocorydine (72) Glaucine (72)	Aurotensine (72)	Protopine (72)
Hunnemannia fumariaefolia Sweet	F58, $C_{20}H_{15}O_3N(OMe)_2$ m.p. 174° (81)		Allocryptopine (81) Protopine (81) Hunnemannine (81)
Papaver armeniacum (Lestib.) Lam.	Armepavine (82)		
P. bracteatum Lindl.	Isothebaine (83, 83a) Oripavine (83a) Bracteine, $C_{16}H_{10}(NMe)(OMe)_2(OH)_2$ (83a) Bractamine, $C_9H_8(NMe)(OMe)(OH)$ (83a)		
P. caucasicum Bieb. as	Floripavine (84)		
P. floribundum Desf.	Oripavine (84) Floribundine (84) Armepavine (84)		
P. dubium L.	Aporeine (85) Aporeidine (85)		
P. hybridum L.	Rhoeadine (86)		
P orientale L.	Glaucidine (87) Isothebaine (88) Thebaine (82, 88) Oripavine (82)		Protopine (87)
P. rhoeas L.	Rhoeadine (89, 90)		
P. somniferum L.	Hydrocotarnine (91) Narcotine (91) Narcotoline (92) Gnoscopine (93) Narceine (94) Nornarceine (95) Papaverine (91) Xanthaline (96) Laudanidine (97) Laudanine (98) Laudanosine (91) Codamine (19) Morphine ψ-Morphine (99) Codeine Neopine (100) Thebaine Porphyroxine (101) Meconidine (102) Lanthopine (102)		Protopine (103) Cryptopine (104)
Pteridophyllum racemosum Sieb. and Zucc.			Protopine (105) Allocryptopine (105)

TABLE 1—(*Continued*)

Plant	Aporphines and others	Protoberberines	Protopines
Roemeria refracta DC.	Roemerine (106, 107) *l*-Ephedrine (107, 108, 109) *d*-ψ-Ephredrine (107, 108, 109)		
Sanguinaria canadensis L.	Chelerythrine (110) Sanguinarine (76) Oxysanguinarine (111)		Allocryptopine (110) Protopine (110)
Stylophorum diphyllum (Michx.) Nutt	Chelidonine (72)	*l*-Stylopine (72)	Protopine (72)

authenticity because the characterization was based largely upon color reactions. It is now known that all of the dehydro compounds behave in essentially the same way, and the only certain method of identifying berberine is by reduction to the tetrahydro base and proper characterization of this. The list of occurrences shown for berberine in Tables 1 and 2 is therefore subject to corrections.

2. Isolation, Detection, Determination

Its earliest isolation under the name "xanthopicrit" by Chevalier and Pelletan (177) from *Zanthoxylum caribaeum* is of historical interest only. The subsequent isolation under the name of berberine from *Berberis vulgaris* (180) and its further examination by Fleitmann (181) served only to facilitate the work of Perrins (167), who not only determined the correct formula, $C_{20}H_{19}O_5N$, but showed that the products from the two sources were identical.

When berberine is the chief alkaloid in a plant extract its isolation is conveniently effected by making use of the sparing solubility of its sulfate in dilute sulfuric acid. The hydrochloride, hydriodide, and nitrate are easily recrystallized from water or precipitated from acetic acid solutions on the addition of the appropriate ions in the form of salts (182). The phosphate (183) is a bright yellow, non-deliquescent crystalline substance soluble in 14.3 parts of water at 16°. Berberine can be purified through its addition compound with acetone (184, 185, 186).

The free base crystallizes from water or preferably dilute alcohol as a hydrate (5.5 moles water) in brilliant yellow needles, which when dried in the air have a fine, silky luster (182). If dried at 100° the crystals lose three moles of water and their luster; at 110° they turn yellow-brown and at 160° decomposition sets in. The solubility of berberine in cold water is 1 part in 4.5 parts at 21° and in alcohol it is 1 in 100.

Many procedures for the estimation of berberine have been published (187–198). There is no question but that most of these methods give

TABLE 2

Plant	Alkaloid
	I. BERBERIDACEAE
Berberis aetnensis Presl.	Berberine (112)
B. aquifolium Pursh as *Mahonia aquifolium* Nutt.	Berberine (113), Oxyacanthine (113), Berbamine (113)
B. buxifolia Lam.	Berberine (114, 115)
B. darwinii Hook.	Berberine (115, 116)
B. fortunei Lindl. (*M. fortunei* Hort.)	Oxyacanthine (116a), Berbamine (116a), Jatrorrhizine (116a), Berberine (116a), Palmatine (116a)
B. insignis Hook. f. and Thoms.	Umbellatine (117)
B. japonica R. Br. (*M. japonica* Thunb.)	Isotetrandrine (117a), Berbamine (117a), Jatrorrhizine (117a), Berberine (117a), Palmatine (117a)
B. laurina (Billb.) Thunb.	Berberine (118), Hydrastine (118)
B. nepalensis Spreng. (*M. nepalensis* DC.)	Umbellatine (119), Neprotine (119)
B. nervosa Pursh	Berberine (120)
B. swaseyi Buckley (*M. swaseyi* Fedde)	Berberine (121, 122), Berbamine (121)
B. thunbergii DC. var. *maximowiczii* Regel	Berbamine (123), Oxyberberine (123), Jatrorrhizine (123), Columbamine (123), Palmatine (123), Shobakunine (123), Berberine (123), Oxyacanthine (123)
B. trifoliolata Moric. (*M. trifoliolata* Fedde)	Berberine (122)
B. umbellata Wall.	Umbellatine (124)
B. vulgaris L.	Berberine (125), Palmatine (126), Jatrorrhizine (126), Columbamine (126), Oxyacanthine (125, 127), Berbamine (125), Berberrubine (126), $C_{19}H_{22}ON_2$ (m.p. 256°) (128)
B. vulgaris L. as *B. heteropoda* Schrenk	Berberine (129), Palmatine (129), Jatrorrhizine (129), Columbamine (129), Oxyacanthine (129), Berbamine (129)
M. acanthifolia Don	Oxyacanthine (130), Berberine (130), Neprotine (130), Palmatine (130), Jatrorrhizine (130)
M. borealis Takeda	Oxyacanthine (131), Berberine (131), Neprotine (131), Palmatine (131), Jatrorrhizine (131)
M. griffithii Takeda	Oxyacanthine (132), Berbamine (132), Berberine (132), Neprotine (132), Palmatine (132)
M. leschenaultii Takeda	Oxyacanthine (133), Berberine (133), Neprotine (133), Palmatine (133), Jatrorrhizine (133)

TABLE 2—(*Continued*)

Plant	Alkaloid
M. manipurensis Takeda	Oxyacanthine (133), Berberine (133), Neprotine (133), Jatrorrhizine (133)
M. philippinensis Takeda	Berberine (134), Jatrorrhizine (134), Shobakunine (134)
M. sikkimensis Takeda	Oxyacanthine (133), Berberine (133), Neprotine (133)
M. simonsii Takeda	Oxyacanthine (131), Berberine (131), Neprotine (131), Palmatine (131), Jatrorrhizine (131)
Nandina domestica Thunb.	Berberine (135), Nandinine (136, 137, 138), Domesticine (138, 139), Isodomesticine (138), Nandazurine (137), Domestine (139, 140), Jatror rhizine (135), Protopine (141)
	II. ANONACEAE
Anona muricata L.	Muricine (142), Muricinine (142)
A. reticulata L.	Anonaine (143, 144)
A. squamosa L.	Anonaine (144)
Artabotrys suaveolens Blume	Isocorydine (Artabotrine) (145, 146, 147), Suaveoline (146), Artabotrinine (148)
Asimina triloba Dun.	Anolobine (149)
Unona discreta L.f. (*Xylopia discreta* (L.f.) Sprague and Hutchinson)	Xylopine (150), Xylopinine (150), Discretine (150) Discretinine (150)
Xylopia polycarpa Oliver (*Coelocline polycarpa* A. DC.)	Berberine (151)
	III. MENISPERMACEAE
Archangelisia flava (L.) Merrill	Berberine (152), Jatrorrhizine (152), Columbamine (152), Shobakunine (152)
Cocculus leaeba DC.	Palmatine (153)
Coscinium blumeanum Miers	Berberine (154), Jatrorrhizine (154), Palmatine (154)
C. fenestratum Colebr.	Berberine (155, 156, 157)
Fibraurea tinctoria Lours. (*F. chloroleuca* Miers)	Palmatine (158), Jatrorrhizine (158)
Jateorhiza columba Miers (*J. palmata* Miers)	Palmatine (159), Columbamine (159, 160), Jatrorrhizine (159)
Sinomenium acutum Rehder and Wilson	Sinactine (161), Tuduranine (162), Acutumine (161)
Tinospora bakis Miers	Palmatine (153)
	IV. RANUNCULACEAE
Coptis orientalis Maxim. as *C. japonica* Makino	Berberine (163), Palmatine (163, 164), Columbamine (163), Coptisine (165), Worenine (164)

TABLE 2—(*Continued*)

Plant	Alkaloid
C. occidentalis Torr. and Gray	Berberine (166)
C. teeta Wall.	Berberine (167, 168)
C. trifolia (L.) Salisb.	Berberine (166)
Hydrastis canadensis L.	Berberine (167), Canadine (169), Hydrastine (170, 171)
Thalictrum foliolosum DC.	Berberine (172), Thalictrine (172)
	V. RUTACEAE
Evodia meliaefolia Benth.	Berberine (173)
Phellodendron amurense Rupr.	Berberine (163, 174), Palmatine (163)
Toddalia aculeata Pers.	Berberine (173), Toddaline ($C_{20}H_{21}O_4N$, m.p. 269–270°) (175), Toddalinine ($C_{19}H_{15}O_4\frac{1}{2}N \cdot H_2O$, m.p. 180–200°) (175)
Zanthoxylum brachyacanthum F. Muell.	1-α-Canadine methochloride (176), Allocryptine (176)
Z. caribaeum Lam. (*Z. clava-herculis* DC.)	Berberine (167, 177), *N*-(2-*p*-anisylethyl)-*N*-methylcinnamamide (178)
Z. ochroxylum DC.	α-Xantherine, $C_{24}H_{23}O_6N$, m.p. 186–187° (179) β-Xantherine (179)

reasonably reliable results if only berberine is present, but in the presence of other protoberberines the methods are arbitrary to a certain degree. Various reagents have been proposed for the detection of berberine. Among them are potassium ferrocyanide (199), picrolonic acid (200), silicoduodecitungstic acid (201), Reinecke salt (202), and 2-nitro-1,3-indandione (203). Most of these lack specificity.

3. STRUCTURE OF BERBERINE

A study of the work which resulted in the correct constitutional formula for berberine can begin advantageously with the researches of Perkin dealing with the oxidation of the alkaloid by permanganate (182, 204). These papers, particularly the second, are models of reporting and skill which commend them to the attention of all serious students of organic chemistry.

In the first paper, Perkin gives a short history of the discovery of and earlier work on berberine, taking great pains to confirm the empirical formula of Perrins (167) which was based on the analysis of salts and therefore were actually written as $C_{20}H_{17}O_4N$. The physical properties of the alkaloid and many of its salts were described, as well as a number of color reactions.

Previous work on the oxidation of berberine by permanganate included that of Schmidt and Schilbach (205), who obtained considerable amounts of hemipinic acid. Perkin confirmed these findings using the method of Goldschmidt, who had shown that permanganate oxidation of papaverine yielded *m*-hemipinic acid also obtained by Wegscheider from narcotine.

In the second paper (204) Perkin described the oxidation of berberine by amounts of permanganate insufficient to effect oxidation to hemipinic acid as the main product. The following five products, each retaining all of the carbon atoms, were obtained: oxyberberine, $C_{20}H_{17}O_5N$; dioxyberberine, $C_{20}H_{17}O_6N$; berberal, $C_{20}H_{17}O_7N$; anhydroberberilic acid, $C_{20}H_{17}O_8N$; and berberilic acid, $C_{20}H_{19}O_9N$.

Anhydroberberilic acid seemed to be the substance most promising for further investigation since hydrolysis with sulfuric acid decomposed it quantitatively into hemipinic acid and a new compound, $C_{10}H_{11}O_4N$, which contained a carboxyl and an amino group. This readily lost water yielding a lactam, $C_{10}H_9O_3N$, which yielded an *N*-nitroso derivative and must therefore contain a secondary nitrogen. The nitroso derivative when heated with dilute alkali evolved nitrogen and yielded a hydroxy acid, $C_{10}H_{10}O_5$, which readily lactonized to an anhydride, $C_{10}H_8O_4$. The above facile ring closures indicate that the carboxyl and the side chain are ortho to each other. Furthermore, no methoxyl groups are present but all of the diagnostic reactions for a methylenedioxy group are positive. It seemed therefore probable that the lactam, $C_{10}H_9O_3N$, might be the *N*-desmethyl derivative of oxyhydrastine (206, 207), and it was indeed converted into the latter in the following way. The anhydride, $C_{10}H_8O_4$ (IV), was treated in chloroform solution with phosphorus pentachloride to yield the acid chloride of an ω-chloroethyl compound (V), which with methanol yielded the methyl ester (VI). This methyl ester when heated

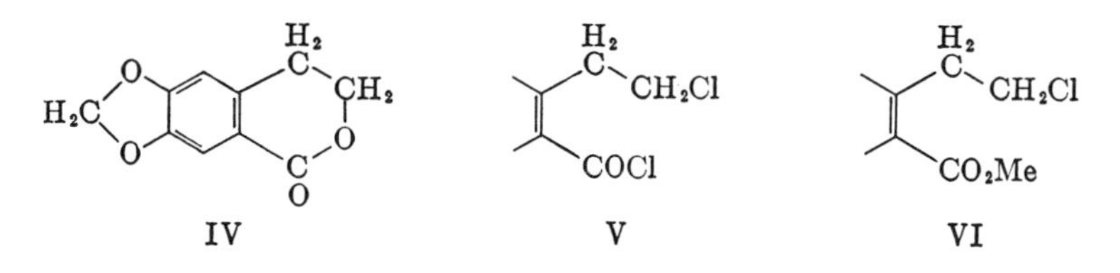

with methylamine and subsequently with aqueous potash gave an almost quantitative yield of oxyhydrastine (VII), the constitution of which was already known with reasonable certainty, although Perkin overlooked this

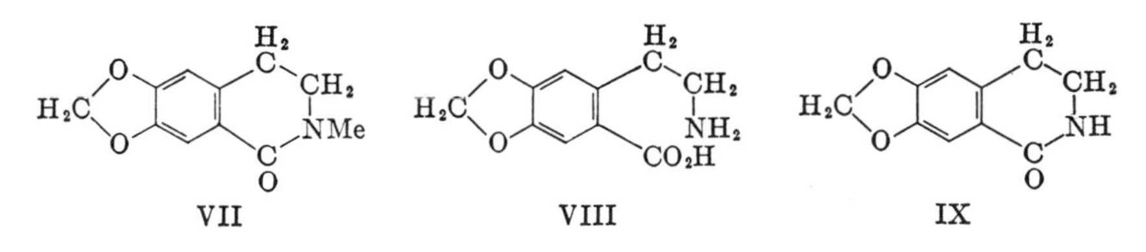

fact at the time and only in a later paper with Robinson (208) made the necessary corrections which are here embodied. Therefore the compound $C_{10}H_{11}O_4N$ and its lactam are VIII and IX, respectively. Since, moreover, anhydroberberilic acid is readily formed by heating VIII with hemipinic acid it must be represented by X. Berberilic acid is therefore the phthalamic acid corresponding to X. Two isomers are possible and indeed

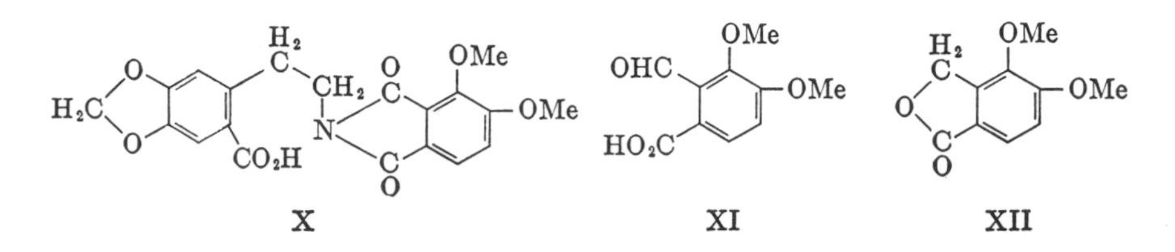

X XI XII

two forms were recorded.

The compound which, however, yielded the most important clue to the structure of berberine was berberal, which unfortunately was difficult of access. This when heated with dilute sulfuric acid suffered hydrolysis to the compound IX and pseudopianic acid (XI), which though not identical with opianic acid bore a striking resemblance to it. It was reducible to pseudomeconine (XII), and its oxime on heating yielded hemipinimide. Berberal was regenerated when the amino acid VIII and pseudopianic acid were heated to 180–200° and was represented by XIII. This was altered

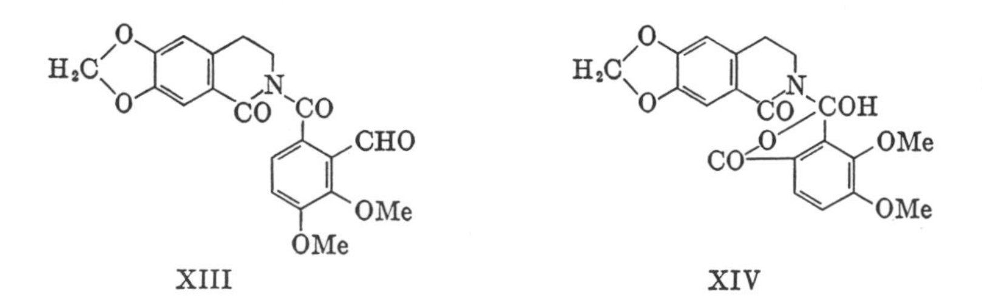

XIII XIV

to XIV (208) largely because of Liebermann's work (209, 210) which showed that opianic acid reacts as hydroxymeconine with aniline and that the carbon of the aldehyde becomes united with the nitrogen. Based on anhydroberberilic acid and the erroneous formula of berberal it was possible to write a formula for berberine which indeed explained most of its known reactions. It was not recognized however that one molecule of water in berberine is constitutional, but this did not invalidate the essential correctness of the structure of tetrahydroberberine. It remained for Gadamer (184, 211, 212) to point out that berberine is a quaternary ammonium compound and that the free base is in fact $C_{20}H_{18}O_4N \cdot OH$. When it is heated with concentrated alkali it undergoes the Cannizzaro reaction (212) yielding equimolecular quantities of dihydroberberine and oxyberberine, and the formula XV was therefore proposed for berberine and this was subsequently accepted by Perkin and Robinson (208). This formula, which

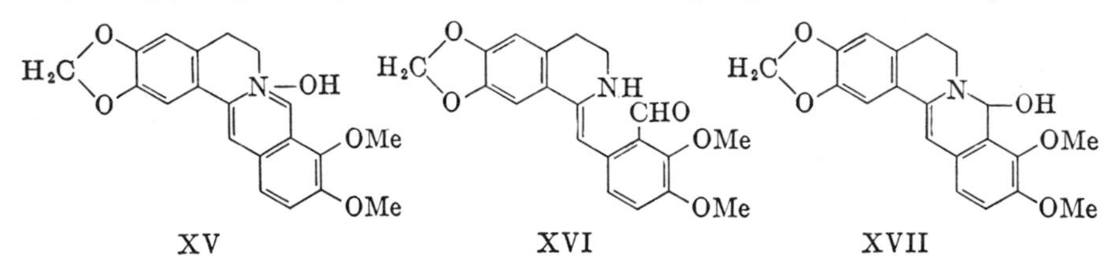

XV XVI XVII

corresponds to that of its salts, is known as the ammonium form. The so-called aldehyde form (XVI) was postulated to account for the formation of an oxime and the condensation products with acetone, chloroform, etc. Tinkler's observation (213) that Gadamer's berberinium hydroxide (XV) showed the same absorption spectra as its salts indicates that the base formed by adding barium hydroxide to berberine sulfate is indeed XV. When an excess of alkali is added to the soluble ammonium form the so-called berberinal is precipitated and this is the form which was described by Perkin as berberine. This provides an absorption spectrum almost identical with α-methyldihydroberberine (214) which is a carbinol and formally resembles the *C*-hydroxy forms of cotarnine and hydrastine. Therefore, the carbinol form of berberine is represented by XVII, dihydroberberine is XVII in which the hydroxyl has been replaced by hydrogen, and oxyberberine is XVIII.

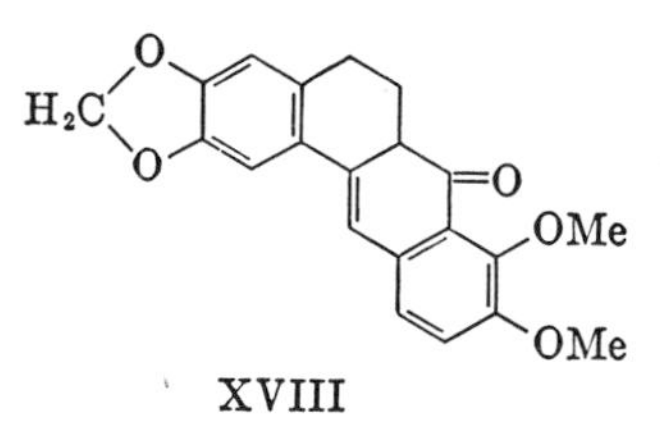

XVIII

4. Other Degradation Products and Synthesis of Berberine

The importance of berberal (XIV) in determining the structure of berberine has already been pointed out. The condensation of opianic acid with noroxyhydrastine yields isoberberal (XIX), and it was this compound

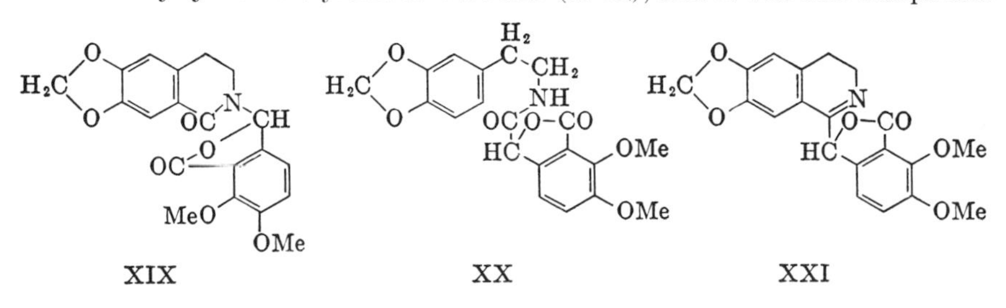

XIX XX XXI

that was studied in some detail because of the ready accessibility of opianic acid (204).

Oxyberberine (XVIII) is the first product of the oxidation of berberine. It may be reduced to tetrahydroberberine at a lead cathode in alcoholic sulfuric acid (215). Its synthesis is therefore a synthesis of berberine. The general procedure for the synthesis of this type of compound is described in connection with the synthesis of cryptopine, and oxyberberine itself was prepared by this procedure. Another synthesis of oxyberberine was achieved by Perkin, Rây, and Robinson (216). The β-piperonylethylimide of meconinecarboxylic acid (XX) was heated with phosphoryl chloride to yield an uncharacterized isoquinoline derivative, presumably XXI, which when reduced with zinc in acetic acid suffered reduction of the doubl bond, opening of the lactone ring, lactam formation, and dehydration to yield oxyberberine. This ready elimination of water was later observed in ophiocarpine (6).

IV. Canadine

Canadine was first isolated from *Hydrastis canadensis* by Schmidt (169). It has since been isolated from *Corydalis cheilantheifolia* (33), along with berberine, *C. ophiocarpa* (6), *C. ternata* (50), and *C. cava* Schweigg. et Kort., (56) (*C. cava* = *C. tuberosa*). The naturally occurring form is optically active and the *dl*-form is conveniently obtainable from berberine by reduction with zinc and dilute hydrochloric acid. Strictly speaking it should be named tetrahydroanhydroberberine, but by common usage the term tetrahydroberberine is now generally accepted. Both forms (*l*-, m.p. 135° $[\alpha]_D$ $-299°$; and *dl*-, m.p. 171°) crystallize readily from hot methanol, in which they are moderately soluble. The salts with inorganic acids are for the greater part sparingly soluble in cold water, the hydrochlorides being well adapted for recrystallization and purification.

l-Canadine with methyl iodide yields a mixture of α- and β-methiodides, the former being convertible into the latter by heating to its melting point (230°). This isomerism is due to the introduction of another center of asymmetry at the nitrogen atom and already had been studied (211, 217, 218), but it was Pyman (219) who elucidated the nature of the products obtained when the methohydroxides are dehydrated. Since the nitrogen in tetrahydroberberine is common to two rings, its methohydroxide (XXII)

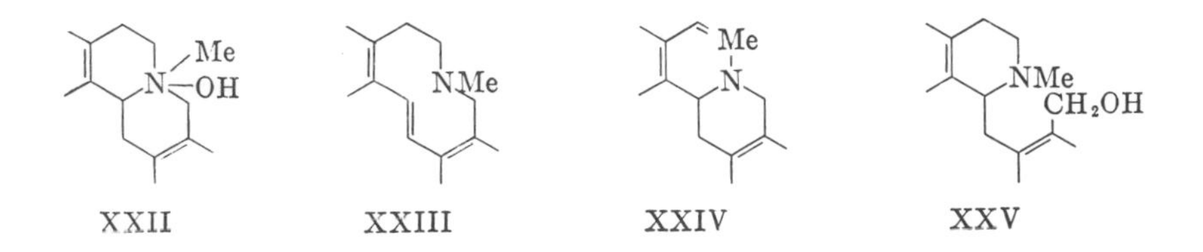

XXII XXIII XXIV XXV

can theoretically undergo ring scission to yield three products (XXIII, XXIV, XXV). Furthermore, if XXII is optically active the optical activity should be retained in XXIV and XXV but not in XXIII. When *l*-canadine was the starting material Pyman did indeed obtain three compounds but only one was optically active. It proved to be XXIV. A second compound proved to be XXIII, and this structure was confirmed by the observation that on heating with acids it was convertible into metho salts of *dl*-canadine, and when heated alone it was converted into the third compound also of structure XXIV but optically inactive. No evidence of the presence of the carbinol (XXV) was obtained.

It should be noted that α-*l*-canadine methochloride was isolated from *Zanthoxylum brachyacanthum* by Jowett and Pyman (176).

Synthesis. Pictet and Gams (220) in 1911 announced a synthesis of berberine via tetrahydroberberine by condensing 1-(3,4-dimethoxybenzyl)-6,7-methylenedioxytetrahydroisoquinoline (XXVI) with methylal in the presence of hydrogen chloride. The entering methylene group was considered as having entered ortho to the methoxyl group. Tetrahydro-

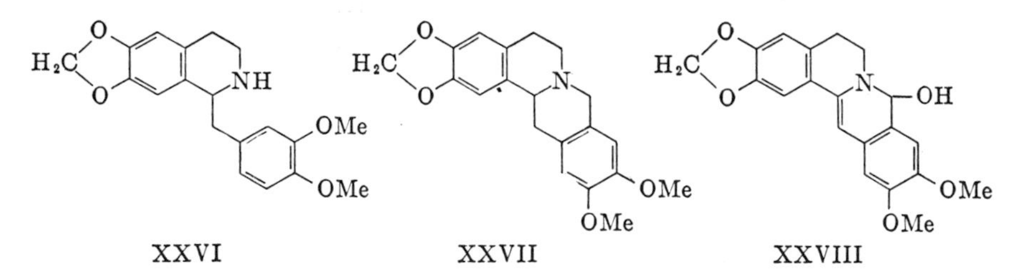

XXVI XXVII XXVIII

berberine was at that time a well-known compound and comparison of the synthetic base with that derived from berberine was reputedly carried out, but Haworth, Perkin, and Rankin (221) showed that the product is tetrahydro-ψ-berberine (XXVII), condensation having taken place para to a methoxyl group. Pictet and Gams' synthetic berberine was therefore ψ-berberine (XXVIII), which on treatment with alkalis suffers dismutation like berberine to yield equimolecular quantities of ψ-oxyberberine and dihydro-ψ-berberine.

A synthesis of oxyberberine is also a synthesis of tetrahydroberberine, and the resolution of the latter by means of bromocamphorsulfonic acid (211) to *l*-canadine completed the synthesis of this natural base.

V. Palmatine

Palmatine, $C_{21}H_{23}O_5N$, was first isolated from *Jateorhiza palmata* by Gadamer (222), who determined the correct formula. Günzel (160) isolated it subsequently under the name of columbamine, and Feist (159) showed the probable identity with Gadamer's base. It has since been isolated from the following plants: *Coptis orientalis* as *C. japonica* (163, 164), *Berberis vulgaris* as *B. heteropoda* (129), *B. thunbergii* (123), *B. vulgaris* (126), *Mahonia philippinensis* (134), *Coscinium blumeanum* (154), *Fibraurea tinctoria* (*F. chloroleuca*) (158), *Phellodendron amurense* (163), *Tinospora bakis* (153), and *Cocculus leaeba* (153).

In many of its source plants it is associated with one or two of its *O*-desmethyl ethers, namely, jatrorrhizine and columbamine, which form sparingly soluble iodides along with that of palmatine. The mixed iodides are digested with aqueous alkali in which the phenolic compounds dissolve leaving the sparingly soluble palmatine iodide which may be purified by recrystallization from much boiling water.

Structure. Reduction of palmatine yields *dl*-tetrahydropalmatine, and this can readily be reoxidized to palmatine. It differs from berberine in having four methoxyls, the methylenedioxy group of the latter being replaced by two methoxyls in the former. Since it yields corydaldine and hemipinic acid on oxidation with permanganate Feist and Sandstede (223) suggested structure XXIX, which should be rewritten to conform to the carbinol form analogous to XVII for berberine. Like berberine it forms

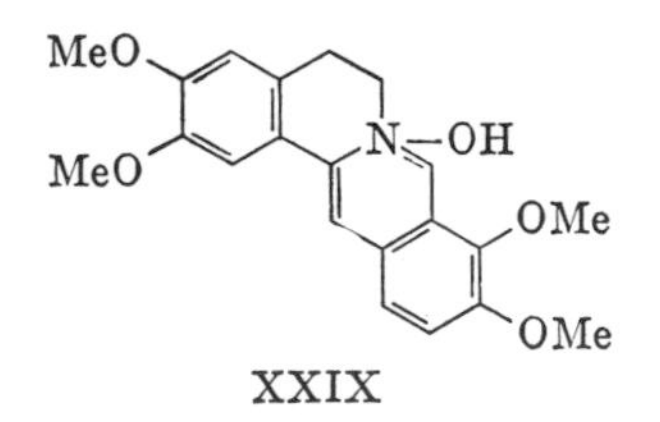

XXIX

addition compounds with chloroform, acetone, etc.

VI. Shobakunine

An alkaloid, shobakunine, isolated from *Mahonia philippinensis* (134) and *Archangelisia flava* (152), was shown to be a mixture, possibly molecular, of berberine and palmatine, and its reduction product, tetrahydroshobakunine, was either a compound or mixture of *dl*-canadine and of *dl*-tetrahydropalmatine.

VII. Tetrahydropalmatine

The *d*-form of this alkaloid was first isolated from *Corydalis tuberosa* by Späth, Mosettig, and Tröthandl (58) but has since been isolated in the *l*-, *d*- (m.p. 142°), and/or *dl*- (m.p. 151°) forms from the following plants: *Corydalis ambigua* (*dl*-) (25, 26), *C. aurea* (*l*-, *dl*-) (5, 28), *C. caseana* (*l*-) (32), *C. decumbens* (*d*-) (38), *C. lutea* (*l*-), (40), *C. micrantha* (*l*-) (37), *C.*

montana (*dl*-) (29), *C. nobilis* (*dl*-, *d*-) (41), *C. ochroleuca* (*l*-) (43), *C. pallida* (*dl*-, *d*-) (45), and *C. platycarpa* (*l*-) (46).

Tetrahydropalmatine yields a hydrochloride which is moderately soluble in boiling water and only sparingly soluble in cold water. This property, together with the fact that the hydrochloride is readily extractable from hydrochloric acid solutions of plant extracts by means of chloroform, renders its isolation and purification a simple procedure. The hydrochloride of the *dl*-form is appreciably less soluble than that of the *d*- or *l*-forms and separates in stout prisms even from hot aqueous solutions. The alkaloid is readily oxidized by air and slowly becomes yellow owing to the formation of palmatine. This oxidation can be readily completed by means of alcoholic iodine solutions when palmatine iodide is formed, or it may be brought about by heating in dilute acetic acid with mercuric acetate (224).

Structure and Synthesis. In addition to the proof of the structure of tetrahydropalmatine by virtue of its preparation from palmatine and the reverse oxidation, the resolution of the *dl*-base was accomplished by means of *d*- and *l*-tartaric acids in succession, the *d*-base *d*-tartrate and the *l*-base *l*-tartrate being the forms of least solubility (225). The *d*- and *l*-bases had $[\alpha]_D^{20}$ +291° (ethanol) and —294° (ethanol), respectively, the natural *d*-base having $[\alpha]_D^{17}$ +292.5° (58). Späth and Mosettig (226) have also related tetrahydropalmatine directly to tetrahydroberberine, that is to canadine. The *d*-, *l*-, and *dl*-forms of canadine were demethylenated by means of phloroglucinol and sulfuric acid yielding the base XXX in its three possible forms, the *d*-form having $[\alpha]_D^{13}$ +307° (ethanol). These when

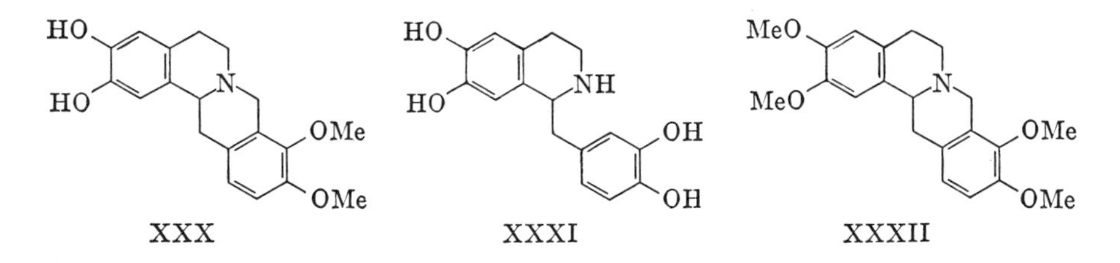

O-methylated with diazomethane yielded the three forms of tetrahydropalmatine, the *d*-form having $[\alpha]_D^{14}$ +288.9°. It was identical with the natural alkaloid.

Still another synthesis was achieved by Späth and Kruta (227), who showed that tetrahydropapaveroline (XXXI) on condensation with formaldehyde yielded two products which on complete *O*-methylation gave a separable mixture of tetrahydropalmatine (XXXII) and norcoralydine (analogous to XXVII). It is to be noted that in the former case the condensation took place in a position ortho to a hydroxyl group. In the latter condensation it occurred in the position para to a hydroxyl in analogy with the synthesis of tetrahydro-ψ-berberine and of tetrahydro-ψ-epiberberine (XXXIII) (221, 228).

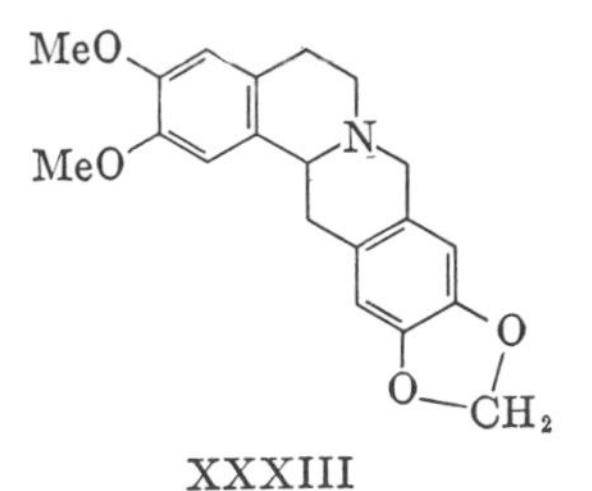

XXXIII

VIII. Jatrorrhizine and Columbamine

Jatrorrhizine (jateorhizine) and columbamine are an isomeric pair of quaternary bases generally isolated in the form of their sparingly soluble iodides. They have been recorded from the following plants: *Coptis japonica* (163) (columbamine only), *Berberis vulgaris* as *B. heteropoda* (129), *B. thunbergii* (123), *B. vulgaris* (126), *Mahonia philippinensis* (134) (jatrorrhizine only), *Archangelisia flava* (152), *Coscinium blumeanum* (154) (jatrorrhizine only), *Fibraurea tinctoria* as *F. chloroleuca* (158) (jatrorrhizine only), and *Jateorhiza columba* as *J. palmata* (159, 160). It should be noted that while most of the above-recorded occurrences are highly probable, some at least require confirmation.

The mixture of the iodides are separable from the palmatine iodide by virtue of their phenolic nature and, therefore, their solubility in aqueous alkali. Jatrorrhizine generally being the major constituent it has been obtained in a satisfactory state of purity by direct crystallization of the iodide, but columbamine has only been isolated in pure form as its tetrahydro derivative. The structures of these alkaloids are discussed under corypalmine, which is tetrahydrojatrorrhizine, and isocorypalmine, which is tetrahydrocolumbamine.

IX. Corypalmine and Isocorypalmine

The *d*-form of corypalmine, $C_{20}H_{23}O_4N$, was isolated from *Corydalis cava* by Späth, Mosettig, and Tröthandl (58). It has subsequently been isolated in either the *d*- or *l*-form from *C. caseana* (32), *C. cheilantheifolia* (33), *C. ochroleuca* (43), *C. ophiocarpa* (6), *C. thalictrifolia* (51), and *Dicentra oregana* (69). The *d*-form has $[\alpha]_D^{16}$ +280° (chloroform). It is almost insoluble in methanol and crystallizes readily in colorless stout prisms when hot methanol is added to its concentrated solution in hot chloroform. A specimen of the *l*-form melted at 246° (*in vacuo*) (51) although the generally accepted melting point is about 236° (*in vacuo*) (58). The *d*-form of isocorypalmine was first isolated from *C. tuberosa* by Knörck (229) and examined by Gadamer, Späth, and Mosettig (59). It has also been isolated in the *d*- or *l*-form from *C. caseana* (32) (where it was described as casealutine), *C. lutea* (40), *C. nobilis* (41), *C. ochroleuca* (43), and *C. platycarpa* (46). The *d*-form has $[\alpha]_D$ +303°. It crystallizes from chloroform–methanol in stout colorless prisms which are practically insoluble in cold methanol. In an open tube its melting point is indefinite due to rapid oxidation. In an evacuated tube it melts sharply and without decomposition at 241°. The *dl*-form melts at 223° (59).

Constitution. *dl*-Corypalmine is identical with tetrahydrojatrorrhizine and *dl*-isocorypalmine is identical with tetrahydrocolumbamine and both are monophenolic, being converted by methylation with diazomethane into *dl*-tetrahydropalmatine.

The position of the free hydroxyl in corypalmine (XXXIV) was deter-

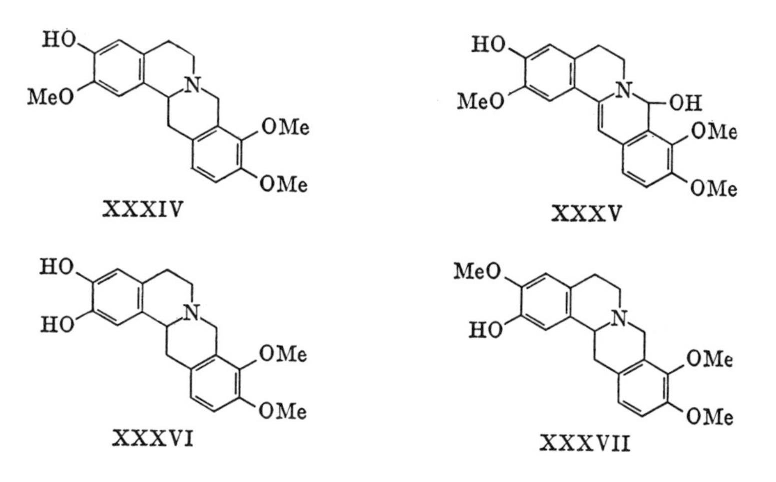

mined (230) by the oxidation of its *O*-ethyl ether (which was later obtained crystalline, m.p. 120°) with permanganate to 7-methoxy-6-ethoxy-1-keto-1,2,3,4-tetrahydroisoquinoline (XLI) melting at 173°. Jatrorrhizine therefore has formula XXXV.

At the time of its discovery there was not available enough *d*-isocorypalmine for the determination of its structure by degradative methods, but Späth and Mosettig (231) prepared it from *d*-canadine by, first, demethylenation to XXXVI (2,3-dihydroxy-9,10-dimethoxytetrahydroprotoberberine, m.p. 252–253°) by means of phloroglucinol and sulfuric acid and, then, by incomplete methylation with diazomethane. In addition to the non-phenolic tetrahydropalmatine, there was formed a separable mixture of *d*-corypalmine and *d*-isocorypalmine (XXXVII), which were identical with the natural *d*-corypalmine and *d*-isocorypalmine, respectively. Columbamine is therefore XXXVIII. It should be added that the oxidation of isocorypalmine *O*-ethyl ether (m.p. 82°) yields the

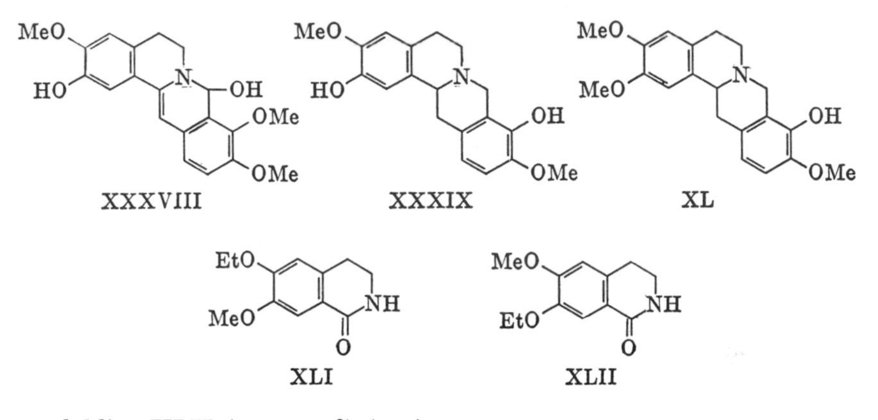

corydaldine XLII (m.p. 195°) (232).

The analogous alkaloid with a free hydroxyl at position 9 is not known as a natural product, but Späth and Burger (232) have prepared it by reducing palmatrubine. The *dl*-base (XL) melts at 149° and its *O*-ethyl ether melts at 115°.

X. Scoulerine

This is the name given to an alkaloid by one of us (47), but it was first isolated in the *d*-form from *Corydalis tuberosa* by Knörck (229). The *l*-form was subsequently found in *C. caseana* (32), *C. micrantha* (37), *C. montana* (29), *C. scouleri* (47), and *C. sibirica* (49). Furthermore, it was isolated as a molecular compound, $[\alpha]_D$ −69.9°, composed of the *l*- and *dl*-forms, under the name of aurotensine from *C. aurea* (5, 28), *C. ochotensis* (42), *Fumaria officinalis* (77), *Glaucium flavum* (79), and *G. serpieri* (72).

Scoulerine hydrochloride is virtually insoluble in cold water and was thus separable from the total base mixture. The free base recrystallized from methanol yielded fine gray needles, m.p. 204°. The *l*- and *dl* mixture, aurotensine, can be recrystallized from ether plus methanol to give pale pink rectangular plates melting at 126–127°.

Constitution. *d*-Scoulerine, $C_{19}H_{21}O_4N$, contains two methoxyl groups, two phenolic hydroxyls, and on methylation yields *d*-tetrahydropalmatine (58). The *O,O*-diethyl ether (m.p. 155°), later obtained crystalline from *l*-scoulerine (233), on partial oxidation with permanganate yields the corydaldine XLII, and on further oxidation it yields a separable mixture of 4-methoxy-5-ethoxyphthalic and 4-methoxy-3-ethoxyphthalic acids, characterized as their ethylimides. Scoulerine therefore is XXXIX.

Aurotensine on methylation with diazomethane yielded a mixture from which *dl*-tetrahydropalmatine was readily separated in a pure form. The diethyl ether on ethylation and oxidation yielded the same products which were obtained from scoulerine (233).

XI. Sinactine

Sinactine, $C_{20}H_{21}O_4N$, is of interest in that the *dl*-form had been obtained by Perkin (234) from cryptopine before it was discovered by Goto and Sudzuki (161) as the levorotatory form in *Sinomenium acutum*. It has since been isolated from *Fumaria officinalis* (77), where it occurs as a mixture of the *l*- and *dl*- forms. It crystallizes from hot methanol in stout prisms which have $[\alpha]_D$ −312° (chloroform) and melt at 176°. Its hydrochloride (m.p. 272°) is sparingly soluble in water and serves as a convenient compound for isolation and purification. The alkaloid is readily oxidized by air, but the dehydro compound has not been recognized as a naturally occurring alkaloid.

Structure and Synthesis. When Buck and Perkin (228) attempted to apply the Pictet and Gams synthesis (220) of berberine to epiberberine they obtained an isomer, tetrahydro-ψ-epiberberine (XXXIII). Subsequently, Haworth and Perkin achieved a total synthesis which is detailed in connection with the synthesis of cryptopine. Oxidation of sinactine with iodine in boiling alcohol yields epiberberinium iodide, from which the chloride was prepared by treatment with silver chloride, and this was identical with epiberberinium chloride prepared from cryptopine (235). Finaly, Späth and Mosettig (236) resolved the *dl*-tetrahydroepiberberine (m.p. 170°) (XLIII) from cryptopine by means of *d*- and *l*-tartaric acids in succession and showed that the *l*-form, $[\alpha]_D^{15}$ −302° (chloroform), was identical with the natural alkaloid. The *d*-form had the same numerical value for its optical rotation and melted at 178–179°.

It should be added that oxidation of sinactine with permanganate in neutral solution has yielded 6,7-dimethoxy-1-keto-1,2,3,4-tetrahydroisoquinoline, but 3,4-methylenedioxyphthalic acid could not be obtained by this method (34).

XII. Cheilanthifoline

Cheilanthifoline, $C_{19}H_{19}O_4N$, has been isolated in small amounts by one of the writers from *Corydalis cheilantheifolia* (34), *C. scouleri* (47), and *C. sibirica* (49). It crystallizes in stout plates from methanol, in which it is moderately soluble; $[\alpha]_D^{20}$ − 311° (methanol), m.p. 184°.

Its structure (XLIV) follows in part from the fact that its *O*-methyl

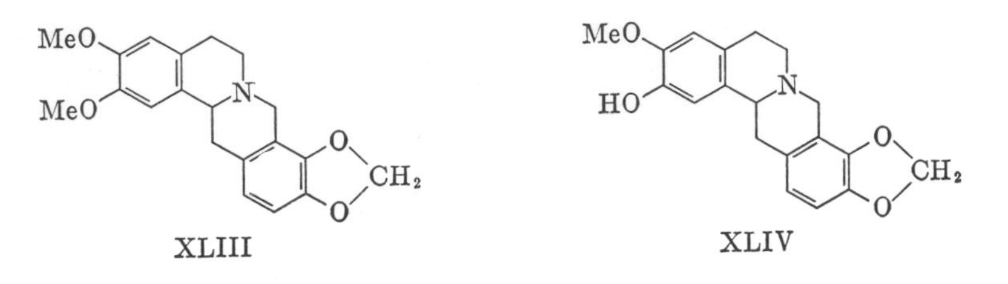

ether is identical with *l*-sinactine, there being only one hydroxyl and one methoxyl in the alkaloid. The position of the free hydroxyl follows from the observation that oxidation of its *O*-ethyl ether yields 6-methoxy-7-ethoxy-1-ketotetrahydroisoquinoline (XLII) (34).

6-Methoxy-7-ethoxy-1-ketotetrahydroisoquinoline.—A solution of cheilanthifoline *O*-ethyl ether (75 mg.) in 50 cc. of water containing a drop of concentrated hydrochloric acid was treated with an aqueous solution of sodium carbonate until a slight but permanent turbidity was produced. The well-cooled mixture was then treated with an aqueous solution of potassium permanganate (135 mg.). When the latter was used up, the solution was heated and filtered and the cooled filtrate extracted with ether. The residue from the ether extract was dissolved in hot water, and the solution cooled, filtered, and again extracted with ether. The residue from this extract was slowly sublimed *in vacuo*. The brilliant colorless crystals thus obtained melted sharply at 195°.

XIII. Ophiocarpine

Ophiocarpine, $C_{20}H_{21}O_5N$, has been isolated only from *Corydalis ophiocarpa* (6), in which it is present to the extent of *ca.* 0.25%. It is sparingly soluble even in hot methanol and crystallizes in stout prisms which melt at 188° when its hot concentrated solution in chloroform is treated with hot methanol; $[\alpha]_D^{24}$ −284°. It yields a sparingly soluble hydrochloride, and its methiodide, which is also sparingly soluble, crystallizes from hot water, even in the presence of sodium hydroxide, in stout prisms.

Ophiocarpine gives Gaebel's test for the methylenedioxy group, contains two methoxyls, and a non-phenolic hydroxyl. The last is eliminated as water on prolonged boiling of the alkaloid with hydrochloric acid, and when the anhydro compound is oxidized with iodine in hot alcohol and again reduced with zinc in acetic acid there is obtained *dl*-canadine, m.p. 171°. When the alkaloid is oxidized in neutral solution with permanganate, it yields 6,7-methylenedioxy-1-keto-1,2,3,4-tetrahydroisoquinoline (IX), and therefore the hydroxyl must be in position 8, 13, or 14. If the hydroxyl were in either positions 8 or 14, the hydrochloride should be yellow like that of hydrastinine and, furthermore, if it were in the former position the action of alkali should convert it into an equimolecular mixture of the 8-keto and 8-hydroxy compounds. Ophiocarpine is however stable to prolonged heating with alkali.

Finally, the methiodide of a compound with a hydroxyl at position 14 would be expected to be identical with the hydriodide of allocryptopine. Ophiocarpine methiodide does not yield allocryptopine on treatment with alkali. There remains only position 13 for the hydroxyl, and ophiocarpine is therfore XLV. It should be noted that this is the only example of a

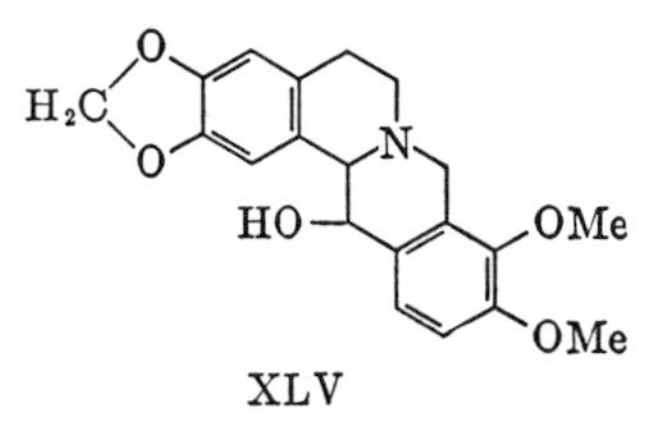

XLV

hydroxyprotoberberine and that the hydroxyl is in the same position that it occupies in the phthalideisoquinolines, and one of these, *l*-adlumine, is also present in *C. ophiocarpa*.

It is of interest to note that a likely biogenetic route to allocryptopine, which is copresent with ophiocarpine, is by way of the 14-hydroxy derivative of ophiocarpine, which need only be dehydrated and *N*-methylated to achieve such a transformation.

XIV. Capaurine and Capauridine

Capaurine and capauridine are respectively the *l*- and *dl*-forms of an alkaloid, $C_{21}H_{25}O_5N$, which has been obtained from *Corydalis aurea* (5), *C. micrantha* (37), *C. montana* (29), and *C. pallida* (45). Capaurine, $[\alpha]_D^{24}$ −271° (chloroform), is readily soluble in chloroform and only sparingly soluble in methanol and crystallizes in large stout polyhedra, melting at 164°, when hot methanol is added to a concentrated solution of the alkaloid in chloroform. Capauridine is optically inactive and only sparingly soluble in chloroform. It separates from its concentrated solution in chloroform in colorless prisms, melting at 208°, particularly if a little methanol is added.

Constitution. Capaurine has one phenolic hydroxyl and four methoxyl groups. That it belongs to the protoberberine type was rendered plausible by the fact that it is oxidized to a quaternary iodide with iodine in alcohol, and this iodide is reducible with zinc and acetic or hydrochloric acid to the optically inactive tetrahydro base which is identical with capauridine. Furthermore, the *O*-methyl ether of capurine, melting at 152°, $[\alpha]_D^{24}$ −254° (methanol), has five methoxyls and on racemization by successive oxidation and reduction yields capauridine *O*-methyl ether, m.p. 142°.

Complete oxidation of capaurine with permanganate yields hemipinic acid and the *O*-methyl ether yields a mixture of 3,4,5-trimethoxyphthalic acid and hemipinic acid (3). These results are in accord with several possible formulas for capaurine, the most probable being XLVI. The *O*-methyl ether furthermore on mild oxidation with permanganate yielded a compound, $C_{22}H_{23}O_8N$, m.p. 192°, which on hydrolysis gave ψ-opianic

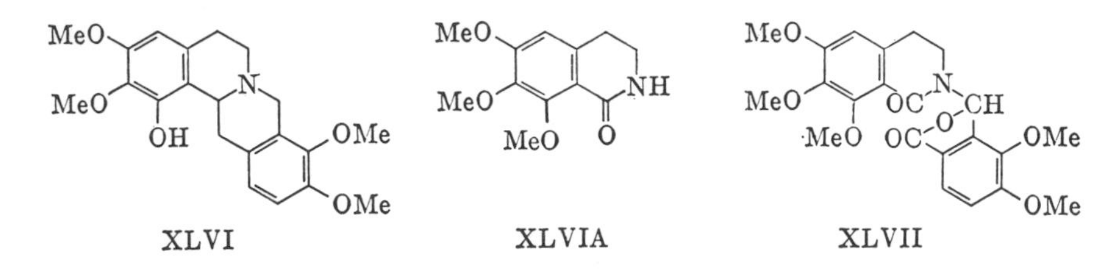

XLVI XLVIA XLVII

acid (XI) and 6,7,8-trimethoxy-1-keto-1,2,3,4-tetrahydroisoquinoline, melting at 138°, (XLVIA). The compound $C_{22}H_{23}O_8N$ is therefore a derivative (XLVII) of berberal (XIV). These observations still leave disputable the position of the free hydroxyl in capaurine. The *O*-ethyl ether of capaurine (m.p. 134°) was therefore oxidized with permanganate, and there was obtained an acid which proved to be 3-ethoxy-4,5-dimethoxyphthalic acid (identified as its *N*-ethylimide, m.p. 76°).

The acid had already been prepared by Späth, but a more convenient route was discovered. When pyrogallol trimethyl ether is condensed with succinic anhydride in nitrobenzene with aluminum chloride it can yield either β-2-hydroxy-3,4-dimethoxybenzoylpropionic acid (XLVIII),

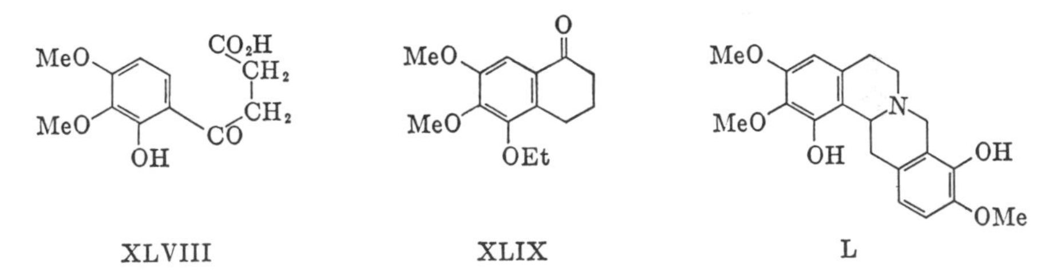

XLVIII XLIX L

or its methyl ether, or a mixture, the relative proportions depending upon the conditions (237). The compound XLVIII is difficult to alkylate but, when reduced by Clemmensen's method, the resulting γ-arylbutyric acid is readily ethylated, and this substance when cyclized yields the keto-tetrahydronaphthalene XLIX. The latter on oxidation with permanganate yielded 3-ethoxy-4,5-dimethoxyphthalic acid, characterized as the anhydride, *N*-methylimide, and *N*-ethylimide, identical with the corresponding derivatives obtained from the oxidation of capaurine *O*-ethyl ether. The corresponding trimethoxy acid was prepared by a parallel series of reactions.

The corydaldine (XLVIA) was prepared by two methods. In the first, the *N*-carbethoxy derivative of β-3,4,5-trimethoxyphenethylamine was heated in xylene with a mixture of phosphoryl chloride and phosphorus pentoxide. In the second method, which is analogous to one used by Mohunta and Rây (238), the azide of β-3,4,5-trimethoxyphenylpropionic acid was decomposed in dry benzene to the corresponding isocyanate, and the latter then cyclized in toluene with phosphoryl chloride.

Capaurine and capauridine are therefore represented by XLVI (3).

XV. Capaurimine

Capaurimine, $C_{20}H_{23}O_5N$, has been found only in *Corydalis montana* (29) and *C. pallida* (45). It crystallizes from chloroform–methanol in stout prisms which melt at 212° and have $[\alpha]_D^{24}$ —287° (chloroform). It has two phenolic hydroxyls and three methoxyls and on methylation with diazomethane yields capaurine *O*-methyl ether. On ethylation with diazoethane it yields an *O*,*O*-diethyl ether which on complete oxidation with permanganate gave a mixture of 3-ethoxy-4,5-dimethoxy- and 3-ethoxy-4-methoxyphthalic acids, both identified as their *N*-methylimides. Capaurimine is therefore L (4).

XVI. Stylopine and Coptisine

Occurrence. l-Stylopine, $C_{19}H_{17}O_4N$, was first isolated by Schlotterbeck and Watkins (239) from *Stylophorum diphyllum.* Its true nature was, however, not recognized until Späth and Julian (56) isolated the *d*-form of it from *Corydalis tuberosa* and showed that it was identical with *d*-tetrahydrocoptisine. It has since been found in *C. ambigua* (26), *Fumaria officinalis* (as *dl*-tetrahydrocoptisine, 2.5 p.p.m.) (77), *C. ternata* (50), *C. lutea* (0.01%) (40), *C. nobilis* (0.007%) (41), *C. claviculata* (0.005%) (35), *Stylophorum diphyllum* and *Dicranostigma franchetianum* (72), *C. cheilantheifolia* (33), *C. platycarpa* (*dl*-stylopine 0.0008%) (46), *C. thalictrifolia* (*d*-stylopine) (51), *Dactylicapnos macrocapnos* (*l*- and *dl*-stylopine 0.009%) (62), and *C. cornuta* (*d*-stylopine 0.02%) (36).

The pure optically active forms of stylopine melt at 202° and the pure *dl*-form melts at 221°. Mixtures of the racemic with one of the active forms occur in plants and when recrystallized several times often melt at 206°.

Constitution. Haworth and Perkin (240) had already synthesized *dl*-stylopine (*dl*-tetrahydrocoptisine) in the course of their synthesis of protopine, but at that time the alkaloid was not recognized as a natural product. When oxidized with iodine it yields coptisine iodide, which has been isolated in this form from *Coptis japonica* (165). Coptisine is also present in *Corydalis ambigua* (26), and of course traces could no doubt be found in all plants which contain stylopine.

Aside from the above-mentioned synthesis the best proof of the structure of stylopine is that of Späth and Posega (241), who reduced protopine to the carbinol, dehydrated this to the quaternary chloride, and then following Perkin's procedure eliminated methyl chloride by distillation in a high vacuum. The resulting product (LI) was identical with *dl*-tetrahydro-

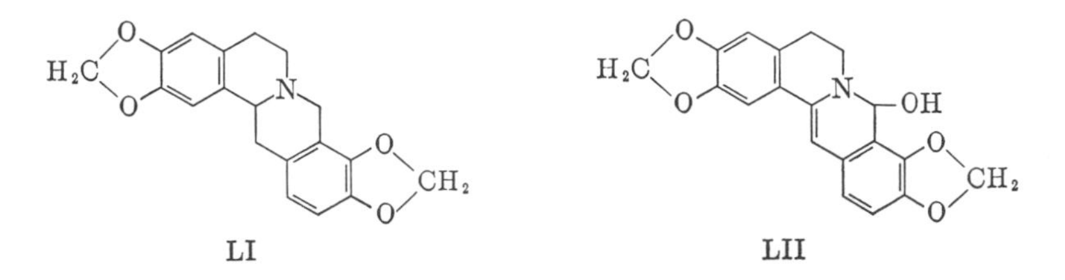

coptisine. This had already been resolved first by means of *d*-bromocamphor-π-sulphonic acid to yield the *l*-base, and then the *d*- and *dl*-bases from the mother liquor were resolved into the pure *d*-base by means of *d*-tartaric acid (56). The resolved *d*-stylopine had $[\alpha]_D^{15}$ +310.5° whereas the natural base had $[\alpha]_D^{15}$ +310°, chloroform being the solvent in both instances. The base from *S. diphyllum* is levorotatory, $[\alpha]_D$ —315.2° (chloroform).

It should also be noted that Kitasato (165) demethylenated coptisine to the corresponding tetrahydroxy compound, and this when methylated with diazomethane yielded palmatine. Coptisine is therefore LII.

The more difficult transformation of four methoxyl groups to two methylenedioxy groups was also achieved by Späth and Posega (241). It was possible to demethylate tetrahydropalmatine to the above tetrahydroxy compound, and this was bismethylenated in small yield to stylopine. The reaction was carried out in a sealed tube by heating the base with methylene iodide.

XVII. Corydaline

Corydaline, $C_{22}H_{27}O_4N$, was first isolated, obviously in impure form, from *Corydalis tuberosa* by Wackenroder (242). It has since been found in *C. ambigua* (24), *C. aurea* (28), *C. montana* (29), and *C. platycarpa* (46). It crystallizes from hot methanol in stout hexagonal prisms and has $[\alpha]_D^{20}$ +300° (chloroform). In most plants it is associated with its oxidation product, dehydrocorydaline, and the alkaloid F57 (29) has recently been shown to be one of the forms of inactive corydaline (243). The dehydro base only was isolated from what was regarded as *C. vernyi* Franch. et Sav. by Makoshi (39), but it remained for Asahina and Motigase (38) to show that the plant source was *C. decumbens*.

Corydaline has only been found in the *d*-form, which melts at 136°. It is readily soluble in choroform, moderately so in ether, and sparingly in methanol or ethanol, from which two solvents it crystallizes in well-developed six-sided plates.

Constitution. Many formulas have been suggested at various times for corydaline. The first, $C_{18}H_{19}O_4N$, due to Wicke (244) was modified by a number of authors until Freund and Josephi (52) arrived at the correct formula.

In the course of work leading to the elucidation of the structure of corydaline at the time that these researches were undertaken the structures of none of the protoberberines were known, and most of this work is of historical interest only. Had the later work on berberine and tetrahydropalmatine been available the determination of the structure of corydaline would have been an easy task. That it contains the same nuclear structure is indicated by its ready oxidation to dehydrocorydaline. Unlike the reduction of palmatine which gives a single product, the *dl*-tetrahydro base, the reduction of dehydrocorydaline gives rise to a mixture of meso- and racemic corydaline (245). The mesocorydaline has been resolved by means of *d*-camphorsulfonic acid, but the *d*-base is not identical with *d*-corydaline. It is obvious therefore that corydaline contains two asymmetric carbons.

Furthermore, corydaline, like tetrahydropalmatine, has four methoxyls, but its formula contains CH_2 more, which indicates that it should be a *C*-methyl derivative of the latter. The final products of its oxidation by permanganate are hemipinic and *m*-hemipinic acid, and it is possible to isolate, along with a number of other products, the compound called corydaldine (LIII) (246), the structure of which has been adequately proved by

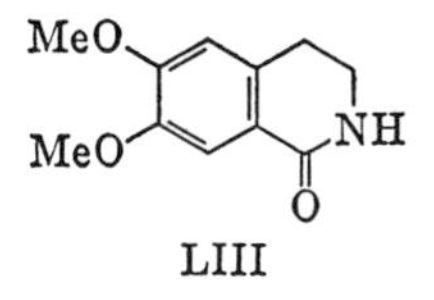

LIII

two syntheses. The first synthesis (247) was achieved by first reacting β-veratrylethylamine with ethyl chloroformate and ring-closing the resulting urethan with phosphoric oxide in boiling xylene. The second synthesis (238) depended upon the formation of the isocyanate, corresponding to the above amine, by heating the azide of β-veratrylpropionic acid in boiling toluene. Ring closure was effected by phosphoryl chloride.

The above results show that the methyl group can occupy only one of two possible positions (8 or 13), and the solution of this problem remained the chief one following Dobbie and Lauder's (246) suggested structure (LIV) for dehydrocorydaline. Späth and Lang (248) showed that the

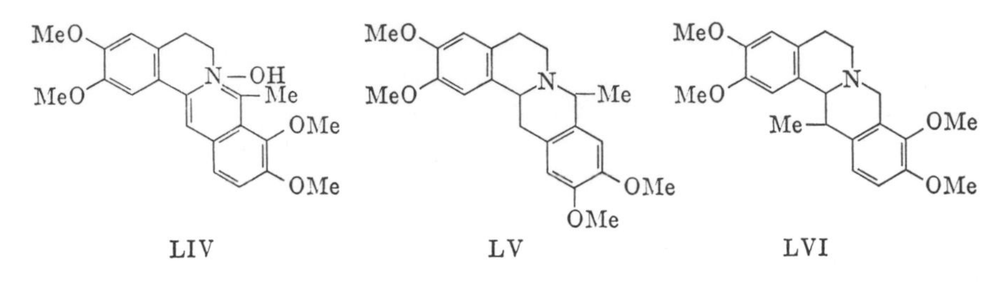

product obtained by reacting methylmagnesium iodide with palmatine yielded neither meso- nor racemic corydaline on reduction and it is known that bases of the protoberberine type react with alkylmagnesium halides to yield only 8-alkyl substituted products (214). Furthermore, Pictet and Chou (2) had already shown that dehydronorcoralydine on treatment with methylmagnesium iodide and subsequent reduction yielded coralydine (LV), in which the methyl group is in the 8 position. Coralydine was previously obtained by condensing tetrahydropapaverine with acetal in the presence of hydrochloric acid (249). Gadamer, who had published a number of papers dealing with the position of the methyl group, finally pointed out in collaboration with von Bruchhausen (250) that dehydrocorydaline gives the Cannizzaro reaction with 30 % sodium hydroxide solution yielding an equimolecular mixture of oxydehydrocorydaline and dihydrodehydrocorydaline. This reaction is strictly analogous to the similar behavior of berberine and is explicable only if there is no methyl at position 8, and therefore corydaline is LVI.

In a later study of this problem Späth and Mosettig (251) by an Emde degradation obtained trimethylamine in the third stage, thus indicating that the nitrogen forms a part of two rings. They also prepared the compound LVII by first condensing 1-(2,3-dimethoxybenzyl)-6,7-dimethoxy-

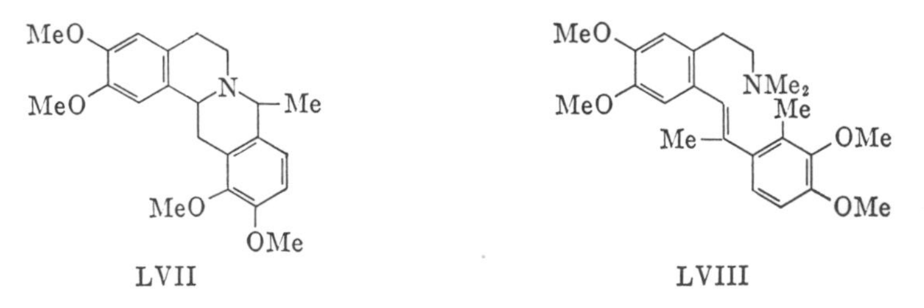

tetrahydroisoquinoline with diethyl formal, oxidizing the resulting base to the berberinium type of compound, reacting with methylmagnesium iodide, and reducing the resulting methyl dihydro base to the tetrahydro base (m.p. 111–112°). This was not identical with either of the optically inactive forms of corydaline but on oxidation might be expected to yield the same two hemipinic acids.

Freund and Fleischer (252) had studied the action of methyl iodide on berberine–acetone. Reduction of the adduct yielded 13-methylberberine. This reaction followed by reduction when applied to palmatine–acetone by von Bruchhausen (253) yielded *dl*-corydaline, melting at 135–136°. Furthermore, von Bruchhausen and Stippler (254) succeeded in degrading corydaline methochloride to an anhydro base analogous to that (XXIII) derived from tetrahydroberberine. The methosulfate of the anhydro base when reduced with sodium amalgam gave a compound (LVIII) which when oxidized with permanganate yielded 2-methyl-3,4-dimethoxyacetophenone. By the use of ozone as oxidizing agent it was possible also to obtain 4,5-dimethoxy-2-(β-dimethylaminoethyl) benzoic acid.

Synthesis. The first synthetic evidence for the structure of corydaline was provided by Koepfli and Perkin (255), who condensed β-veratrylethylamine with 3,4-dimethoxy-α-methylhomophthalic anhydride to yield the amide LIX. The action of phosphoryl chloride on the methyl ester of LIX yielded the isoquinoline, probably LX, but formulated with

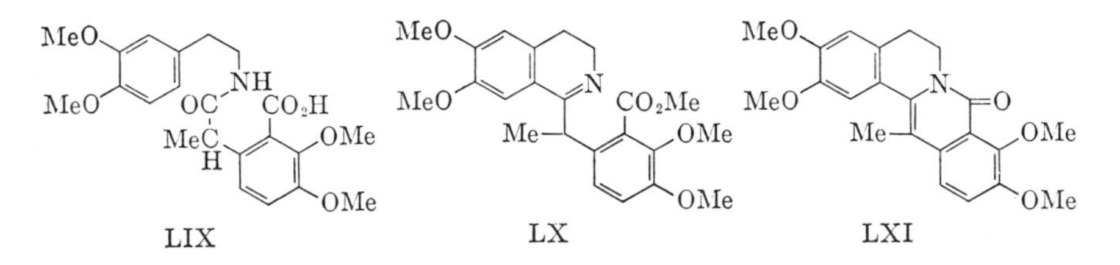

the double bond outside the ring. However, when this substance was heated to 150° a second ring closure, that is, lactam formation, took place, and the product (LXI) was identical with oxydehydrocorydaline (250) prepared by Gadamer and von Bruchhausen.

The synthesis of the homophthalic acid was a rather involved one, requiring as primary starting material β-veratrylbutyric acid. It was necessary to block the 6-position with a bromine atom, ring-close to the corresponding 4-bromo-6,7-dimethoxy-3-methyl-1-indanone, and then treat the isonitroso derivative of this with *p*-toluenesulfonyl chloride in the presence of alkali. The resulting carboxy nitrile on hydrolysis and debromination with sodium amalgam afforded the desired acid. Similar syntheses are described in greater detail in the chapter on protopine and cryptopine.

The synthesis of corydaline itself was accomplished by Späth and Kruta (1) following their earlier work on the synthesis of tetrahydropalmatine (227). Methyltetrahydropapaveroline (LXII) was condensed with formaldehyde and the mixture of products methylated with diazomethane.

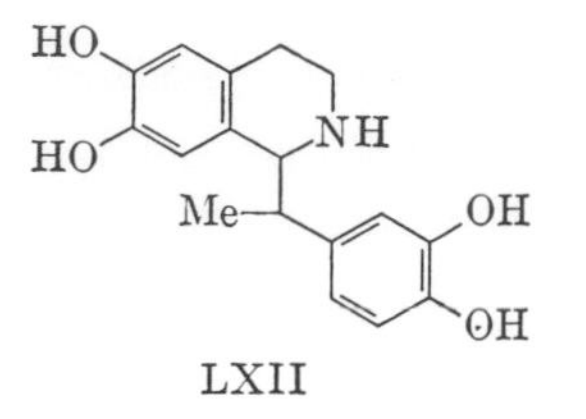

LXII

Condensation would obviously take place at either the 2- or the 6-position of the benzyl ring, but it was possible to isolate both the meso- and racemic corydalines from the reaction mixture. The tetrahydroxy base (LXII) was obtained from its tetramethyl ether, which was prepared from papaverine. For this purpose papaverine was condensed with formaldehyde (256) and the methylenepapaverine so formed was reduced first catalytically to methylpapaverine (257) and then electrolytically to the tetrahydro base—presumably a mixture of the meso- and racemic forms.

XVIII. Corybulbine

Corybulbine, $C_{21}H_{25}O_4N$, first isolated from *C. tuberosa* (258), was subsequently found in *C. ambigua* (24) and *C. platycarpa* (46). It crystallizes from hot methanol in colorless needles, $[\alpha]_D$ +303.3° (chloroform). It is sparingly soluble in most solvents except acetone or chloroform. When heated in an open tube its melting point varies greatly with the rate of heating because of its rapid oxidation. *In vacuo* it melts at 242° without change of color.

Constitution. Corybulbine oxidizes slowly in air, and with iodine in alcohol it is converted into a quaternary iodide which on reduction yields *dl*-corybulbine (259, 260), melting at 220–222°. Since it contains one phenolic hydroxyl and three methoxyls, and since it is convertible to corydaline on *O*-methylation, it must be one of the four possible *O*-desmethylcorydalines (261). Späth and Dobrowsky (247) confirmed these findings and located the position of the free hydroxyl. The *O*-ethyl ether on complete oxidation with permanganate yielded 4-methoxy-5-ethoxypthalic acid identified as its *N*-ethylimide. Mild oxidation of corybulbine *O*-ethyl ether gave 1-keto-7-methoxy-6-ethoxy-1,2,3,4-tetrahydroisoquinoline (XLI), and therefore corybulbine is LXIII.

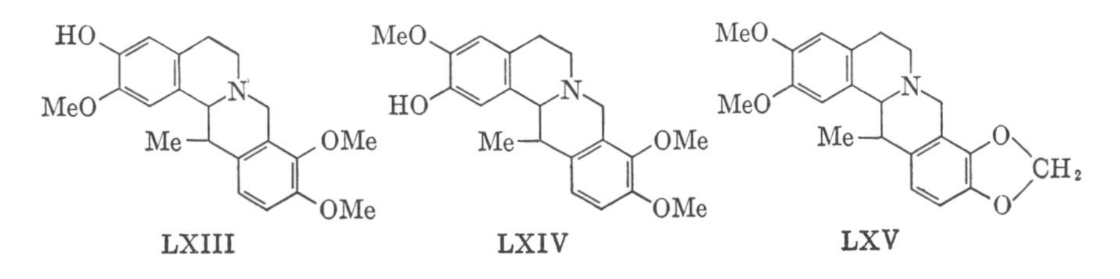

LXIII LXIV LXV

XIX. Isocorybulbine

Isocorybulbine, $C_{21}H_{25}O_4N$, was first isolated by Gadamer, Ziegenbein, and Wagner (53) from *C. tuberosa* and has not been found elsehwere. It crystallizes from hot ethanol in colorless plates which melt at 179–180° $[\alpha]_D$ +299.8° (chloroform).

Constitution. Gadamer and Bruns (260) and Bruns (259) showed that isocorybulbine on oxidation with iodine in alcohol yielded a quaternary iodide, which on reduction regenerated *dl*-isocorybulbine. Isocorybulbine is isomeric with corybulbine and like it on *O*-methylation yields corydaline. The *O*-ethyl ether on mild oxidation gives 1-keto-6-methoxy-7-ethoxy-1,2,3,4-tetrahydroisoquinoline (XLII) (247), and therefore isocorybulbine is LXIV. Subsequently, Späth and Holter (262) by partial demethylation of corydaline with hydrochloric acid at 100° for twenty-five minutes obtained a product from which they separated both corybulbine and isocorybulbine. In the meantime von Bruchhausen and Saway (263) and Gadamer and Saway (264) confirmed these results by independent syntheses of the reference compounds and by a combined Hofmann and Emde degradation and oxidation of corybulbine *O*-ethyl ether.

XX. Thalictrifoline

Thalictrifoline, $C_{21}H_{23}O_4N$, occurs, along with dehydrothalictrifoline, in *C. thalictrifolia* (51). It crystallizes from hot methanol in stout colorless prisms melting at 155°, $[\alpha]_D^{25}$ +218° (methanol).

Constitution. The empirical formula of thalictrifoline and its ready oxidation indicates that it is a methyl homologue of either canadine or sinactine, that is, corydaline in which two of the methoxyls are replaced by a methylenedioxy group. On oxidation with iodine in methanol it is transformed into a quaternary iodide, which on reduction with zinc and hydrochloric acid yields *dl*-thalictrifoline, m.p. 151°, which was also obtained by reduction of the naturally occurring dehydrothalictrifoline chloride. Complete oxidation of thalictrifoline yielded *m*-hemipinic acid, and therefore its structure was written as LXV. This was confirmed by demethylenation to a dihydroxy base and methylation of the latter. The new base proved to be an optically active stereoisomer of corydaline, presumably that of mesocorydaline, and on racemization by iodine oxidation and subsequent reduction was converted into mesocorydaline.

XXI. Thalictricavine

Thalictricavine, $C_{21}H_{23}O_4N$, was obtained (265) from some mother liquors from the commercial preparation of bulbocapnine from *C. tuberosa*. It concentrated in the corydaline fraction from which alkaloid it was partly separable because it was a slightly weaker base. Complete separation from corydaline was possible by virtue of its very sparing solubility in methanol, from which it crystallized in colorless stout needles which melted at 149° when placed in the bath at 140° and rapidly heated. When slowly heated from room temperature it sintered slightly at 149–150° but did not melt completely even at 175°; $[\alpha]_D$ +292° (chloroform).

It is isomeric with thalictrifoline and has the same functional groups. When demethylenated with phloroglucinol and sulfuric acid it yields a dihydroxy base (m.p. 246°, *in vacuo*) which on methylation is converted into corydaline. Thalictricavine is therefore either steroisomeric with thalictrifoline or it is thalictrifoline with the pairs of vicinal ether groups interchanged as in LXVI.

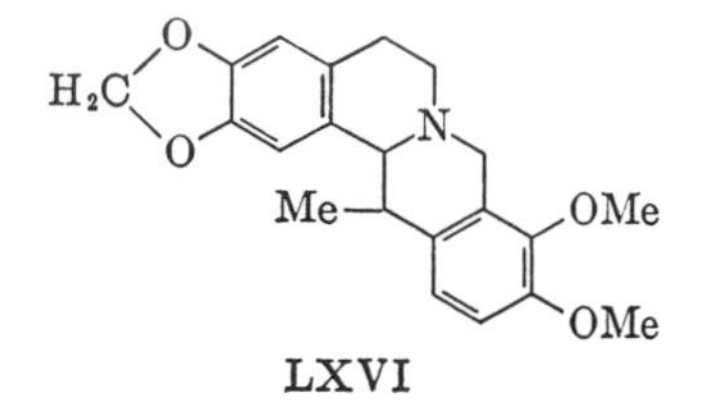

LXVI

When it was racemized by oxidation to the dehydro base followed by reduction, *dl*-thalictricavine, m.p. 209° (*in vacuo*), was obtained, and hence thalictricavine was probably not a stereoisomer of thalictrifoline. The correct structure was shown to be LXVI when it was possible to isolate 4,5-methylenedioxyphthalic (hydrastic) acid as its ethylimide from the oxidation products of the alkaloid.

XXII. Nandinine

Nandinine, $C_{19}H_{19}O_4N$, was isolated by Kitasato (137, 138) from *Nandina domestica* in a crystalline and apparently homogeneous condition after Eijkman (136) had shown the presence of alkaloids and Iwakawa (266) had separated an alkaloid melting at 78°. Nandinine has $[\alpha]_D$ +63.2° (ethanol).

Constitution. Frerichs and Stoepel (267, 268) had already shown that when berberine hydrochloride is heated with urea to 200° it loses one methoxyl group to yield a product to which they ascribed the name berberrubine and which they regarded as the 9-*O*-desmethyl derivative of berberine. Späth and Burger (232) showed that the free hydroxyl was as mooted and that tetrahydroberberrubine (m.p. 167°) has structure LXVII.

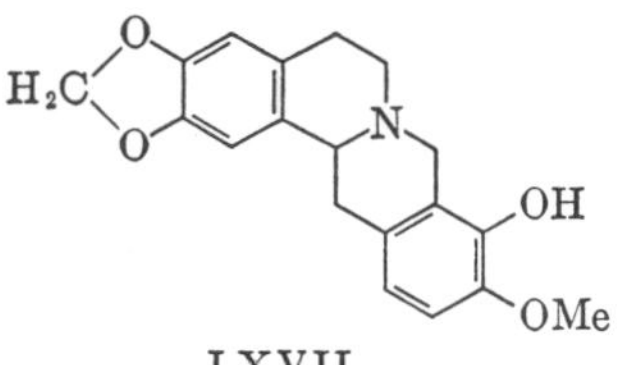

LXVII

Subsequently Kitasato (138) methylated nandinine, which was shown to be phenolic and contain one methoxyl, to a base, melting at 139° and having $[\alpha]_D$ +246–273°, which was regarded as being identical with *d*-canadine. The latter however was recorded as melting at 132° with $[\alpha]_D$ +297°, although a higher value had been recorded. Furthermore, tetrahydroberberrubine was deracemized with *d*-bromocamphor-π-sulfonic acid, and the *d*-base, $[\alpha]_D$ +62.9°, thus obtained proved to be identical with nandinine. In addition, the *O*-ethyl ether of nandinine after racemization proved to be identical with tetrahydroberberrubine *O*-ethyl ether.

Späth and Leithe (225) reinvestigated the resolution of tetrahydroberberrubine with α-bromo-*d*-camphor-π-sulfonic acid and from the first fraction obtained a base having $[\alpha]_D$ +52°. This when fractionally crystallized from a variety of solvents ultimately yielded the *d*-base (m.p. 195–196°) of $[\alpha]_D^{15}$ +303° (chloroform) and $[\alpha]_D^{15}$ +298° (ethanol). The *l*-base was similarly obtained from the first fractionation and had $[\alpha]_D^{15}$ −304° (chloroform). These results were taken to indicate that Kitasato's conclusions were in error.

In view of the observations on aurotensine and scoulerine (233) it is highly probable that Kitasato was quite correct in his conclusions. He did fail however to recognize that he was working with a compound which was not optically pure. That nandinine is a molecular compound of the *d*- plus the *dl*-forms is fairly evident and serves to explain adequately all of the observations. In this connection it is qute obvious that racemization of the *O*-ethyl ether should give *dl*-tetrahydroberberrubine *O*-ethyl ether. It may also be pointed out that most plant sources of stylopine give a partial racemate which can be positively identified by complete racemization (72).

XXIII. Worenine

Occurrence. Worenine was isolated from *Coptis japonica* (164). The base was separated from coptisine by virtue of the greater solubility of its nitrate or sulfate in alcohol or hot water. Worenine, mixed with berberine, was thus separated from coptisine, and reduction of this mixture afforded a separable mixture of tetrahydroberberine and tetrahydroworenine, the latter, $C_{20}H_{19}NO_4$, melting at 212–213°.

Constitution. Tetrahydroworenine contains one more methyl group than does tetrahydrocoptisine but is devoid of methoxyl or *N*-methyl and would therefore seem to be tetrahydrocoptisine methylated either at C_8 or C_{13}. Kitasato prepared the C_8 methyl derivative and found it to be dissimilar from tetrahydroworenine since the methyl group in the new base is believed to be at C_{13}, and tetrahydroworenine would therefore have structure LXVIII.

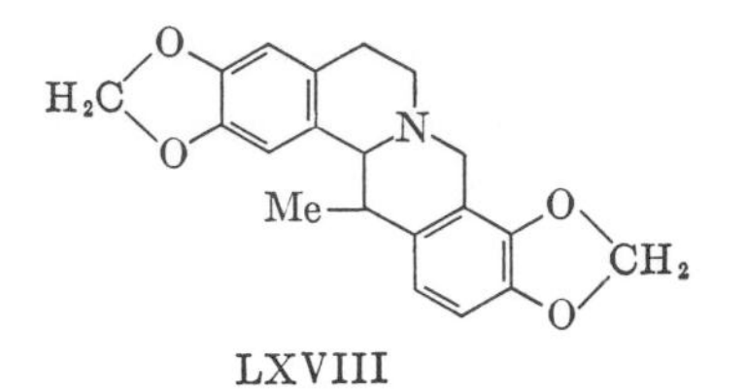

LXVIII

XXIV. Umbellatine

Occurrence. Umbellatine, $C_{21}H_{21}O_8N$, was first isolated from *Berberis umbellata* by Chatterjee (124) from the air-dried stem bark. It has since been isolated from *B. insignis*, where 1.52% of the total alkaloid content consisted of umbellatine (117) and from *B. nepalensis* (*Mahonia nepalensis* DC.) (119).

The base hydrochloride crystallizes from water giving yellow needles decomposing above 200°. The free base obtained from the hydrochloride as yellow needles melts 206–207° (decomp.). The base, which contains 5.5 moles of water of crystallization up to 110°, is optically inactive, soluble in alcohol and hot water, and slightly soluble in cold water, chloroform, and alcohol. It is insoluble in benzene, ethyl acetate, ether, and petroleum ether.

Constitution. Chatterjee (269) compared the near-ultraviolet absorption spectra of umbellatine and berberine and observed curves of marked similarity. The base contains a methylenedioxy group, two methoxyls and two hydroxyls. An *N*-methyl group can be detected by the Herzig-Meyer method.

Umbellatine on oxidation with permanganate (270) yielded an acid which was identified as 3,4-dimethoxyphthalic acid by conversion to its *N*-ethylimide.

Umbellatine is included here because of its occurrence in *Berberis* species, but a correct structural formula cannot yet be written for it.

XXV. Neprotine

Occurrence. Neprotine was found to be present with umbellatine in *Berberis nepalensis* (119) and assigned the formula $C_{19}H_{21}O_6N$. The two alkaloids appear to be waste products of metabolism since they are stored mainly in dead and other cells which take no part in metabolic activities.

The base decomposes above 200° without melting, is optically inactive, and forms elongated prisms which crystallize slowly. It is readily soluble in alcohol and water, very slightly soluble in chloroform, and insoluble in petroleum ether, ether, ethyl acetate, and acetone.

While insufficient work has been carried out on the constitutional formula of this alkaloid, it is believed to belong to the protoberberine group.

XXVI. Thalictrine

Thalictrine, $C_{20}H_{27}O_4N$, was isolated along with berberine from the rhizomes of *Thalictrum foliolosum* (172). It crystallizes with three moles of water of crystallization from dilute alcohol and has $[\alpha]_D^{25}$ +308°. The base melts at 208° and forms a picrate melting at 207–208°.

Diagnostic tests indicate two methoxyls and an *N*-methyl group, and from these meager data the authors (172) have assigned a tentative formula which need not be reproduced.

XXVII. Coreximine

Occurrence. Coreximine, $C_{19}H_{21}O_4N$, has been isolated only from *Dicentra eximia* (0.007 %) (28). It crystallizes with great facility when a concentrated solution of it in chloroform is diluted with methanol. The colorless stout prisms thus obtained melt at 262° to an orange-colored liquid.

Structure. Coreximine has two methoxyls and two phenolic hydroyls, and when methylated with diazomethane it yields a tetramethoxy compound, melting at 177°. Ethylation similarly yields a dimethoxydiethoxy base melting at 131° (28). The tetramethoxy compound is isomeric but not identical with tetrahydropalmatine, and like the latter it is readily oxidized in air to a yellow base, and when racemized by oxidation with mercuric acetate followed by reduction with zinc and hydrochloric acid it gave rise to a base (m.p. 157°) identical with norcoralydine (LXIX) (227). Coreximine is therefore a bisdesmethyl derivative of LXIX (271). Four such compounds are possible if vicinal hydroxy compounds are excluded.

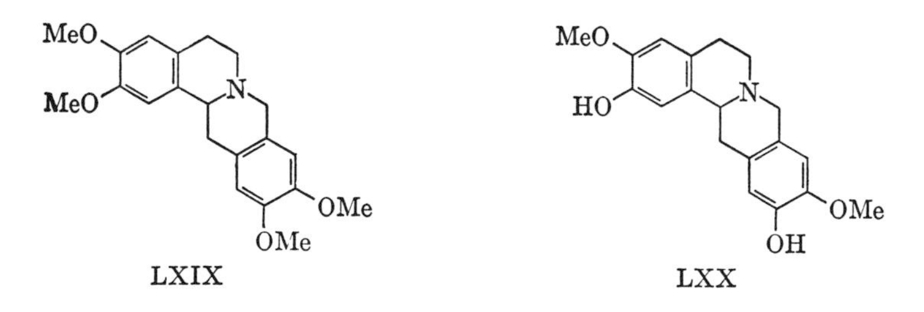

When th *O,O*-diethyl ether of coreximine was oxidized under conditions which favor the formation of corydaldines there was obtained 1-keto-6-methoxy-7-ethoxytetrahydroisoquinoline (XLII), and this serves to locate one hydroxyl at position 2 (LXX). The location of the second hydroxyl could not be carried out by further oxidation of the diethyl ether because only 4-methoxy-5-ethoxyphthalic acid could be formed. It was then assumed that the natural synthesis of coreximine involved ring closure of a benzylisoquinoline and that this could only occur if the condensation position were para to a hydroxyl. On this basis coreximine should be LXX. A synthesis of the *O,O*-diethyl ether of LXX proved this supposition to be correct. It was identical (m.p. 170°) with a specimen of racemized coreximine *O,O*-diethyl ether (m.p. 169°) (272). This is the only known example of a naturally occurring protoberberine with the oxygen substituents in positions 10 and 11, that is, the positions occupied in the so-called ψ-berberines, and is an observation which lends strong support to the assumption that benzylisoquinolines are intermediates in the biosynthesis of more complex types such as the aporphines, cularine, and the protoberberines.

XXVIII. References

1. E. Späth and E. Kruta, *Ber.*, **62**, 1024 (1929).
2. A. Pictet and T. Q. Chou, *Ber.*, **49**, 370 (1916).
3. R. H. F. Manske and H. L. Holmes, *J. Am. Chem. Soc.*, **67**, 95 (1945).
4. R. H. F. Manske, *J. Am. Chem. Soc.*, **69**, 1800 (1947).
5. R. H. F. Manske, *Can. J. Research*, **9**, 436 (1933).
6. R. H. F. Manske, *Can. J. Research*, **17B**, 51 (1939).
7. R. H. F. Manske, *Can. J. Research*, **8**, 210 (1933).
8. J. O. Schlotterbeck and H. C. Watkins, *Pharm. Arch.*, **6**, 17 (1903).
9. P. A. Foote, *J. Am. Pharm. Assoc.*, **21**, 246 (1932).
10. T. O. Soine and O. Gisvold, *J. Am. Pharm. Assoc.*, *Sci. Ed.*, **33**, 185 (1944).
11. A. C. Santos and P. Adkilen, *J. Am. Chem. Soc.*, **54**, 2923 (1932).
12. R. H. F. Manske, *Can. J. Research*, **21B**, 140 (1943).
13. J. F. Eijkman, *Rec. trav. chim.*, **3**, 182 (1884).
14. P. Murrill and J. O. Schlotterbeck, *Ber.*, **33**, 2802 (1900).
15. J. A. Battandier, *Compt. rend.*, **114**, 1122 (1892); **120**, 1276 (1895).
16. I. Maccío, *Arch. farm. y. bioquím. Tucumán*, **3**, 27 (1946).
17. R. H. F. Manske, unpublished data.
18. E. Schmidt and F. Selle, *Arch. Pharm.*, **228**, 441 (1890).
19. J. Gadamer and A. Stichel, *Arch. Pharm.*, **262**, 488 (1924).
20. J. Gadamer and K. Winterfeld, *Arch. Pharm.*, **262**, 589 (1924).
21. E. Späth and F. Kuffner, *Ber.*, **64**, 1127 (1931).
22. W. Awe, *Arzneimittel-Forsch.*, **1**, 287 (1951).
23. J. O. Schlotterbeck, *Am. J. Pharm.*, **74**, 584 (1902).
24. K. Makoshi, *Arch. Pharm.*, **246**, 381 (1908).
25. T. Q. Chou, *et al.*, *Chinese J. Physiol.*, **2**, 203 (1928); **3**, 69 (1929); **3**, 301 (1929); **7**, 35 (1933); **8**, 155 (1934); **10**, 507 (1936).
26. Huang-Minlon, *Ber.*, **69**, 1737 (1936).
27. R. H. F. Manske, *J. Am. Chem. Soc.*, **74**, 2864 (1952).
28. R. H. F. Manske, *Can. J. Research*, **16B**, 81 (1938).
29. R. H. F. Manske, *Can. J. Research*, **20B**, 49 (1942).
30. O. Haars, *Arch. Pharm.*, **243**, 154 (1905).
31. G. Heyl, *Apoth. Ztg.*, **25**, 36 (1910).
32. R. H. F. Manske and M. R. Miller, *Can. J. Research*, **16B**, 153 (1938).
33. R. H. F. Manske, *Can. J. Research*, **20B**, 57 (1942).
34. R. H. F. Manske, *Can. J. Research*, **18B**, 100 (1940).
35. R. H. F. Manske, *Can. J. Research*, **18B**, 97 (1940).

36. R. H. F. Manske, *Can. J. Research*, **24B**, 66 (1946).
37. R. H. F. Manske, *Can. J. Research*, **17B**, 57 (1939).
38. Y. Asahina and S. Motigase, *J. Pharm. Soc. Japan*, **No. 463**, 766 (1920).
39. K. Makoshi, *Arch. Pharm.*, **246**, 401 (1908).
40. R. H. F. Manske, *Can. J. Research*, **17B**, 89 (1939).
41. R. H. F. Manske, *Can. J. Research*, **18B**, 288 (1940).
42. R. H. F. Manske, *Can. J. Research*, **18B**, 75 (1940).
43. R. H. F. Manske, *Can. J. Research*, **17B**, 95 (1939).
44. R. H. F. Manske, *Can. J. Research*, **15B**, 159 (1937).
45. R. H. F. Manske, *Can. J. Research*, **18B**, 80 (1940).
46. R. H. F. Manske, *Can. J. Research*, **21B**, 13 (1943).
47. R. H. F. Manske, *Can. J. Research*, **14B**, 347 (1936).
48. R. H. F. Manske, *Can. J. Research*, **8**, 407 (1933).
49. R. H. F. Manske, *Can. J. Research*, **14B**, 354 (1936).
50. J. Go, *J. Pharm. Soc. Japan*, **49**, 801, 814 (1929); **50**, 933, 940 (1930).
51. R. H. F. Manske, *Can. J. Research*, **21B**, 111 (1943).
52. M. Freund and W. Josephi, *Ber.*, **25**, 2411 (1892).
53. J. Gadamer, H. Ziegenbein, and H. Wagner, *Arch. Pharm.*, **240**, 19, 81 (1902).
54. J. J. Dobbie and A. Lauder, *J. Chem. Soc.*, **63**, 485 (1893).
55. J. Gadamer, *Arch. Pharm.*, **249**, 224 (1911).
56. E. Späth and P. L. Julian, *Ber.*, **64**, 1131 (1931).
57. E. Schmidt, *Arch. Pharm.*, **246**, 575 (1908).
58. E. Späth, E. Mosettig, and O. Tröthandl, *Ber.*, **56**, 875 (1923).
59. J. Gadamer, E. Späth, and E. Mosettig, *Arch. Pharm.*, **265**, 675 (1927).
60. R. H. F. Manske, unpublished data.
61. J. Gadamer, *Arch. Pharm.*, **249**, 30 (1911).
62. R. H. F. Manske, *Can. J. Research*, **21B**, 117 (1943).
63. R. H. F. Manske, *Can. J. Research*, **27B**, 653 (1949).
64. R. H. F. Manske, *Can. J. Research*, **7**, 258 (1932).
65. R. H. F. Manske, *Can. J. Research*, **15B**, 274 (1937).
66. R. H. F. Manske, *Can. J. Research*, **7**, 265 (1932).
67. R. H. F. Manske, *Can. J. Research*, **8**, 592 (1933).
68. R. H. F. Manske, *Can. J. Research*, **10**, 521 (1934).
69. R. H. F. Manske, *Can. J. Research*, **10**, 765 (1934).
70. Y. Asahina, *Arch. Pharm.*, **247**, 201 (1909).
71. P. W. Danckwortt, *Arch. Pharm.*, **260**, 94 (1922).
72. R. H. F. Manske, *Can. J. Research*, **20B**, 53 (1942).
73. R. H. F. Manske, unpublished data.
74. R. H. F. Manske, unpublished data.
75. R. Fischer and M. E. Tweeden, *Pharm. Arch.*, **5**, 117 (1902).
76. R. Fischer, *Arch. Pharm.*, **239**, 421 (1901).
77. R. H. F. Manske, *Can. J. Research*, **16B**, 438 (1938).
78. R. A. Konovalova, S. Yunosov, and A. P. Orekhov, *J. Gen. Chem. (U.S.S.R.)*, **9**, 1939 (1939).
79. R. H. F. Manske, *Can. J. Research*, **17B**, 399 (1939).
80. R. Fischer, *Arch. Pharm.*, **239**, 426 (1901).
81. R. H. F. Manske, L. Marion, and A. E. Ledingham, *J. Am. Chem. Soc.*, **64**, 1659 (1942).
82. R. Konowalowa, S. Yunussoff, and A. Orechoff, *Ber.*, **68**, 2158 (1935).
83. B. L. Konson and P. P. Saksonov, *Farmakol. i Toksikol.*, **9**, No. 4, 14 (1946).
83a. V. V. Kiselev and R. A. Konovalova, *J. Gen. Chem. (U.S.S.R.)*, **18**, 142 (1948).

84. R. Konowalowa, S. Yunussoff, and A. Orechoff, *Ber.*, **68,** 2277 (1935).
85. V. Pavesi, *Gazz. chim. ital.*, **37I,** 629 (1907).
86. V. Pavesi, (from) *Atti reale ist. botan. univ. Pavia*, **9** (1906); *Chem. centr*, **1906, I,** 690.
87. J. Gadamer, *Arch. Pharm.*, **252,** 274 (1914).
88. W. Klee, *Arch. Pharm.*, **252,** 211 (1914).
89. W. Awe, *Arch. Pharm.*, **274,** 439 (1936).
90. E. Späth, L. Schmid, and H. Sternberg, *Monatsh.*, **68,** 33 (1936).
91. O. Hesse, *Ann.* (*Suppl.*), **8,** 261 (1872).
92. F. Wrede, *Forschungen u. Fortschr.*, **14,** 173 (1938).
93. T. Smith and H. Smith, *Pharm. J. Trans.*, **52,** 794 (1892).
94. M. Freund, *Ann.*, **277,** 20 (1893).
95. P. Rabe and A. McMillian, *Ann.*, **377,** 223 (1910).
96. B. Dobson and W. H. Perkin, Jr., *J. Chem. Soc.*, **99,** 135 (1911).
97. O. Hesse, *Ann.*, **282,** 208 (1894).
98. O. Hesse, *Ann.*, **153,** 47 (1870).
99. O. Hesse, *Ann.*, **234,** 253 (1886).
100. C. F. van Duin, R. Robinson, and J. C. Smith, *J. Chem. Soc.*, **1926,** 903.
101. J. N. Rakshit, *Ber.*, **59,** 2473 (1926).
102. E. Machiguchi, *J. Pharm. Soc. Japan*, **No. 529,** 185 (1926).
103. O. Hesse, *Ber.*, **4,** 693 (1871).
104. J. Smiles, *Pharm. J.*, [2]**8,** 595 (1867).
105. K. Kohei and Y. Ando, *J. Pharm. Soc. Japan*, **71,** 625 (1951).
106. R. A. Konovalova, S. Yunosov, and A. P. Orekhov, *Bull. soc. chim.*, [5]**6,** 811 (1939).
107. R. A. Konovalova, S. Yunosov, and A. P. Orekhov, *J. Gen. Chem.* (*U.S.S.R.*), **9,** 1356 (1939).
108. R. A. Konovalova, S. Yunosov, and A. P. Orekhov, *Bull. soc. chim.*, [5]**6,** 1479 (1939).
109. R. A. Konovalova, S. Yunosov, and A. P. Orekhov, *J. Gen. Chem. U.S.S.R.*), **9,** 1507 (1939).
110. E. Schmidt, G. König, and W. Tietz, *Arch. Pharm.*, **231,** 136 (1893).
111. E. Späth, F. Schlemmer, G. Schenck, and A. Gempp. *Ber.*, **70,** 1677 (1937).
112. A. G. Perkin, *J. Chem. Soc.*, **71,** 1194 (1897).
113. H. Pommerehne, *Arch. Pharm.*, **233,** 127 (1895).
114. Arata, *Rêpert. pharm.*, **1892,** 45.
115. F. Richert, *Rev. centro estud. agronomia y veterinaria univ. Buenos Aires*, **11** 11 (1918).
116. B. T. Cromwell, *Biochem. J.* (*London*), **27,** 860 (1933).
116a. M. Tomita and T. Abe, *J. Pharm. Soc. Japan*, **72,** 773 (1952).
117. R. Chatterjee, *J. Am. Pharm. Assoc.*, *Sci. Ed.*, **30,** 247 (1941).
117a. M. Tomita and T. Abe, *J. Pharm. Soc. Japan*, **72,** 735 (1952).
118. L. Gurguel, O. deA. Costa, and R. D. da Silva, *Bol. assoc. brasil. farm.*, **15,** 11 (1934).
119. R. Chatterjee, *J. Am. Pharm. Assoc.*, *Sci. Ed.*, **33,** 210 (1944).
120. Neppach, *Am. J. Pharm.*, **1878,** 373.
121. G. A. Greathouse and N. E. Rigler, *Plant Physiol.*, **15,** 563 (1940).
122. G. A. Greathouse and G. M. Watkins, *Am. J. Botany*, **25,** 743 (1938).
123. H. Kondo and M. Tomita, *Arch. Pharm.*, **268,** 549 (1930).
124. R. Chatterjee, *J. Indian Chem. Soc.*, **17,** 289 (1940).
125. O. Hesse, *Ber.*, **19,** 3190 (1886).

126. E. Späth and N. Polgar, *Monatsh.*, **52,** 117 (1929).
127. E. Späth and A. Kolbe, *Ber.*, **58,** 2280 (1925).
128. F. von Bruchhausen and H. Schultze, *Arch. Pharm.*, **267,** 617 (1929).
129. A. Orekhov, *Arch. Pharm.*, **271,** 323 (1933).
130. R. Chatterjee and M. P. Guha, *J. Am. Pharm. Assoc., Sci. Ed.*, **39,** 577 (1950).
131. R. Chatterjee, M. P., Guha, and S. K. Sen, *J. Am. Pharm. Assoc., Sci. Ed.*, **40,** 36 (1951).
132. R. Chatterjee and M. P. Guha, *J. Am. Pharm. Assoc., Sci. Ed.*, **39,** 181 (1950).
133. R. Chatterjee and M. P. Guha, *J. Am. Pharm. Assoc., Sci. Ed.*, **40,** 229 (1951).
134. E. R. Castro, A. C. Santos, and P. Valenzuela, *Univ. Philippines Nat. and Appl. Sci. Bull.*, **2,** 401 (1932).
135. M. Tomita, Y. Inubushi, S. Ishii, and M. Yamagata, *J. Pharm. Soc. Japan*, **71,** 381 (1951).
136. J. F. Eijkman, *Rec. trav. chim.*, **3,** 197 (1884).
137. Z. Kitasato, *J. Pharm. Soc. Japan*, **No. 522,** 695 (1925).
138. Z. Kitasato, *Acta Phytochim. Japan*, **3,** 175 (1927).
139. Z. Kitasato, *J. Pharm. Soc. Japan*, **No. 536,** 843 (1926).
140. H. Maniwa, R. Sakae, and I. Kan, *J. Pharm. Soc. Japan*, **No. 536,** 833 (1926).
141. T. Ohta, *J. Pharm. Soc. Japan*, **69,** 502 (1949).
142. T. M. Meyer, *Ing. Ned.-Indië*, **8,** No. 6, VII, 64 (1941).
143. A. C. Santos, *Philippine J. Sci.*, **43,** 561 (1930); **47,** 357 (1932).
144. F. R. Reyes and A. C. Santos, *Philippine J. Sci.*, **44,** 409 (1931).
145. J. M. Marañon, *Philippine J. Sci.*, **38,** 259 (1929).
146. A. C. Santos and F. R. Reyes, *Univ. Philippines Nat. and Appl. Sci. Bull.*, **2,** 407 (1932).
147. E. Schlittler and H. U. Huber, *Helv. Chim. Acta*, **35,** 111 (1952).
148. G. Barger and L. J. Sargent, *J. Chem. Soc.*, **1939,** 991.
149. R. H. F. Manske, *Can. J. Research*, **16B,** 76 (1938).
150. E. N. Parabirsing, Dissertation, 1952.
151. J. Stenhouse, *Ann.*, **95,** 108 (1855); **105,** 360 (1858).
152. A. C. Santos, *Univ. Philippines Nat. and Appl. Sci. Bull.*, **1,** 153 (1931).
153. L. Beauquesne, *Bull. sci. pharmacol.*, **45,** 7 (1938).
154. M. Tomita and C. Tani, *J. Pharm. Soc. Japan*, **61,** 251 (1941).
155. J. Stenhouse, *J. Chem. Soc.*, **20,** 187 (1867).
156. N. S. Varier and P. P. Pillai, *Current Sci. (India)*, **12,** 228 (1943).
157. R. Child and W. R. N. Nathanael, *Current Sci. (India)*, **12,** 255 (1943).
158. M. Tomita and C. Tani, *J. Pharm. Soc. Japan*, **61,** 247 (1941).
159. K. Feist, *Arch. Pharm.*, **245,** 586 (1907).
160. E. Günzel, *Arch. Pharm.*, **244,** 257 (1906).
161. K. Goto and H. Sudzuki, *Bull. Chem. Soc. Japan*, **4,** 220 (1929).
162. K. Goto, *Ann.*, **521,** 175 (1935).
163. Y. Murayama and K. Shinozaki, *J. Pharm. Soc. Japan*, **No. 530,** 299 (1926).
164. Z. Kitasato, *J. Pharm. Soc. Japan*, **No. 542,** 315 (1927).
165. Z. Kitasato, *Proc. Imp. Acad. (Tokyo)*, **2,** 124 (1926).
166. C. E. Mollett and B. V. Christensen, *J. Am. Pharm. Assoc.*, **23,** 310 (1934).
167. J. D. Perrins, *J. Chem. Soc.*, **15,** 339 (1862).
168. D. Hooper, *Pharm. J.*, [4]**34,** 482 (1912).
169. E. Schmidt, *Arch. Pharm.*, **232,** 136 (1894).
170. M. Freund and W. Will, *Ber.*, **19,** 2797 (1886).
171. J. D. Perrins, *Pharm. J.*, [2]**3,** 546 (1862).
172. S. K. Vashistha and S. Siddiqui, *J. Indian Chem. Soc.*, **18,** 641 (1941).

173. A. G. Perkin and J. J. Hummel, *J. Chem. Soc.*, **67,** 413 (1895).
174. Y. Murayama and J. Takada, *J. Pharm. Soc. Japan,* **No. 550,** 1035 (1927).
175. B. B. Dey and P. P. Pillay, *Arch. Pharm.*, **271,** 477 (1933).
176. H. A. D. Jowett and F. L. Pyman, *J. Chem. Soc.*, **103,** 290 (1913).
177. M. Chevalier and G. Pelletan, *J. chim. med.*, **2,** 314 (1826).
178. F. B. LaForge and W. F. Barthel, *J. Org. Chem.*, **9,** 250 (1944).
179. M. Leprince, *Bull. sci. pharmacol.*, **18,** 337 (1911).
180. J. A. Buchner and C. A. Buchner, *Ann.*, **24,** 228 (1837).
181. T. Fleitmann, *Ann.*, **59,** 160 (1846).
182. W. H. Perkin, Jr., *J. Chem. Soc.*, **55,** 63 (1889).
183. F. Shedden, *Pharm. J.*, [4]**11,** 89 (1900).
184. J. Gadamer, *Arch. Pharm.*, **243,** 31 (1905).
185. F. L. Pyman, *J. Chem. Soc.*, **99,** 1690 (1911).
186. G. M. Robinson and R. Robinson, *J. Chem. Soc.*, **111,** 958 (1917).
187. H. M. Gordin and A. B. Prescott, *Arch. Pharm.*, **237,** 439 (1899).
188. J. Troeger and O. Linde, *Arch. Pharm.*, **238,** 4 (1900).
189. H. M. Gordin, *Arch. Pharm.*, **239,** 638 (1901).
190. H. M. Gordin, *Arch. Pharm.*, **240,** 146 (1902).
191. E. Richter, *Arch. Pharm.*, **252,** 192 (1914).
192. R. Wasicky and M. Joachimowitz, *Arch. Pharm.*, **255,** 497 (1917).
193. H. Neugebauer and K. Brunner, *Pharm. Ztg.*, **81,** 1416 (1936).
194. H. Neugebauer and K. Brunner, *Pharm. Ztg.*, **82,** 1212 (1937).
195. L. Davis, *Pharm. Post.* **48,** 1, 21 (1915).
196. W. Awe, *Deut. Apoth. Ztg.*, **52,** 1359 (1937).
197. K. Feist, *Süddeut. Apoth. Ztg.*, **79,** 429 (1939).
198. E. Brochmann-Hanssen, *Pharm. Acta Helv.*, **21,** 23 (1946).
199. H. I. Cole, *Philippine J. Sci.*, **23,** 97 (1923).
200. H. Almgren, *Svensk Farm. Tidŝkr.*, **28,** 377 (1924).
201. E. O. North and G. D. Beal, *J. Am. Pharm. Assoc.*, **13,** 889, 1001 (1924).
202. L. Rosenthaler, *Arch. Pharm.*, **265,** 319 (1927).
203. L. Rosenthaler, *Scientia Pharm.*, **9,** 4 (1938).
204. W. H. Perkin, Jr., *J. Chem. Soc.*, **57,** 992 (1890).
205. E. Schmidt and C. Schilbach, *Arch. Pharm.*, **225,** 164 (1887).
206. M. Freund and W. Will, *Ber.*, **20,** 2400 (1887).
207. M. Freund and S. Lachmann, *Ber.*, **22,** 2322 (1889).
208. W. H. Perkin, Jr., and R. Robinson, *J. Chem. Soc.*, **97,** 305 (1910).
209. C. Liebermann, *Ber.*, **19,** 2275 (1886).
210. C. Liebermann, *Ber.*, **29,** 174 (1896).
211. J. Gadamer, *Arch. Pharm.*, **239,** 648 (1901).
212. J. Gadamer, *Chem. Ztg.*, **26,** 291 (1902).
213. C. K. Tinkler, *J. Chem. Soc.*, **99,** 1340 (1911).
214. M. Freund and H. Beck, *Ber.*, **37,** 4673 (1904).
215. W. H. Perkin, Jr., *J. Chem. Soc.*, **113,** 764 (1918).
216. W. H. Perkin, Jr., J. N. Rây, and R. Robinson, *J. Chem. Soc.*, **127,** 740 (1925).
217. J. W. McDavid, W. H. Perkin, Jr., and R. Robinson, *J. Chem. Soc.*, **101,** 1218 (1912).
218. A. Voss and J. Gadamer, *Arch. Pharm.*, **248,** 43 (1910).
219. F. L. Pyman, *J. Chem. Soc.*, **103,** 817 (1913).
220. A. Pictet and A. Gams, *Ber.*, **44,** 2480 (1911).
221. R. D. Haworth, W. H. Perkin, Jr., and J. Rankin, *J. Chem. Soc.*, **125,** 1686 (1924).
222. J. Gadamer, *Arch. Pharm.*, **240,** 450 (1902).

223. K. Feist and G. Sandstede, *Arch. Pharm.*, **256,** 1 (1918).
224. J. Gadamer, *Arch. Pharm.*, **253,** 274 (1915).
225. E. Späth and W. Leithe, *Ber.*, **63,** 3007 (1930).
226. E. Späth and E. Mosettig, *Ber.*, **59,** 1496 (1926).
227. E. Späth and E. Kruta, *Monatsh.*, **50,** 341 (1928).
228. J. S. Buck and W. H. Perkin, Jr., *J. Chem. Soc.*, **125,** 1675 (1924).
229. K. F. Knörck, Dissertation, Marburg, 1926.
230. E. Späth and E. Mosettig, *Ber.*, **58,** 2133 (1925).
231. E. Späth and E. Mosettig, *Ber.*, **60,** 383 (1927).
232. E. Späth and G. Burger, *Ber.*, **59,** 1486 (1926).
233. R. H. F. Manske, *Can. J. Research*, **18B,** 414 (1940).
234. W. H. Perkin, Jr., *J. Chem. Soc.*, **113,** 492 (1918).
235. K. Goto and Z. Kitasato, *J. Chem. Soc.*, **1930,** 1234.
236. E. Späth and E. Mosettig, *Ber.*, **64,** 2048 (1931).
237. P. C. Mitter and S. De, *J. Indian Chem. Soc.*, **16,** 35 (1939).
238. L. M. Mohunta and J. N. Rây, *J. Chem. Soc.*, **1934,** 1263.
239. J. O. Schlotterbeck and H. C. Watkins, *Ber.*, **35,** 7 (1902).
240. R. D. Haworth and W. H. Perkin, Jr., *J. Chem. Soc.*, **1926,** 1769.
241. E. Späth and R. Posega, *Ber.*, **62,** 1029 (1929).
242. Wackenroder, *Berz. Jahrb.*, **7,** 220 (1826).
243. R. H. F. Manske, unpublished data.
244. H. Wicke, *Ann.*, **137,** 274 (1866).
245. J. Gadamer and W. Klee, *Arch. Pharm.*, **254,** 295 (1916).
246. J. J. Dobbie and A. Lauder, *J. Chem. Soc.*, **81,** 145 (1902).
247. E. Späth and A. Dobrowsky, *Ber.*, **58,** 1274 (1925).
248. E. Späth and N. Lang, *Ber.*, **54,** 3064 (1921).
249. A. Pictet and S. Malinowski, *Ber.*, **46,** 2688 (1913).
250. J. Gadamer and F. von Bruchhausen, *Arch. Pharm.*, **259,** 245 (1921).
251. E. Späth and E. Mosettig, *Ann.*, **433,** 138 (1923).
252. M. Freund and K. Fleischer, *Ann.*, **409,** 266 (1915).
253. F. von Bruchhausen, *Arch. Pharm.*, **261,** 28 (1923).
254. F. von Bruchhausen and H. Stippler, *Arch. Pharm.*, **265,** 152 (1927).
255. J. B. Koepfli and W. H. Perkin, Jr., *J. Chem. Soc.*, **1928,** 2989.
256. W. Kœnigs, *Ber.*, **32,** 3599 (1899).
257. E. Späth and N. Polgar, *Ber.*, **59,** 2787 (1926).
258. M. Freund and W. Josephi, *Ann.*, **277,** 1 (1893).
259. D. Bruns, *Arch. Pharm.*, **241,** 634 (1903).
260. J. Gadamer and D. Bruns, *Arch. Pharm.*, **239,** 39 (1901).
261. J. J. Dobbie, A. Lauder, and P. G. Paliatseas, *J. Chem. Soc.*, **79,** 87 (1901).
262. E. Späth and H. Holter, *Ber.*, **59,** 2800 (1926).
263. F. von Bruchhausen and K. Saway, *Arch. Pharm.*, **263,** 602 (1925).
264. J. Gadamer and K. Saway, *Arch. Pharm.*, **264,** 401 (1926).
265. R. H. F. Manske, *J. Am. Chem. Soc.* **75,** 4928 (1953).
266. K. Iwakawa, *Mitt. med. Ges. Tokyo*, **24,** 15 (1910).
267. G. Frerichs, *Arch. Pharm.*, **248,** 276 (1910).
268. G. Frerichs and P. Stoepel, *Arch. Pharm.*, **251,** 321 (1913).
269. R. Chatterjee, *J. Indian Chem. Soc.*, **19,** 233 (1942).
270. R. Chatterjee, *J. Indian Chem. Soc.*, **19,** 385 (1942).
271. R. H. F. Manske, *J. Am. Chem. Soc.*, **72,** 4796 (1950).
272. R. H. F. Manske and W. R. Ashford, *J. Am. Chem. Soc.*, **73,** 5144 (1951).

CHAPTER 30

The Aporphine Alkaloids

R. H. F. MANSKE

The Dominion Rubber Research Laboratory, Guelph, Ontario

Page

I. Introduction 119
II. Glaucine 120
III. Glaucentrine 122
IV. Boldine 123
V. Laurotetanine 125
VI. *N*-Methyllaurotetanine 126
VII. Dicentrine 126
VIII. Actinodaphnine 127
IX. Domesticine 128
X. Nantenine 128
XI. Phanostenine 129
XII. Crebanine 129
XIII. Corydine 129
XIV. Isocorydine 130
XV. Corytuberine 130
1. Structures of Corytuberine, Corydine, and Isocorydine 131
XVI. Suaveoline 132
XVII. Bulbocapnine 132
XVIII. Laurepukine 134
XIX. Isothebaine 135
XX. Tuduranine 136
XXI. Laureline 137
XXII. Pukateine 138
XXIII. Anolobine 139
XXIV. Stephanine 141
XXV. Roemerine 141
XXVI. Anonaine 142
XXVII. Other Aporphines 142
XXVIII. References 143

I. Introduction

The aporphine alkaloids (I) are derivable from the benzylisoquinolines by the abstraction of two hydrogens in such a manner that the two benzene nuclei now form part of a 9,10-dihydrophenanthrene. Since the bio-

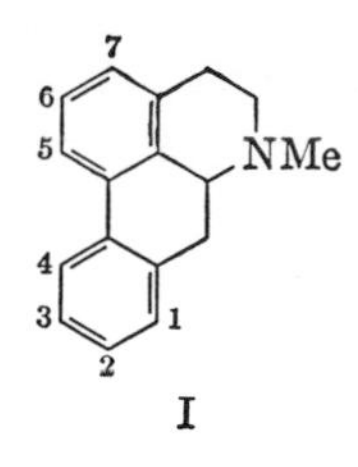

synthesis of these alkaloids almost certainly proceeds from the benzylisoquinolines and since the latter are derived from precursors in which the oxygen substituents are in the 3- and 4-positions (i.e., the vanillin positions) it follows that aporphines can have the substituents only in the 2-, 3-, 4-, 5-, or 6-positions.

The majority of the aporphines have four oxygen atoms. Some however—isothebaine, tuduranine, pukateine, laureline, anolobine, artabotrinine, and possibly others—have only three oxygen atoms, whereas anonaine and roemerine have only two oxygens. The three artifacts, apomorphine, apocodeine, and morphothebaine, are obtained from morphine or morphine derivatives and have been discussed in Volume II.

The aporphines occur most abundantly in the Papaveraceae in which case the nitrogen is methylated, but they are also widespread in the Anonaceae, Lauraceae, and Monimiaceae, in which families they frequently occur as secondary amines. Those having the greater number of oxygens will be discussed first, and the tertiary amines will be discussed before the secondary amines. In all cases the non-phenolic bases, if they occur naturally, will be discussed before the corresponding phenolic bases.

II. Glaucine

Glaucine, $C_{21}H_{25}O_4N$, is the only naturally occurring tetramethoxyaporphine. It is also the first aporphine to have been isolated (1) as well as the first to have been synthesized.

Glaucine was obtained in a pure condition and its correct formula determined by Fischer (2), who, like previous investigators, isolated it form *Glaucium flavum* Crantz. (*G. luteum* Scop.) and characterized it thoroughly not only by color and precipitation reactions but by the formation of a number of salts. It was subsequently isolated from *Corydalis tuberosa* DC. by Gadamer (3), and more recently from *C. ternata* Nakai (*l*-glaucine) (4), *G. fimbrilligerum* Boiss. (5), *G. serpieri* Heldr. (6), *Dicentra eximia* (Ker) Torr. (7), *D. formosa* Walp. (8), and *D. oregana* Eastwood (9). It crystallizes from ethyl acetate or, better, from ether, in almost colorless prisms which melt at 120°; $[\alpha]_D$ +113.3° (c = 5.04 in ethanol) (2). It is readily soluble in most organic solvents except benzene and hexane. The hydriodide is the only characteristic salt and because of its sparing solubility is useful in the isolation of glaucine from plant extracts (10). The hydrochloride is readily soluble in chloroform and is extractable from aqueous solutions (2), and this property, which has been shown to be shared by many other alkaloid hydrochlorides, has been used in an effective procedure for separating alkaloids into two groups (11).

Structure. The structure of glaucine was arrived at by Gadamer (12) by a process of intuitive reasoning supplemented by a synthesis. Corytuberine dimethyl ether and glaucine were known to be isomeric, and if a relation to papaverine were admitted only two structures were available for the two alkaloids. Pschorr (13), utilizing his well-known phenanthrene synthesis, had attempted to convert papaverine into an aporphine (IV) via the nitro (II) and the amino (III) derivatives. When papaverine is nitrated it yields 6′-nitropapaverine (II), from which the methochloride

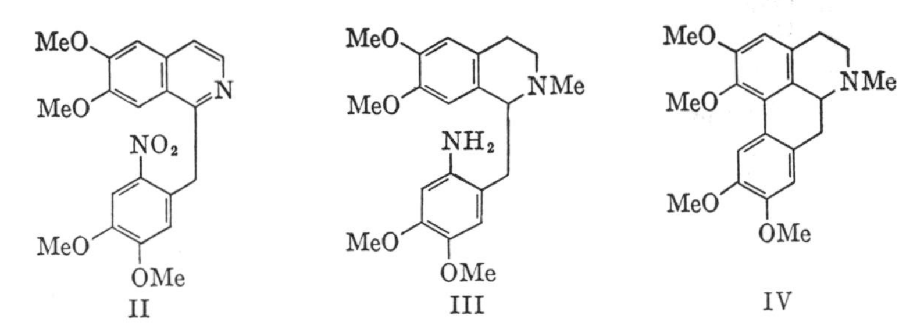

can be obtained by dissolving the methosulfate in a warm saturated solution of potassium chloride and allowing to cool. Reduction of the methochloride yields aminolaudanosine which when diazotized and decomposed with copper powder loses nitrogen and thereby couples the two benzene nuclei with the formation of a phenanthrene derivative (IV). Pschorr failed to isolate the aporphine from his reaction mixture because he attempted to eliminate impurities by extracting the acid solution with chloroform. Gadamer (12) repeated the synthesis and obtained from the chloroform extract of the acid solution a base which was purified and resolved at the same time by successive conversion to *l*-glucine *d*-bitartrate, and *d*-glaucine *l*-bitartrate. The last proved to be identical with the *l*-bitartrate of natural *d*-glaucine, $[\alpha]_D$ +33°, and the free base regenerated from it was *d*-glaucine, $[\alpha]_D$ +115.4° (c = 2.6 in ethanol). The *l*-glaucine regenerated from its *d*-bitartrate had the same numerical value for its optical rotation. Both bases melted at 119–120°, and the *dl*-glaucine melted at 137–139°.

Subsequently, glaucine was subjected to Hofmann degradation (14), and the methiodide (m.p. 222°) as well as the tetramethoxyvinylphenanthrene (m.p. 142°) were shown to be identical with the same derivatives prepared from boldine dimethyl ether (15). The corresponding tetramethoxyphenanthrene-8-carboxylic acid melts at 213° (15).

III. Glaucentrine

Glaucentrine, $C_{20}H_{23}O_4N$, has been found in very small amounts in *D. eximia* (7), *D. formosa* (8), and *D. oregana* (9). From the purified hydrochloride, which melts with decomposition at 237–238°, it is possible to prepare the free base in a crystalline condition, which then melts at 148°.

Structure. Glaucentrine has one phenolic hydroxyl, and upon methylation with diazomethane it is converted into *d*-glaucine. It can therefore have one of four possible structures, and with this in view it was converted into its *O*-ethyl ether whose *l*-acid tartrate melted at 189°. Since there was inadequate alkaloid available to degrade it to known fragments two trimethoxyethoxyaporphines were synthesized and resolved by means of *d*- and *l*-tartaric acid, respectively (16). The first of these, the 2,5,6-trimethoxy-3-ethoxy compound, yielded the *d*- and *l*-acid tartrates, m.p. 212°, $[\alpha]_D^{22}$ ∓56.5°, of which neither was identical with the ether derived from glaucentrine. The second base, 2,3,6-trimethoxy-5-ethoxyaporphine, yielded *d*- and *l*-acid tartrates melting at 189° which had $[\alpha]_D^{25}$ ∓102°. The latter was identical with glaucentrine *O*-ethyl ether *l*-acid tartrate, and the methiodide of the regenerated base (m.p. 225°) was also identical with that of glaucentrine *O*-ethyl ether. Glaucentrine is therefore V. The syntheses followed the now well-known sequence in which an appropriately

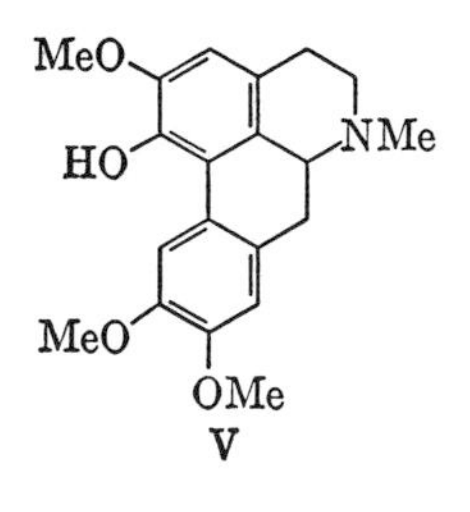

V

substituted β-arylethylamine is reacted with a 6-nitrodialkoxyphenylacetic acid and the resultant amide cyclized by means of any one or a mixture of the reagents such as phosphorus pentoxide, phosphorus pentachloride, and phosphorus oxychloride, in benzene or a homologue. (This well-known ring closure is discussed in detail in the chapter on the benzylisoquinolines (chap. 28)). The resultant 1-(6-nitrobenzyl) dihydroisoquinoline is converted to its methiodide and then reduced, whereby the nitro group is converted to an amino group and the hetero ring is reduced to the *N*-methyltetrahydro compound (analogous to III). Subsequent diazotization and ring closure have been somewhat modified from Pschorr's original procedure but in no case is the yield good.

IV. Boldine

Boldine, $C_{19}H_{21}O_4N$, was the name given to an impure alkaloid preparation obtained by Bourgoin and Verne (17) from *Peumus boldus* Molina (*Boldea fragrans* C. Gay) (Monimiaceae). This plant has received a number of names, the most unfortunate being *Pneumus* (there being no such genus). The alkaloid was subsequently observed by Merck (18) to crystallize with chloroform, and when repeatedly crystallized from this solvent the crystals melt at 162–163°, $[\alpha]_D$ +72.7° (19). The writer (20) has obtained crystalline boldine in the following manner.

An alcoholic extract of the leaves of *Peumus boldus* is largely freed of solvent, rendered just acid to Congo red with hydrochloric acid, diluted with water to one liter for every kilo of plant material, heated on the steam bath with enough paraffin to form a copious layer, and thoroughly stirred. The mixture is then allowed to settle and cool without being disturbed, finally in a refrigerator. After several days it is possible to decant the lower aqueous layer from the mixture of solidified resin and paraffin without much contamination. It is filtered through a layer of charcoal and extracted with chloroform until the extract is colorless. This extraction removes much colored material and some alkaloid, but no boldine. The aqueous solution is then basified with ammonia and again extracted with chloroform. The residue from the chloroform extract is dissolved in dilute aqueous oxalic acid and the filtered solution extracted with ether until the residue from the extract is colorless. A large volume of purified ether is then added to the aqueous solution, a layer of water interposed, and then a layer of aqueous ammonia run in without mixing. The mixture is then shaken very vigorously and allowed to settle. The virtually colorless ether solution is separated, clarified with a little charcoal, evaporated to the consistency of a thin sirup, and treated with a drop of methanol to dispel a slight turbidity. Boldine then crystallizes in the course of a short time in colorless stout polyhedra which melt at 179° and on analysis give the theoretical value for two methoxyls. The yield is *ca.* 0.1%.

Structure. Warnat (14, 15) determined the correct empirical formula and showed that boldine had two methoxyls and two phenolic hydroxyls, and that its dimethyl ether was identical with glaucine. He showed, furtheremore, that when it reacts with an excess of benzoyl chloride it yields an *O,O,N*-tribenzoyl derivative (m.p. 173°) which is optically inactive and no longer basic. Späth and Tharrer (19) carried out the Hofmann degradation of boldine diethyl ether without paying much attention to the characterization of intermediates and obtained a dimethoxydiethoxyvinylphenanthrene (m.p. 112–113°) which was oxidized to the corresponding phenanthrenecarboxylic acid. This upon decarboxylation gave rise to 4,6-dimethoxy-3,7-diethoxyphenanthrene (m.p. 133–134°) (VI), which was prepared synthetically as follows. The anhydrous sodium salt of 4-methoxy-3-ethoxyphenylacetic acid was condensed with 2-nitrovanillin ethyl ether in the presence of acetic anhydride to yield the stilbenecar-

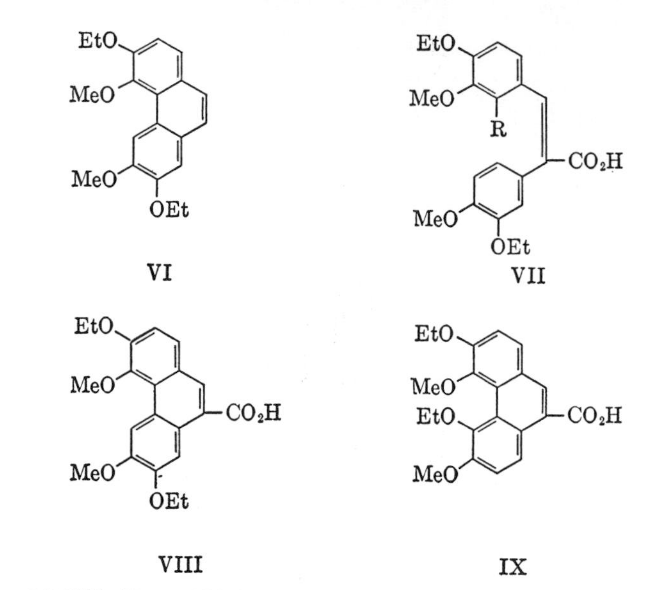

boxylic acid VII (R = NO_2), which was reduced to the amino compound (VII, R = NH_2) by means of ferrous sulfate and ammonia, and this latter compound was diazotized and treated with copper powder. An excellent yield of a mixture of phenanthrenecarboxylic acids was obtained. This was separable into a sparingly soluble acid (m.p. 224°) and a more soluble one (m.p. 193–195°). Evidently ring closure had taken place in the two possible ways (VIII and IX). The higher-melting acid, which was obtained in 50% yield, was decarboxylated by heating with quinoline and copper powder and yielded a dimethoxydiethoxyphenanthrene melting at 134–135° which proved to be identical with the phenanthrene obtained from the degradation of the alkaloid. Since the oxygen atoms in glaucine are in positions 3, 4, 6, and 7 and since they are in the same positions in boldine the synthetic tetraalkoxyphenanthrene of melting point 134–135° must be VI and its acid precursor must be VIII. Consequently, the lower-melting acid must be IX. The 4,6-dimethoxy-3,5-diethoxyphenanthrene derived from it melted at 88°.

The structure (X) of boldine thus determined was independently and

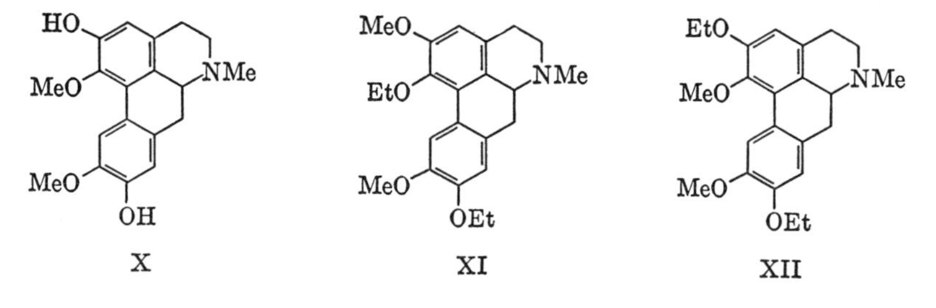

almost simultaneously established by Schlittler (21) by a synthesis of its diethyl ether. The well-known sequence of reactions already outlined was employed for this purpose. The compound first prepared (XI) when reacted with ethyl chloroformate yielded a urethan melting at 106–107°. The reaction product of boïdine diethyl ether and ethyl chloroformate melted at 115°. The second compound (XII) when reacted with ethyl chloroformate yielded a urethan melting at 114–115°, and this was identical with the above compound of natural origin.

V. Laurotetanine

Laurotetanine, $C_{19}H_{21}O_4N$, was obtained by Greshoff (22) from *Litsea chrysocoma* Blume and from several other plants of the Lauraceae family, namely, *L. citrata* Blume (*Tetranthera citrata* Nees) and *Actinodaphne procera* Nees, as well as from the Combretaceae *Illigera pulchra* Blume. Although it was obtained in crystalline condition it was not chemically characterized. It was shown to be a powerful tetanic poison, the lethal dose for the toad (*Bufo melanostictus* Schneid.) being 1 mg.; for the hen, given subcutaneously, 15 mg. (death in 20 minutes); and for the guinea pig, 30 mg., death occurring in 30 minutes. Filippo (23) reviewed the chemistry and source plants of laurotetanine, gave a melting point (134°), suggested the formula $C_{19}H_{23}O_5N$, unaware that he was dealing with a hydrate, described a number of salts, prepared a phenylthiocarbamide (m.p. 211–212°), and gave a series of color reactions and precipitation reactions. He also determined the presence of three methoxyls and a phenolic hydroxyl and showed that the alkaloid is secondary by the preparation of a neutral *O,N*-dibenzoyl derivative (m.p. 194° (?)). Gorter (24), working with laurotetanine obtained from *L. cubeba* Pers., showed that the alkaloid is a monohydrate which only loses all of its water at 80° over phosphorus pentoxide. It melts at 125° and has $[\alpha]_D^{25}$ +98.5°, and the dibenzoyl derivative was shown to melt at 169–170°. When methylated with diazomethane it yields an amorphous *O*-methyl ether, which on further methylation was to have been converted into *O,N*-dimethyllaurotetanine. This compound was regarded as isomeric but not identical with glaucine and was termed isoglaucine, a structure being given for it. Barger and Silberschmidt (10) subsequently showed that isoglaucine is a misnomer and that *O,N*-dimethyllaurotetanine methiodide is identical with glaucine methiodide. Späth and Strauhal (25) also demonstrated the identity of *O,N*-dimethyllaurotetanine and glaucine, although the position of the hydroxyl was also left undetermined.

The correct structure of laurotetanine (XIII) was determined by Barger

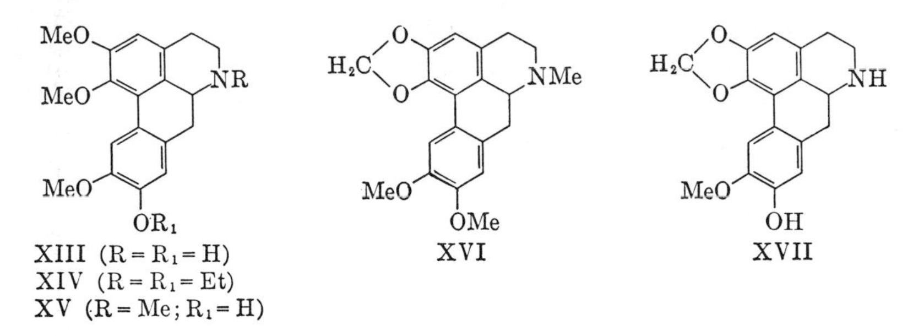

and coworkers (26) by a synthesis of the trimethoxyethoxy-*N*-ethylnoraporphine XIV and its Hofmann degradation to the corresponding vinylphenanthrene (143°) which was identical with that similarly obtained from laurotetanine by exhaustive ethylation. The reaction products of XIV with ethyl chloroformate (m.p. 129–130°) and with benzoyl chloride (m.p. 138°) were identical with those obtained from *O,N*-diethyllaurotetanine, which itself could not be crystallized. The isomer of XIV in which the methoxyl and the ethoxyl in the lower ring are interchanged was also synthesized. Its derivatives were different from those derived from laurotetanine. It had previously been shown (25) that the hydroxyl must be in the ring shown in XIII because permanganate oxidation of laurotetanine yielded 4,5-dimethoxybenzene-1,2,3-tricarboxylic acid. The above aporphine syntheses were carried out by reactions similar to those already outlined under glaucine. Späth and Tharrer (27) almost simultaneously degraded laurotetanine *O*-ethyl ether to 3,4,6-trimethoxy-7-ethoxyphenanthrene (m.p. 114–116°) via the 1-vinyl and 1-carboxy derivatives and showed that it was identical with a synthetic specimen of the same compound.

VI. *N*-Methyllaurotetanine

N-Methyllaurotetanine, $C_{20}H_{23}O_4N$, was obtained from the tertiary phenolic fraction of the alkaloids from *L. citrata* by Späth and Suominen (28). The alkaloid and its derivatives were amorphous for the greater part. However, the *O*-ethyl ether was exhaustively degraded to a nitrogen-free compound which proved to be 3,4,6-trimethoxy-7-ethoxy-1-vinylphenanthrene (m.p. 140–141°), identical with a specimen already prepared from laurotetanine (27). The structure of this alkaloid is therefore XV.

VII. Dicentrine

Dicentrine, $C_{20}H_{21}O_4N$, was first isolated from *Dicentra pusilla* Sieb. and Zucc. by Asahina (29) along with a small amount of protopine, although Heyl (30) had already isolated an alkaloid from *D. formosa* which was later shown to be dicentrine (8). Dicentrine melts at 169°, has $[\alpha]_D$ +62° (chloroform), and yields sparingly soluble and easily crystallized salts, particularly the hydrochloride, the hydrobromide, and the nitrate. The alkaloid was shown to be tertiary and to have two methoxyls. Dicentrine was later isolated from *D. eximia* (7), *D. oregana* (9), and *Stephania capitata* Spreng. (31, 32).

Gadamer (3, 12) recognized the possible relation of dicentrine to glaucine, and he pointed out that the neutral acetyldicentrine (m.p. 202°) described by Heyl (30) was undoubtedly formed by scission of the pyridine ring. Perkin and his coworkers (33, 34), utilizing the series of reactions by which Gadamer (12) synthesized glaucine, substituted the 6,7-methylenedioxy analogue of III and effected ring closure by Pschorr's method. The synthetic *dl*-base melted at 181° and when resolved with the active tartaric acid yielded the sparingly soluble *l*-dicentrine *d*-bitartrate and *d*-dicentrine *l*-bitartrate, successively. The *d*-dicentrine prepared from the tartrate was identical with the natural alkaloid, which therefore has structure XVI. The methine prepared from dicentrine melts at 158–159° (7).

The conversion of dicentrine into *d*-glaucine was achieved by Osada (35). The methylenedioxy group was hydrolyzed to two hydroxyls by heating with phloroglucinol in diluted sulfuric acid, and the resulting phenolic base methylated with diazomethane.

VIII. Actinodaphnine

Actinodaphnine, $C_{18}H_{17}O_4N$, was isolated by Krishna and Ghose (36) from *Actinodaphne hookeri* Meissn. (Lauraceae) and more thoroughly examined by Ghose, Krishna, and Schlittler (37), who determined its structure (XVII). Actinodaphnine melts at 210–211° and has $[\alpha]_D^{20}$ +32.8° (ethanol). It was shown that the nitrogen is secondary by the formation of a phenylthiocarbamido derivative (m.p. 181°). There are present one methoxyl, one phenolic hydroxyl, and a methylenedioxy group. When the alkaloid was methylated with diazomethane it yielded a non-phenolic base which on treatment with methyl iodide generated a mixture from which dicentrine could be isolated. It remained therefore to determine only the position of the hydroxyl. When actinodaphnine was *O*-ethylated with diazoethane and then *N*-methylated with methyl iodide there was obtained *O*-ethyl-*N*-methylactinodaphnine (m.p. 198–199°), which was first demethylenated with phloroglucinol and sulfuric acid and then *O*-methylated with diazomethane. The product was then exhaustively degraded by Hofmann's method to yield ultimately 3,4,6-trimethoxy-7-ethoxy-1-vinylphenanthrene, which appears to be identical with the compound similarly obtained from laurotetanine. It can be added that a number of oxidation products of actinodaphnine or of its derivatives all confirm the proposed structure XVII.

IX. Domesticine

Domesticine, $C_{19}H_{19}O_4N$ was obtained by Kitasato (38) from *Nandina domestica* Thunb. (Berberidaceae) along with isodomesticine. The former melts at 115–117° and has $[\alpha]_D$ +60.5°. Isodomesticine was obtained in the amorphous condition, but its *O*-methyl ether (m.p. 139°, $[\alpha]_D$ +101 to +102° in chloroform) was identical with domesticine *O*-methyl ether. Both alkaloids are tertiary, and contain one methoxyl, one phenolic hydroxyl, and a methylenedioxy group. The absorption spectra indicate that these alkaloids are aporphines. Oxidation of domesticine with permanganate was stated to yield 4,5-methylenedioxybenzene-1,2,3-tricarboxylic acid (38), but this cannot be so in view of the work of Kitasato and Shishido (39) who synthesized epidicentrine and resolved it and showed that the *d*-base (m.p. 138–139°, $[\alpha]_D$ +102° in chloroform) was identical with domesticine *O*-methyl ether. There remained the determination of the position of the hydroxyl, and this was achieved by a synthesis of domesticine *O*-ethyl ether (m.p. 132°) (40). Both syntheses followed the well-known routes leading to aporphines. In the first case 6,7-dimethoxy-1-(3,4-methylenedioxybenzyl)isoquinoline and in the second case the corresponding 6-methoxy-7-ethoxy compound were the essential intermediates.

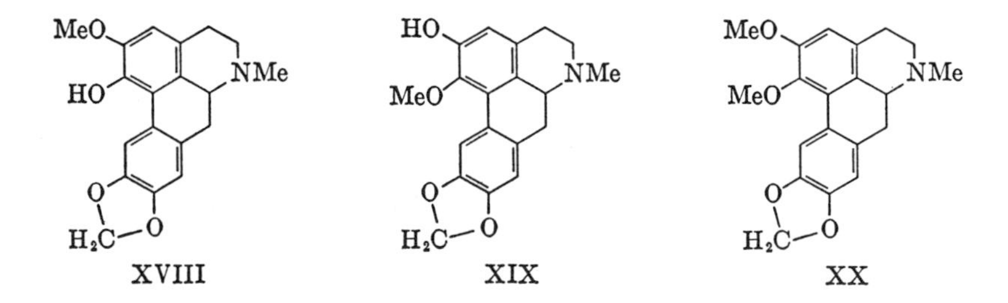

The ethoxy derivative of XVIII was resolved by means of the tartaric acids, and the *l*-bitartrate gave the free *d*-base melting at 131° ($[\alpha]_D^{14}$ +111°) identical with domesticine *O*-ethyl ether. Domesticine is therefore XVIII. The writer is of the opinion that the evidence is not sufficient to establish the existence of isodomesticine. It is most unlikely that a compound of formula XIX suggested by implication for isodomesticine (38) could survive biological methylation.

X. Nantenine

Nantenine, $C_{20}H_{21}O_4N$, obtained from the seeds of *N. domestica* by Takase and Ohashi (41), melts at 138.5° and has $[\alpha]_D^{17}$ +111°. It was also, and independently, isolated by Maniwa and coworkers (42) who named it domestine and proposed the accepted empirical formula. In the meantime Kitasato (43) methylated the phenolic domesticine and showed that the product was identical with nantenine and with domestine. The structure of nantenine is therefore XX.

XI. Phanostenine

Phanostenine, $C_{19}H_{19}O_4N$, was first described by Tomita (44) as obtained from *Stephania sasakii* Hayata; m.p. 210°, $[\alpha]_D^{20}$ —36.7° (chloroform). It was subsequently isolated from *S. capitata* (45) and shown to have the above formula. It has one methoxyl and one hydroxyl, and upon methylation with diazomethane affords an alkaloid shown to be *l*-dicentrine (m.p. 160–165°) because when admixed with *d*-dicentrine there was formed the known *dl*-dicentrine (m.p. 176°). Phanostenine can therefore have only one of two possible structures, namely, XVI, with one of the two methoxyls replaced by hydroxyl.

XII. Crebanine

Crebanine, $C_{20}H_{21}O_4N$, present in *S. sasakii* (44) and in *S. capitata* (45) melts at 126°. It is non-phenolic and upon oxidation by permanganate afforded hemipinic acid. It was submitted to Hofmann degradation, the nitrogen-free compound oxidized, and the latter utimately decarboxylated to yield a phenanthrene derivative (m.p. 111–112°) which was stated to be identical with a synthetic specimen of 1,2-dimethoxy-5,6-methylene dioxyphenanthrene (46, 47). In view of these observations crebanine must be XXI in which the methoxyls are in positions not accountable for by

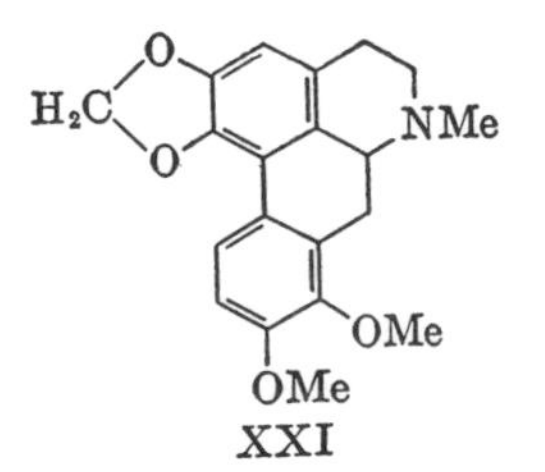

XXI

known biosynthetic routes. The writer would welcome confirmation of this structure before accepting it unreservedly.

XIII. Corydine

Corydine, $C_{20}H_{23}O_4N$, was first prepared and described by Gadamer and Ziegenbein (48), although the name had already been used by Merck (49) for an amorphous mixture of unknown products. In addition to the original source plant, *C. tuberosa*, corydine also occurs in *C. ternata* (4), *Dicentra canadensis* Walp. (50), *D. eximia* (7), *D. formosa* (8), *D. oregana* (9), and in

Glaucium fimbrilligerum (5). When crystallized from dilute alcohol the crystals retain solvent of crystallization and melt with effervescence indefinitely at 103–105°. When crystallized from dry ethyl acetate or dry ether corydine is obtained in virtually colorless prisms which melt at 149° (50, 51); $[\alpha]_D^{25}$ +205° (chloroform). It is also obtainable in a form containing half a mole of ethanol and then melts with effervescence at 124–125° (45). Corydine hydrochloride is sparingly soluble in water, and when dry it is virtually insoluble in chloroform. It dissolves in alkali hydroxide solutions but is rapidly extractable therefrom by means of ether.

XIV. Isocorydine

Isocorydine, $C_{20}H_{23}O_4N$, was first obtained by the partial methylation of corytuberine (52). It has subsequently been isolated from *C. lutea* (L.) DC. (53) (described as luteanine), *C. platycarpa* Makino (54), *C. ternata* (4), *D. canadensis* (50), *G. flavum* Crantz (55), *G. serpieri* Heldr. (56), and *Dicranostigma lactucoides* Hook. f. and Thoms. (57). The alkaloid artabotrine isolated from *Artabotrys suaveolens* Blume (58, 59) has been shown to be identical with isocorydine (60). The pure alkaloid melts at 186° and has $[\alpha]_D^{15}$ +195° (chloroform). It is only sparingly soluble in cold methanol, from which solvent it may be conveniently crystallized. It is sparingly soluble in most organic solvents except chloroform, in which it is readily soluble. The salts in general are crystalline, the hydrochloride being only moderately soluble in methanol. Characteristic is the reaction product of isocorydine with ethyl chloroformate and alkali. This reaction, which was discovered by Gadamer and Knoch (61), results in the scission of the hydropyridine ring of aporphine with the formation of a urethan which in the present instance melts at 110–112° (54).

Isocorydine is phenolic but only sparingly soluble in aqueous alkali, and ether extracts it readily from such solutions, on account of which it has been looked upon as a new and non-phenolic alkaloid on several occasions.

XV. Corytuberine

Corytuberine, $C_{19}H_{21}O_4N$, was first isolated and named by Dobbie and Lauder (62) from commercial corydaline (ex *C. tuberosa*), although it had undoubtedly been obtained earlier from *C. nobilis* Pers. (63). The accepted formula is due to Gadamer (52). Corytuberine is insoluble or only sparingly soluble in virtually all organic solvents and is best recrystallized from hot water in which it is also sparingly soluble, and is then obtained as a pentahydrate, which becomes anhydrous over sulfuric acid. It melts at 240° with slight decomposition and has $[\alpha]_D^{20}$ +282° (ethanol). The hydrochloride is crystalline and only moderately soluble in water.

1. STRUCTURES OF CORYTUBERINE, CORYDINE, AND ISOCORYDINE

The interrelation of these alkaloids was demonstrated by Gadamer (52). It was shown that corytuberine has two methoxyls and two phenolic hydryoxyls, and that partial methylation with diazomethane yields a mixture of corydine and isocorydine, each of which has three methoxyls and one phenolic hydroxyl. Benzoylation of corytuberine (Schotten-Baumann) generates a separable mixture of a monobenzoyl (m.p. 211–214°) and a dibenzoyl derivative (m.p. 135–140°). When the alkaloid is heated with an excess of benzoyl chloride a tribenzoyl derivative (m.p. 140–142°) is formed. This is a neutral substance and is evidently formed by the scission of the nitrogen ring of an aporphine molecule. Complete *O*-methylation generates a non-phenolic tetramethoxy compound, namely corytuberine *O,O*-dimethyl ether which, though never obtained crystalline, can be characterized by the formation of an *l*-acid tartrate which is only moderately soluble in ethanol, melts at 219–224°, and has $[\alpha]_D^{20}$ +150° (water). The Hofmann degradation of this ether ultimately gave rise to a tetramethoxyvinylphenanthrene which was regarded as having structure XXII although no proof of the positions of the methoxyls was given. Zinc dust dust distillation of it, however, gave 1-ethylphenanthrene, so that the

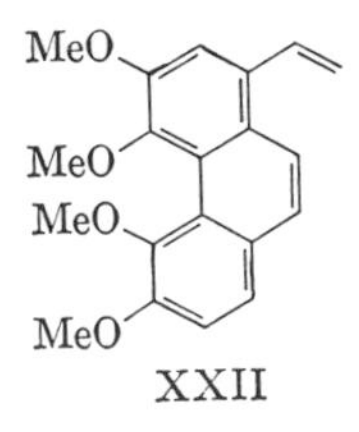

XXII

nuclear structure of corytuberine as an aporphine was reasonably certain. Späth and Hromatka (64) synthesized the tetramethoxyaporphine XXIII and resolved their synthetic base by means of the tartaric acids. The *l*-bitartrate was identical with the *l*-bitartrate obtained from a base prepared by the methylation of corydine (m.p. 212–214°,$[\alpha]_D$ +147°). The synthesis was strictly analogous to that of glaucine except that the ultimate starting materials were 3,4-dimethoxyphenethylamine and 2-nitro-3,4-dimethoxyphenylacetic acid. Gulland and Haworth (65) had already carried out the synthesis of corytuberine dimethyl ether by the same route. They recorded for *d*-corytuberine dimethyl ether *l*-bitartrate, m.p. 219–222°, $[\alpha]_D$ +149.7° (water).

There remained the location of the two hydroxyls which Gadamer (52) had relegated to one nucleus without adequate evidence. Go (66) had made an attempt to solve this problem by demethylenating bulbocapnine *O*-ethyl ether and methylating the resulting dihydroxy base. His conclusions were shown to be in error by Späth and Berger (67), who showed that corytuberine diethyl ether on oxidation gave rise to 4-methoxy-3-ethoxyphthalic acid and therefore corytuberine can have only two possible structures, one of which (the correct one) is XXIV. It was also shown that bulbocapnine methyl ether (XXV) on demethylenation (m.p. 118–120°) followed by partial methylation yields a base identical with corydine, and again therefore corydine may have only two possible formulas, one of which (the correct one) is XXVI.

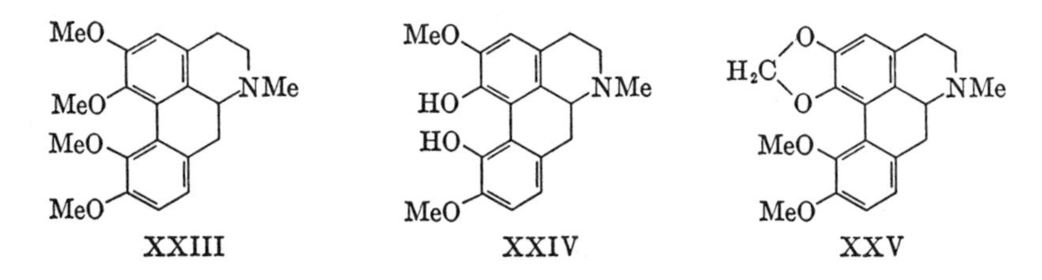

For isocorydine, however, there is therefore only one possible structure, namely XXVII, and a final decision to confirm XXVI for corydine was possible by oxidizing the mixed corytuberine monoethyl ethers to a mixture of 4-methoxy-3-ethoxyphthalic acid and 5-methoxy-4-ethoxybenzene-1,2,3-tricarboxylic acid. The latter was prepared synthetically from methylnoropianic acid (68) by *O*-ethylation followed by nitration, reduction, Sandmeyer introduction of a cyano group, and hydrolysis. It can therefore be said that the structures of corytuberine (XXIV), corydine (XXVI), and isocorydine (XXVII) are known with certainty.

XVI. Suaveoline

Suaveoline, $C_{19}H_{21}O_4N$, is an alkaloid described by Barger and Sargent (69). It melts at 232° and has $[\alpha]_D^{15}$ +164°. It was described as very soluble in chloroform and moderately so in methanol, and it therefore does not appear to be identical with corytuberine although it yields corytuberine dimethyl ether methiodide on methylation with diazomethane followed by reaction with methyl iodide. Barger and Sargent state that they were able to convert suaveoline into artabotrine (isocorydine), but they do not record the essential experiment in which this was accomplished. Schlittler and Huber (60) evidently overlooking this lack of experimental proof suggested certain structures for suaveoline the plausibility of which is uncertain. Nevertheless, the analytical data seem to indicate that this alkaloid is a dihydroxydimethoxyaporphine.

XVII. Bulbocapnine

Bulbocapnine, $C_{19}H_{19}O_4N$, was first isolated from *C. tuberosa* by Freund and Josephi (70), who ascribed to it the accepted formula and described a number of its salts and derivatives. It was stated to melt at 199°, but the writer has repeatedly observed a melting point of 202° (corr.) or even slightly higher; $[\alpha]_D$ +237° (chloroform). The nitrate is sparingly soluble in water or in methanol and can serve as a means of purifying the alkaloid. It has also been isolated from *C. decumbens* Pers. (71), *C. bulbosa* DC. 72), and *D. canadensis* (50).

After earlier observations by a number of investigators Gadamer and Kuntze (73) showed that the nitrogen is tertiary and has a methyl group and that the four oxygens are accounted for by a hydroxyl, a methoxyl, and a methylenedioxy group, and that exhaustive methylation of the *O*-methyl ether (m.p. 131°) via the methine (amorphous) ultimately gave rise to a compound which was correctly surmised to be 1-vinyl-3,4-methylenedioxy-5,6-dimethoxyphenanthrene (m.p. 101°). It was convertible into the corresponding phenanthrenecarboxylic acid (m.p. 228°), and when distilled with zinc dust generated 1-ethylphenanthrene (m.p. of the picrate, 138–140°), thus establishing the aporphine structure of bulbocapnine. On this basis the correct structure (XXVIII) of bulbocapnine was arrived at, although much of it was based upon analogy with corytuberine and corydine.

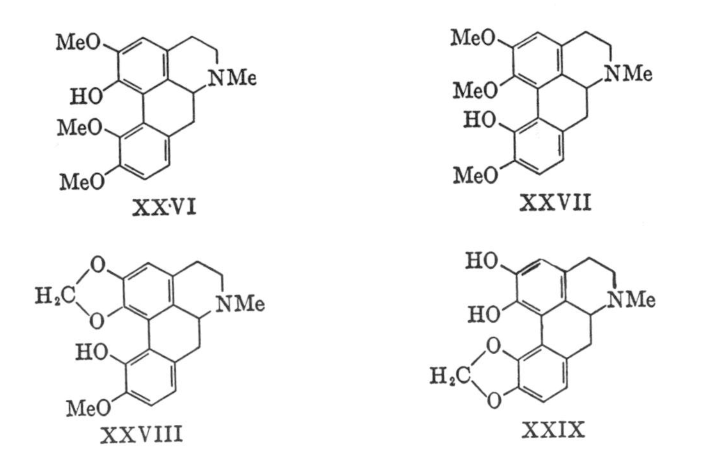

It was possible to racemize bulbocapnine *O*-methyl ether and *O*-benzoylbulbocapnine by first oxidizing with iodine and subsequently reducing with zinc in dilute acid. The *dl-O*-methyl ether melted at 136° and was resolvable into the *l*- and *d*-derivatives ($[\alpha]_D$ ±247° in chloroform) by means of *d*- and *l*-tartaric acid, respectively. Hydrolysis of the *dl-O*-benzoylbulbocapnine (m.p. 201–202°) with sodium methylate yielded *dl*-bulbocapnine (m.p. 209–210°). As in other aporphines, it was possible to effect scission of the nitrogen ring in bulbocapnine by treatment with benzoyl chloride at its boiling point.

The correctness of structure XXVIII for bulbocapnine was established by Späth, Holter, and Posega (74), who obtained three significant oxidation products under three separate experimental conditions. In the first place the methine of bulbocapnine upon nitric acid oxidation yielded mellophanic acid (benzene-1,2,3,4-tetracarboxylic acid) (m.p. 233–236°; tetramethyl ester, m.p. 129°). The formation of this acid from an alkaloid is now regarded as sufficient evidence to prove that the alkaloid is an aporphine. Oxidation of bulbocapnine with permanganate gave rise to oxyhydrastine (1-keto-2-methyl-6,7-methylenedioxytetrahydroisoquinoline), and consequently the methylenedioxy group is in the position shown. Oxidation of bulbocapnine *O*-methyl ether and of the *O*-ethyl ether by permanganate generated respectively hemipinic acid and 4-methoxy-3-ethoxyphthalic acid, the latter identified as its *N*-ethylimide. The isolation of these products proves not only that the *O*-methyl ether has structure XXV but that the phenolic hydroxyl is in the sterically hindered 4-position (XXVIII). The possible alternate positions 1 and 2 for the hydroxyl and methoxyl, respectively, are unlikely on biogenetic grounds and disproved by the later synthesis of bulbocapnine *O*-methyl ether which was achieved by Gulland and Haworth (75). The reactions used were those which had become so well known and involved the preparation of 2-nitro-3,4-dimethoxyphenylacetic acid as well as 3,4-methylenedioxyphenethylamine as the two essential starting materials. The ultimate *dl*-bulbocapnine *O*-methyl ether (m.p. 135°) was identical with a specimen prepared from bulbocapnine (73).

XVIII. Laurepukine

Laurepukine, $C_{18}H_{17}O_4N$, is the name given to an alkaloid obtained from *Laurelia novae-zelandae* A. Cunn. (Monimiaceae) by Barger and Girardet (76). The free base crystallizes in colorless hexagonal plates which melt at 230–231° with $[\alpha]_D$ −222° (chloroform), −252° (ethanol). The sulfate is virtually insoluble in cold water. Analytical data show that this alkaloid has two phenolic hydroxyls, an *N*-methyl, and a methylenedioxy group and its absorption spectrum is such that it must be an aporphine alkaloid (77). When it is methylated with nitrosomethylurethan in alcohol in the presence of potassium hydroxide there is formed an *O,O*-dimethyl ether (m.p. 134°; $[\alpha]_D$ −314° (chloroform), −211° (ethanol)) which is not identical with bulbocapnine *O*-methyl ether (78). Since all of the possible aporphines with methoxy or methylenedioxy groups in positions 2, 3, 5, 6 and 3, 4, 5, and 6 are known with the exception of 3,4-methylenedioxy-5,6-dimethoxyaporphine, it is assumed that the last is laurepukine dimethyl ether and, therefore, that laurepukine is XXIX. Alternate structures with oxygen substituents in positions 1 and 2 or 6 and 7 are excluded on biogenetic grounds. The presence of laureline and pukateine of known structure in the same plant indicates that the chosen positions for the substituents are the correct ones.

XIX. Isothebaine

Isothebaine, $C_{19}H_{21}O_3N$, was first isolated from *Papaver orientale* L. by Gadamer and Klee (79) and properly characterized and further examined by Klee (80), who showed that the plant during active growth contained almost exclusively thebaine but as it reached maturity the plant, and particularly the roots of it, contained very little thebaine but mostly isothebaine. It was postulated that the plant converted the thebaine into isothebaine.

Few color reactions of alkaloids are either specific or striking and in general serve merely to confirm what is either suspected or already known. However, isothebaine gives with concentrated nitric acid a beautiful dark violet color which persists for a long time. Most alkaloids with this reagent give colors, if any, which range from fugitive red to yellow.

Isothebaine crystallizes from ether in strongly refractive prisms which melt at 203–204° and have $[\alpha]_D$ +285.1° (ethanol). The free base is readily soluble in chloroform, methanol, and ethanol. The sulfate and the hydrochloride are readily soluble in water, whereas the nitrate is only sparingly soluble.

Isothebaine was shown to have one phenolic hydroxyl, two methoxyls, and an *N*-methyl group, and since heating with acetic anhydride yielded a neutral diacetyl derivative (from a tertiary base) it was looked upon as an aporphine alkaloid. From the *O*-methyl ether (amorphous, $[\alpha]_D$ +234.5°; *l*-bitartrate, m.p. 226–227°, $[\alpha]_D$ + 143°) on Hofmann degradation via its methosulfate, and a mixture of optically active and inactive methines, there was obtained a vinylphenanthrene which upon permanganate oxidation formed a trimethoxyphenanthrenecarboxylic acid (m.p. 170–171°). The decarboxylation of this acid proved to be difficult but was finally achieved by heating it in acetic acid in a sealed tube to 220°. The resulting trimethoxyphenanthrene yielded a picrate which melted, when not further purified, at 160°. This was assumed to be identical with 3,4,5-trimethoxyphenanthrene (XXX), first obtained by Vongerichten and Ditt-

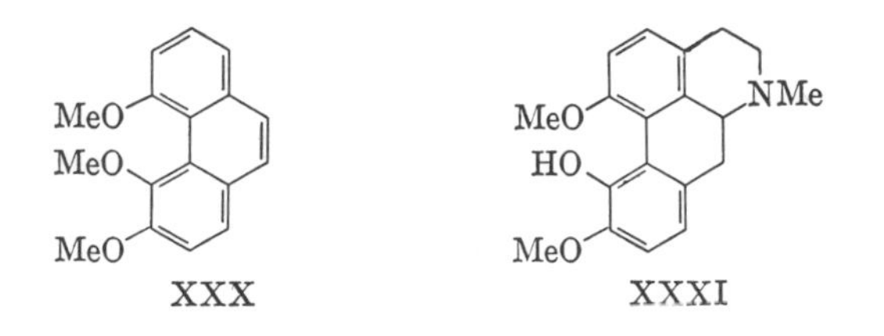

mer (81) by methylating the product obtained on alkali fusion of morphenol, and subsequently synthesized by Pschorr and Koch (82) and found to melt at 167°. On this basis isothebaine was given the structure XXXI. The free hydroxyl was put as shown because of its sterically hindered position.

Attempts to synthesize isothebaine *O*-methyl ether by routes which have been so successful with other aporphines have thus far failed. Gulland and coworkers (83) failed in the Bischler-Napieralski ring closure to yield a 1-benzyl-7-methoxyisoquinoline. This failure is due to the fact that the position of ring closure lacks the activation which is conferred by a para alkoxyl. Schlittler and Müller (84) attempted to achieve a synthesis employing the Pomeranz-Fritsch reactions, after an earlier attempt (85) using the method employed by Gadamer, Oberlin, and Schoeler (86) for aporphine itself had failed. The reaction failed at the last stage and is another confirmation that ketimines, presumably because of their lesser stability than aldimines, are not suitable reactants in this otherwise useful synthesis. Failing a synthesis the earlier degradation (80) to a trimethoxyphenanthrene was repeated. The ultimate compound was obtained crystalline (m.p. 78.5°) and it as well as its picrate (m.p. 159°) were identical with a synthetic specimen of 3,4,5-trimethoxyphenanthrene and its picrate, respectively, prepared by the known method (82). This work seemed to settle beyond dispute the structure of isothebaine *O*-methyl ether. However, Kiselev and Konovalova (87) also repeated the Hofmann degradation of isothebaine. In the main their results agree with or extend the first work (80). They obtained mellophanic acid by nitric acid oxidation of the nitrogen-free product obtained in the degradation, thus confirming that this alkaloid is an aporphine. Their ultimate trimethoxyphenanthrene picrate melted at 158–159°. For comparison they prepared 3,4,5-trimethoxyphenanthrene from morphenol (81) and obtained a picrate which melted at 163–164°, some sintering taking place at 160–161°. A mixture of the picrates from the two sources melted at 142–145°, leading the authors to the conclusion that isothebaine methyl ether has a structure other than that hitherto accepted.

XX. Tuduranine

Tuduranine, $C_{18}H_{19}O_3N$, was obtained by Goto (88) from *Menispermum acutum* Thunb. (*Sinomenium acutum* Rehd. and Wils.) (Menispermaceae) along with sinomenine. It melts not quite sharply at 125° and forms a sparingly soluble hydrochloride which decomposes at 286° and has $[\alpha]_D$ $-148°$. Its Hofmann degradation gave as final product a trimethoxyvinylphenanthrene (m.p. 93.5°), which was oxidized to a trimethoxyphenanthrenecarboxylic acid melting at 199°. When the Hofman degradation is carried through with diethyl sulfate and/or ethyl iodide there is ultimately formed a dimethoxyethoxyphenanthrene (m.p. 108°). Tuduranine has one phenolic hydroxyl, two methoxyls, and is a secondary base. Its *O*,*N*-dimethyl ether was synthesized by Goto and coworkers (89) starting from 2-nitro-4-methoxyphenylacetic acid and 3,4-dimethoxyphenethylamine. An unusually high yield (24 %) was obtained in the last step of the synthesis. The resulting 3,5,6-trimethoxyaporphine (XXXII) was resolved with *d*- and *l*-tartaric acids, respectively, to yield the *l*-base (m.p.

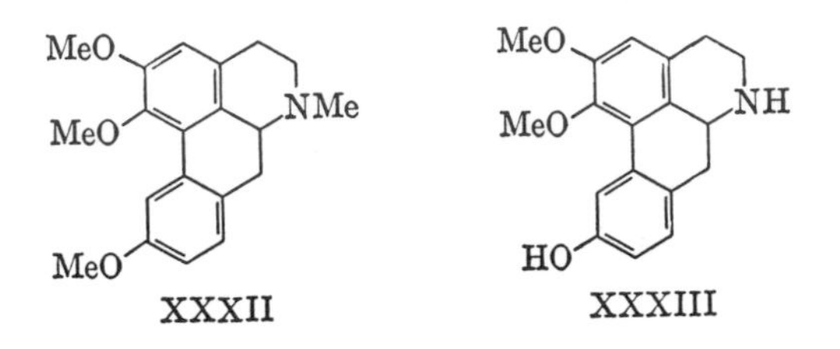

108°, $[\alpha]_D^{12}$ −137°) identical with *O*,*N*-dimethyltuduranine, and the *d*-base (m.p. 108, $[\alpha]_D^{12}$ + 138°). The tartrates melted at 204°. Subsequent syntheses of the 5- and 6-ethyl analogues of XXXII (90) with ethyl on nitrogen proved that neither of these compounds was identical with *O*,*N*-diethyltuduranine. However, the 3,*N*-diethyl analogue of XXXII was synthesized in the same way as was XXXII except the 2-nitro-4-ethoxyphenylacetic acid was used in the first stage and ethyl iodide in the penultimate stage. The synthetic base was then subjected to the Hofmann degradation to 3-ethoxy-5,6-dimethoxy-8-vinylphenanthrene (m.p. 106–108°) and to the corresponding phenanthrenecarboxylic acid (m.p. 178–180) (91) which proved to be identical with the corresponding degradation products of tuduranine for which structure XXXIII is therefore proved.

XXI. Laureline

Laureline, $C_{19}H_{19}O_3N$, occurs along with pukateine and laurepukine in *Laurelia novae-zelandae* (76). It forms a sparingly soluble hydrochloride (m.p. 280°) and hydrobromide. The nitrate, phosphate, and oxalate are readily soluble whereas the hydriodide is virtually insoluble in water, and the *d*-bitartrate (m.p. 220°, $[\alpha]_D$ −25°) is practically insoluble in ethanol and can be recrystallized from hot water. The free base crystallizes from dry ether in plates which melt at 97°; $[\alpha]_D$ −98.5° (ethanol). When repeatedly recrystallized from hexane it melts at 114° (92).

Laureline has one methoxyl, an *N*-methyl, and a methylenedioxy group. Oxidation with permanganate yields 4-methoxyphthalic acid, so that if laureline is an aporphine, which seemed most probable, it should have structure XXXIV. When degraded by Hofmann's method it yielded

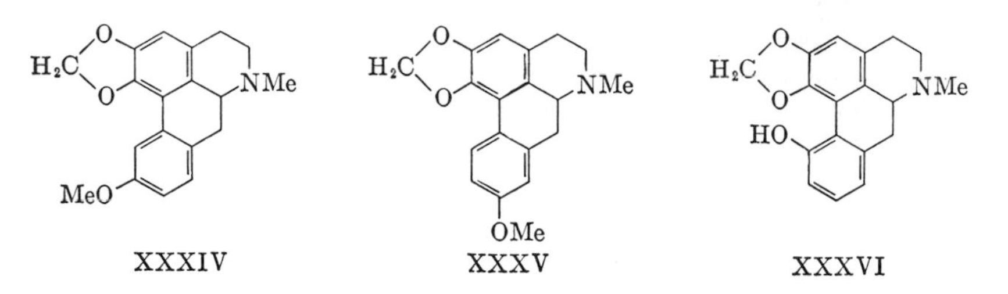

XXXIV XXXV XXXVI

via its methiodide (m.p. 223°) and its methine (m.p. 171°) a vinylphenanthrene (m.p. 158°), which in view of what follows must be 3-methoxy-5,6-methylenedioxy-8-vinylphenanthrene. The oxidation of the latter gave the corresponding phenanthrenecarboxylic acid (m.p. 279–281°), which on decarboxylation generated 3-methoxy-5,6-methylenedioxyphenanthrene (m.p. 132°; picrate, m.p. 172°).

The synthesis of laureline (92) from 3,4-methylenedioxyphenethylamine and 2-nitro-4-methoxyphenylacetic acid offered no unusual features, and the purification of it was facilitated by the very sparing solubility of its hydrochloride. Resolution of the synthetic base was easily achieved by means of *d*- and *l*-tartaric acids. The tartrates crystallized readily from ethanol and the *l*-base *d*-tartrate and the *d*-base *l*-tartrate were the sparingly soluble ones (m.p. 210–211°, $[\alpha]_D \mp 24°$). The former was identical with natural *l*-laureline *d*-tartrate, and the base (m.p. 114°) regenerated therefrom was identical with *l*-laureline. A Hofmann degradation on synthetic *dl*-laureline yielded products which were identical with those obtained from the natural alkaloid, and therefore it has structure XXXIV.

Faltis, Wagner, and Adler (93) repeated the synthesis and resolution of laureline by the same route and reported essentially the same results throughout. They also confirmed the properties of the products of a Hofman degradation. They furthermore synthesized XXXV, which they termed isolaureline, by using 3,4-methylenedioxyphenethylamine and 2-nitro-5-methoxyphenylacetic acid. The *dl*-base (m.p. 109–110°) upon resolution with the tartaric acids yielded *l*- and *d*-isolaureline (m.p. 108–109°); $[\alpha]_D \mp 39°$.

XXII. Pukateine

Pukateine, $C_{18}H_{17}O_3N$ (76) crystallizes easily and melts at 200° (94). It is readily soluble in chloroform, moderately in hydrolytic solvents, and virtually insoluble in ethers and hydrocarbons; $[\alpha]_D^{15}$ −220° (ethanol). The hydrochloride is crystalline but the salts are not characteristic. Pukateine is soluble in alkali and is recoverable from its alkaline solution by treatment with carbon dioxide. In addition to the phenolic hydroxyl there is present in the molecule an *N*-methyl and a methylenedioxy group, but the *O*-methyl ether (m.p. 137°, $[\alpha]_D$ −261° (ethanol)) is not identical though isomeric with laureline.

Diagnostic reactions, namely, heating with excess acetic anhydride or with benzoyl chloride, and reacting with ethyl chloroformate, indicated that pukateine is an aporphine, and the formation of mellophanic acid by nitric acid oxidation gave strong support to this view. Oxidation with permanganate in acetone destroyed the phenolic nucleus and yielded 3,4-methylenedioxyphthalic acid after sublimation. When *O*-methylpukateine methiodide was oxidized with permanganate there was formed 3-methoxyphthalic acid, and therefore structure of XXXVI can be written for pukateine.

Hofmann degradation of pukateine *O*-methyl ether via the methiodide (m.p. 240–241°) and a mixture of methines which was optically active generated a vinylphenanthrene which upon permanganate oxidation formed what, in view of later confirmation, must be 4-methoxy-5,6-methylenedioxyphenanthrene-8-carboxylic acid (m.p. 216–217°) and which upon decarboxylation generated 4-methoxy-5,6-methylenedioxyphenanthrene, isolated as its picrate (m.p. 183–184°).

A synthesis of *O*-methylpukateine was achieved by Barger and Schlittler (95) in which 2-nitro-3-methoxyphenylacetic acid and 3,4-methylenedioxyphenethylamine were employed. The known series of reactions proceeded without novelty, albeit the yield in the final step was low. The synthetic *dl*-base was resolved with *d*- and with *l*-tartaric acid to yield *l*-base *d*-tartrate and *d*-base *l*-tartrate (m.p. 232; 225°) $[\alpha]$ ∓146° in 25% ethanol), respectively. The synthetic *l*-base *d*-tartrate and the free base (m.p. 136°) derived therefrom were identical with the corresponding products from pukateine, which therefore is XXXVI.

Laureline and pukateine are essentially desoxy derivatives of laurepukine (XXIX), whose biosynthesis from norlaudanosine is reasonable and understandable, and Faltis (93) has suggested a mechanism whereby norlaudanosine may yield both of the three-oxygen bases. While there is good reason to believe that norlaudanosine is indeed the precursor, the suggested mechanism lacks experimental verification.

XXIII. Anolobine

Anolobine, $C_{17}H_{15}O_3N$, was obtained from the bark of *Asimina triloba* Dunal (96). It is sparingly soluble in methanol and crystallizes well from a mixture of chloroform and methanol and then melts at 262° to a tar with some sintering at a lower temperature; $[\alpha]_D^{27}$ −22.5° (chloroform-methanol). The hydrochloride is sparingly soluble and may serve as a salt for purifying the alkaloid.

Anolobine has one hydroxyl and a methylenedioxy and is a secondary base. When reacted with diazomethane it generates anolobine *O*-methyl ether (m.p. 97°, $[\alpha]_D$ −27.9° in methanol) which readily undergoes the Hofmann degradation to yield first a mixture of secondary, tertiary, and quaternary salts, and from the latter a methine which crystallized from dry ether in colorless needles (m.p. 99°). The vinylphenanthrene obtained in the last stage appeared to be partly polymeric and upon oxidation with permanganate in acetone generated a very small amount of what was probably a methoxymethylenedioxyphenanthrenecarboxylic acid and a fair amount of 4-methoxyphthalic acid. Assuming the 5,6-positions for the methylenedioxy there were therefore only two possible structures for anolobine. Since anolobine *O*-methyl ether is not identical with laureline

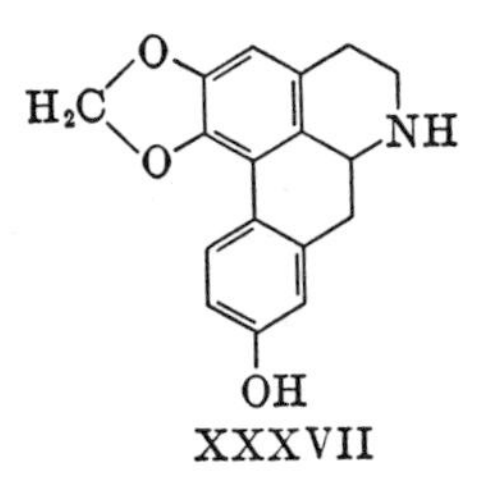

XXXVII

it must be XXXVII.

Govindachari (97) recorded a synthesis of *dl*-2-methoxy-5,6-methylenedioxynoraporphine from 3,4-methylenedioxyphenethylamine and 2-nitro-5-methoxyphenylacetic acid. The free base was not prepared but it was reacted with ethyl chloroformate to yield a product (m.p. 169–170°) not identical with the product (m.p. 245–247°) similarly obtained from anolobine *O*-methyl ether, and consequently it was concluded that the suggested structure of anolobine was wrong (98). Marion (99) repeated the synthesis with the same starting materials but carried the reaction to the tertiary *O*,*N*-dimethylanolobine isolated as its sparingly soluble hydrochloride (m.p. 266°; picrate, m.p. 226°). This via its methiodide (m.p. 241°) readily yielded the methine (m.p. 100°; picrate, m.p. 258°) which was identical with a specimen of *O*,*N*-dimethylanolobine methine and therefore anolobine is XXXVII.

Barger and Sargent (69) have suggested that the alkaloid artabotrinine, $C_{18}H_{17}O_3N$, obtained from *Artabotrys suaveolens* may be identical with *O*-methylanolobine. It yields a sparingly soluble hydrochloride (m.p. 273–274°, $[\alpha]_D$ −42°) and the free base which could not be crystallized had $[\alpha]_D^{18}$ −18.9° in chloroform. Upon *N*-methylation with formic acid and formaldehyde it formed a tertiary base, $C_{19}H_{19}O_3N$, which melted at 132–133° and had $[\alpha]_D^{16}$ −53.6° in ethanol.

XXIV. Stephanine

Stephanine, $C_{19}H_{19}O_3N$, was isolated along with chondodendrine, *d*-dicentrine, cycleanine, and crebanine from *S. capitata* (31, 32). It melts at 155°. Its absorption spectrum is such as to allocate it to the aporphines. It has one methoxyl and presumably a methylenedioxy group, and when oxidized with permanganate it generated 3-methoxyphthalic acid. Hofmann degradation of stephanine followed by oxidation and decarboxylation gave a phenanthrene derivative ($C_{16}H_{12}O_3$, m.p. 87–88°) which was assumed to be 1-methoxy-5,6-methylenedioxyphenanthrene. If this were correct stephanine would have structure XXXVIII, which in the writer's opinion

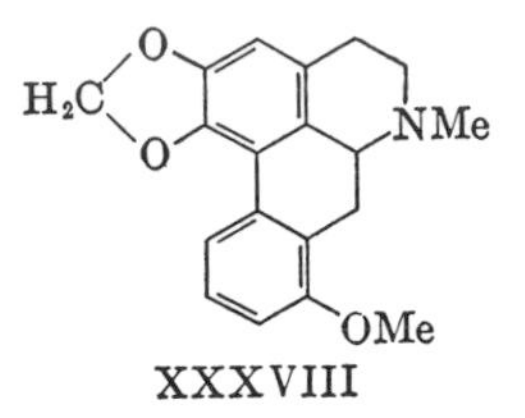

XXXVIII

is very doubtful and requires rigorous proof.

XXV. Roemerine

Roemerine, $C_{18}H_{17}O_2N$, was isolated from *Roemeria refracta* DC. by Orekhov and collaborators (100) along with *l*-ephedrine and *d*-ψ-ephedrine. It melts at 101–102° and yields a sparingly soluble hydrochloride. When distilled with zinc dust it yielded phenanthrene, and on Hofmann degradation via its methiodide (m.p. 215–216°) it generated a series of products which Barger and Weitnauer (101) regarded as identical with those obtained from anonaine. When the methylenedioxy group is replaced by two methoxyls via the dihydroxy base (m.p. 162°) there is obtained a dimethoxyaporphine which was subjected to Hofmann degradation. The ultimate product, 3,4-dimethoxyphenanthrene-1-carboxylic acid, proved that roemerine is XXXIX (102), the *dl*-form of which had already been synthesized (101).

Marion and Grassie (103), evidently unaware of this synthesis, repeated it using the same precursors as those already used. They did however resolve the *dl*-base with *d*- and with *l*-tartaric acids and obtained the natural *l*-roemerine, $[\alpha]_D$ −79.9°, as well as *d*-roemerine, $[\alpha]_D$ +80.2°. Roemerine exhibits dimorphism; a low-melting (87°) form was at first obtained, but later when the form melting at 102° was obtained only that form could be crystallized.

XXVI. Anonaine

Anonaine, $C_{17}H_{15}O_2N$, was obtained from the bark of *Anona reticulata* L. by Santos (104). It was subsequently isolated from the seeds of *A. squamosa* L. (105, 106) and shown to be identical with that originally obtained by Trimurti (107) from the leaves. It melts at 122–123° and has $[\alpha]_D^{20}$ −52° in chloroform. It was more thoroughly examined by Barger and Weitnauer (101), who established the correct formula, determined its structure, and achieved a synthesis. Diagnostic reactions indicated a methylenedioxy group, thus accounting for both oxygens, and a secondary nitrogen (nitroso derivative, m.p. 229–230°; *N*-acetyl derivative, m.p. 229–230°). The *N*-methylanonaine was obtainable by reaction with formic acid and formaldehyde, and Hofmann degradation via *N*-methylanonaine methiodide (m.p. 217°) gave a methine base (m.p. 87–90°) and a vinylphenanthrene (m.p. 87°) which on oxidation generated a phenanthrenecarboxylic acid (m.p. 240°) which could be decarboxylated to what was evidently 3,4-methylenedioxyphenanthrene (m.p. of picrate, 168°).

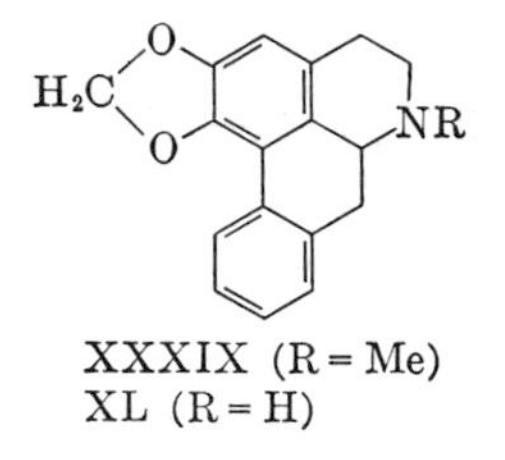

XXXIX (R = Me)
XL (R = H)

The synthesis of anonaine from 3,4-methylenedioxyphenethylamine and *O*-nitrophenylacetic acid proceeded with satisfactory yields, and the isolation of the base as its virtually insoluble hydrochloride (m.p. 285°) facilitated its purification (acetyl derivative, m.p. 217°). Hofmann degradation yielded a series of products identical with those from the natural alkaloid, and therefore anonaine is XL.

XXVII. Other Aporphines

Most of the alkaloids isolated from plants of the Anonaceae family have proved to be aporphines, and for this reason it may be suspected that muricine and muricinine (108) isolated from *Anona muricata* L. may also be aporphines.

Muricine, $C_{19}H_{21}O_4N$, was obtained only as its hydrobromide (m.p. 242–243°). It was stated to contain three methoxyls but to be insoluble in alkali and therefore presumably non-phenolic. The writer would like to suggest that, since *N*-methyl is absent, muricine is probably des-*N*-methylisocorydine or des-*N*-methylcorydine. The former would be expected to dissolve in alkali only with difficulty.

Muricinine, $C_{18}H_{19}O_4N$, isolated as its perchlorate, melts at 206–208°, contains two methoxyls, is alkali soluble, and gives a green color with ferric chloride. It could be des-*N*-methylcorytuberine.

XXVIII. References

1. J. M. Probst, *Ann.*, **31,** 241 (1839).
2. R. Fischer, *Arch. Pharm.* **239,** 426 (1901).
3. J. Gadamer, *Arch. Pharm.*, **249,** 224 (1911).
4. J. Go, *J. Pharm. Soc. Japan*, **49,** 801, 814 (1929); **50,** 933, 940 (1930).
5. R. A. Konovalova, S. Yunusov, and A. P. Orekhov, *J. Gen. Chem.* (*U.S.S.R.*), **9,** 1939 (1939).
6. R. H. F. Manske, *Can. J. Research*, **20B,** 53 (1942).
7. R. H. F. Manske, *Can. J. Research*, **8,** 592 (1933).
8. R. H. F. Manske, *Can. J. Research*, **10,** 521 (1934).
9. R. H. F. Manske, *Can. J. Research*, **10,** 765 (1934).
10. G. Barger and R. Silberschmidt, *J. Chem. Soc.*, **1928,** 2919.
11. R. H. F. Manske, *Can. J. Research*, **8,** 210 (1933).
12. J. Gadamer, *Arch. Pharm.*, **249,** 680 (1911).
13. R. Pschorr, *Ber.*, **37,** 1926 (1904).
14. K. Warnat, *Ber.*, **59,** 85 (1926).
15. K. Warnat, *Ber.*, **58,** 2768 (1925).
16. R. H. F. Manske, E. H. Charlesworth, and W. R. Ashford, *J. Am. Chem. Soc.*, **73,** 3751 (1951).
17. E. Bourgoin and C. Verne, *Bull. soc. chim. France*, [2]**18,** 481 (1872).
18. E. Merck, *Jahresber.*, **36,** 110 (1922).
19. E. Späth and K. Tharrer, *Ber.*, **66,** 904 (1933).
20. R. H. F. Manske, unpublished data.
21. E. Schlittler, *Ber.*, **66,** 988 (1933).
22. M. Greshoff, *Ber.*, **23,** 3546 (1890).
23. J. D. Filippo, *Arch. Pharm.*, **236,** 601 (1898).
24. K. Gorter, *Bull. jard. bot. Buitenzorg*, [III] **3,** 180 (1921).
25. E. Späth and F. Strauhal, *Ber.*, **61,** 2395 (1928).
26. G. Barger, J. Eisenbrand, L. Eisenbrand, and E. Schlittler, *Ber.*, **66,** 450 (1933).
27. E. Späth and K. Tharrer, *Ber.*, **66,** 583 (1933).
28. E. Späth and E. E. Suominen, *Ber.*, **66,** 1344 (1933).
29. Y. Asahina, *Arch. Pharm.*, **247,** 201 (1909).
30. G. Heyl, *Arch. Pharm.*, **241,** 313 (1903).
31. M. Tomita and H. Shirai, *J. Pharm. Soc. Japan*, **62,** 381 (1942).
32. H. Shirai, *J. Pharm. Soc. Japan*, **64,** 44 (1944).
33. R. D. Haworth, W. H. Perkin Jr., and J. Rankin, *J. Chem. Soc.*, **127,** 2018 (1925).
34. R. D. Haworth, W. H. Perkin Jr., and J. Rankin, *J. Chem. Soc.*, **1926,** 29.
35. S. Osada, *J. Pharm. Soc. Japan*, **48,** 423 (1928).
36. S. Krishna and T. P. Ghose, *J. Indian Chem. Soc.*, **9,** 429 (1932).
37. T. P. Ghose, S. Krishna, and E. Schlittler, *Helv. Chim. Acta*, **17,** 919 (1934).
38. Z. Kitasato, *Acta Phytochim.* (*Japan*), **3,** 175 (1927).
39. Z. Kitasato and H. Shishido, *Ann.*, **527,** 176 (1937).
40. H. Shishido, *Bull. Chem. Soc. Japan*, **12,** 150 (1937).
41. T. Takase and H. Ohashi, *J. Pharm. Soc. Japan*, No. **535,** 742 (1926).
42. H. Maniwa, R. Sakae, and I. Kan, *J. Pharm. Soc. Japan*, No. **536,** 833 (1926).
43. Z. Kitasato, *J. Pharm. Soc. Japan*, No. **536,** 843 (1926).

44. M. Tomita, *J. Pharm. Soc. Japan*, **59,** 207 (1939).
45. M. Tomita and H. Shirai, *J. Pharm. Soc. Japan*, **63,** 233 (1943).
46. M. Tomita and S. Shirai, *J. Pharm. Soc. Japan*, **62,** 27 (1942).
47. H. Shirai, *J. Pharm. Soc. Japan*, **62,** 517 (1942).
48. J. Gadamer and H. Ziegenbein, *Arch. Pharm.*, **240,** 94 (1902).
49. E. Merck, *Arch. Pharm.*, **231,** 133 (1893).
50. R. H. F. Manske, *Can. J. Research*, **7,** 258 (1932).
51. J. Gadamer, *Arch. Pharm.*, **249,** 669 (1911).
52. J. Gadamer, *Arch. Pharm.*, **249,** 641 (1911).
53. R. H. F. Manske, *Can. J. Research*, **20B,** 57 (1942).
54. R. H. F. Manske, *Can. J. Research*, **21B,** 13 (1943).
55. R. H. F. Manske, *Can. J. Research*, **17B,** 399 (1939).
56. R. H. F. Manske, *Can. J. Research*, **20B,** 53 (1942).
57. R. H. F. Manske, unpublished data.
58. J. M. Marañon, *Philippine J. Sci.*, **38,** 259 (1929).
59. A. C. Santos and F. R. Reyes, *Univ. Philippines Nat. and Appl. Sci. Bull.*, **2,** 407 (1932).
60. E. Schlittler and H. U. Huber, *Helv. Chim. Acta*, **35,** 111 (1952).
61. J. Gadamer and F. Knoch, *Arch. Pharm.*, **259,** 135 (1921).
62. J. J. Dobbie and A. Lauder, *J. Chem. Soc.*, **63,** 485 (1993).
63. R. H. F. Manske, *Can. J. Research*, **18B,** 288 (1940).
64. E. Späth and O. Hromatka, *Ber.*, **61,** 1692 (1928).
65. J. M. Gulland and R. D. Haworth, *J. Chem. Soc.*, **1928,** 1834.
66. J. Go, *J. Pharm. Soc. Japan*, **49,** 821 (1929).
67. E. Späth and F. Berger, *Ber.*, **64,** 2038 (1931).
68. C. Liebermann, *Ber.*, **29,** 2030 (1896).
69. G. Barger and L. J. Sargent, *J. Chem. Soc.*, **1939,** 991.
70. M. Freund and W. Josephi, *Ann.*, **277,** 1 (1893).
71. Y. Asahina and S. Motigase, *J. Pharm. Soc. Japan*, **No. 463,** 766 (1920).
72. O. Haars, *Arch. Pharm.*, **243,** 154 (1905).
73. J. Gadamer and F. Kuntze, *Arch. Pharm.*, **249,** 598 (1911).
74. E. Späth, H. Holter, and R. Posega, *Ber.*, **61,** 322 (1928).
75. J. M. Gulland and R. D. Haworth, *J. Chem. Soc.*, **1928,** 1132.
76. G. Barger and A. Girardet, *Helv. Chim. Acta*, **14,** 481 (1931).
77. A. Girardet, *J. Chem. Soc.*, **1931,** 2630.
78. A. Girardet, *Helv. Chim. Acta*, **14,** 504 (1931).
79. J. Gadamer and W. Klee, *Arch. Pharm.*, **249,** 41 (1911).
80. W. Klee, *Arch. Pharm.*, **252,** 211 (1914).
81. E. Vongerichten and O. Dittmer, *Ber.*, **39,** 1718 (1906).
82. R. Pschorr and W. Koch, *Ann.*, **391,** 40 (1912).
83. R. K. Callow, J. M. Gulland, and R. D. Haworth, *J. Chem. Soc.*, **1929,** 1444.
84. E. Schlittler and J. Müller, *Helv. Chim. Acta*, **31,** 1119 (1948).
85. J. Müller, *Helv. Chim. Acta.* **31,** 1111 (1948).
86. J. Gadamer, M. Oberlin, and A. Schoeler, *Arch. Pharm.*, **263,** 81 (1925).
87. V. V. Kiselev and R. A. Konovalova, *J. Gen. Chem.* (*U.S.S.R.*), **19,** 148 (1949).
88. K. Goto, *Ann.*, **521,** 175 (1936).
89. K. Goto, R. Inaba, and H. Nozaki, *Ann.*, **530,** 142 (1937).
90. K. Goto and H. Sisido, *Proc. Imp. Acad.* (*Tokyo*), **15,** 8 (1939).
91. K. Goto and H. Shishido, *Ann.*, **539,** 262 (1939).
92. E. Schlittler, *Helv. Chim. Acta*, **15,** 394 (1932).
93. F. Faltis, G. Wagner, and E. Adler, *Ber.*, **77,** 686 (1944).

94. B. C. Aston, *J. Chem. Soc.*, **97,** 1381 (1910).
95. G. Barger and E. Schlittler, *Helv. Chim. Acta*, **15,** 381 (1932).
96. R. H. F. Manske, *Can. J. Research*, **16B,** 76 (1938).
97. T. R. Govindachari, *Current Sci. (India)*, **10,** 76 (1941).
98. T. R. Govindachari, *Current Sci. (India)*, **11,** 238 (1942).
99. L. Marion, *J. Am. Chem. Soc.*, **66,** 1125 (1944).
100. R. A. Konovalova, S. Yunusov, and A. P. Orekhov, *J. Gen. Chem. (U.S.S.R.)*, **9,** 1356 (1939).
101. G. Barger and G. Weitnauer, *Helv. Chim. Acta*, **22,** 1036 (1939).
102. S. Yunusov, R. A. Konovalova, and A. P. Orekhov, *J. Gen. Chem. (U.S.S.R.)*, **9,** 1868 (1939).
103. L. Marion and V. Grassie, *J. Am. Chem. Soc.*, **66,** 1290 (1944).
104. A. C. Santos, *Philippine J. Sci.*, **43,** 561 (1930).
105. F. R. Reyes and A. C. Santos, *Philippine J. Sci.*, **44,** 409 (1931).
106. A. C. Santos, *Philippine J. Sci.*, **47,** 357 (1932).
107. N. Trimurti, *J. Indian Inst. Sci.*, **7,** 232 (1924).
108. T. M. Meyer, *Ing. Ned.-Indië*, **8,** No. 6, VII, 64 (1941).

CHAPTER 31

The Protopine Alkaloids

R. H. F. MANSKE

Dominion Rubber Research Laboratory, Guelph, Ontario

	Page
I. Introduction	147
II. Occurrence	148
1. Isolation and Purification of Protopine	148
III. Cryptopine	149
1. Occurrence and Properties	149
2. Constitution	150
3. The Structures of the Degradation Fragments	154
IV. Cryptocavine	155
1. Constitution	155
2. Synthesis	156
V. Protopine	157
1. Occurrence and Properties	157
2. Constitution	158
3. Synthesis	159
VI. Allocryptopine	159
1. Constitution	160
2. Synthesis	160
VII. Hunnemanine	160
1. Constitution	161
VIII. Cryptopalmatine	161
IX. Corycavine	162
1. Properties	162
2. Constitution	162
X. Corycavamine	163
XI. Corycavidine	163
XII. References	164

I. Introduction

The protopine alkaloids form a natural group which is characterized by the presence of a ten-membered *N*-hetero-ring containing one carbonyl. That they are to be classed as isoquinoline alkaloids follows not from the actual presence of an isoquinoline nucleus but from the fact that they almost certainly are derived from isoquinolines into which they are reconvertible at least *in vitro*. Their congeners if any are also isoquinolines, and it is evident that the biosynthetic mechanism which gives rise to them involves intermediates analogous to, if not identical with, those which give rise to genuine isoquinolines.

II. Occurrence

While isoquinolines are elaborated by a number of natural orders, there are only two exceptions to the statement that the protopine bases are found only in the Papaveraceae. These exceptions are the occurrence of α-allocryptopine (β-homochelidonine) in *Zanthoxylum brachyacanthum* F. Müll. and in *Z. coco* Gill. (*Fagara coco* (Gill.) Engl.), plants belonging to the Rutaceae, and of protopine in *Nandina domestica* Thunb. (Berberidaceae).

Protopine has been found in all papaveraceous plants which have been exhaustively examined. In some plants, *Papaver somniferum* L., it is present only in minute amounts, while in others, *Dicentra spectabilis* Lem., it is the chief or perhaps only alkaloid. The writer has been able to isolate it from nearly fifty species.

1. Isolation and Purification of Protopine

The dried and ground roots of *Dicentra spectabilis* are extracted in a Soxhlet apparatus with methanol until the extract is practically colorless. Most of the methanol is recovered by distillation and the residue treated with one to two liters of water for every kilo of plant material and enough hydrochloric acid to render the mixture just acid to Congo red. A current of steam is passed into the heated mixture to remove some remaining methanol. The mixture is set aside without agitation until cool and then placed in a refrigerator for at least two days. The clear aqueous solution is decanted from the fats and resins, which have agglomerated and hardened, through a thin filter cake prepared from a mixture of charcoal and Filtercel. The The filtrate is extracted with chloroform until the extract is almost colorless. The first contact of the chloroform with the aqueous solution generally causes the separation of a dark resin, insoluble in both media, which usually adheres to the walls of the separatory funnel. The aqueous solution is preferably filtered again, then basified with an excess of ammonia, and again exhausted with chloroform. If the extraction is prolonged a turbidity generally develops due to the gradual crystallization of magnesium ammonium phosphate. The combined chloroform extract is evaporated somewhat to remove adhering water, filtered, and evaporated to dryness. The thin sirupy residue is treated with small successive amounts of methanol, the solution being evaporated somewhat after each addition to remove the chloroform completely. At this point a turbidity may have developed, in which case the solution is filtered while hot if crystallization has not occurred. In any event the alkaloid crystallizes with great facility from the hot solution if the high-melting form is available for seeding. The yield of tan-colored crystals melting at 205–207° is 0.5 to 0.7%. Some purification can be effected by recrystallizing from chloroform–methanol, but the brilliant colorless polyhedra of the pure alkaloid are not obtainable by recrystallization alone.

Either of the two following procedures can be used to obtain colorless protopine. (*1*) The crude base (1 g.) is dissolved in hot 5% acetic acid (10 cc.), boiled with charcoal, filtered, and while hot treated with solid potassium nitrate (1 g.) when the sparingly soluble nitrate will crystallize while the solution is still hot. After cooling, the protopine nitrate is separated by filtration and washing and shaken in contact with ammonia and chloroform. The separated and virtually colorless chloroform layer on evaporation to a sirup and treatment with about 10 cc. hot methanol will yield protopine melting at 211°. (*2*) The crude base (1 g.) is dissolved in 2% oxalic acid (25 cc.) and the filtered solution extracted with several successive portions of ether. A layer of fresh ether is then added to the aqueous solution contained in a separatory funnel and a layer of water (25 cc.) cautiously run in. This is followed by the similar cautious addition of an excess of ammonia, and the mixture is then shaken vigorously. The ether layer is immediately separated, filtered with the aid of a little charcoal, and evaporated. Frequently the protopine crystallizes while the ether solution is being manipulated or during its evaporation. In any case the form which separates from ether is generally the low-melting (205°) form which consists of minute bulky needles. Recrystallization from chloroform–methanol yields the high-melting form, particularly if crystals for seeding are available.

Allocryptopine, cryptocavine, and cryptopine are widely distributed, particularly in the Fumariaceae division of the Papaveraceae, while the *C*-methyl derivatives are rare and found exclusively in *Corydalis tuberosa* DC.

III. Cryptopine

1. Occurrence and Properties

Cryptopine, $C_{21}H_{23}O_5N$, was first isolated from the thebaine fraction of the opium alkaloids (1), and this was its only known source when W. H. Perkin, Jr., began and successfully completed his classical researches on its structure. It has since been found in the following plants, albeit always as a minor constituent—*Corydalis sempervirens* (L.) Pers. (2), *C. scouleri* Hook. (3), *C. sibirica* Pers. (4), *C. nobilis* Pers. (5), *Dicentra cucullaria* (L). Bernh. (6), *D. chrysantha* Walp. (7), and *D. ochroleuca* Engelm. (7). It is conveniently separated from the protopine mother liquors as its hydrobromide, which is sparingly soluble in dilute methanol and crystallizes in glistening micaceous plates. The acid oxalate is sparingly soluble in water and also serves as a salt suited for purification. Many of the salts separate from hot water as gelatinous masses which can however be crystallized by warming slightly, preferably in the presence of some methanol, but none of them have characteristic sharp melting points. The free base, m.p. 221°, is only sparingly soluble in most solvents except in chloroform. It crystallizes with great facility if the residue from its solution in chloroform is dissolved in hot metahnol. The most striking color reaction of cryptopine is that obtained when a trace of it in acetic acid is treated with sulfuric acid. The reddish-violet color which is immediately produced is permanent for several hours but gradually changes to a dirty blue. All of the protopine alkaloids give the same color reaction.

Cryptopine has been examined pharmacologically by a number of investigators (8–11). It depresses the higher nervous centers, causes spinal paralysis in frogs, and convulsions in mammals. None of its effects are such as to suggest its use in medicine.

2. Constitution

The work of Pictet and Kramers (12) and of Danckwortt (13) indicated only that cryptopine was saturated, contained two methoxyls, one methyl on a tertiary nitrogen atom, probably a carbonyl, and also a methylenedioxy group. The earlier observation that *m*-hemipinic acid could be obtained by oxidizing the alkaloid with permanganate (14) is significant only historically and serves to emphasize the difficulties that were encountered when the chemistry of the alkaloids was being born.

The memoirs of W. H. Perkin, Jr. (15, 16), which record the labors leading to the complete elucidation of the structures of cryptopine and of protopine, will ever stand as examples of skill in planning and executing structural research as well as in faithful reporting. It should be pointed out that chemists of to-day having relegated an alkaloid to the protopine group will have little difficulty in establishing the positions of the substituents. This fortunate state of affairs is due to the fact that Perkin discovered a series of reactions by which these alkaloids could be split into two fragments which retain the nitrogen and all of the carbon atoms.

Cryptopine (I) reacts with methyl sulfate yielding a methosulfate, $B \cdot Me_2SO_4$, which when reduced with sodium amalgam in acid solution undergoes an Emde degradation as well as a reduction of the ketonic group yielding tetrahydromethylcryptopine (II), which on dehydration with

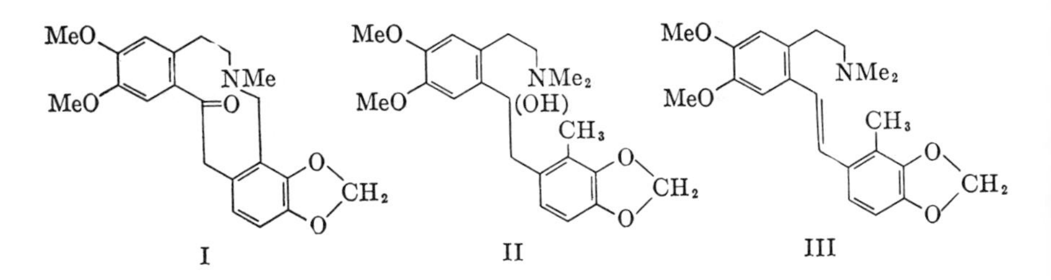

acetyl chloride is convertible into anhydrotetrahydromethylcryptopine (III). Oxidation of the latter (III) yields the products which would be expected if cleavage took place at the double bond, namely 4,5-dimethoxy-2-(β-dimethylaminoethyl) benzaldehyde (IV) and 2-methyl-3,4-methylenedioxybenzaldehyde (V), as well as the further oxidation products of these.

From the former (IV) there is formed by further oxidation the formyl derivative of 4,5-dimethoxy-2-(β-methylaminoethyl) benzoic acid by oxidation of the aldehyde to a carboxyl and the oxidation of an *N*-methyl group to a formyl group (cf. oxidation of tropine, Vol. I, p. 286). The aldehyde (V) readily undergoes oxidation to the corresponding acid, and it was these four compounds which were isolated in the original work. If the structures of compounds IV and V be taken as proved the compound III must have the structure shown. It could however arise not only from II by dehydration but also from an isomer of II in which the hydroxyl group is present at the site of the adjacent —CH_2 group, and Perkin spared no pains to determine the site of the ketonic group.

If cryptopine is reduced with sodium amalgam under mildly acid conditions it yields a dihydro compound (VI). When the latter is digested

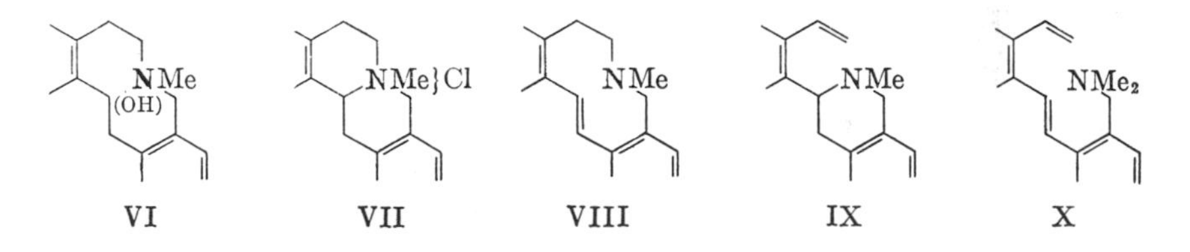

with acetyl chloride or phosphoryl chloride it yields a separable mixture of two quaternary chlorides formed empirically by the substitution of chlorine for hydroxyl. These are both represented by VII, the isomerism being due to the fact that the quaternary nitrogen and the carbon originally carrying the hydroxyl group are asymmetric. These compounds are so similar to the two methochlorides of canadine (17) that the partial formula VII is applicable to both, the difference being attributable only to the interchange of alkoxy groups in the nuclei not shown. Either form of isodihydrocryptopine chloride (VII) when digested with methanolic potash yields a mixture of anhydrodihydrocryptopine A (VIII) and B (IX), which are identical with Pyman's (18) *N*-methylisotetrahydroberberines A and B, respectively, but for the interchange of the two methoxyls and the methylenedioxy group. Bases of the type of A when heated with acids regenerate the original quaternary salts (VII) and when digested with dilute alcohol isomerize to the more stable bases B. Further degradation of either VIII or IX via the methosulfates and alkali treatment yields methylisoanhydrocryptopine (X). This close analogy with the berberine derivatives is carried still further in that both series by a last Hofmann degradation yield a separable mixture of α- and β-isocryptopidol (α- and β-isoberberidol) (XI), the isomerism being obviously of the cis-trans type. Further study of compound XI derived from cryptopine was not continued because of

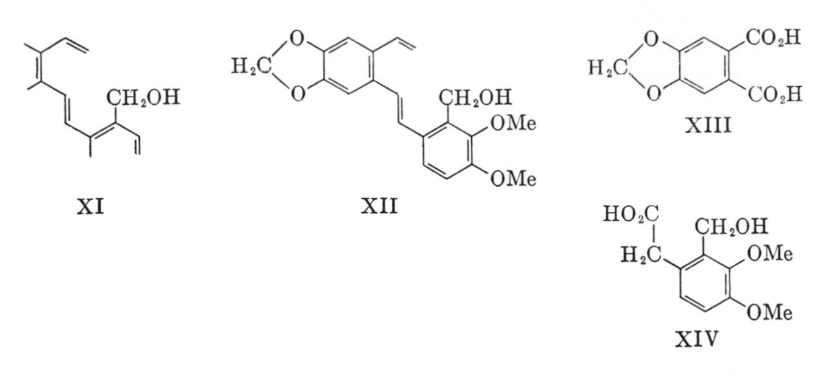

paucity of material, but the compound (XII) from berberine corresponding to XI was submitted to oxidation. Four compounds were obtained, two of which, hydrastic acid (XIII) and 2-hydroxymethyl-3,4-dimethoxyphenylacetic acid (XIV), clearly confirm the structure of XII, although no mechanism was suggested to account for the unusual formation of XIV from XII.

The degradation of cryptopine methosulfate with alkali and subsequent manipulations of the resultant products yielded a series of compounds whose formation could be reasonably explained only on the basis of formula I. In the first stage there is obtained a mixture of β- and γ-methylcryptopines. A third, α-methylcryptopine, was shown to be polymorphic with the β-form. The β- and γ-forms were not interconvertible and were represented by XV and XVI, respectively, and on exhaustive methylation yielded the same substance, anhydrocryptodiol (XVII), the pyran ring of

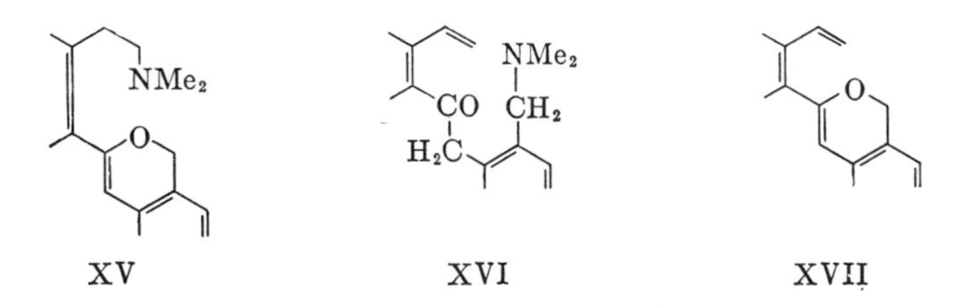

which is evidently formed by dehydration of the intermediate benzyl alcohol. The γ-form yielded derivatives diagnostic of a ketone, and this is the simplest derivative of cryptopine which shows the presence of such a group. The β-form is inert to ketone reagents and does not form an acetyl derivative. The acetyl derivative which the γ-form yields is regarded as an enol acetate.

Some further transformation products of cryptopine deserve mention because of their intrinsic interest to the organic chemist and because their formation and structures can best be explained on the basis of the accepted structure of the alkaloid.

When cryptopine is treated with phosphoryl chloride, isocryptopine chloride is formed, which is formulated as XVIII. When this is digested

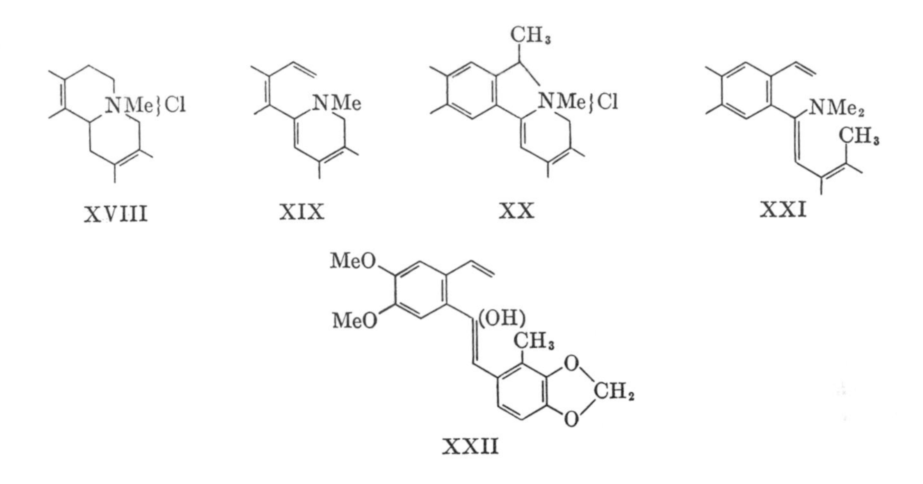

with strong alkali, hydrogen chloride is eliminated with the formation of anhydrocryptopine (XIX), which on reduction with sodium amalgam in acid solution is converted into a dihydro derivative, the cyclic double bond only being reduced, and on oxidation converted to ketoanhydrocryptopine (XIX with CO instead of CH_2). The quaternary metho-salts of XIX on treatment with alkali regenerate XIX by elimination of methanol, a reaction which at the time of its discovery was unique. The same metho-salts also eliminate methanol when warmed with acids, but in this reaction XIX is not regenerated but a new ring is formed yielding ψ-cryptopine salts (XX). Emde reduction of anhydrocryptopine methosulfate yields dihydroanhydromethylcryptopine (XXI), the methosulfate of which on heating with alkali yielded the nitrogen-free hydroxycryptopidine (XXII). The oxidative fission of XXII to 2-methyl-3,4-methylenedioxybenzoic acid and 2-vinyl-4,5-dimethoxybenzaldehyde clearly demonstrates its constitution.

Reduction of anhydrocryptopine methosulfate in an acid medium brings about the same ring scission that the Emde conditions cause, but the heterocyclic double bond is simultaneously reduced yielding the dihydro derivative of XXI, the vinyl side chain remaining unchanged.

A series of reduction products are obtained when isocryptopine chloride (XVIII) is reduced in alkaline and in acid media with sodium amalgam. The most interesting of these is dihydroanhydrodihydrocryptopine A, the dihydro derivative of VIII, which can also be obtained by reducing the latter with the same reagent in acid solution.

The elimination of the methyl group as methyl chloride from isocryptopine chloride (XVIII) by heating to 260° *in vacuo* yields dihydroanhydroepiberberine (XXIII) (19). That it is correctly represented by XXIII

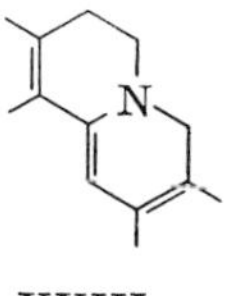

XXIII

follows from the fact that its methosulfate on decomposition with alkali yields anhydrocryptopine (XIX). The substance XXIII is of importance because on reduction with zinc or tin and hydrochloric acid it yields a dihydro derivative (XXIX), which was named tetrahydroanhydroepiberberine, and this was subsequently shown to be identical with *dl*-sinactine (20, 21). The dihydro derivative of XXIII was also obtainable by heating the α-isomer of isodihydrocryptopine chloride (VII) *in vacuo* to 230°.

3. The Structures of the Degradation Fragments

2-Methyl-3,4-methylenedioxybenzaldehyde (V).—The elucidation of the structure of this aldehyde and the corresponding acid provided the evidence necessary for the interpretation of the constitution of anhydrotetrahydromethylcryptopine (III). The acid was recognized as one of the possible methylenedioxytoluic acids, but attempts to oxidize it to a methylenedioxyphthalic acid were unsuccessful. Barger's method (22) of converting a methylenedioxy group into two hydroxyls when applied to the acid yielded a dihydroxytoluic acid which on *O*-methylation afforded a dimethoxytoluic acid, and this in turn could be oxidized to hemipinic acid (XXIV). The dimethoxytoluic acid is therefore either XXVA or XXVB.

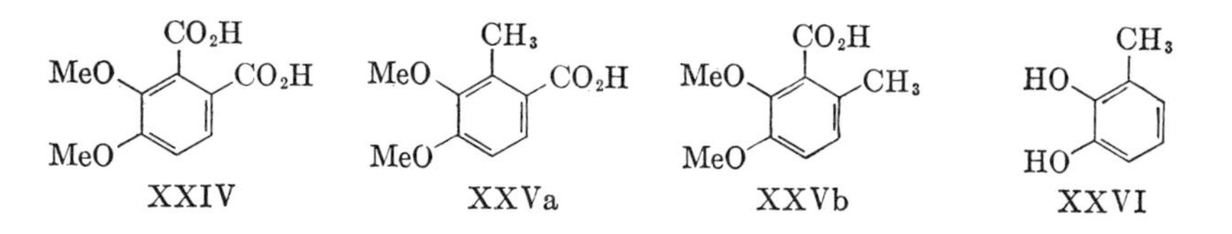

A decision between these two formulas was possible when it was observed that the dihydroxytoluic acid lost carbon dioxide when heated to 170–180° with water. The resulting dihydroxytoluene proved to be isohomocatechol (XXVI), and therefore the degradative aldehyde has formula V.

4,5-Dimethoxy-2-(β-dimethylaminoethyl)benzaldehyde (IV).—This base yielded an oxime and seemed to be the methyl derivative of 4,5-dimethoxy-2-(β-methylaminoethyl)benzaldehyde, which Pyman (23) had obtained by oxidizing laudanosine with manganese dioxide and sulfuric acid. This on treatment with methyl iodide yielded a separable mixture from which the base (IV) and the methiodide of this were obtained. The properties of the degradative and synthetic compounds were identical.

The methiodide of IV on treatment with alkali evolved trimethylamine and yielded 4,5-dimethoxy-2-vinylbenzaldehyde, a reaction strictly analogous to the decomposition of trimethylhydrastylammonium iodide (24).

The structure of one of the oxidation products obtained along with IV was shown to be *N*-formyl-4,5-dimethoxy-2-(β-methylaminoethyl)benzoic acid. When heated in the dry state or with dilute sulfuric acid to 150° it loses formic acid and suffers ring closure to 1-keto-2-methyl-6,7-dimethoxytetrahydroisoquinoline identical with that previously obtained by Pyman (23).

IV. Cryptocavine

This alkaloid has been isolated by the writer from *D. chrysantha* (7), *C. sibirica* (4), *C. ochotensis* Turcz. (25), *Fumaria officinalis* L. (26), and *C. ophiocarpa* Hook. f. et Thoms. (27). It yields a sparingly soluble hydrobromide which salt is useful in its isolation and purification. The free base is sparingly soluble in most solvents. It is however moderately soluble in chloroform and crystallizes in colorless fine prisms, melting at 223°, when the chloroform solution is concentrated to a sirup and treated with hot methanol.

1. Constitution

Cryptocavine is isomeric with cryptopine ($C_{21}H_{23}O_5N$), and like the latter has two methoxyls, one methylenedioxy, and an *N*-methyl, and is optically inactive. It gives the same color reaction with sulfuric acid and melts only 2° higher. A mixture of the two begins to sinter at about 200° and is completely liquid at 205–210°. The analytical figures first obtained did not differentiate between the accepted formula and the next homologue, and it was regarded at one time as a *C*-methylcryptopine. The degradative experiments (28) via the methosulfate and the tetrahydro base obtained therefrom by Emde degradation in the manner described for cryptopine yielded a compound which on dehydration was similar to but not identical with III. When subjected to oxidation this product yielded not the expected 2-methyl-3,4-methylenedioxyacetophenone, but the aldehyde (V), the corresponding acid, and the amino aldehyde (IV)—products identical with those obtained from cryptopine. Since there was no reason to assume the loss of a *C*-methyl group it was obvious that the unsaturated compound had the structure III. Since however its precursor could not be II it was assumed that tetrahydromethylcryptocavine had structure XXVIA,

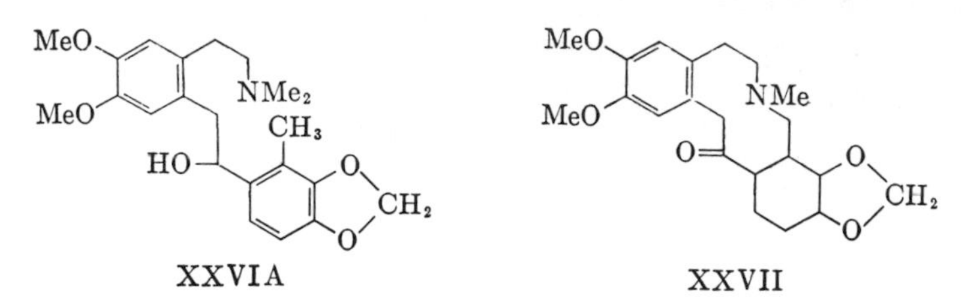

and therefore cryptocavine must be XXVII. That the anhydro compound derived from XXVIA was not identical with III was disconcerting, but explicable because it is capable of existing as cis- and trans-isomers. The structure for cryptocavine is convincing evidence for the suggested biosynthesis of the protopine bases (p. 5), particularly since the ketonic oxygen is in the position which the aliphatic oxygen occupies not only in the phthalideisoquinolines but in ophiocarpine. It should be pointed out that the latter two bases accompany cryptocavine in one plant (27).

2. Synthesis

The correctness of the nuclear structure of cryptopine received final verification in a synthesis achieved by Haworth and Perkin (29). The first stage consisted in the condensation of 3,4-methylenedioxyhomophthalic acid with β-veratrylethylamine to yield the imide, which on partial

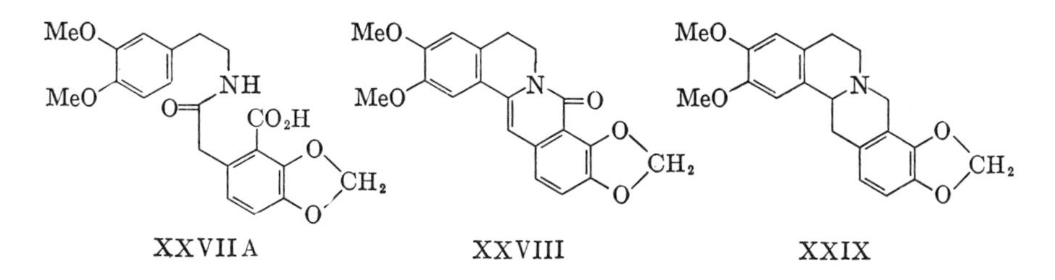

hydrolysis yielded the acid amide XXVIIA, the methyl ester of which on treatment with phosphoryl chloride underwent double ring closure to oxyepiberberine (XXVIII), identical with the compound already prepared from isocryptopine chloride (XVIII) (19) via XXIII and its dehydro derivative by treatment of the last with alkali. Electrolytic reduction of XXVIII in ethanolic sulfuric acid yielded the tetrahydro compound XXIX. The mixture of α- and β-methochlorides (VII) of the latter, obtained via the methiodide, was digested with an aqueous suspension of silver hydroxide and the resulting methohydroxide decomposed by evaporating the aqueous solution *in vacuo* (18) to yield VIII. When the latter was treated in chloroform–ether solution with perbenzoic acid it yielded an amine oxide which when heated with hydrochloric acid in acetic acid isomerized to cryptopine (I) identical in all respects with a specimen of natural origin.

The mechanism of this isomerization is obscure, but it can be assumed that the penultimate intermediate is a compound with two vicinal hydroxyls, formed by the addition of two such groups to the double bond in VIII, dehydration of which could yield either of two vinyl alcohols in which the hydroxyls substitute one or other of hydrogens on the ethylenic carbons. These enols would be expected to ketonize readily, but only one of them could yield cryptopine. The authors (29) do not indicate the yield obtained and failed to report an examination of the mother liquors. It would seem to the writer that such an examination might well have disclosed the presence of the other isomer which is now known as cryptocavine.

Synthesis of 3,4-Methylenedioxyhomophthalic Acid.—When β-3,4-methylenedioxyphenylpropionic acid is dehydrated with phosphorus pentoxide in boiling benzene it yields 5,6-methylenedioxy-1-indanone, which can be converted to 4,5-methylenedioxyhomophthalic acid (XXX) (30). In order to effect ring closure of the indanone ortho to the methylenedioxy group the 6-position of the arylpropionic acid was blocked by a bromine atom

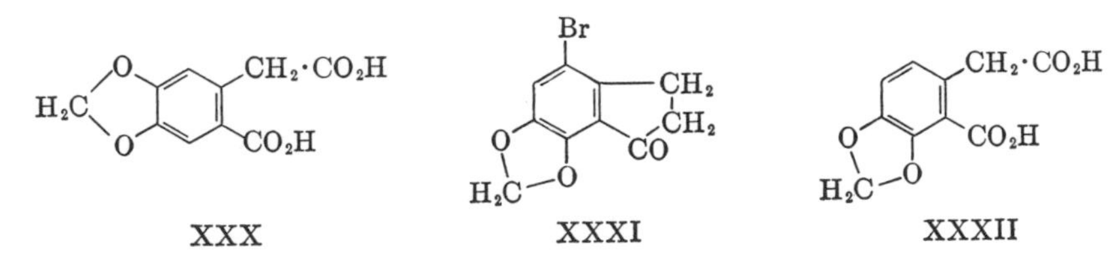

(31). This was accomplished by brominating the acid in acetic acid, and the resulting bromoarylpropionic acid was identical with a specimen prepared from 6-bromopiperonal of known orientation. Ring closure yielded XXXI, which was converted into its isonitroso derivative by the action of methyl nitrite and concentrated hydrochloric acid. Beckmann rearrangement of the latter in the presence of phosphorus pentachloride (32) gave an *o*-carboxyphenylacetonitrile, which on hydrolysis and subsequent reduction with sodium amalgam to eliminate the bromine yielded XXXII.

V. Protopine

1. Occurrence and Properties

Protopine was first isolated from opium by Hesse (33). The amount present is very small and it remained for Danckwortt (13) to find it in *Dicentra spectabilis* in useful quantities. It is without doubt the most widespread of all alkaloids, having been isolated, sometimes as macleyine, fumarine, etc., from the following plants: *Adlumia fungosa* Greene (34), *Argemone mexicana* L. (35), *Bocconia arborea* S. Wats. (36), *B. cordata* Willd. (37), *B. frutescens* L. (38), *Ceratocapnos* spp. (39), *Chelidonium majus*

L. (40), *Corydalis ambigua* Cham. et Sch. (41), *C. aurea* Willd. (42), *C. caseana* A. Gray (43), *C. cheilantheifolia* Hemsl. (44), *C. claviculata* (L.) DC. (45), *C. cornuta* Royle (46), *C. crystallina* Engelm. (47), *C. decumbens* Pers. (48), *C. incisa* (Thunb.) Pers. (49), *C. lutea* (L.) DC. (50), *C. micrantha* (Engelm.) Gray (47), *C. montana* (Engelm.) Britton (51), *C. nobilis* Pers. (52), *C. ochotensis* (25), *C. ophiocarpa* (27), *C. pallida* Pers. (53), *C. platycarpa* Makino (54), *C. scouleri* (3), *C. sempervirens* (2), *C. sibirica* (4), *C. bulbosa* DC. (55), *C. ternata* Nakai (56), *C. thalictrifolia* Franch. (57), *C. tuberosa* DC. (58), *Dactylicapnos macrocapnos* Hutchinson (59), *Dicentra canadensis* (Goldie) Walp. (60), *D. chrysantha* (7), *D. cucullaria* (6), *D. eximia* (Ker) Torr. (61), *D. formosa* Walp. (62), *D. ochroleuca* (7), *D. oregana* Eastwood (63), *D. pusilla* Sieb. et Zucc. (64), *D. spectabilis* Lem. (7), *Dicranostigma franchetianum* (Prain) Fedde (65), *D. lactucoides* Hook. f. et Thoms. (66), *Eschscholtzia californica* Cham. (67), *Fumaria officinalis* (26), *Glaucium corniculatum* Curt. (39), *G. fimbrilligerum* (68), *G. flavum* Crantz. (69), *G. serpieri* Heldr. (70), *Hunnemannia fumariaefolia* Sweet (71), *Hypecoum procumbens* L. (72), *Nandina domestica* (73), *Papaver orientale* L. (74), *Petrocapnos* spp. (39), *Platycapnos* spp. (39), *Sanguinaria canadensis* L. (75), *Sarcocapnos* spp. (39), *Stylophorum diphyllum* Nutt. (70), and *Pteridophyllum racemosum* Sieb. et Zucc. (76). The above references are by no means complete, but those given may be consulted for more complete literature. The writer has also isolated protopine from the following (unpublished): *Cysticapnos vesicarius* (L.) Fedde, *Platycapnos spicatus* (L.) Bernh., *Fumaria capreolata* L., and *Hypecoum leptocarpum*, Hook. f. et Thoms. A review of its known sources to 1912 is given by Danckwortt (13).

2. Constitution

Gadamer (77) and Danckwortt (13) had already recognized the possibility that protopine, $C_{20}H_{19}O_5N$, containing CH_4 less than cryptopine, may be similarly constituted, the only difference being the replacement of two methoxyls in the latter by a methylenedioxy group in the former. Perkin (15, 16) recognized this similarity and demonstrated that many of the characteristic changes which cryptopine undergoes are exhibited by protopine in a similar manner. On this basis alone structure XXXIII

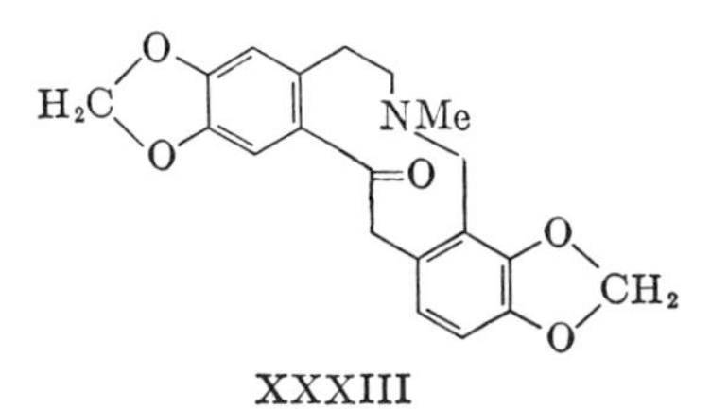

XXXIII

can be formulated for protopine with great assurance. Isoprotopine chloride (XVIII) is readily obtained when the alkaloid is treated with phosphoryl chloride, and this by the action of methanolic potassium hydroxide yields anhydroprotopine (XIX). Similarly, the methosulfate on treatment with alkali gives a separable mixture of α- and γ-methylprotopine (XV and XVI), and dihydroprotopine (VI) on treatment with benzoyl chloride yields isodihydroprotopine chloride (VII).

3. Synthesis

The synthesis of protopine (31) was achieved in a manner strictly analogous to that used for cryptopine. The intermediate analogous to XXVIIA (methylenedioxy group replacing two methoxyls) was obtained from β-3,4-methylenedioxyphenethylamine by condensation with 3,4-methylenedioxyhomophthalic acid and partial hydrolysis of the imide thus formed. The subsequent steps followed those already outlined. Here too, yields in the ultimate step are not recorded and the possibility of forming a cryptocavine analog are not to be overlooked.

VI. Allocryptopine

Allocryptopine, $C_{21}H_{23}O_5N$, like protopine occurs in two allotropic modifications, the α-form melting at 160° and the β-form melting at 170°. The older names of β- and γ-homochelidonine were based upon an assumed relation to chelidonine and are no longer acceptable. It is readily separable from protopine, with which it is nearly always associated, by reason of the fact that its hydrochloride and nitrate are readily soluble in water. It may also be separated from many associated alkaloids by extracting an aqueous solution of their hydrochlorides with chloroform (34). The protopine alkaloids remain in the aqueous phase.

The free alkaloid is sparingly soluble in methanol and readily soluble in chloroform and crystallizes in stout monoclinic prisms when its solution in chloroform is evaporated to a thin resin and dissolved in boiling methanol. The writer has not encountered the higher-melting β-modification.

Allocryptopine has been found in plants outside of the Papaveraceae first by Jowett and Pyman (78) in *Zanthoxylum brachyacanthum* and then in *Z. coco* (79), from the latter of which it was first recorded under the name of α-fagarine (80).

In the Papaveraceae it occurs in the following plants, albeit generally in quantities of the order of 0.1% or less: *Bocconia arborea* (36), *B. cordata* (37), *B. frutescens* (38), *Chelidonium majus* (40), *Corydalis aurea* (42), *C. caseana* (43), *C. cheilantheifolia* (44), *C. ophiocarpa* (27), *C. scouleri* (3), *Dactylicapnos macrocapnos* (59), *Dicentra cucullaria* (6), *D. oregana* (63), *Eschscholtzia californica* (67), *Glaucium fimbrilligerum* (68), *Hunnemannia fumariaefolia* (71), *Sanguinaria canadensis* (75), and *Pteridophyllum racemosum* (76).

1. Constitution

Perkin having recognized certain characteristic reactions for cryptopine and protopine, it remained for Gadamer (81) to demonstrate that the same reactions were also characteristic of allocryptopine. Indeed the formation of dihydroberberine methochloride (VII) from allocryptopine (XXXIV)

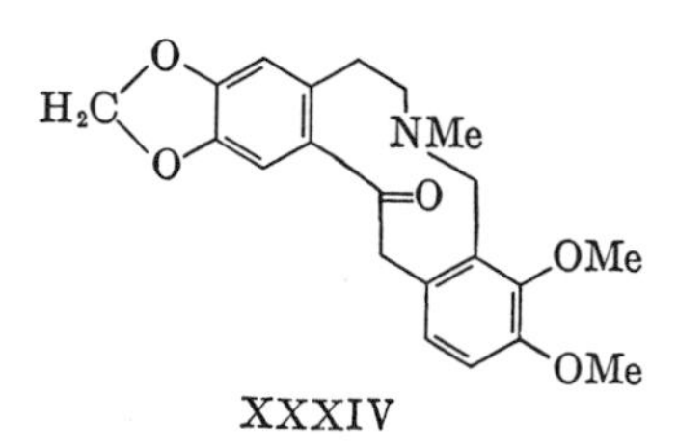

XXXIV

and phosphoryl chloride is only explicable on the formula shown. Its reduction to its dihydro derivative (VI) by sodium amalgam in dilute sulfuric acid and the conversion of the latter into tetrahydroanhydroberberine methochloride (VII) by the action of phosphoryl chloride are further confirmation of its structure.

2. Synthesis

The synthesis of allocryptopine by Haworth and Perkin (82) was the first application of the process already outlined for cryptopine and protopine. This choice was made because the starting material, tetrahydroberberine ((XXIX) with the methylenedioxy and the methoxy groups interchanged) was readily available. Furthermore, Pyman (18) had already made a full investigation of the decomposition of the methohydroxide to VIII. This was converted to the amine oxide, which was isomerized by heating its solution in acetic acid with hydrochloric acid for one hour in boiling water. The synthetic base was identical in all respects with allocryptopine.

VII. Hunnemanine

Hunnemanine, $C_{20}H_{21}O_5N$, has been isolated only from *Hunnemannia fumariaefolia* (71) in which it is present to the extent of 0.18 %. It is readily separable from the associated bases because of its solubility in alkaline solution, from which it is precipitated quantitatively by carbon dioxide, but not well by ammonium chloride.

Hunnemanine crystallizes from chloroform–methanol in stout colorless polyhedra melting at 209°. It is readily soluble in chloroform, sparingly in alcohols, and virtually insoluble in ether and alkanes. When a minute quantity is dissolved in a drop of acetic acid and then treated with sulfuric acid there is developed an immediately deep red-orange color which quickly changes to purple.

1. Constitution

Hunnemanine contains a methylenedioxy group as well as one methoxyl and one phenolic hydroxyl. When methylated with diazomethane in methanolic suspension it gives rise to allocryptopine (XXXIV). It is therefore one of the two possible *O*-desmethylallocryptopines. That it is XXXV in which the hydroxyl occupies the sterically hindered position

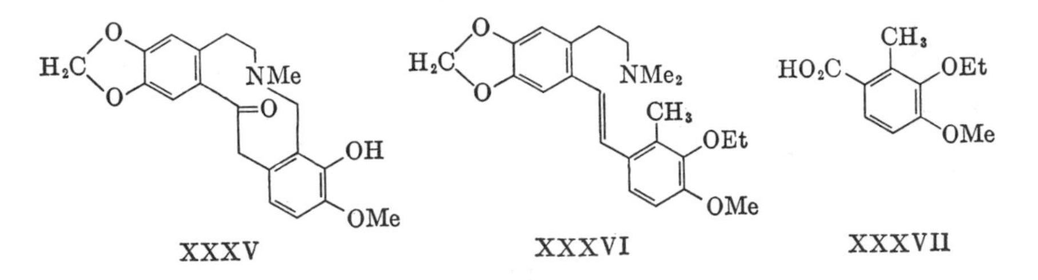

was proved by preparing the *O*-ethyl ether and degrading this to XXXVI by Perkin's method (15) via the methosulfate and the tetrahydro base (analogous to II). The unsaturated compound (XXXVI) on oxidation yielded among other products an acid which was shown to be 2-methyl-3-ethoxy-4-methoxybenzoic acid (XXXVII) by a synthesis. For this purpose 2-ethoxy-3-methoxytoluene was converted into an aldehyde by the Gattermann synthesis. Oxidation of the aldehyde yielded an acid identical with the degradative acid. This observed identity proved not only the structure of the acid but proved that the aldehyde group entered ortho to the methyl. Incidentally, this is added proof of the nuclear structure of allocryptopine.

VIII. Cryptopalmatine

This is the name given to the tetramethoxy analog of cryptopine and allocryptopine by Haworth, Koepfli, and Perkin (83), who synthesized it by the general method (82) from tetrahydropalmatine, involving the compounds VIII and its amine oxide. Cryptopalmatine $C_{22}H_{27}O_5N$, crystallizes from ether in colorless prisms melting at 148–150° and imparts a reddish-violet color to sulfuric acid.

The writer has searched for this alkaloid in vain. It seemed likely that it should be present in *Dicentra cucullaria* (6), which contains cryptopine and allocryptopine along with protopine. An exhaustive search in the mother liquors from these bases derived from 100 kilos of plant material failed thus far to yield it.

IX. Corycavine

1. Properties

Corycavine was first isolated by Freund and Josephi (84) from *Corydalis tuberosa*, but their formula as well as those of Ziegenbein (85) and of Gaebel (86) were in error. It was the formula, $C_{21}H_{21}O_5N$, of Gadamer and von Bruchhausen (87) which indicated a homologous relation to protopine, a relation obscured by the earlier formulas. It crystallizes from hot ethanol in colorless rhombic tablets melting at 221° *in vacuo* and slightly lower (217–218°) in an open tube. The salts crystallize readily and for the most part are sparingly soluble in water (86). The acid oxalate is very sparingly soluble in methanol or in water but sufficiently soluble in hot water to be recrystallized. In the writer's experience it is well suited not only for isolating the alkaloid but for purifying it as well. With sulfuric acid the alkaloid yields a greenish solution which rapidly changes to reddish-violet.

2. Constitution

Gadamer and von Bruchhausen (87), who showed that corycavine contains CH_2 more than protopine, regarded it as a homolog of the latter, and demonstrated that it showed the reaction characteristic of the protopine alkaloids (15). Reduction with sodium amalgam in acid solution yielded dihydrocorycavine, and this as well as the unreduced base on treatment with phosphoryl chloride yielded a quaternary chloride. These compounds are formulated as VII and XVIII, respectively, with a methyl group substituting one of the hydrogens.

Furthermore, the methosulfate of corycavine on reduction with sodium amalgam yielded a tetrahydromethylcorycavine, which on dehydration with acetyl chloride gave rise to an unsaturated compound analogous to III. The position of the methyl group in the anhydro compound and therefore in corycavine (XXXVIII) was determined by oxidizing the former in aqueous suspension with permanganate. In addition to 4,5-methylenedioxy-2-(β-dimethylaminoethyl)benzaldehyde, which was also obtained for

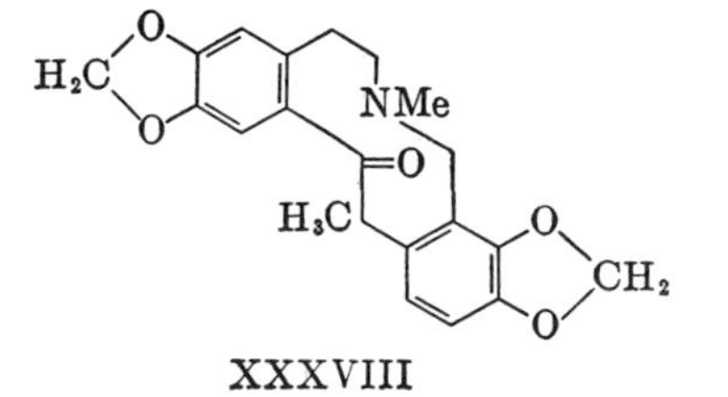

XXXVIII

H₃C
OC
CH₃
O
CH₂
O

XXXIX

the first time from protopine in parallel experiments, there was obtained 2-methyl-3,4-methylenedioxyacetophenone (XXXIX).

X. Corycavamine

Corycavamine was obtained by Gadamer, Ziegenbein, and Wagner (88) from *Corydalis tuberosa*. It was purified by recrystallizing the sparingly soluble nitrate from hot water. The hydrochloride and hydriodide are crystalline and sparingly soluble in water.

The free base, $C_{21}H_{21}O_5N$, crystallizes in rhombs, melting at 147–148°, from alcohol in which it is sparingly soluble, and is optically active, $[\alpha]_D^{20}$ +166.6° (chloroform). It is isomeric with corycavine, and like the latter it contains an *N*-methyl and two methylenedioxy groups. When heated to 180° it becomes optically inactive and is then identical with corycavine. It is therefore assumed that melting has resulted only in racemization about the carbon carrying the methyl group, and corycavamine accordingly is XXXVIII. Von Bruchhausen (89) has suggested that corycavamine is XXXVIII and that corycavine is the enolic form.

XI. Corycavidine

Gadamer (90) obtained a small amount of corycavidine, $C_{22}H_{25}O_5N$, from *Corydalis tuberosa*. It crystallized from hot chloroform in a solvated form, but the chloroform of crystallization is readily lost and the base then melts at 212–213° and is optically active, $[\alpha]_D^{20}$ +203.1° (chloroform). The nitrate and hydrochloride crystallize readily from water, but the latter is more soluble than that of corycavine. Corycavidine like corycavamine when heated (209°) becomes racemized, the racemic modification melting at 193–195°. It dissolves in sulfuric acid to a yellow solution which on warming undergoes a number of color changes ultimately becoming green.

Corycavidine differs by plus CH_4 from corycavine, a difference attributable to the substitution of two methoxyls in the former for a methylenedioxy group in the latter. Indeed only in one respect does corycavidine not give the reactions characteristic of the protopine alkaloids—namely, it is not converted into a quaternary chloride by the action of acetyl chloride under the usual conditions (89).

However, its methosulfate when reduced with sodium amalgam in dilute sulfuric acid yields tetrahydromethylcorycavidine (analogous to II), which is dehydrated to its anhydro compound (analogous to III) by evaporation with dilute hydrochloric acid. This anhydro compound when oxidized with permanganate in acetone solution yielded among related products 4,5-methylenedioxy-2-(β-dimethylaminoethyl)benzaldehyde and 2-methyl-3,4-dimethoxyacetophenone (XLI). Formula XL is therefore ascribable

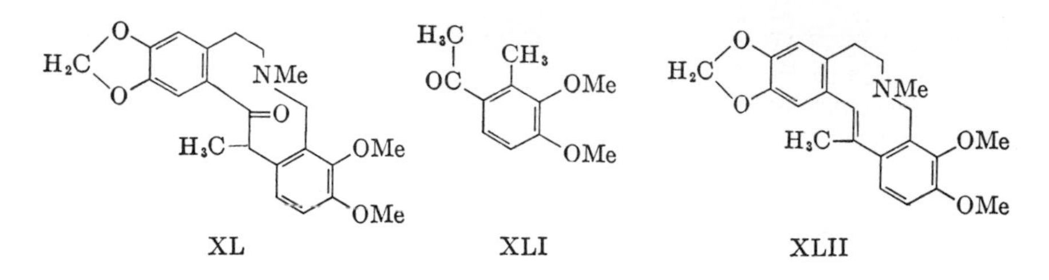

to corycavidine. Confirmation of the assigned structure was obtained by first reducing corycavidine to its dihydro derivative (m.p. 147–148°), which in contrast to the parent alkaloid readily yielded the quaternary chloride, isodihydrocorycavidine chloride (analogous to VII) on reaction with acetyl chloride. The quaternary chloride on digestion with methanolic potassium hydroxide yielded the compound XLII (m.p. 160–161°).

The compound XLII was prepared from berberine by the method of Freund and Fleischer (91), which consists in first reacting dihydroberberine with methyl iodide. A methyl group enters the position corresponding to that in XLII. This 4-methyldihydroberberine (yellow prisms) (m.p. 121–133°) on reduction yielded the tetrahydro compound, which on treatment with methyl iodide and subsequently with methanolic alkali (cf. isocryptopine chloride) gave XLII.

The ketone XLI (m.p. 70–71°; semicarbazone, m.p. 235–236°) was prepared in good yield by the Friedel-Crafts reaction of acetyl chloride on 2,3-dimethoxytoluene.

Von Bruchhausen (89) also isolated a small amount of racemic corycavidine, m.p. 193–194°, from a slightly impure base which Gadamer (90) had obtained from *C. tuberosa*.

XII. References

1. J. Smiles, *Pharm. J.*, [2]**8**, 595 (1867).
2. R. H. F. Manske, *Can. J. Research*, **8**, 407 (1933).
3. R. H. F. Manske, *Can. J. Research*, **14B**, 347 (1936).
4. R. H. F. Manske, *Can. J. Research*, **14B**, 354 (1936).
5. R. H. F. Manske, *Can. J. Research*, **18B**, 288 (1940).,
6. R. H. F. Manske, *Can. J. Research*, **7**, 265 (1932).
7. R. H. F. Manske, *Can. J. Research*, **15B**, 274 (1937).
8. R. S. A. Heathcote, *J. Pharmacol.*, **25**, 35 (1925).
9. F. Mercier, *Compt. rend. soc. biol.*, **127**, 1018 (1938).
10. F. Mercier, J. Delphaut, and P. Blache, *Compt. rend. soc. biol.*, **127**, 1022 (1938).
11. F. P. Ludueña, *Rev. soc. argentina biol.*, **14**, 339 (1938).
12. A. Pictet and G. H. Kramers, *Ber.*, **43**, 1329 (1910).
13. P. W. Danckwortt, *Arch. Pharm.*, **250**, 590 (1912).
14. D. R. Brown and W. H. Perkin, Jr., *Proc. Chem. Soc.*, **7**, 166 (1891).
15. W. H. Perkin, Jr., *J. Chem. Soc.*, **109**, 815–1028 (1916).
16. W. H. Perkin, Jr., *J. Chem. Soc.*, **115**, 713–790 (1919).

17. A. Voss and J. Gadamer, *Arch. Pharm.*, **248,** 43 (1910).
18. F. L. Pyman, *J. Chem. Soc.*, **103,** 817 (1913).
19. W. H. Perkin, Jr., *J. Chem. Soc.*, **113,** 492 (1918).
20. K. Goto and Z. Kitasato, *J. Chem. Soc.*, **1930,** 1234.
21. E. Späth and E. Mosettig, *Ber.*, **64,** 2048 (1931).
22. G. Barger, *J. Chem. Soc.*, **93,** 563 (1908).
23. F. L. Pyman, *J. Chem. Soc.*, **95,** 1266 (1909).
24. M. Freund, *Ber.*, **22,** 2329 (1889).
25. R. H. F. Manske, *Can. J. Research*, **18B,** 75 (1940).
26. R. H. F. Manske, *Can. J. Research*, **16B,** 438 (1938).
27. R. H. F. Manske, *Can. J. Research*, **17B,** 51 (1939).
28. R. H. F. Manske and L. Marion, *J. Am. Chem. Soc.*, **62,** 2042 (1940).
29. R. D. Haworth and W. H. Perkin, Jr., *J. Chem. Soc.*, **1926,** 1769.
30. W. H. Perkin, Jr. and R. Robinson, *J. Chem. Soc.*, **91,** 1073 (1907).
31. R. D. Haworth, W. H. Perkin, Jr., and T. S. Stevens, *J. Chem. Soc.*, **1926,** 1764.
32. R. D. Haworth and H. S. Pink, *J. Chem. Soc.*, **127,** 1368 (1925).
33. O. Hesse, *Ber.*, **4,** 693 (1871).
34. R. H. F. Manske, *Can. J. Research*, **8,** 210 (1933).
35. A. C. Santos and P. Adkilen, *J. Am. Chem. Soc.*, **54,** 2923 (1932).
36. R. H. F. Manske, *Can. J. Research*, **21B,** 140 (1943).
37. P. Murrill and J. O. Schlotterbeck, *Ber.*, **33,** 2802 (1900).
38. E. R. Miller, *J. Am. Pharm. Assoc.*, **18,** 12 (1929).
39. J. A. Battandier, *Compt. rend.*, **114,** 1122 (1892).
40. F. Selle, *Arch. Pharm.*, **228,** 441 (1890).
41. K. Makoshi, *Arch. Pharm.*, **246,** 381 (1908).
42. R. H. F. Manske, *Can. J. Research*, **9,** 436 (1933).
43. R. H. F. Manske and M. R. Miller, *Can. J. Research*, **16B,** 153 (1938).
44. R. H. F. Manske, *Can. J. Research*, **20B,** 57 (1942).
45. R. H. F. Manske, *Can. J. Research*, **18B,** 97 (1940).
46. R. H. F. Manske, *Can. J. Research*, **24B,** 66 (1946).
47. R. H. F. Manske, *Can. J. Research*, **17B,** 57 (1939).
48. Y. Asahina and S. Motigase, *J. Pharm. Soc. Japan*, **No. 463,** 766 (1920).
49. R. H. F. Manske, *J. Am. Chem. Soc.*, **72,** 3207 (1950).
50. R. H. F. Manske, *Can. J. Research*, **17B,** 89 (1939).
51. R. H. F. Manske, *Can. J. Research*, **20B,** 49 (1942).
52. R. H. F. Manske, *Can. J. Research*, **18B,** 288 (1940).
53. R. H. F. Manske, *Can. J. Research*, **18B,** 80 (1940).
54. R. H. F. Manske, *Can. J. Research*, **21B,** 13 (1943).
55. O. Haars, *Arch. Pharm.*, **243,** 154 (1905).
56. J. Go, *J. Pharm. Soc. Japan*, **49,** 801 (1929).
57. R. H. F. Manske, *Can. J. Research*, **21B,** 111 (1943).
58. J. Gadamer, *Arch. Pharm.*, **249,** 224 (1911).
59. R. H. F. Manske, *Can. J. Research*, **21B,** 117 (1943).
60. R. H. F. Manske, *Can. J. Research*, **7,** 258 (1932).
61. R. H. F. Manske, *Can. J. Research*, **8,** 592 (1933).
62. R. H. F. Manske, *Can. J. Research*, **10,** 521 (1934).
63. R. H. F. Manske, *Can. J. Research*, **10,** 765 (1934).
64. Y. Asahina, *Arch. Pharm.*, **247,** 201 (1909).
65. R. H. F. Manske, *Can. J. Research*, **20B,** 53 (1942).
66. R. H. F. Manske, unpublished data.
67. R. Fischer, *Arch. Pharm.*, **239,** 421 (1901).

68. R. A. Konovalova, S. Junusov, and A. P. Orekhov, *J. Gen. Chem.* (*U.S.S.R*), **9**, 1939 (1939).
69. R. H. F. Manske, *Can. J. Research*, **17B**, 399 (1939).
70. R. H. F. Manske, *Can. J. Research*, **20B**, 53 (1942).
71. R. H. F. Manske, L. Marion, and A. E. Ledingham, *J. Am. Chem. Soc.*, **64**, 1659 (1942).
72. E. Schmidt, *Arch. Pharm.*, **239**, 395 (1901).
73. T. Ohta, *J. Pharm. Soc. Japan*, **69**, 502 (1949).
74. W. Klee, *Arch. Pharm.*, **252**, 211 (1914).
75. G. König and W. Tietz, *Arch. Pharm.*, **231**, 145 (1893).
76. K. Kohei and Y. Ando, *J. Pharm. Soc. Japan*, **71**, 625 (1951).
77. J. Gadamer, Habilitations Schrift, Breslau, 1912, p. 25.
78. H. A. D. Jowett and F. L. Pyman, *J. Chem. Soc.*, **103**, 290 (1913).
79. C. E. Redemann, B. B. Wisegarver, and G. A. Alles, *J. Am. Chem. Soc.*, **71**, 1030 (1949).
80. V. Deulofeu, R. Labriola, and J. DeLanghe, *J. Am. Chem. Soc.*, **64**, 2326 (1942).
81. J. Gadamer, *Arch. Pharm.*, **257**, 298 (1919).
82. R. D. Haworth and W. H. Perkin, Jr., *J. Chem. Soc.*, **1926**, 445.
83. R. D. Haworth, J. B. Koepfli, and W. H. Perkin, Jr., *J. Chem. Soc.*, **1927**, 2261.
84. M. Freund and W. Josephi, *Ann.*, **277**, 1 (1893).
85. H. Ziegenbein, *Arch. Pharm.*, **234**, 492 (1896).
86. G. O. Gaebel, *Arch. Pharm.*, **248**, 207 (1910).
87. J. Gadamer and F. von Bruchhausen, *Arch. Pharm.*, **260**, 97 (1922).
88. J. Gadamer, H. Ziegenbein, and H. Wagner, *Arch. Pharm.*, **240**, 81 (1902).
89. F. von Bruchhausen, *Arch. Pharm.*, **263**, 570 (1925).
90. J. Gadamer, *Arch. Pharm.*, **249**, 30 (1911).
91. M. Freund and K. Fleischer, *Ann.*, **409**, 188 (1915).

CHAPTER 32

Phthalideisoquinoline Alkaloids

JAROSLAV STANEK

Charles University, Praha, Czechoslovakia, and

R. H. F. MANSKE,

Dominion Rubber Research Laboratory, Guelph, Ontario

	Page
I. Introduction	168
II. Constitution	169
1. Narcotine	169
2. Cotarnine	170
3. Opianic Acid	172
4. Narcotoline	173
5. Hydrastine	173
6. Adlumine and Corlumine	176
7. Corlumidine	177
8. Bicuculline, Capnoidine, and Adlumidine	178
9. Bicucine	178
10. Cordrastine	178
11. Narceine	179
12. Nornarceine	179
III. Syntheses	180
1. Narcotine	180
2. Hydrastine	181
3. Bicuculline	182
4. Adlumine	183
IV. Discovery, Isolation, and Properties	183
1. *l*-α-Narcotine	183
2. α-Gnoscopine	184
3. β-Gnoscopine	185
4. Narcotoline	185
5. Hydrastine	185
6. *dl*-α-Hydrastine	186
7. *dl*-β-Hydrastine	187
8. Bicuculline	187
9. Adlumidine	188
10. Capnoidine	188
11. Adlumine	188
12. Corlumine	189
13. Corlumidine	189
V. Physiology and Pharmacology	189
VI. References	190

I. Introduction

The term phthalideisoquinoline is applied to a group of eleven known alkaloids which are all derived from the parent substance I by the substitu-

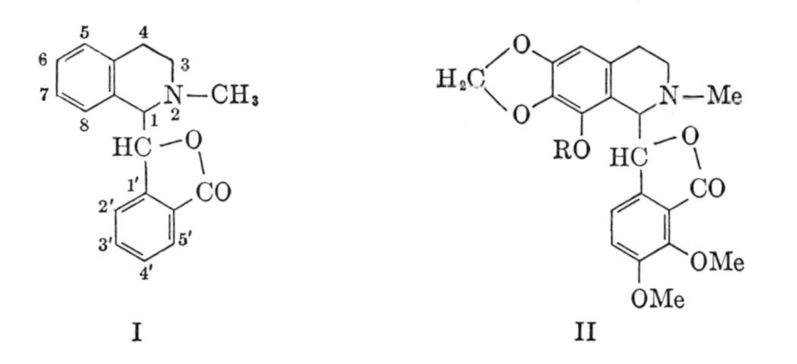

I II

tion of a hydroxyl or methoxyl at position 8, and/or methoxyl and methylenedioxy groups at positions 6, 7, 4′, and 5′. The nitrogen at position 2 always has a methyl group, and in one example (corlumidine) there is a hydroxyl at position 7. Those so far known are narcotine (II, R = Me), narcotoline (II, R = H), hydrastine (III), bicuculline (IV), capnoidine

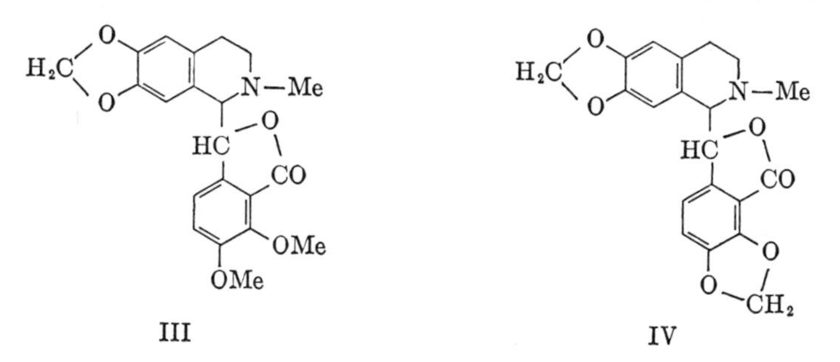

III IV

(IV), adlumidine (IV), *d*- and *l*-adlumine (V, R = Me), corlumine (V, R = Me), corlumidine (V, R = H), and cordrastine (VI). Gnoscopine

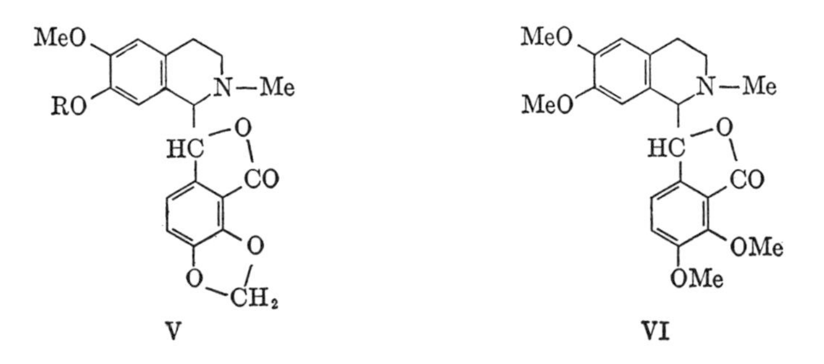

V VI

is *dl*-narcotine and has been isolated from opium, but, in view of the facile racemization of narcotine, there is the possibility that gnoscopine may be an artifact.

The alkaloids narceine (VII) and hydroxynarcotine (nornarceine) (VIII)

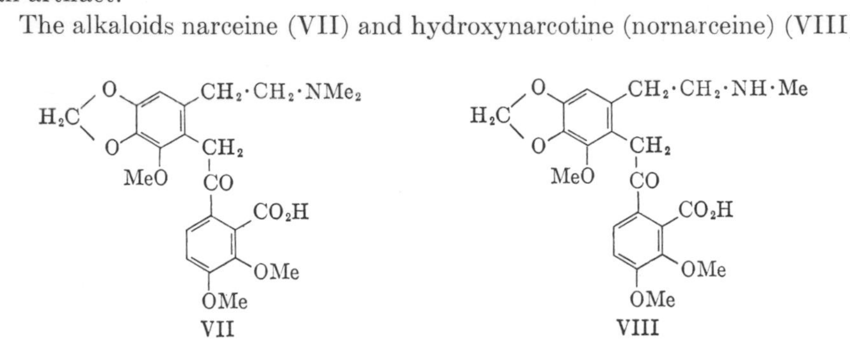

are derivable from narcotine by simple reactions and probably occur as such in opium, but they are not phthalideisoquinolines. With the exception of hydrastine, which has been found only in plants of the Ranunculaceae and Berberidaceae families, all of the phthalideisoquinolines have been found in plants of the Papaveraceae family. Reviews on this group have been published (1, 2, 3).

II. Constitution

The determination of the structure of a new phthalideisoquinoline at present has become such a simple problem that it can be considered to be a routine procedure. This is due to the fact that mild oxidative scission results in two fragments which contain all of the carbon atoms of the alkaloid as well as the nitrogen. There remains only the identification of these fragments, and at the present time most of these have become known substances. This state of knowledge, however, had not been realized at the time that work was started on narcotine and hydrastine, the structures of the two respective fragments having to be determined as part of the problem. The work which led to the structures of these two alkaloids will therefore be presented in some detail.

1. Narcotine

There are three closely related reactions by which narcotine may be cleaved into two fragments which still contain all of the carbon atoms. Wöhler (4) observed that when narcotine is heated in dilute sulfuric acid it yields two substances, a base, cotarnine, and an acid, opianic acid. Hydrolysis with water at 150° or with boiling dilute acids results in hydrocotarnine and opianic acid, whereas heating with zinc and hydrochloric or sulfuric acid generates hydrocotarnine and meconin. These reactions are restated in the following diagram.

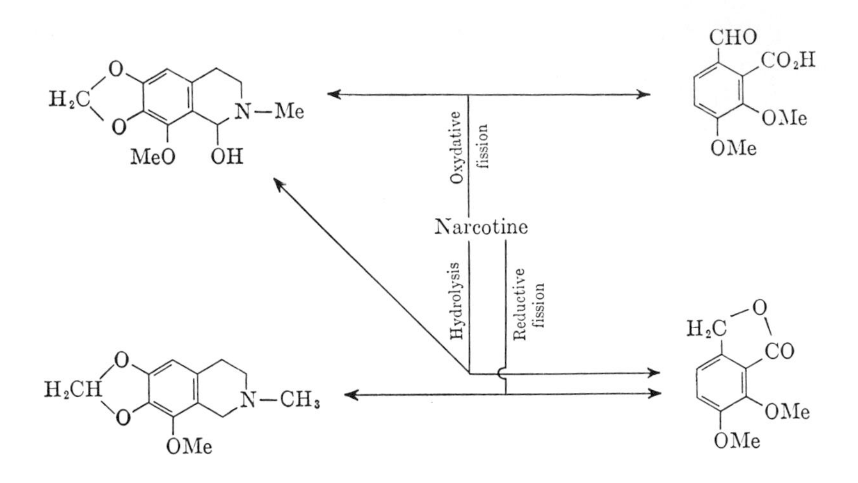

It is evident that formula II (R = Me) adequately accounts for the above reactions (5), and a subsequent synthesis (6) amply confirms it. The lactone group persists in narcotine as shown by its reactions with alkali. Only after prolonged warming in alcoholic alkali is an alkali salt formed, and this rapidly regenerates narcotine on acidification. The crux of the problem resolved itself into determining the structure of the fission products.

2. Cotarnine

This base, $C_{12}H_{15}O_4N$, m.p. 132°, which was first obtained by Wöhler (4) may also be prepared from narcotine by dilute nitric acid oxidation (7–12) as well as by chromic acid or by permanganate (13). The free base is colorless but the salts are yellow. It contains one methoxyl group, a methylenedioxy group, and an *N*-methyl, and on reduction yields hydrocotarnine, $C_{12}H_{15}O_3N$.

Oxidation of cotarnine by permanganate yields cotarnic acid (14), $C_8H_6O_3(COOH)_2$, m.p. 178°, which must be an *o*-dicarboxylic acid since it readily forms an anhydride. This acid on heating with hydriodic acid and red phosphorus yields gallic acid, and therefore the alkoxy groups are vicinal in cotarnine but their positions remained to be established (5). Cotarnine reacts with aniline as though it were an aromatic aldehyde to yield an anil (15), which reacts with methyl iodide to form a quaternary salt, which in turn when heated with hydrochloric acid loses the *O*-methyl group and the aniline moiety yielding a substance which now can be formulated as IX. That the methoxyl was ortho to the aldehyde follows

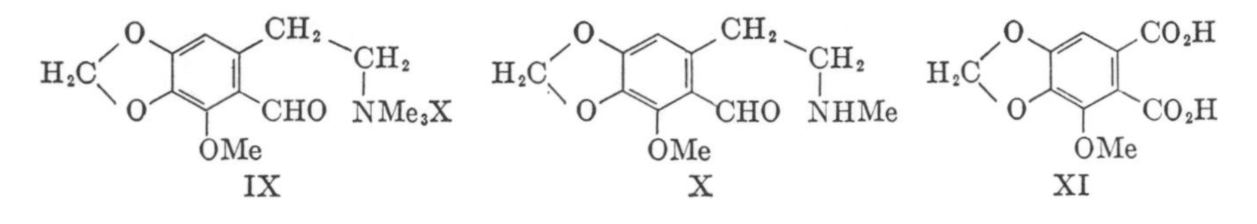

by analogy with the similar behavior of *o*-methoxybenzaldehyde anil (but not that of anisaldehyde), which yields *o*-hydroxybenzaldehyde when first treated with methyl iodide and then hydrolyzed with hydrochloric acid. Cotarnine can therefore be written as X, and cotarnic acid should be XI. A synthesis of cotarnic acid confirmed this structure as follows (16): 5,6-Methylenedioxy-1-indanone (XII) was nitrated, the nitro group entering position 7, that is ortho to the carbonyl—but for the present purpose

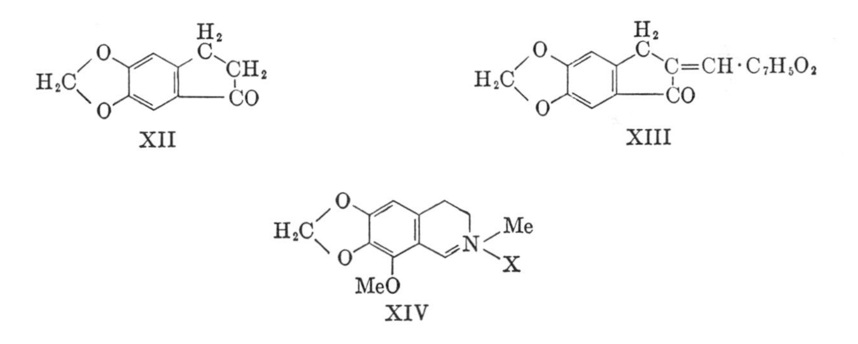

its position of entry being unimportant—, the nitro group replaced by a hydroxyl via the amino group, and the hydroxyl was then methylated. The condensation of the methoxy compound with piperonal yielded an unsaturated compound (XIII) which on oxidation gave cotarnic acid (XI).

Cotarnine reacts with methyl iodide as though it were a secondary base, there being formed a mixture of cotarnine hydriodide, more properly, cotarninium iodide, and methylcotarnine methiodide. Roser (14) therefore suggested that cotarnine is X and that its yellow salts are quaternary ring compounds representable by XIV, thus accounting for the loss of water in salt formation. Decker (17) preferred the carbinolamine structure XV, since he argued that the secondary amine and the aldehyde functions

are not likely to coexist in such a favorable spatial arrangement without reacting. Electrical conductivity measurements of aqueous solutions of cotarnine indicate that at least two species are present (18), and these could be represented by X and XV. A third form may be XIV (X = OH). Ultraviolet absorption spectra (19) do not show evidence of structure X. The solid cotarnine and its solutions in non-hydrolytic solvents are satisfactorily represented by XV, but in hydrolytic solvents it exists largely in the form of XIV (X = OH). That the salts are true cyclic compounds follows from the observation that cotarnine when oxidized with nitric acid yields apophyllenic acid (20). The nature of this acid as an *N*-methylpyridinium compound (XVI) was recognized by von Gerichten (21), and its synthesis was achieved by Roser (22) by heating a mixture of methyl iodide and cinchomeronic acid (pyridine-3,4-dicarboxylic acid) in methanol at 100°.

A synthesis of cotarnine was finally recorded by Salway (23) who, starting from β-(3-methoxy-4,5-methylenedioxyphenyl)propionic acid (24), converted this through its amide to β-3-methoxy-4,5-methylenedioxyphenethylamine. The last was converted into its phenylacetyl derivative, which was then cyclized with phosphoric oxide to a mixture of two isoquinolines (XVII and XVIII) which were separated as their respective

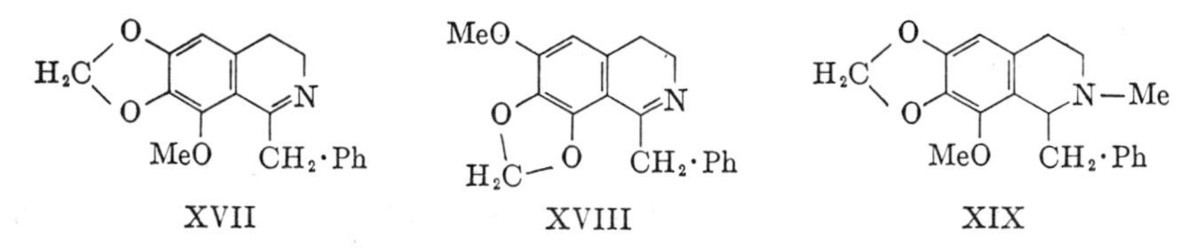

hydrochlorides (m.p. 192° and 174°). The methochloride of the former (XVII) was reduced with tin and hydrochloric acid to 1-benzylhydrocotarnine (XIX), and this when oxidized with manganese dioxide in dilute sulfuric acid yielded cotarnine (XV).

The isomeric dihydroisoquinoline (XVIII) was also taken through a parallel series of reactions and gave rise to an isomer of cotarnine, namely, neocotarnine (XX), m.p. 124°.

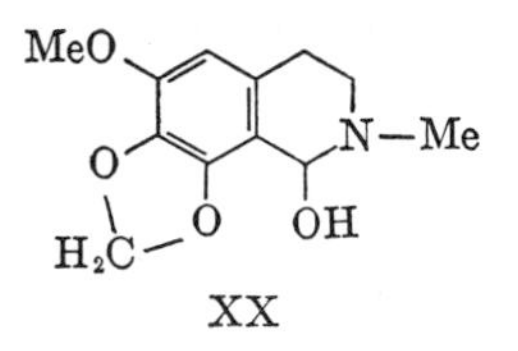

3. Opianic Acid

Opianic acid, m.p. 145°, is an *o*-aldehydo carboxylic acid which on oxidation yields hemipinic acid (XXI), and on reduction it gives rise to

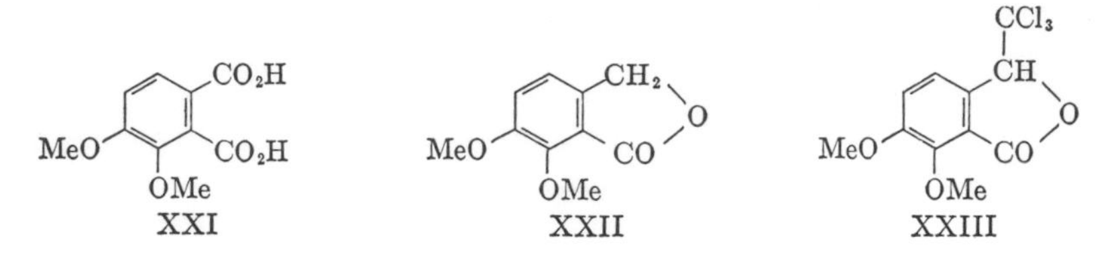

meconin (XXII), m.p. 102°, a constituent of opium (25) and of *Hydrastis canadensis* L. (26). The first synthesis of meconin is that of Fritsch (27), who condensed methyl 2,3-dimethoxybenzoate with chloral in the presence of sulfuric acid. The trichloromethylmeconin (XXIII) thus obtained was heated with alkali to hydrolyze the trichloromethyl group to a carboxyl, and when the resulting hydroxy dicarboxylic acid was decomposed by cautious heating meconin was obtained as a sublimate. A much more direct and useful synthesis was achieved by heating 2,3-dimethoxybenzoic acid with formaldehyde and concentrated hydrochloric acid (28). These syntheses of meconin are also syntheses of opianic acid. The former can be oxidized to opianic acid in almost quantitative yield by heating with manganese dioxide in 10% sulfuric acid (29).

4. Narcotoline

This alkaloid is monophenolic and on methylation with diazomethane gives rise to narcotine. Hydrolytic fission with dilute acetic acid yields meconin, and therefore the hydroxyl is in the isoquinoline nucleus and narcotoline is II (R = H).

5. Hydrastine

The correct empirical formula, $C_{21}H_{21}O_6N$, was proposed by Eijkman (30) and by Freund and Will (31) following earlier ones by Mahla (32) and Power (33). Oxidative fission yields opianic acid (31, 34, 35) and a new base, hydrastinine, $C_{11}H_{13}O_3N$, m.p. 116–117°, but, unlike narcotine, hydrastine does not suffer hydrolysis when heated with water or dilute sulfuric acid at 200° (36) and is not cleaved by reducing agents such as zinc or tin and hydrochloric acid or sodium amalgam (35).

Oxidative Fission of Hydrastine (37). Hydrastine (1 g.) is dissolved in a mixture of nitric acid (sp. gr. 1.42) (2 ml.) and water (8 ml.) and the solution maintained at 75° for 20 min. To the cold solution a strong aqueous solution of potassium hydroxide is added until strongly alkaline when hydrastinine (0.4 g.) separates in the crystalline condition. It may be recrystallized from dry ether.

The chemical reactions of hydrastinine bear the closest analogy to those of cotarnine. It is colorless as free base or in non-hydrolytic solvents, but in hydrolytic solvents it is yellow and fluorescent as are its salts which are formed by the loss of a molecule of water and are properly named hydrastinium salts. Like cotarnine it reacts with carbonyl reagents forming, for example, an oxime and with acetic anhydride or with benzoyl chloride it yields derivatives characteristic of a secondary base. These reactions, together with the observation that oxidation leads to hydrastic acid (XXIV), m.p. 175°, led Roser (38) to propose formula XXV for hydrastinine. Added support for this formula is found in the fact that treatment

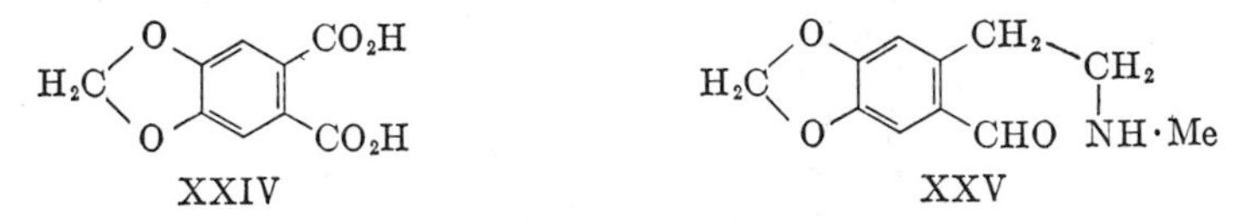

of hydrastinine with strong alkali (Cannizzaro) brings about an oxidation-reduction reaction and gives rise to hydrohydrastinine (XXVI), m.p. 66°, and oxyhydrastinine (XXVII), m.p. 97–98° (39), which were presumed to be formed by ring closure of the corresponding carbinol and carboxylic acid

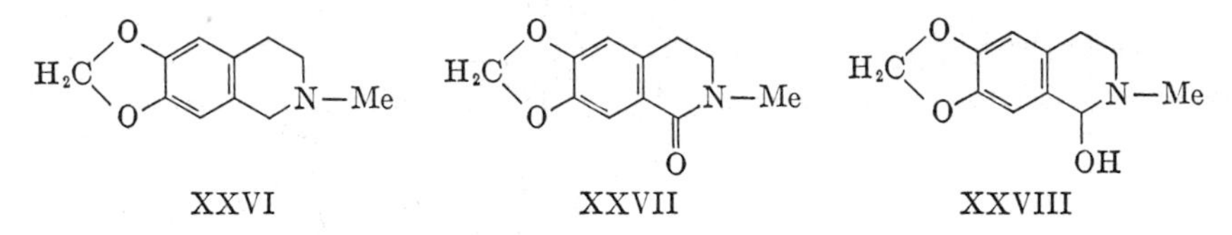

intermediates. Hydrohydrastinine is also readily obtainable by reducing hydrastinine with zinc and hydrochloric acid (34), whereas oxidation with nitric acid yields apophyllenic acid (XVI). It should be pointed out that the dismutation referred to above does not necessarily require a free aldehyde group (40), and hydrastinine is satisfactorily represented by XXVIII (41) whereas its salts are analogous to those of cotarnine (XIV) (42). It should be pointed out that the position of the methylenedioxy group in hydrastine follows from the structure of hydrastic acid (XXIV), which can be converted into bisnormetahemipinic acid (43) and which, however, was not synthesized until 1907 (44). For this purpose 5,6-methylenedioxy-1-indanone was first prepared by cyclizing β-(3,4-methylenedioxyphenyl)-propionic acid with phosphoric oxide in benzene. The ketone on oxidation with dilute nitric acid readily yielded hydrastic acid. A later synthesis was described by Stevens and Robertson (45).

The synthesis of hydrastinine itself was first accomplished by Fritsch (46). Aminoacetal was condensed with piperonal and the product (XXIX) cyclized by treatment for ten days at 0° with 72% sulfuric acid which had

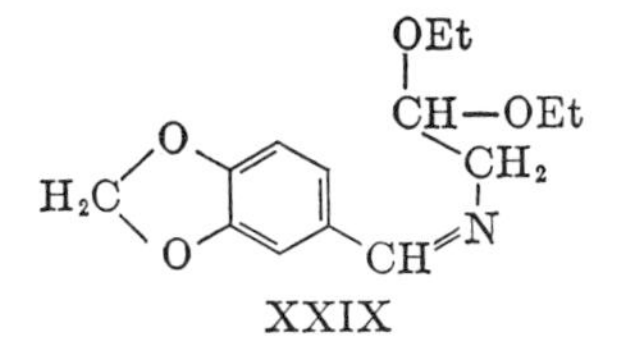

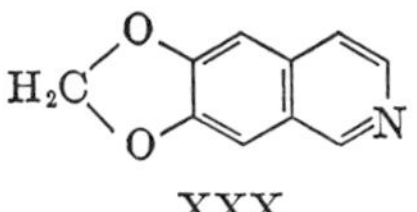

been saturated with hydrogen chloride. The resultant isoquinoline (XXX) obtained in 23% yield was converted into its methiodide, which was then reduced with tin and hydrochloric acid. The resulting base was identical with hydrohydrastinine (XXVI), which had already been reconverted to hydrastinine (39).

There have been recorded a number of other syntheses of hydrohydrastinine, some of which are in the patent literature, but most of them depend upon the formation of the isoquinoline ring from β-3,4-methylenedioxyphenethylamine or of its *N*-methyl derivative (47, 48) or upon the *N*-methylation of norhydrohydrastinine (49). When the above phenethylamine as its hydrochloride is heated with aqueous formaldehyde in a sealed tube for three hours at 130° it generates hydrohydrastinine in 88% yield (50). There takes place not only the now well-known ring closure of the isoquinoline, but also the *N*-methylation reaction studied in detail by Hess, Merck, and Uibrig (51, 52).

The preparation of hydrohydrastine from hydrocotarnine by sodium–alcohol reduction (53) is another example of the many in which this reduction serves to replace a methoxyl in derivatives of pyrogallol trimethyl ethers with hydrogen (54, 55). The yield is about 40%. The by-products formed were thoroughly investigated and were mostly derived from the action of the reducing reagents on the methylenedioxy group, which suffered scission to yield phenols. The four possible compounds—6-hydroxy-, 7-hydroxy-, 6-hydroxy-8-methoxy-, and 7-hydroxy-8-methoxy-*N*-methyltetrahydroisoquinoline—were isolated and characterized. The first two were shown to result from the intermediate hydrohydrastine, while the last two were formed from the hydrocotarnine without the prior elimination of the methoxyl.

There is considerable interest in a number of other reactions of hydrastinine which are characteristic of carbinolamines of this type. It reacts with methyl iodide in indifferent solvents to yield a mixture of hydrastinium iodide and methylhydrastine methiodide (56), which when warmed with alkali generates trimethylamine and hydrastal (XXXI), the oxidation of which yields hydrastic acid. In methanol, hydrastinine reacts with methyl

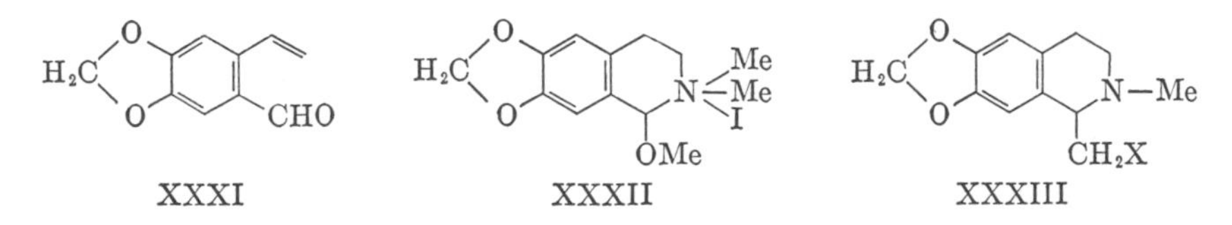

iodide to yield XXXII. This reaction was one of the first known examples of the reactivity of the hydroxyl group in carbinolamines of the type here discussed. Not only do these compounds form ethers with great ease, but they react with a large variety of compounds, CH_3X, having an active methylene group, the product of the reaction with acetone being XXXIII ($X = CO \cdot CH_3$) (57). The reaction product with nitromethane, XXXIII ($X = NO_2$), m.p. 121–122° (42), is useful for characterizing hydrastinine. These compounds, however, are often unstable to acids, and the last mentioned on treatment with picric acid regenerates nitromethane and yields hydrastinine picrate, m.p. 173° (58). It is due to the reactivity of these carbinolamines that a relatively simple synthesis of the phthalide-isoquinolines was possible.

The evident close relation between hydrastine and berberine and their copresence in plants has often been a matter of comment. It is, therefore, of more than passing interest that the former is convertible into the latter by chemical means (59), although in the authors' opinion the biosynthesis of hydrastine is by way of berberine or canadine. When hydrastine is reduced with lithium aluminum hydride, a glycol (XXXIIIA), m.p. 142°, is obtained

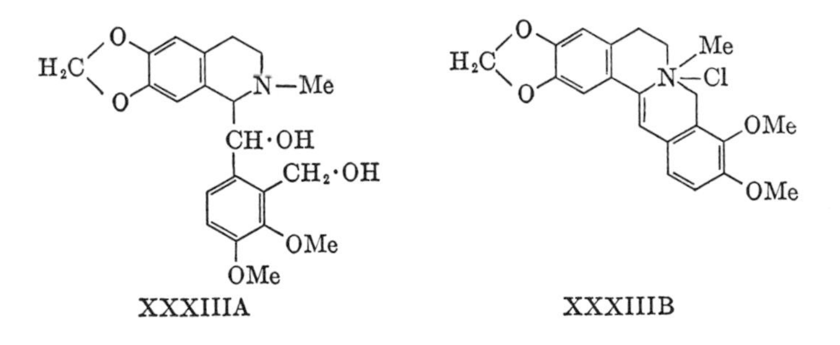

which is convertible by the action of thionyl chloride into dihydroanhydroberberinium methochloride (XXXIIIB), which in turn on heating *in vacuo* at 160–170° generates methyl chloride and yields dihydroanhydroberberine. Ring closure in this instance with the resultant quaternary salt formation was accompanied by the elimination of the secondary hydroxyl (XXXIIIA) as water, so that alkaloids of the type of ophiocarpine were not accessible by this route.

6. Adlumine and Corlumine

These alkaloids, $C_{21}H_{21}O_6N$, are isomeric with hydrastine and have been shown to be stereoisomeric but not optical antipodes. Owing to the presence of two asymmetric centers in the molecule, four optically active forms are possible. Two of these are the naturally occurring *d*- and *l*-adlumines and the third is corlumine. That they all have the structure V (R = Me) was shown by the observation that they all yield 1-hydroxy-2-methyl-5,6-dimethoxytetrahydroisoquinoline (XXXIV) (60) (lodal) and 2-carboxy-3,4-methylenedioxybenzaldehyde (XXXV) on hydrolytic oxidation with

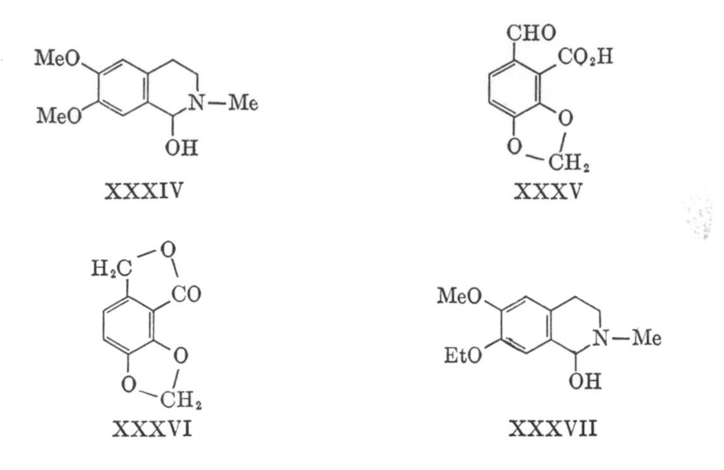

XXXIV XXXV XXXVI XXXVII

dilute nitric acid (61–64). The isoquinoline fragment, m.p. 123–124°, was characterized by its own properties (picrate, m.p. 170°), and by conversion to its two dismutation products on treatment with alkali, namely, 1-keto-2-methyl-6,7-dimethoxytetrahydroisoquinoline, m.p. 126°, and 2-methyl-6,7-dimethoxytetrahydroisoquinoline, m.p. 84°.

The acidic scission product was a new compound, but it was easily convertible into the phthalide (XXXVI) either by reduction with sodium amalgam or by heating with alkali. The phthalide had already been synthesized (65).

7. Corlumidine

Corlumidine, $C_{20}H_{19}O_6N$, is phenolic and on methylation yields corlumine. It must therefore have one of two possible structures. The *O*-ethyl ether on hydrolytic scission yields the phthalide (XXXVI) and a base (XXXVII) (picrate, m.p. 181°) whose identity was established by a synthesis. Corlumidine therefore is V (R = H) (63). The synthesis of XXXVII was accomplished by a reaction which, with this group of compounds, is well known and which provides convincing proof of the structure of their salts (cf. XIV). The dihydroisoquinoline (XXXVIII) (66) was

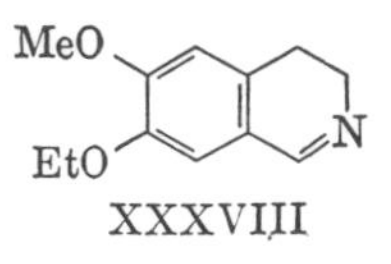

XXXVIII

converted into its methiodide, and the latter on treatment with strong alkali suffered the shift of the resultant hydroxyl and yielded XXXVII.

8. Bicuculline, Capnoidine, and Adlumidine

Bicuculline, capnoidine, and adlumidine, $C_{20}H_{17}O_6N$, are three stereoisomers, the last two being optical antipodes. Their structures (IV) follow from the observation that they all yield hydrastinine and the aldehyde XXXV on dilute nitric acid oxidation (67, 68). Equal weights of capnoidine and adlumidine when mixed and recrystallized yielded an apparently homogeneous compound which is the *dl*-form.

9. Bicucine

Bicucine, $C_{20}H_{19}O_7N \cdot H_2O$, is the name given to a substance frequently encountered along with bicuculline. There is no evidence that it occurs as such in the plants, and it appears therefore to be an artifact. That it is

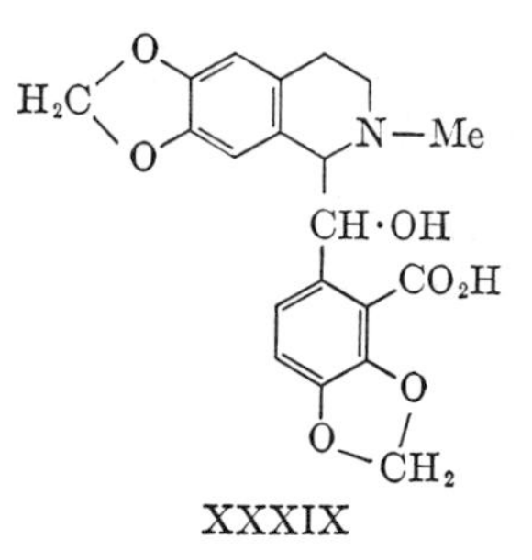

XXXIX

the hydroxy acid (XXXIX) corresponding to its lactone, bicuculline, follows not only from the fact that it shows mutarotation in dilute acid but from the fact that mild acid treatment regenerates bicuculline (69). Its stability however is unusual in this series, and it is one of the few amino acids which is precipitated from its alkaline solution by carbon dioxide or by ammonium chloride.

10. Cordrastine

Cordrastine, $C_{22}H_{25}O_6N$, m.p. 196°, is the name given to an alkaloid which was provisionally assigned structure VI. The basis for this was the exceptionally good correspondence of the analytical figures, including methoxyl, with those for such a structure and the fact that gentle heating with manganese dioxide in sulfuric acid gave rise to a solution which exhibited the expected brilliant fluorescence (64) characteristic of hydrastinine. There was insufficient alkaloid for degradation experiments, and the alkaloid has not been found again. Its source was *Corydalis aurea* Willd. (62, 64).

11. Narceine

Narceine, $C_{23}H_{27}O_8N \cdot 3H_2O$. While this alkaloid is not a phthalideisoquinoline its close relation to narcotine recommends its discussion here. It has three methoxyls, a methylenedioxy, and two *N*-methyl groups as well as a carboxyl and a carbonyl. The best evidence of its structure (VII) is its formation from narcotine methochloride by decomposition with one mole of alkali in a current of steam (70). The product was called pseudonarceine, and its identity with narceine was established later (71, 72). This reaction may result in the intermediate formation of an unsaturated

XL XLI

lactone (XL), which after hydrolysis would isomerize to VII. Independent structural proof was afforded by Freund and Oppenheim (73), who obtained the oximino derivative (XLI) of narceine by reaction with ethyl nitrite. This compound on heating is cleaved into hemipinic acid and a base which on exhaustive methylation generates trimethylamine and 3-methoxy-4,5-methylenedioxy-6-vinylbenzonitrile, m.p. 156°, (XLII),

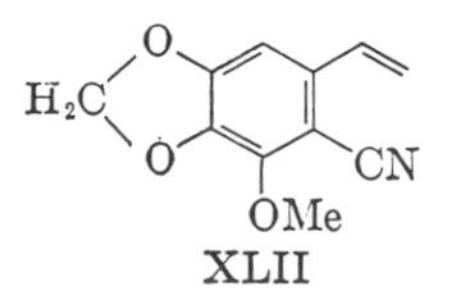

XLII

thus accounting for all of the carbon atoms in recognizable substances. The nitrile (XLII) (cotarnonitrile) had previously been obtained by Roser (74) from cotarnine by heating the oxime of *N*-methylcotarnine methochloride with alkali and can only have the assigned structure.

12. Nornarceine

Nornarceine, $C_{22}H_{25}O_8N$, has been isolated from opium under the name of oxynarcotine and may be a primary constituent although it may also have arisen as a result of the partial hydrolysis of narcotine, which when heated in acetic acid suffers this change (75, 76) along with racemization. Rabe (75) has pointed out that this change is strictly analogous to the cinchonine-cinchotoxine conversion (77). The identity of nornarceine with Beckett and Wright's oxynarcotine was definitely established (76).

III. Syntheses

1. Narcotine

The first attempt to recombine the fission products of narcotine were made by Liebermann (78). When opianic acid and hydrocotarnine are digested with 73% sulfuric acid a new base isomeric with narcotine is obtained. This compound which was named isonarcotine, m.p. 194°, was given formula XLIII by Jones, Perkin, and Robinson (79). Other ortho aldehydic acids behave like opianic acid, and phenol ethers with a free

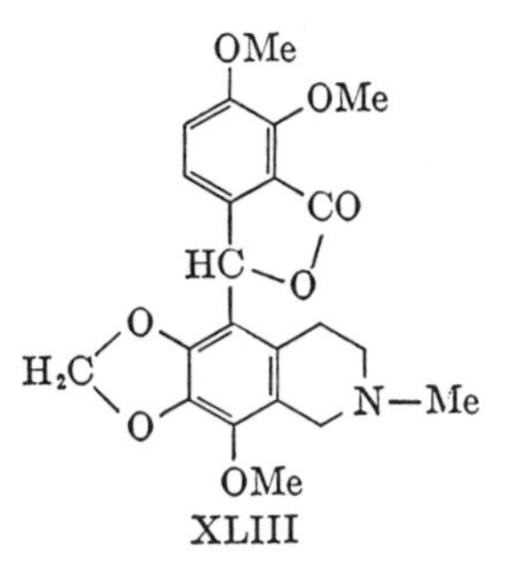

XLIII

ortho or para position give analogous condensation products. The attempted condensation of cotarnine with meconin in sulfuric acid did not yield narcotine (78) but Perkin and Robinson (80) observed that when these compounds are merely heated in alcoholic solution a small yield of *dl*-narcotine (gnoscopine) is obtained. Condensing agents of the type of potassium carbonate were of no advantage. That gnoscopine was in fact *dl*-narcotine was proved by its resolution with the aid of *d*-bromocamphorsulfonic acid. The least soluble salt was that of *l*-narcotine, identical in all respects with the natural alkaloid. It was also possible to isolate pure *d*-narcotine from the regenerated bases of the more soluble sulfonates, and a complete resolution by means of *l*-bromocamphorsulfonic acid was also achieved. That this condensation yielded a base identical with natural gnoscopine was a fortuitous one. There are two asymmetric centers in the phthalideisoquinolines and two racemic forms could have been expected. An analogous condensation takes place with the substituted meconins, and with nitromeconin (XLIV) the yield is almost quantitative.

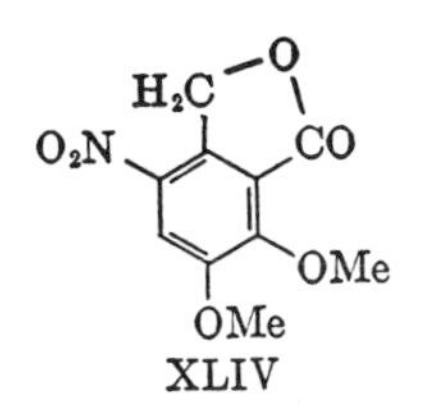

XLIV

Hope and Robinson (81) showed that the condensation product of nitromeconin and cotarnine was not the nitro derivative of natural gnoscopine, which they then called α-gnoscopine. When the nitro group is eliminated via the amino and the hydrazino groups, or via the amino and iodo groups, it yields a racemic narcotine different from α-gnoscopine and termed β-gnoscopine, which they could not deracemize. On the other hand when iodomeconin is condensed with cotarnine it yields iodo-α-gnoscopine different from that obtained from the nitro compound and convertible by reduction into α-gnoscopine. Both of the gnoscopines were convertible into narceine, indicating that the only differences were stereochemical ones, and β-gnoscopine was partly isomerized to α-gnoscopine by heating in a sealed tube with 80% ethanol at 100° for about 100 hours. The *d*- and *l*-forms of β-gnoscopine were ultimately obtained by Marshall, Pyman, and Robinson (82) by subjecting the *l*-α- and *d*-α-narcotines to the prolonged action of hot methanolic potassium hydroxide. The former, i.e., natural *l*-narcotine, yielded *l*-β-narcotine and the latter yielded *d*-β-narcotine. When equal quantities of the *d*- and *l*-β-narcotines were mixed and crystallized an almost quantitative yield of β-gnoscopine was obtained.

2. Hydrastine

The synthesis of hydrastine, being parallel to that of narcotine, was reported by Hope and Robinson in 1912 (83) and extensively described later (84). The yield of condensation product approaches 90% when hydrastinine and nitromeconin are boiled for a short time in ethanol solution. In this case, however, the product is a mixture of the two possible racemic forms, the separation of which was difficult. Separation was more readily effected after the nitro group had been reduced to the amino group, and there were thus obtained a sparingly soluble aminohydrastine-a and a more soluble aminohydrastine-b, both still racemic. These amino compounds were convertible into *dl*-hydrastine-a and *dl*-hydrastine-b, respectively. In the latter case the yield was very small, the main product being a didehydrohydrastine, m.p. 183°, which was regarded as

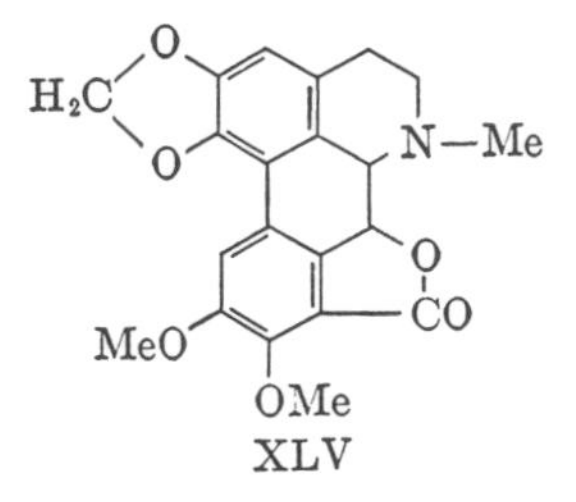

XLV

having structure XLV, and evidently formed by a reaction analogous to the Pschorr phenanthrene synthesis. Neither isomer was resolved, but in a later paper (82) arguments were adduced to show that natural hydrastine is *l*-β-hydrastine and therefore its stereochemical configuration is not that of natural narcotine. It was indicated that hydrastine-a is *dl*-β-hydrastine and therefore the racemic natural base. This supposition was later substantiated when it was possible, although with difficulty, to resolve hydrastine-a with *d*-bromocamphorsulfonic acid and with *d*-8-camphorsulfonic acid to natural *l*-hydrastine (85). At the same time a new synthesis of the phthalideisoquinolines was developed. For this purpose a dialkoxy-*N*-methyl-β-arylethylamine was first condensed with a dialkoxyphthalidecarboxylic acid to give XLVI, which on cyclodehydration yielded XLVII.

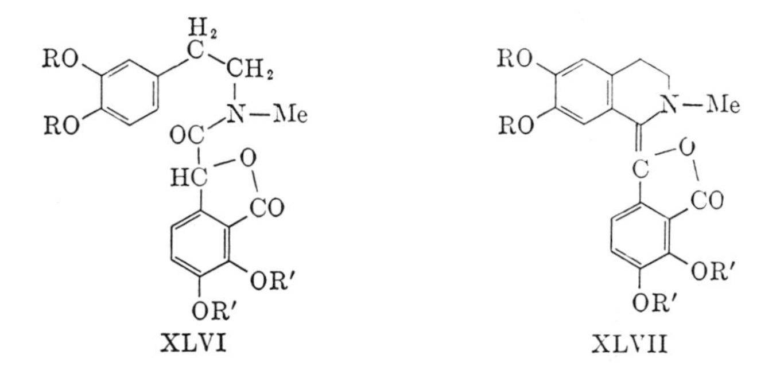

XLVI XLVII

and which in turn on reduction yielded two racemic stereoisomeric phthalideisoquinolines. For the synthesis of hydrastine R is CH_2 (/ \) and R′ is —OMe. A synthesis of the two *dl*-cordrastines (R = R′ = OMe) was also reported, but it was not possible to resolve them so that the uncertainty of the structure of cordrastine still remains.

3. Bicuculline

The synthesis of bicuculline was achieved by Groenewoud and Robinson (86) by condensing hydrastinine with 6-nitro-4,5-methylenedioxyphthalide (XLVIII), which was readily obtained by nitrating methylenedioxyphthalide (XXXVI). The resulting nitro-*x*-bicuculline was converted

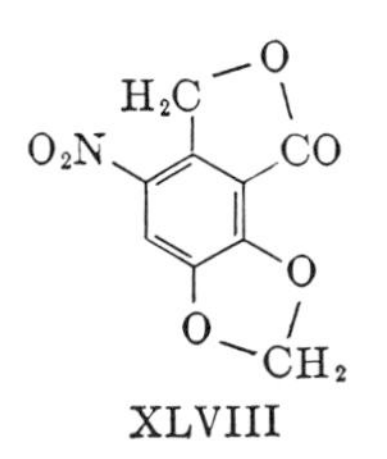

XLVIII

into *x*-bicuculline by the elimination of the nitro group via the amino and the iodo groups. It was easily resolvable by means of the hydrogen *d*- and *l*-tartrates (85). The stereochemical relation of bicuculline, and therefore those of adlumidine and capnoidine, to that of hydrastine are unknown, as are those of adlumine and corlumine.

4. Adlumine

The nitro *x*-base, m.p. 180–181°, was obtainable by condensing lodal (XXXIV) with the nitrophthalide XLVIII and its reduction to the corresponding amino derivative, m.p. 218–219°, was reported (86). The nitro compound is unusually phototropic, its pale orange color changing to a dark red on exposure to light for two hours.

IV. Discovery, Isolation, and Properties

1. *l*-α-Narcotine

l-α-Narcotine was probably first observed by Derosne in 1804 (87), but its isolation may be attributed to Robiquet (88), who assigned to it the formula $C_{23}H_{25}O_7N$. The accepted formula was first proposed by Matthiessen and Foster (89). The alkaloid opianine (90, 91) was shown by Hesse (92, 93) to be narcotine. A base regarded by Wertheim (94) as a homologue of narcotine has not been encountered again.

Narcotine has been found only in opium or in the source plant, *Papaver somniferum* L., the content in opium being of the order of 0.7 to 6.4% (95–98), although some Persian opium may contain as much as 11.2% (99), while a Chinese variety of *P. somniferum* is stated to be devoid of this alkaloid (100) as well as of papaverine. The seeds contain detectable amounts of the alkaloid, and the content in the dried plant is from 0.008 to 0.276% (101) and depends upon the state of maturity of the plant. The reported presence of narcotine in a number of fruits and vegetables and its confusion with vitamin C are erroneous, or at best unconfirmed (102–106).

The isolation of narcotine from opium is simplified by the fact that most of it remains in the water-insoluble residue when opium is processed for the manufacture of morphine. The narcotine is then extractable from this residue with dilute acids, and after regeneration from the extract it may be purified by recrystallization from ethanol (107). The acid oxalate, m.p. 174°, has also been used to separate it from its chief contaminant, namely, papaverine (92, 108, 109). Its salt with camphorsulfonic acid is practically insoluble in water whereas that of the other opium salts are quite soluble (110). The free base may be quickly purified by passing a chloroform or benzene solution through a column of calcium hydroxide, most of the impurities being absorbed (111).

Narcotine is polymorphic (112, 113), being obtained in anhydrous stout needles when slowly crystallized from ethanol. It melts sharply at 176°. Most of the salts, though generally crystalline, are readily soluble in water and have varying amounts of water of crystallization. In dilute solution they are largely dissociated because of the weakly basic nature of narcotine (114), and the free base may be extracted in part from such solutions by immiscible solvents (115–117). Numerous methods for its detection and estimation have been published (95, 118–147).

Tables 1 and 2 give the solubility of narcotine and its specific rotation, respectively, in a number of solvents. It should be noted that the value of

TABLE 1

SOLUBILITY OF NARCOTINE

Solvent	Solubility, g. in 100 cc.	References
Water	0.01	314
	0.005	315
	0.004	109
Hydrochloric acid, 1%	10.0	315
Ethanol	0.5	315
	0.35	109
Ether	0.4	315
	0.56	319
	0.6	109
Chloroform	70.0	315
	35	109
Carbon tetrachloride	1.04	316
Trichloroethylene	5.15	317
Acetone	4.2	314
Isoamyl alcohol	0.325	318
Benzene	4.614	318
	8.3	319
	4.0	109
Aniline	25	320
Pyridine	2.3	320
Piperidine	1.7	320
Diethylamine	0.4	320

the specific rotation is greatly influenced not only by the nature of the solvent but by the concentration (148, 149).

The UV-absorption spectrum of narcotine has been frequently determined (150–153) and suggested as a quantitative method for its determination (151). Narcotine is fluorescent in ultraviolet light, the color of the emitted light depending upon the wave length of the incident light (154–157).

2. α-Gnoscopine

α-Gnoscopine (*dl*-α-narcotine) was found by Smith and Smith (158) in opium, and whether or not it is an artifact is still in doubt. It melts at 232–233° (75, 80, 158), is readily soluble in chloroform, slightly so in benzene, and very sparingly so in ethanol—much less so than narcotine. The hydrochloride is the trihydrate and melts at 220° (158), 238° (76); picrate, m.p. 185° (158, 159) 188° (80). The *d*-α-narcotine was obtained by resolution of α-gnoscopine and when *l*-bromocamphorsulfonic acid is used the salt of *d*-α-narcotine (m.p. 80–90°) (80) separates first. The *l*-α-narcotine salt melts at 180–186°.

3. β-Gnoscopine

β-Gnoscopine is only known as a synthetic compound (81). It melts at 180°; hydrochloride, m.p. 224–226°. When heated in ethanol it is transformed into α-gnoscopine almost quantitatively. No suitable acid

TABLE 2

SPECIFIC ROTATION OF NARCOTINE

Solvent	$[\alpha]_D$	References
Ethanol	−185.0°	321
Chloroform	−207.35°	321
	−207.5°	93
Benzene	−229°	322
Oxalic acid in water	+62°	322
Hydrochloric acid:		
2 mol:1 mol narcotine	+47.0°	321
10 mol:1 mol narcotine	+50.0°	321
2 mol:1 mol narcotine in 80% ethyl alcohol	+104.5°	321

was found with which it could be resolved. *l*-β-Narcotine prepared by the epimerization of *l*-α-narcotine in ethanolic potassium hydroxide (82) melts at 176° and has $[\alpha]_D$ −101° in chloroform. The *d*-β-narcotine similarly obtained from *d*-α-narcotine has the same physical properties; $[\alpha]_D$ +103° in chloroform.

4. Narcotoline

Narcotoline, $C_{21}H_{21}O_7N$, forms colorless prisms, m.p. 202°, 189° (160); $[\alpha]_D$ −189° in chloroform, +5.8 in $N/10$ hydrochloric acid. It occurs to the extent of 0.05 % in some varieties of opium (160, 161) and was separated from the alkali soluble alkaloids after the morphine had been removed.

5. Hydrastine

Hydrastine, $C_{21}H_{21}O_6N$, is conveniently separated from the mother liquors of plant extracts from which the associated berberine has first been removed as sulfate. It was first encountered in *Hydrastis canadensis* L.

by Durand (162) and subsequently by Perrins (163), Mahla (32), and Power (33). More recently it has been found in *Berberis laurina* Billb. (164, 165, 166), in which it may occur to the extent of 1.4%. In *H. canadensis* the content varies from about 1.5 to 3.9% (167, 168). It is chiefly present in the rhizomes, with less amounts in the leaves and rootlets (169, 170), and only traces in the unripe seeds (169).

Hydrastine crystallizes from ethanol in colorless crystals which melt at 132–133° (30, 31, 33) 135° (32), or according to Dott (172) at 145°; picrate, m.p. 190° (171). Its solubility in water is 0.003 (173), in ethanol, 0.83 (30, 33), in ether 1.2 (30), in chloroform 7.14 (167), in carbon tetrachloride, 0.12 (173), in ethyl acetate, 4.0 (173), in petroleum ether, 0.073 (173), and in benzene 5.3 (30), all in 100 ml. of solvent at room tempera-

TABLE 3

SPECIFIC ROTATION OF HYDRASTINE

Solvent	[α]	References
Ethanol, absolute	−49.8°	167, 174
Ethanol, 97%	12.5°	174
Ethanol, 95%	0.0°	174
Ethanol, 93%	+30.0°	174
Ethanol, 85%	+37.5°	174
Ethanol, 50%	+115.0°	174
Chloroform	−67.8° (c = 2.552)	31, 167
	−57.5° (c = 3.042)	30
	−63.8° (c = 2)	174
Acetone	−85°	174
Hydrochloric acid (2HCl to 1 base)	+127.3°	31, 167

ture. Its specific rotation varies with the concentration and solvent as shown in Table 3.

The UV-absorption spectrum has been recorded by a number of investigators (152, 153, 175, 176), and the infrared spectrum has also been determined (177). The free base and its salts fluoresce in ultraviolet light (157, 158), and this property has been recommended as an assay method in biological material (179), but it has been indicated that this fluorescence is due to decomposition products of the alkaloid (180, 181). There is extensive literature on the identification and quantitative determination of hydrastine (118, 120, 121, 166, 167, 182–197), the methods depending upon sublimation and color reactions for identification and titrimetry for assay.

6. *dl*-α-Hydrastine

dl-α-Hydrastine (hydrastine-b) (84) is a synthetic compound melting at 150–151°; picrate, m.p. 197°. Its resolution was not achieved.

7. *dl*-β-Hydrastine

dl-β-Hydrastine (hydrastine-a) is the racemic form of natural hydrastine (84, 85, 198) and crystallizes in colorless prisms which melt at 137°; hydrochloride, m.p. 165°; picrate, m.p. 219°. It has been resolved into natural hydrastine and *d*-β-hydrastine, m.p. 131–132°, $[\alpha]_D$ +42.2° (chloroform).

Narcotine and hydrastine yield sparingly soluble precipitates with a number of inorganic complex acids, such as silicotungstic (199–206), phosphotungstic (199), ferro- and ferricyanic (207–210), chloroplatinic (92, 211–214), and many others including double compounds with heavy metals (213, 215–218). Many color reactions have been observed, but a large number of these depend upon some type of condensation with one of the fission products, and few if any are exclusively diagnostic or specific (160, 167, 219–224).

The remaining phthalideisoquinoline alkaloids have all been isolated by one of the present authors by a procedure outlined in an early publication (225). They have been given serial numbers as well as trivial names. Alkaloid F38, $C_{20}H_{19}O_6N$, m.p. 256°, may belong to this group, but it has not been further investigated (226).

8. Bicuculline

Bicuculline, $C_{20}H_{17}O_6N$, has been found in the following plants—*Adlumia fungosa* Green (0.036%) (67, 225), *Corydalis aurea* Willd. (0.06%) (69), *C. caseana* A. Gray (0.2%) (227, 228, 229), *C. crystallina* Engelm. (0.02%) (230), *C. nobilis* Pers. (0.09%) (227), *C. ochroleuca* Koch (0.026%) (229), *C. platycarpa* Makino (0.0007%) (231), *C. scouleri* Hook. (0.2%) (232), *C. sempervirens* (L.) Pers. (64, 233), *C. sibirica* Pers. (0.1%) (234), *Dicentra chrysantha* Walp. (0.03%) (235), *D. ochroleuca* Engelm. (0.05%) (235), and *D. cucullaria* (L.) Bernh. (64, 236). It crystallizes from chloroform–methanol in colorless stout prisms which melt at 177°, resolidify, and remelt again at 196°. The high-melting form separates in pale yellow polyhedra if a hot solution in chloroform–methanol is inoculated with it. It is much more sparingly soluble in chloroform or other solvents than that melting at 177°. Bicuculline has $[\alpha]_D^{25}$ +130.5° (chloroform), but in dilute hydrochloric acid it is levorotatory. When heated with alkali the lactone ring is opened and it is possible to isolated the corresponding hydroxy acid in a pure state. Its solution in $N/10$ potassium hydroxide is levorotatory, $[\alpha]^{25}$ −115.4°, while its solution in acid shows mutarotation owing to the closing of the lactone ring. The hydrochloride melts at 259° (dec.) and is very soluble in chloroform. The methiodide on decomposition with alkali gave *N*-methylbicuculleine, m.p. 250°, the open-chain analogue of narceine.

Isolation of Bicuculline (64, 67, 225). A plant extract in dilute hydrochloric acid freed largely from resinous material but containing all of the alkaloids is extracted with chloroform until only little is removed. The solvent is distilled from the extract, and the residue is boiled with water and a few drops of hydrochloric acid, allowed to cool, and filtered. The solution is then basified with a slight excess of aqueous potassium hydroxide and the precipitate recovered by filtering and washing with water. If the temperature during the basification is not allowed to rise appreciably, very little of the bicuculline is hydrolyzed to bicucine. The dried base or mixture of bases is then dissolved in chloroform, and the solution is boiled until it is anhydrous. A slight turbidity is eliminated by filtering it with the aid of charcoal or other filter aid, and the chloroform is then evaporated over a steam bath. While the residual resin is still hot and fluid there is added about ten times its volume of hot methanol and boiling is continued until the chloroform has been mostly removed. If crystals for seeding are available the hot solution will deposit bicuculline on inoculation. Otherwise the vessel should be closed and set in a warm place to prevent the bicuculline from separating as an oil.

9. Adlumidine

Adlumidine, $C_{20}H_{17}O_6N$, was first obtained by Schlotterbeck (37, 237) from *Adlumia fungosa* (*A. cirrhosa* Raf.) but given an erroneous formula. It was later reisolated from this plant (0.044 %) (225) as well as from *Corydalis thalictrifolia* Franch. (238) and from *C. incisa* Thunb. (0.005 %) (68). The earlier formula was revised to the one now in use when its structure was determined (68). Adlumidine crystallizes in colorless rhombic plates from chloroform–methanol and is only very sparingly soluble in alcohol, ether, or hexane. It melts at 238° and has $[\alpha]_D^{25}$ +116.2° (chloroform).

10. Capnoidine

Capnoidine, $C_{20}H_{17}O_6N$, the optical antipode of adlumidine, has been isolated from *Corydalis sempervirens* (233), *C. scouleri* (0.002 %) (232), and *C. crystallina* (0.025 %) (230). When repeatedly recrystallized from chloroform–methanol it was obtained in stout polyhedra which melted at 238°; $[\alpha]_D^{22}$ −113.2° (chloroform). The hydrochloride is sparingly soluble in methanol, insoluble in chloroform, and melts at 244° (233). When equal quantities of capnoidine and adlumidine in admixture are crystallized from chloroform–methanol an apparently homogeneous *dl*-form, melting sharply at 205°, is obtained.

11. Adlumine

Adlumine, $C_{21}H_{21}O_6N$, melts at 180° and has $[\alpha]_D^{22}$ ± 42.5° (chloroform). The *dl*-form obtained by recrystallizing a mixture of equal amounts of the components melts at 190°. Schlotterbeck's alkaloid of this name (37, 237) was impure and his formula was erroneous. Pure *d*-adlumine was again isolated from Schlotterbeck's plant source, *Adlumina fungosa* (0.05 %) (225). It crystallizes in large rhombic tablets when a supersaturated methanolic solution is inoculated with a crystal.

l-Adlumine has been isolated from *C. scouleri* (0.002 %) (232) *C. ophiocarpa* Hook. f. et Thoms. (0.03 %) (239), and *C. sempervirens* (64). The hydrochloride is only moderately soluble in chloroform.

12. Corlumine

Corlumine, $C_{21}H_{21}O_6N$, was isolated from *C. scouleri* (62, 232), *C. sibirica* (0.12 %) (62, 234), *C. nobilis* (0.04 %) (227), and *D. cucullaria* (trace) (227). It is moderately soluble in hot methanol and crystallizes from this solvent in colorless stout prisms which melt at 159°; $[\alpha]_D^{25}$ +77° (chloroform); in absolute ethanol it is optically inactive, while in acid solution it is levorotatory. The hydrochloride is very soluble in chloroform.

13. Corlumidine

Corlumidine, $C_{20}H_{19}O_6N$, has been found only in *C. scouleri* (0.02 %) (62, 232). It crystallizes from boiling chloroform, in which it is only sparingly soluble, in stout almost colorless prisms which melt at 236°; $[\alpha]_D^{23}$ +80° (chloroform).

V. Physiology and Pharmacology

Owing to the ready availability of narcotine its effects on the animal organism have been studied extensively, but the observations have not indicated any extensive use in medicine. It is effective neither as a prophylactic nor as a curative in malaria (240). It has only a mild narcotic action (241, 242, 243), and as an analgesic it is much weaker than morphine (244, 245), although it has been recorded that it potentiates the activity of morphine four- to sevenfold (246). The cramps due to the action of cocaine are also augmented by the simultaneous use of narcotine. It does not lower the basal metabolic rate appreciably (247), nor does it shorten the induction period in nitrous oxide narcosis (248). Its effect on respiration is one of acceleration (249, 250), and its effect on smooth muscle of the intestine (251–254), of the bladder (255), of the gall bladder (251, 252, 256, 257), and of the uterus (251, 252, 258–261) is depressive, while the amplitude of the peristaltic pulses is increased (262–265).

Narcotine has a paralytic action on the frog's heart (266–270), this action being antagonized by ephedrine and augmented by atropine (268). It is absorbed in the intestines and slightly in the stomach (271, 272), slowing down the digestive process (272) and inhibiting the hunger contractions of the stomach (271). It is rapidly eliminated from the blood stream and absorbed in the body tissues, and only eliminated in the urine in traces (315).

It has a mitotic action which is very much weaker than that of colchicine (273), but the growth of wheat seedlings is inhibited (274, 275, 276).

It should be noted that the claim that narcotine and its des-*O*-methyl derivatives have antiscorbutic action (105, 106, 277–284), has been repeatedly denied (102, 103, 161, 285–294).

Narcotoline is similar to but weaker than narcotine in its effects.

Hydrastine resembles strychnine in some of its responses (295), producing convulsions in the frog which may be followed by paralysis. Unlike narcotine, which is a depressor, hydrastine has a pressor effect (296, 297, 298). It is more toxic than narcotine (296) or morphine (299), has a paralytic action on intestines (296, 300), and inhibits the contraction of smooth muscles (251, 252, 254, 301). It is strongly antagonistic to adrenaline, totally suppressing the renal vasoconstriction due to small doses of the latter (302–305). It is slightly antispasmodic (306) and has a mild sedative effect on respiration by diminishing the amplitude and frequency (307).

Hydrastine is about equally distributed between corpuscles and plasma, but erythrocytes have a superior fixing tendency for it (308, 309). It is eliminated from the urine in about four days, only about 4% being recovered.

Bicuculline and *d*-adlumine were compared with hydrastine as convulsants, cardiac depressors, and uterine and intestinal stimulants, in all effects those of bicuculline being qualitatively and quantitatively similar to those of hydrastine except that its convulsant action is about 100 times stronger, in which respect *d*-adlumine is much weaker. The depressant action of *d*-adlumine on the frog's heart is antagonized by atropine (310).

Corlumine is 30 times as potent a convulsant as *d*-adlumine but less so than bicuculline. It has little effect on the perfused heart of the frog (311).

None of these alkaloids have found regular use in medicine, but hydrastinine, the basic fission fragment, is a useful oxytocic styptic and has found some use as a uterine stimulant (312, 313).

VI. References

1. R. Robinson, *Ann. Rev. Biochem.*, **4**, 497 (1935).
2. E. C. Kipperman, *Polytech. Weekblad*, **35**, 227 (1941); *Chem. Zentr.*, **1941, II**, 1294.
3. K. Josephson, *Svensk Farm. Tidskr.*, **35**, 237 (1931); *Chem. Zentr.*, **1931, II**, 1162.
4. F. Wöhler, *Ann.*, **50**, 1 (1944).
5. W. Roser, *Ann.*, **254**, 334, 359 (1889).
6. W. H. Perkin, Jr. and R. Robinson, *J. Chem. Soc.*, **99**, 775 (1911).
7. T. Anderson, *Ann.*, **86**, 179 (1853).
8. A. Matthiessen and G. C. Foster, *Jahresbericht*, **1861**, 539.
9. J. N. Rakshit, *J. Chem. Soc.*, **113**, 466 (1918).
10. G. S. Ahluwalia, B. D. Kochhar, and J. Nath Rây, *J. Indian Chem. Soc.*, **9**, 215 (1932).
11. K. Topchiev, *J. Appl. Chem.* (*U.S.S.R.*), **6**, 529 (1933); *Chem. Abstr.*, **28**, 2718 (1934).
12. E. V. Seshacharyulu and S. Dutt, *Proc. Acad. Sci. United Provinces Agra and Oudh, India*, **4**, 159 (1934); *Chem. Abstr.*, **29**, 7989 (1935).

13. E. Schmidt, *Arch. Pharm.*, **228,** 49 (1890).
14. W. Roser, *Ann.*, **249,** 156 (1888).
15. M. Freund and F. Becker, *Ber.*, **36,** 1521 (1903).
16. W. H. Perkin, Jr., R. Robinson, and F. Thomas, *J. Chem. Soc.*, **95,** 1977 (1909).
17. H. Decker, *J. prakt. Chem.*, [2]**47,** 222 (1893).
18. A. Hantzsch and M. Kalb, *Ber.*, **32,** 3109 (1899); **33,** 2201 (1900).
19. J. J. Dobbie, A. Lauder, and C. K. Tinkler, *J. Chem. Soc.*, **83,** 598 (1903); **85,** 121 (1904).
20. E. von Gerichten, *Ber.*, **13,** 1635 (1880).
21. E. von Gerichten, *Ann.*, **210,** 79 (1881).
22. W. Roser, *Ann.*, **234,** 116 (1886).
23. A. H. Salway, *J. Chem. Soc.*, **97,** 1208 (1910).
24. A. H. Salway, *J. Chem. Soc.*, **95,** 1204 (1909).
25. Couerbe, *Ann.*, **2,** 272 (1832); **5,** 180 (1833).
26. M. Freund, *Ber.*, **22,** 459 (1899).
27. P. Fritsch, *Ann.*, **301,** 352 (1898).
28. G. A. Edwards, W. H. Perkins, Jr., and F. W. Stoyle, *J. Chem. Soc.*, **127,** 195 (1925).
29. O. Salomon, *Ber.*, **20,** 888 (1887).
30. J. F. Eijkman, *Rec. trav. chim.*, **5,** 290 (1886).
31. M. Freund and W. Will, *Ber.*, **19,** 2797 (1886).
32. F. Mahla, *Am. J. Science*, [2]**36,** 57 (1863); *Jahresbericht*, **1863,** 455. *J. prakt. Chem.*, [1]**91,** 248 (1864).
33. F. B. Power, *Pharm. J.*, [3]**15,** 297 (1884); *Jahresbericht*, **1884,** 1396.
34. M. Freund and W. Will, *Ber.*, **20,** 88 (1887).
35. E. Schmidt and F. Wilhelm, *Arch. Pharm.*, **226,** 346 (1888).
36. E. Schmidt and W. Kerstein, *Arch. Pharm.*, **228,** 49 (1890).
37. J. O. Schlotterbeck and H. C. Watkins, *Pharm. Arch.*, **6,** 17 (1903); *Chem. Centr.*, **1903, I,** 1142; *J. Am. Chem. Soc.*, **25,** 596 (1903). (The name alumidin is used in *Chem. Centr.* obviously by mistake.)
38. W. Roser, *Ann.*, **249,** 172 (1888).
39. W. Freund and W. Will, *Ber.*, **20,** 2400 (1887).
40. Sarah N. McGeogh and T. S. Stevens, *J. Chem. Soc.*, **1934,** 1465.
41. J. J. Dobbie and C. K. Tinkler, *J. Chem. Soc.*, **85,** 1005 (1904).
42. E. Hope and R. Robinson, *J. Chem. Soc.*, **99,** 2114 (1911).
43. M. Freund, *Ann.*, **271,** 383 (1892).
44. W. H. Perkin, Jr., and R. Robinson, *J. Chem. Soc.*, **91,** 1086 (1907).
45. T. S. Stevens and Mary C. Robertson, *J. Chem. Soc.*, **1927,** 2790.
46. P. Fritsch, *Ann.*, **286,** 1 (1895).
47. German Patent 281,546. H. Decker, 1912.
48. German Patent 281,547. H. Decker, 1913.
49. German Patent 270,859. H. Decker, 1911.
50. H. Decker and P. Becker, *Ann.*, **395,** 358 (1913).
51. K. Hess, F. Merck, and C. Uibrig, *Ber.*, **48,** 1885 (1915).
52. K. Hess and C. Uibrig, *Ber.*, **48,** 1974 (1915).
53. F. L. Pyman and F. G. P. Remfry, *J. Chem. Soc.*, **101,** 1595 (1912).
54. S. von Kostanecki and V. Lampe, *Ber.*, **41,** 1327 (1908).
55. H. Thoms and W. Siebeling, *Ber.*, **44,** 2134 (1911).
56. M. Freund, *Ber.*, **22,** 2329 (1889).
57. C. Liebermann and F. Kropf, *Ber.*, **37,** 211 (1904).
58. N. J. Leonard and G. W. Leubner, *J. Am. Chem. Soc.*, **71,** 3408 (1949).

59. R. Mirza and R. Robinson, *Nature*, **166**, 271 (1950).
60. F. L. Pyman, *J. Chem. Soc.*, **95**, 1266 (1909).
61. R. H. F. Manske, *Can. J. Research*, **8**, 404 (1933).
62. R. H. F. Manske, *Can. J. Research*, **14B**, 325 (1936).
63. R. H. F. Manske, *Can. J. Research*, **15B**, 159 (1937).
64. R. H. F. Manske, *Can. J. Research*, **16B**, 81 (1938).
65. W. H. Perkin, Jr. and V. M. Trikojus, *J. Chem. Soc.*, **1926**, 2925.
66. E. Späth and A. Dobrowsky, *Ber.*, **58**, 1274 (1925).
67. R. H. F. Manske, *Can. J. Research*, **8**, 142 (1933).
68. R. H. F. Manske, *J. Am. Chem. Soc.*, **72**, 3207 (1950).
69. R. H. F. Manske, *Can. J. Research*, **9**, 436 (1933).
70. W. Roser, *Ann.*, **247**, 167 (1888).
71. M. Freund and G. B. Frankforter, *Ann.*, **277**, 20 (1893).
72. C. R. Addinall and R. T. Major, *J. Am. Chem. Soc.*, **55**, 1202 (1933).
73. M. Freund and P. Oppenheim, *Ber.*, **42**, 1084 (1909).
74. W. Roser, *Ann.*, **254**, 339 (1889).
75. P. Rabe, *Ber.*, **40**, 3280 (1907).
76. P. Rabe and A. McMillian, *Ann.*, **377**, 223 (1910).
77. W. von Miller and Rhode, *Ber.*, **28**, 1056 (1895).
78. C. Liebermann, *Ber.*, **29**, 183 (1896).
79. E. G. Jones, W. H. Perkin, Jr. and R. Robinson, *J. Chem. Soc.*, **101**, 257 (1912).
80. W. H. Perkin, Jr. and R. Robinson, *J. Chem. Soc.*, **99**, 775 (1911).
81. E. Hope and R. Robinson, *J. Chem. Soc.*, **105**, 2085 (1914).
82. M. A. Marshall, F. L. Pyman, and R. Robinson, *J. Chem. Soc.*, **1934**, 1315.
83. E. Hope and R. Robinson, *Proc. Chem. Soc.*, **28**, 17 (1912).
84. E. Hope, F. L. Pyman F. G. P. Remfry, and R. Robinson, *J. Chem. Soc.*, **1931**, 236.
85. R. D. Haworth, A. R. Pinder, and R. Robinson, *Nature*, **165**, 529 (1950).
86. P. W. G. Groenewoud and R. Robinson, *J. Chem. Soc.*, **1936**, 199.
87. C. Derosne, *Ann. chim.*, [1]**45**, 274 (1804).
88. M. Robiquet, *Ann. chim.*, [2]**5**, 275 (1817).
89. A. Matthiessen and G. C. Foster, *J. Chem. Soc.*, **16**, 343 (1863); *Ann.* (*Suppl.*), **1**, 330 (1861).
90. F. Hinterberger, *Ann.*, **77**, 207 (1851).
91. F. Hinterberger, *J. prakt. Chem.*, [1]**56**, 144 (1852).
92. O. Hesse, *Ann.* (*Suppl.*), **8**, 261 (1872).
93. O. Hesse, *Ann.*, **178**, 241 (1875).
94. T. Wertheim, *J. prakt. Chem.*, [1]**53**, 431 (1851).
95. J. N. Rakshit, *Analyst*, **46**, 481 (1921); *Chem. Abstr.*, **16**, 611 (1922).
96. W. Straub, *Biochem. Z.*, **41**, 419 (1912).
97. E. Both, *Apotheker im Osten*, **1**, 137 (1942); *Chem. Abstr.*, **38**, 3086 (1944).
98. Z. Arima and M. Iwakiri, *Rept. Inst. Sci. Research, Manchoukuo*, **2**, 221 (1938); *Chem. Abstr.*, **33**, 1875 (1939).
99. A. Jermstad, *Schweiz. Apoth. Ztg.*, **60**, 691 (1922); *Chem. Zentr.*, **1923, II**, 209.
100. K. A. Chasovnikova, *Biokhimiya*, **2**, 701 (1937); *Chem. Zentr.*, **1938, II**, 2131; *Chem. Abstr.*, **32**, 1861 (1938).
101. W. Küssner, *E. Merck's Jahresber.*, **54**, 29 (1941).
102. O. Dalmer and T. Moll, *Z. physiol. Chem.*, **209**, 211 (1932).
103. E. Ott and K. Packendorff, *Z. physiol. Chem.*, **210**, 94 (1932).
104. P. Laland, *Z. physiol. Chem.*, **204**, 112 (1932).

105. O. Rygh, *Z. Vitaminforsch.*, **1,** 134 (1932); *Chem. Abstr.*, **27,** 2177 (1933).
106. O. Rygh, A. Rygh, and P. Laland, *Z. physiol. Chem.*, **204,** 105 (1932).
107. Russian Patent 40,979; *Chem. Zentr.*, **1935, II,** 3544.
108. H. de Haan, *Pharm. Weekblad*, **57,** 1483 (1920); *Chem. Abstr.*, **15,** 922 (1921).
109. B. Kljatchkina, *Arch. Pharm.*, **271,** 558 (1933).
110. F. Mercier and J. Détrie, *J. pharm. chim.*, [9]**1,** 287 (1940); *Chem. Abstr.*, **37,** 6407 (1943).
111. Swedish Patent 98,873, H. Willstaedt, 1940; *Chem. Abstr.*, **40,** 990 (1946).
112. P. Gaubert, *Compt. rend.*, **156,** 1161 (1913).
113. R. Kremann and N. Schniderschitz, *Monatsh.*, **35,** 1423 (1914).
114. M. Kolthoff, *Biochem. Z.*, **162,** 289 (1925).
115. R. Fabre and Mlle. E. Parinaud, *Compt. rend.*, **180,** 2077 (1925); *Chem. Abstr.*, **19,** 3000 (1925).
116. P. C. Plugge, *Arch. Pharm.*, **224,** 993 (1886).
117. A. Simmer, *Arch. Pharm.*, **244,** 672 (1906).
118. R. Eder, *Schweiz. Wochschr. f. Chem., und Pharm.*, **51,** 228 (1913); *Chem. Zentr.* **1913, II,** 91.
119. A. Heiduschka and N. J. Meisner, *Arch. Pharm.*, **261,** 102 (1923).
120. M. M. Janot and M. Chaigneau, *Compt. rend.*, **225,** 1371 (1947); *Chem. Abstr.*, **42,** 2728 (1948).
121. A. Mayrhofer, *Pharm. Monatsh.*, **5,** 231 (1924); *Chem. Abstr.*, **19,** 701 (1925).
122. L. Kofler and A. Kofler, *Arch. Pharm.* **272,** 537 (1924).
123. C. K. Glycart, *J. Assoc. Offic. Agr. Chemists*, **20,** 551 (1937); *Chem. Abstr.*, **32,** 305 (1938).
124. H. Beckmann, *Pharm. Ztg.*, **74,** 28 (1929); *Chem. Abstr.*, **23,** 1469 (1929).
125. G. Vanag and Anna Dombrowski, *Ber.*, **75,** 82 (1942).
126. W. F. Whitmore and C. A. Wood, *Mikrochemie ver Mikrochim. Acta*, **27,** 249 (1939).
127. R. Dietzel and W. Paul, *Süddeut. Apoth. Ztg.*, **76,** 474 (1936); *Chem. Zentr.*, **1936, II,** 1577.
128. P. Herzig, *Arch. Pharm.*, **259,** 249 (1922).
129. F. Gallais, *Bull. sci. pharmacol.*, **42,** 278 (1935); *Chem. Zentr.*, **1936, I,** 4761.
130. Schoof, *Bull. acad. roy. méd. Belg.*, [5]**7,** 832 (1927); *Chem. Abstr.*, **22,** 1302 (1928).
131. A. W. van der Haar, *Pharm. Weekblad*, **48,** 1302 (1911); *Chem. Zentr.*, **1912, I,** 292.
132. A. W. van der Haar, *Pharm. Weekblad*, **53,** 1452 (1916); *Chem. Zentr.*, **1917, I,** 607.
133. J. W. de Waal, *Pharm. Weekblad*, **52,** 1423 (1915); *Chem. Zentr.*, **1916, II,** 432.
134. J. W. de Waal, *Pharm. Weekblad*, **53,** 1055 (1916); *Chem. Zentr.*, **1917, I,** 541.
135. A. P. Snesarev, *J. Chem. Ind. (U.S.S.R.)*, **8,** 161 (1931); *Chem. Abstr.*, **25,** 4658 (1931).
136. D. C. M. Adamson, F. P. Handysyde, and H. W. Hodgson, *Quart. J. Pharm. Pharmacol.*, **20,** 218 (1947); *Chem. Abstr.*, **42,** 1384 (1948).
137. E. Anneler, *Festschr. Emil Barell*, **1936,** 344; *Chem. Abstr.*, **31,** 2349 (1937).
138. E. Anneler, *Arch. Pharm.*, **258,** 130 (1920).
139. H. E. Annett, H. D. Sen, and H. D. Singh, *Mem. Dept. Agr. India*, **6,** 1 (1921); *Chem. Abstr.*, **17,** 2167 (1923).
140. V. Brustier, *Bull. soc. chim.*, [4]**39,** 1527 (1926).
141. J. Détrie and J. L. Lelièvre, *Compt. rend., XVII congr. chim. ind.*, **1937,** 174; *Chem. Abstr.*, **32,** 6400 (1938).
142. B. A. Klyachkina and V. F. Sorochinskaya, *Farmatsiya*, **1939,** 8; *Chem. Abstr.*, **34,** 8177 (1940).

143. B. A. Klyachkina, *Khim. Farm. Prom.*, **1933,** 203; *Chem. Abstr.*, **28,** 575 (1934).
144. H. Baggesgaard Rasmussen and F. Reimers, *Pharm. Acta Helv.*, **7,** 249 (1932); *Chem. Zentr.*, **1933, I,** 822.
145. L. Rosenthaler and H. Kocak, *Pharm. Acta Helv.*, **23,** 214 (1948); *Cheml Abstr.*, **43,** 2368 (1949).
146. W. F. Whitmore and C. A. Wood, *Mikrochemie ver Mikrochim. Acta*, **28,** 1 (1939).
147. K. Freudenberg, M. Harder, and Laura Makkert, *Ber.*, **61,** 1760 (1928).
148. J. N. Rakshit, *J. Phys. Chem.*, **34,** 2539 (1930); *Chem. Abstr.*, **25,** 451 (1931).
149. H. E. Annett, *J. Chem. Soc.*, **123,** 376 (1923).
150. P. Steiner, *Compt. rend.*, **176,** 244 (1923); *Chem. Zentr.*, **1923, I,** 1189.
151. P. Steiner, *Ann. med. légale criminol. et police sci.*, **2,** 338 (1922); *Chem. Abstr.*, **20,** 1178 (1926).
152. P. Csókan, *Z. anal. Chem.*, **124,** 344 (1942).
153. Z. Kitasato, *Acta Phytochim. Japan*, **3,** 229 (1927); *Chem. Abstr.*, **22,** 1780 (1928).
154. E. A. Kocsis and Z. Holló, *Z. anal. Chem.*, **124,** 35 (1943).
155. P. W. Danckwortt and E. Pfau, *Arch. Pharm.*, **265,** 68 (1927).
156. E. Bayle and R. Fabre, *Compt. rend.*, **178,** 2181 (1924); *Chem. Zentr.*, **1924, II,** 1158.
157. E. Bayle, R. Fabre, and H. George, *Bull. soc. chim.*, [4]**37,** 89 (1925).
158. T. Smith and H. Smith, *Pharm. J. Trans.*, **52,** 794 (1892); *Ber.*, **26,** 593 R (1893).
159. C. W. Maplethorpe and N. Evers, *Pharm. J.*, **115,** 137 (1925); *Chem. Abstr.*, **20,** 94 (1926).
160 .G. Baumgarten and W. Christ, *Pharmazie*, **5,** 80 (1950).
161. F. Wrede, *Forschungen u. Fortschr.*, **14,** 173 (1938).
162. Durand, *Am. J. Pharm.*, **23,** 112 (1851).
163. J. D. Perrins, *Pharm. J.* [2]**3,** 546 (1862); *Jahresbericht*, **1862,** 381.
164. L. Gurguel, O. de A. Costa, and R. Diaz da Silva, *Bol. assoc. brasil. farm.*, **15,** 11 (1934); *Chem. Abstr.*, **28,** 3521 (1934).
165. O. de A. Costa and R. Diaz da Silva, *Rev. soc. brasil. chim.*, **4,** 199 (1933); *Chem. Zentr.*, **1934, II,** 3526.
166. O. de A. Costa and V. Lucas, *Rev. quím. farm. (Santiago, Chili)*, **4,** 63 (1939); *Chem. Abstr.*, **33,** 7957 (1939).
167. G. Klein, Handbuch der Pflanzenanalyse, Springer, Berlin, 1931–1933.
168. E. Belloni, *Boll. chim. farm.*, **58,** 81 (1919); *Chem. Abstr.*, **14,** 92 (1920).
169. R. Wasicky and Marianne Joachimowitz, *Arch. Pharm.*, **255,** 497 (1917).
170. G. Polacci and M. Galotti, *Boll. soc. ital. biol. sper.*, **17,** 652 (1942); *Chem. Abstr.*, **40,** 7519 (1946).
171. H. Neugebauer and K. Brunner, *Pharm. Ztg.*, **82,** 1212 (1937); *Chem. Abstr.*, **32,** 1862 (1938).
172. D. B. Dott, *Pharm. J.*, **109,** 607 (1922); *Chem. Abstr.*, **17,** 1302 (1923).
173. H. Beckurts and W. Müller, *Apoth. Ztg.*, **18,** 208 (1903); *Chem. Centr.*, **1903, I,** 1141.
174. F. H. Carr and W. C. Reynolds, *J. Chem. Soc.*, **97,** 1328 (1910).
175. J. J. Dobbie and A. Lauder, *J. Chem. Soc.*, **83,** 605 (1903).
176. A. Andant, *Bull. sci. pharmacol.*, **37,** 89 (1930); *Chem. Abst.*, **24,** 3441 (1930).
177. L. Marion, D. A. Ramsay, and R. N. Jones, *J. Am. Chem. Soc.*, **73,** 305 (1951).
178. A. Mayrhofer, *Pharm. Post*, **47,** 547 (1914); *Chem. Zentr.*, **1914, II,** 736.
179. R. Fabre, *Bull. soc. chim. biol.*, **7,** 1024 (1925); *Chem. Abstr.*, **20,** 1632 (1926).
180. A. Slesser and C. B. Jordan, *J. Am. Pharm. Assoc., Sci. Ed.*, **29,** 134 (1940); *Chem. Abstr.*, **34,** 3447 (1940).

181. E. Bayle and R. Fabre, *J. pharm. chim.*, [8]**1**, 248 (1925); *Chem. Abstr.*, **19**, 2260 (1925).
182. G. L. Keenan, *J. Am. Pharm. Assoc., Sci. Ed.*, **37**, 41 (1948); *Chem. Abstr.*, **42**, 3907 (1948).
183. G. Klein and A. Schilhab, *Österr. bot. Z.*, **77**, 14 (1928).
184. A. Viehoever, *J. Assoc. Offic. Agr. Chemists*, **5**, 557 (1922); *Chem. Abstr.*, **16**, 3167 (1922).
185. H. Baggesgaard Rasmussen and S. A. Schou, *Pharm. Zentralhalle*, **65**, 729 (1924); *Chem. Abstr.*, **19**, 702 (1925).
186. H. Baggesgaard Rasmussen and S. A. Schou, *Schweiz. Apoth. Ztg.*, **63**, 30 (1925); *Chem. Zentr.*, **1925, I**, 1514.
187. H. Baggesgaard Rasmussen and S. A. Schou, *Z. Elektrochem.*, **31**, 189 (1925); *Chem. Abstr.*, **19**, 2388 (1925).
188. H. Wales, *Ind. Eng. Chem.*, **18**, 390 (1926); *Chem. Abstr.*, **20**, 1493 (1926).
189. E. M. Eiderman, *Farm. Zhur.*, **1928**, 602; *Chem. Abstr.*, **23**, 3541 (1929).
190. H. Dieterle, *Arch. Pharm.*, **261**, 77 (1923); *Chem. Zentr.*, **1923, IV**, 555.
191. N. Neugebauer, *Pharm. Ztg.*, **78**, 1077 (1933); *Chem. Zentr.*, **1934, I**, 90.
192. R. Dietzel and W. Paul, *Arch. Pharm.*, **273**, 507 (1935).
193. H. M. Gordin and A. B. Prescott, *Arch. Pharm.*, **237**, 439 (1899); *Z. anal. Chem.*, **40**, 437 (1901).
194. H. Neugebauer and K. Brunner, *Pharm. Ztg.*, **81**, 1416 (1936); *Chem. Abstr.*, **31**, 1953 (1937).
195. W. A. Puckmer, *Pharm. Rev.*, **26**, 132 (1908); *Chem. Zentr.*, **1908, II**, 266.
196. E. Rupp, *Apoth. Ztg.*, **24**, 922 (1909); *Chem. Zentr.*, **1910, I**, 206.
197. R. Fischer and H. Frank, *Scientia Pharm.*, **16**, 38 (1948).
198. R. D. Haworth and A. R. Pinder, *J. Chem. Soc.*, **1950**, 1776.
199. G. Denigès, *Ann. chim. anal. et chim. appl.*, **22**, 103 (1917); *Chem. Zentr.*, **1917, II**, 648.
200. A. Heiduschka and L. Wolf, *Schweiz. Apoth. Ztg.*, **58**, 213 (1920); *Chem. Abstr.*, **14**, 3041 (1920).
201. E. O. North and G. D. Beal, *J. Am. Pharm. Assoc.*, **13**, 889 (1924); *Chem. Abstr.*, **19**, 792 (1925).
202. F. E. R. Sas, *Anales soc. españ. fís. y quím.*, **23**, 277 (1925); *Chem. Zentr.*, **1925, II**, 1550.
203. P. Duquénois and M. Ellert, *Bull. soc. chim.*, **6**, 1582 (1939); *Chem. Abstr.*, **34**, 2530 (1940).
204. N. Wattiez, *J. pharm. Belg.*, **2**, 817 (1920); *Chem. Abstr.*, **15**, 145 (1921).
205. F. E. Raurich, *Anales soc. españ. fís. y quím.*, **24**, 647 (1926); *Chem. Abst.*, **21**, 2758 (1927).
206. B. A. Klyatchina, M. K., Strugatzki, and F. D. Silberg, *Bull. Wiss. Chem. Pharm. Forsch. Inst. (U.S.S.R.)*, **1931**, 203; *Chem. Zentr.*, **1932, I**, 1376.
207. H. I. Cole, *Philippine J. Sci.*, **23**, 97 (1923); *Chem. Abstr.*, **17**, 3229 (1923).
208. W. M. Cumming and D. G. Brown, *J. Soc. Chem. Ind. (London)*, **44**, 110 (1925); *Chem. Abstr.*, **19**, 2826 (1925).
209. W. M. Cumming and D. G. Brown, *J. Soc. Chem. Ind. (London)*, **47**, 84 T (1928); *Chem. Abstr.*, **22**, 2028 (1928).
210. Yu, D. Gnesin, *Farm. Zhur.*, **1930**, 293; *Chem. Abstr.*, **25**, 2811 (1931).
211. J. Blyth, *Ann.*, **50**, 29 (1844).
212. F. Wilhelm, *Arch. Pharm.*, **226**, 329 (1888).
213. Alide Gruterink, *Z. anal. Chem.*, **51**, 175 (1912).

214. A. Husemann, *Ann.*, **128,** 305 (1863).
215. F. Litterscheid and K. Thimme, *Ann.*, **334,** 49 (1904).
216. F. Hinterberger, *Ann.*, **82,** 311 (1852).
217. R. Voynnet, *J. Pharm. chim.*, **16,** 344 (1933); *Chem. Abstr.*, **27,** 1991 (1933).
218. J. J. L. Zwikker and A. Kruysse, *Pharm. Weekblad*, **77,** 18 (1940); *Chem. Zentr.*, **1940, I,** 1717.
219. F. Wrede, *Arch. exptl. Pathol. Pharmakol.*, **184,** 331 (1937).
220. L. van Itallie and A. J. Stenhauer, *Arch. Pharm.*, **265,** 696 (1927); *Chem. Abstr.*, **22,** 842 (1928).
221. L. Ekkert, *Magyar Gyógyszerésztud. Társaság Értesitöje*, **5,** 21 (1929); *Chem. Zentr.*, **1929 I,** 1592.
222. M. A. Labat, *Bull. soc. chim.* [4]**5,** 742 (1909).
223. A. Wangerin, *Pharm. Ztg.*, **47,** 916 (1902); *Chem. Centr.*, **1903, I,** 58.
224. M. A. Labat, *Bull. soc. chim. biol.*, **15,** 1344 (1933); *Chem. Abstr.*, **28,** 2300 (1934).
225. R. H. F. Manske, *Can. J. Research*, **8,** 210 (1933).
226. R. H. F. Manske, *Can. J. Research*, **16B,** 438 (1938).
227. R. H. F Manske, *Can. J. Research*, **18B,** 288 (1940).
228. R. H. F. Manske, *Can. J. Research*, **16B,** 153 (1938).
229. R. H. F. Manske, *Can. J. Research*, **17B,** 95 (1939).
230. R. H. F. Manske, *Can. J. Research*, **17B,** 57 (1939).
231. R. H. F. Manske, *Can. J. Research*, **21B,** 13 (1943).
232. R. H. F. Manske, *Can. J. Research*, **14B,** 347 (1936).
233. R. H. F. Manske, *Can. J. Research*, **8,** 407 (1932).
234. R. H. F. Manske, *Can. J. Research*, **14B,** 354 (1936).
235. R. H. F. Manske, *Can. J. Research*, **15B,** 274 (1937).
236. R. H. F. Manske, *Can. J. Research*, **7,** 265 (1931).
237. J. O. Schlotterbeck, *Am. Chem. J.*, **24,** 249 (1900); *Chem. Centr.*, **1900, II,** 576.
238. R. H. F. Manske, *Can. J. Research*, **21B,** 111 (1943).
239. R. H. F. Manske, *Can. J. Research*, **17B,** 51 (1939).
240. R. N. Chopra and R. Knowles, *Indian J. Med. Research*, **18,** 5 (1930); *Chem. Abstr.*, **24,** 5374 (1930).
241. L. Bacialli and P. Maria Niccolini, *Ber. ges. Physiol. u. exptl. Pharmakol.*, **25,** 492 (1924); *Chem. Zentr.*, **1924, II,** 1365.
242. H. C. Wood, *J. Am. Med. Assoc.*, **96,** 1140 (1931); *Chem. Zentr.*, **1931, I,** 3372.
243. R. N. Chopra, B. Mükherjee, and B. B. Dikshit, *Indian J. Med. Research*, **18,** 35 (1930); *Chem. Abstr.*, **24,** 5865 (1930).
244. O. W. Barlow, *J. Am. Med. Assoc.*, **99,** 986 (1932); *Chem. Zentr.*, **1933, I,** 2137.
245. F. Haffner, *Deut. med. Wochschr.*, **55,** 731 (1929); *Chem. Zentr.*, **1929, II,** 189.
246. W. Möhrke, *Arch. exptl. Pathol. Pharmakol.*, **90,** 180 (1921); *Chem. Abstr.*, **15,** 3333 (1921).
247. K. Tin, *Folia Pharmacol. Japon.*, **29,** 1 (1940); *Chem. Abstr.*, **34,** 8054 (1940).
248. O. W. Barlow and M. F. Stormont, *J. Pharmacol. Exptl. Therap.*, **46,** 141 (1932); *Chem. Abstr.*, **27,** 138 (1933).
249. R. Meissner, *Z. ges. exptl. Med.*, **31,** 159 (1923); *Chem. Zentr.*, **1923, I,** 1604.
250. A. Rikl, *Arch. exptl. Pathol. Pharmakol.*, **127,** 173 (1928); *Chem. Abstr.*, **22,** 1407 (1928).
251. T. Ri, *J. Med. Assoc. Formosa*, **35,** 237 (1936); *Chem. Abstr.*, **32,** 9284 (1938).
252. T. Ri, *Ber. ges. Physiol. u. exptl. Pharmakol.*, **94,** 168 (1938); *Chem. Abstr.*, **32,** 9284 (1938).
253. D. I. Macht, *J. Pharmacol. Exptl. Therap.*, **11,** 389 (1918); *Chem. Zentr.*, **1919, III,** 24.

254. H. Guyot, *Schweiz. Apoth. Ztg.*, **61**, 146 (1923); *Chem. Zentr.*, **1923, I**, 1460.
255. D. I. Macht, *J. Pharmacol. Exptl. Therap.*, **9**, 197 (1916); *Chem. Zentr.*, **1917, I**, 1019.
256. S. Hirano, *Folia Pharmacol. Japon.*, **26**, 21 (1938); *Chem. Zentr.*, **1939, I**, 1403.
257. D. I. Macht, *J. Pharmacol. Exptl. Therap.*, **9**, 473 (1917); *Chem. Zentr.*, **1919, III**, 933.
258. J. La Barre, *Arch. intern. pharmacodynamie*, **29**, 179 (1924); *Chem. Zentr.*, **1925, I**, 1628.
259. G. Dellepiane, *Riv. ital. ginecol.*, **12**, 563 (1931); *Arch. ital. biol.*, **87**, 51 (1932); *Chem. Abstr.*, **27**, 1939 (1933).
260. G. Dellepiane, *Boll. soc. ital. biol. sper.*, **6**, 291 (1931); *Chem. Zentr.*, **1934, I**, 727.
261. G. Dellepiane, *Boll. soc. ital. biol. sper.*, **6**, 584 (1931); *Chem. Abstr.*, **26**, 1346 (1932).
262. O. H. Plant and G. H. Miller, *J. Pharmacol. Exptl. Therap.*, **27**, 361 (1926); *Chem. Abstr.*, **20**, 2707 (1926).
263. P. Trendelenburg, *Arch. exptl. Pathol. Pharmakol.*, **81**, 55 (1917); *Chem. Zentr.*, **1917, II**, 401.
264. Jeanne Lévy and O. Gaudin, *Bull. sci. pharmacol.*, **37**, 407 (1930); *Chem. Abstr.*, **24**, 5934 (1930).
265. K. Kin, *Keijo J. Med.*, **3**, 501 (1932); *Chem. Abstr.*, **27**, 3752 (1933).
266. M. Hayashi, *Japan. J. Med. Sci. IV. Pharmacol.*, **6**, 203 (1932); *Chem. Abstr.*, **27**, 1946 (1933).
267. P. J. Hanzlik, *J. Pharmacol. Exptl. Therap.*, **17**, 445 (1921); *Chem. Abstr.*, **15**, 4023 (1921).
268. T. Ri, *J. Med. Assoc. Formosa*, **35**, 1295 (1936); *Chem. Abstr.*, **32**, 9285 (1938).
269. V. V. Sakussov, *Arch. exptl. Pathol. Pharmakol.*, **144**, 331 (1929).
270. L. Adler, *Arch. exptl. Pathol. Pharmakol.*, **91**, 81 (1921); *Chem. Abstr.*, **16**, 3130 (1922).
271. B. B. Dikshit, *Indian J. Med. Research*, **19**, 765 (1932); *Chem. Abstr.*, **26**, 4097 (1932).
272. E. Zunz, *Arch. néerl. physiol.*, **7**, 276 (1922); *Chem. Abstr.*, **17**, 1074 (1923).
273. H. Lettré and Marianne Albricht, *Naturwissenschaften*, **30**, 184 (1942).
274. N. T. Deleano, N. Popovici, and I. Ionesco, *Beitr. Biol. Pflanz.*, **25**, 261 (1938); *Chem. Abstr.*, **33**, 1782 (1939).
275. W. Sigmund, *Biochem. Z.*, **62**, 299 (1914).
276. G. Ciamician and C. Ravenna, *Atti accad. nazl. Lincei, Mem., Classe sci. fis. mat. e nat.*, **28, Sez. I**, 13 (1919); *Chem. Abstr.*, **13**, 2905 (1919).
277. O. Rygh, *Angew. Chem.*, **45**, 307 (1932).
278. O. Rygh, *Tidsskr. Kjemi og Bergvesen*, **12**, 49 (1932); *Chem. Zentr.*, **1932, II**, 3574.
279. O. Rygh, *Norske Videnskaps-Akad. Oslo, Avhandl. I. Mat. Naturv. Klasse*, **1931**, No. 5, 1; *Chem. Abstr.*, **26**, 5994 (1932).
280. O. Rygh, *Ergeb. Physiol. u. exptl. Pharmakol.*, **35**, 387 (1933); *Chem. Abstr.*, **28**, 3455 (1934).
281. O. Rygh and A. Rygh, *Z. physiol. Chem.*, **211**, 275 (1932); *Chem. Zentr.*, **1932, II**, 3574.
282. O. Rygh, *Z. Vitaminforsch.*, **8**, 166 (1938); *Chem. Abstr.*, **33**, 3848 (1939).
283. N. Bezssonoff, *Bull. soc. chim. biol.*, **14**, 682 (1932).
284. British Patent 383,746; *Chem. Zentr.*, **1933, I**, 1480 Nyegaard & Co., 1932.
285. R. L. Grant, S. Smith, and S. S. Zilva, *Biochem. J.*, **26**, 1628 (1932).
286. W. Neuweiler, *Z. Vitaminforsch.*, **9**, 251 (1939); *Chem. Abstr.*, **33**, 8714 (1939).
287. J. Brüggemann, *Z. physiol. Chem.*, **211**, 231 (1932).

288. T. Matsuoka, *J. Agr. Chem. Soc. Japan*, **9**, 416 (1933); *Chem. Abstr.*, **27**, 4282 (1933).
289. T. Matsuoka, *Mem. Coll. Agr., Kyoto Imp. Univ.*, No. **35**, 71 (1935); *Chem. Abstr.*, **30**, 139 (1936).
290. S. Maruyama, *Sci. Papers Inst. Phys. Chem. Research (Tokyo)*, **20**, 259 (1933); *Chem. Abstr.*, **27**, 4284 (1933).
291. S. Maruyama, *Sci. Papers Inst. Phys. Chem. Research (Tokyo)*, **21**, 93 (1933); *Chem. Abstr.*, **27**, 4835 (1933).
292. E. Abderhalden, *Med. Klin. (Munich)*, **28**, 466 (1932); *Chem. Zentr.*, **1932, I,** 2969.
293. N. N. Vorozhtzov and A. T. Troshtzenko, *Bull. Appl. Botany, Genet. Plant Breeding (U.S.S.R.), Suppl.*, **67**, 161 (1934); *Chem. Abstr.*, **28**, 7318 (1934).
294. J. Shimada, *J. Biochem. (Japan)*, **17**, 395 (1933); *Chem. Abstr.*, **27**, 5103 (1933).
295. Helen M. Kipple and J. M. Dille, *Pharm. Arch.*, **11**, 21 (1940); *Chem. Abstr.*, **34**, 6359 (1940).
296. H. Kako, *Folia Pharmacol. Japon.*, **1**, 164 (1925); *Chem. Zentr.*, **1927, I,** 2100.
297. F. Mercier and Raymond-Hamet, *Compt. rend.*, **185**, 363 (1927).
298. Raymond-Hamet, M. and F. Mercier, *Compt. rend. soc. biol.*, **97**, 1465 (1927); *Chem. Abstr.*, **22**, 821 (1928).
299. H. Chernoruzkii, *Biochem. Z.*, **46**, 112 (1912).
300. F. Mercier, *Compt. rend. soc. biol.*, **122**, 965 (1936); *Chem. Abstr.*, **30**, 7685 (1936).
301. D. I. Macht, *J. Pharmacol. Exptl. Therap.*, **9**, 287 (1917); *Chem. Zentr.*, **1919, III,** 935.
302. Raymond-Hamet, M. *Compt. rend.*, **184**, 774 (1927).
303. Raymond-Hamet, M. *Compt. rend. soc. biol.*, **117**, 980 (1934); *Chem. Abstr.*, **29**, 1499 (1935).
304. B. A. Houssay and E. A. Molinelli, *Compt. rend. soc. biol.*, **93**, 1133 (1925); *Chem. Abstr.*, **20**, 1862 (1926).
305. H. Yokoyama, *Folia Pharmacol. Japon.*, **21**, 309 (1936); *Chem. Abstr.*, **30**, 3518 (1936).
306. T. Takase and H. Sato, *J. Pharm. Soc. Japan*, **49**, 1096 (1929); *Chem. Abstr.*, **24**, 1428 (1930).
307. F. Mercier, *Compt. rend. soc. biol.*, **97**, 1468 (1927); *Chem. Abstr.*, **22**, 821 (1928).
308. R. Fabre, *Bull. soc. chim. biol.*, **12**, 954 (1930); *Chem. Abstr.*, **25**, 2195 (1931).
309. R. Fabre, *J. pharm. chim.*, [8]**12**, 339 (1930); *Chem. Abstr.*, **25**, 1591 (1931).
310. A. D. Welch and V. E. Henderson, *J. Pharmacol. Exptl. Therap.*, **51**, 482 (1934); *Chem. Abstr.*, **28**, 7366 (1934).
311. H. V. Rice, *J. Pharmacol. Exptl. Therap.*, **63**, 329 (1938); *Chem. Zentr.*, **1939, II,** 1107.
312. H. Offergeld, *Berlin. klin. Wochschr.*, **50**, 62 (1913); *Chem. Abstr.*, **7**, 3160 (1913).
313. H. Lungberg, *Compt. rend. soc. biol.*, **92**, 644 (1925); *Chem. Abstr.*, **19**, 1905 (1925).
314. G. Guérin, *J. pharm. chim.*, [7]**7**, 438 (1913); *Chem. Zentr.*, **1913, II,** 54.
315. N. Cooper and R. A. Hatcher, *J. Pharmacol. Exptl. Therap.*, **51**, 411 (1934); *Chem. Abstr.*, **28**, 7364 (1934).
316. G. Gori, *Boll. chim. farm.*, **52**, 891 (1913); *Chem. Zentr.*, **1914, I,** 1377.
317. D. H. Wester, *Pharm. Weekblad*, **51**, 1444 (1914).
318. M. Kubly, *Pharm. Z. f. Russland*, **5**, 457 (1866); *Jahresbericht*, **1866**, 823.
319. M. A. Mancini, *Boll. chim. farm.*, **62**, 3 (1923); *Chem. Abstr.*, **17**, 2344 (1923).
320. M. Scholtz, *Arch. Pharm.*, **250**, 418 (1912).
321. O. Hesse, *Ann.*, **176**, 189 (1875).
322. D. B. Dott, *Pharm. J.*, [3]**14**, 582 (1883); *Jahresbericht*, **1884**, 1389.

Chapter 33

Bisbenzylisoquinoline Alkaloids

MARSHALL KULKA

Dominion Rubber Research Laboratory, Guelph, Ontario

	Page
I. Introduction	199
II. Alkaloids Containing One Diphenyl Ether Linkage	203
1. Magnoline	203
2. Dauricine	207
3. Magnolamine	209
4. Aztequine	210
III. Alkaloids Containing Two Diphenyl Ether Linkages	211
1. Oxyacanthine	213
2. Berbamine	215
3. Isotetrandrine	215
4. Tetrandrine	216
5. Repandine	217
6. Daphnandrine	218
7. Fangchinoline	219
8. Pheanthine	220
9. Trilobamine (Daphnoline)	220
10. Aromoline	221
11. Epistephanine	222
12. Hypoepistephanine	223
13. Cepharanthine	223
14. Isochondodendrine	224
15. Methylisochondodendrine (Cycleanine)	227
16. Bebeerine (Chondodendrine)	227
17. Chondrofoline	230
18. Curine	230
19. Tubocurarine Chloride	231
20. *d*-Chondocurine	233
21. Neoprotocuridine and Protocuridine	234
22. Insularine	235
IV. Alkaloids Containing Three Diphenyl Ether Linkages	237
1. Trilobine and Isotrilobine	238
2. Micranthine	240
3. Menisarine and Normenisarine	242
V. References	243

I. Introduction

The bisbenzylisoquinoline or biscoclaurine alkaloids, which comprise a group of over thirty members, possess structures containing two benzylisoquinoline nuclei joined by one, two, or three ether linkages. They occur in plants of the Menispermaceae and related families which include the genera *Berberis*, *Magnolia*, *Daphnandra*, and some *Strychnos* species.

The position and the number of ether linkages in the molecule have served as a convenient criteria for the classification of these alkaloids into subgroups. Franz Faltis (69, 95) was the first to recognize that all members of this class could be considered as offsprings of the benzylisoquinoline compounds coclaurine (I) or norcoclaurine (II). According to his belief

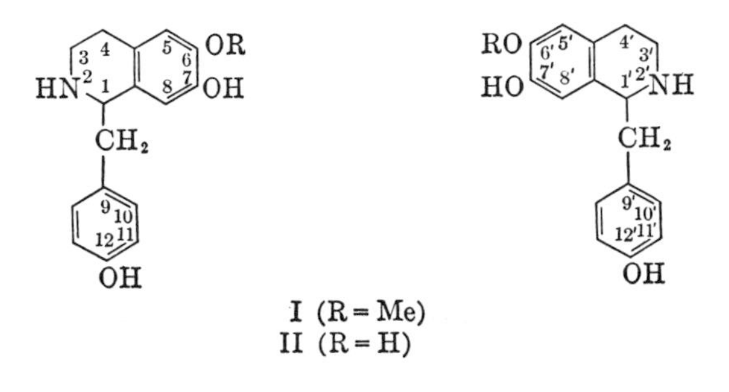

and that of his followers the bisbenzylisoquinoline alkaloids are formed in the plant from two molecules of coclaurine (I) or norcoclaurine (II) by enzymatic dehydrogenation followed by methylation of some or all of the OH and NH groups. The dehydrogenation occurs between a phenolic hydroxyl of one molecule of I or II and a reactive nuclear hydrogen of another molecule. The simplest case is where the ether formation takes place between the 12-hydroxyl of one molecule of II and the 11′-hydrogen of another molecule to form a skeletal structure common to the alkaloids of series A (Diagram 1). If in addition another ether linkage is formed between the 7-OH and 8′-H of II or 8-H and 7′-OH of II skeletal structures are provided which account for the oxyacanthine-berbamine series (B). The only differences between the individual members of series B are the extent of methylation and structural or optical isomerism. A third ether linkage may be introduced into the molecule by dehydrogenation to yield alkaloids of series E. The two diphenyl ether linkages between two molecules of II may be formed at different positions from those in the members of the oxyacanthine-berbamine series (B), and this explains the occurrence of the alkaloids of the series C and D.

The Faltis theory explains the biological synthesis of all the bisbenzylisoquinoline alkaloids except two. The proposed structures of these two (magnolamine and aztequine) contain one more hydroxyl group than a compound formed from two molecules of norcoclaurine (II) by enzymatic dehydrogenation. However, in these cases it may be assumed that the extra hydroxyl is introduced into the molecule either before or after ether formation. Furthermore, the formation of trilobine and of isotrilobine

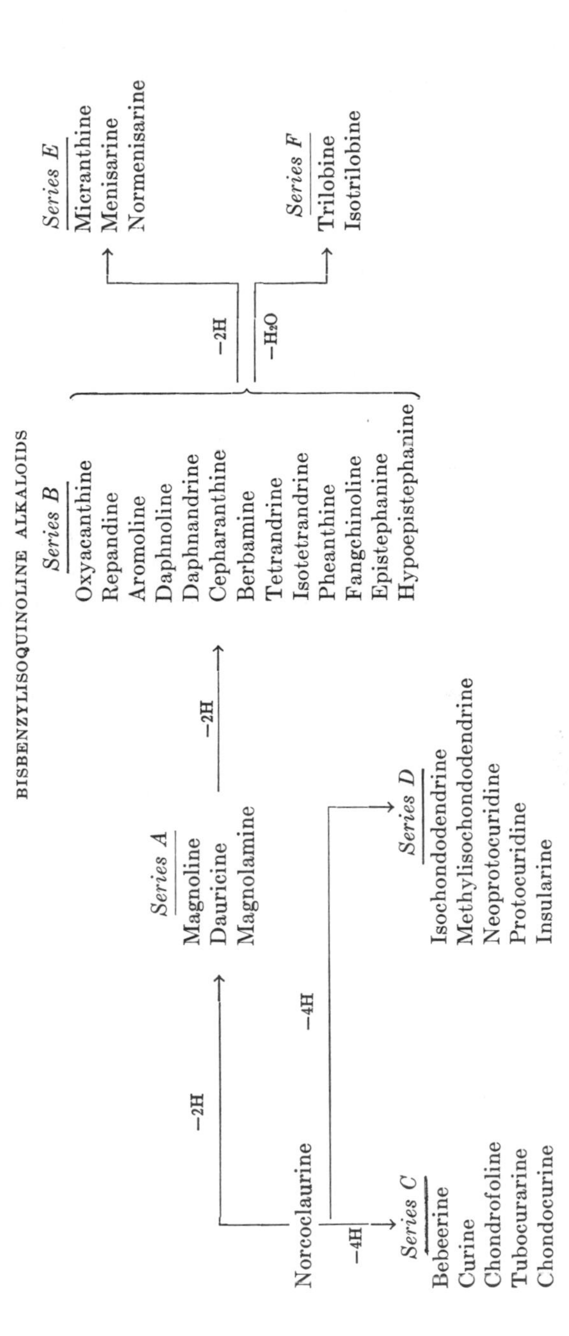

DIAGRAM 1

BISBENZYLISOQUINOLINE ALKALOIDS

by dehydration of the appropriate bisbenzylisoquinoline is not a satisfactory mechanism. There are no known reactions by which diaryl ethers can be formed under comparable conditions, and a mechanism involving a 6,7-dihydroxyisoquinoline and a 6-hydroxyisoquinoline, already joined through their benzyl groups by an ether linkage, seems much more plausible.

In the bisbenzylisoquinoline alkaloids the oxygen bridges between two molecules of II occur mainly at positions 7, 8, 11 and 12, seldom at 6, and never at 5. In general the hetero ring is fully hydrogenated and the secondary nigrogen atoms may or may not be methylated. There are a few examples in which one of the hetero rings contains a tertiary nitrogen, that is, a double bond occurs at the 1,2-position.

Coclaurine (I) and norcoclaurine (II) contain one asymmetric center (at postion 1). When two molecules of I or II are united by ether bridge(s) the resulting unsymmetrical molecule now contains two asymmetric centers and, therefore, four optical isomers are possible. Such optical isomers do occur in nature, especially in the oxyacanthine-berbamine series (B).

The determination of the structures of these alkaloids has been of interest to many investigators for a long time. None of the bisbenzylisoquinoline alkaloids have, as yet, been synthesized, but degradative studies have pointed to structures which are acceptable with certainty. Benzylisoquinolines as well as bisbenzylisoquinolines undergo certain important reactions, and these have been exploited by the various workers for structure determination. The molecule is usually split into two fragments by oxidative degradation and these are then identified. The methylenic group (—CH_2—) in a tetrahydrobenzylisoquinoline is susceptible to facile oxidation, and potassium permanganate causes rupture easily at this point to form a 1-oxotetrahydroisoquinoline and a benzoic acid. The more important degradation method consists of first the exhaustive methylation of the alkaloid at the OH and NH groups and then the treatment of the resulting quaternary ammonium halide (III) with alkali (Hofmann degradation). This ruptures the hetero ring to form the unsaturated methine

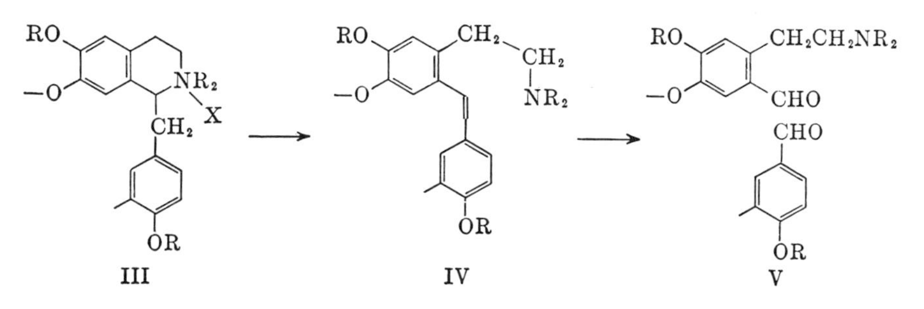

IV. The methine (IV) when treated with oxidizing agents undergoes cleavage at the double bond, ozone yielding the two respective aldehydes (V) and potassium permanganate the corresponding acids. The dimethylamino aldehyde (V) or acid on further degradation according to the method of Hofmann furnishes trimethylamine and an *o*-vinylbenzaldehyde or *o*-vinylbenzoic acid.

Recently a method has been developed which cleaves only the ether-linked oxygen forming the diphenyl ether in the bisbenzylisoquinoline alkaloid. Thus when the alkaloid is methylated and then treated with sodium in liquid ammonia two benzylisoquinoline fragments are formed which may be separated and identified. This method of degradation has solved unsettled problems regarding structural and optical isomerism of many alkaloids, especially those of the oxyacanthine-berbamine series.

The physical constants of the bisbenzylisoquinoline alkaloids and of their derivatives are listed in Table 1.

II. Alkaloids Containing One Diphenyl Ether Linkage

The four alkaloids that belong to this class are magnoline, dauricine, magnolamine and aztequine. They all have the same skeletal structure which, according to Faltis (69, 95), is formed in the plant by enzymatic dehydrogenation of two molecules of norcoclaurine (II), the hydrogen of the 12-hydroxyl of one molecule and the 11′-hydrogen of the other molecule being eliminated. The next step in the biosynthesis is methylation of the phenolic groups, and it is in the degree of methylation that magnoline and dauricine differ from one another. Both magnolamine and aztequine are reported to possess one phenolic hydroxyl more than the bimolecular dehydrogenation product of norcoclaurine (II). This interesting new fact would require modification of the biogenetic theory which would include hydroxylation of the bimolecular dehydrogenation product of II or the addition of dihydroxybenzyltetrahydroisoquinolines to the list of progenitors.

1. Magnoline

The simplest alkaloid of the bisbenzylisoquinoline group, magnoline (VI) (1) occurs in the leaves of *Magnolia fuscata* Andr., which grows on the Caucasian shores of the Black Sea. It is a yellow, crystalline, optically active substance forming vitreous salts with hydrogen halides. The structure of magnoline was established by Proskurnina and Orekhov (2). They methylated it with diazomethane and then oxidized the resulting trimethylmagnoline with potassium permanganate. This yielded 4′,5-dicarboxy-2-methoxydiphenyl ether (VIII, R = CH_3) and 1-oxo-6,7-dimethoxy-*N*-methyltetrahydroisoquinoline (IX, R = CH_3) whose struc-

TABLE 1

PHYSICAL CONSTANTS OF BISBENZYLISOQUINOLINE ALKALOIDS

Alkaloid and derivatives	M.p., °C.	$[\alpha]_D^t$	References
Magnoline (VI)	179	−9.6° (pyridine)	1, 2
Magnoline picrate	162 (dec.)		
Trimethylmagnoline	110		
Dauricine (VII)	115	−139° (methanol) (t = 11)	3
Dauricine methiodide	204		
α-Methyldauricine methine	128		8
Magnolamine (XVII)	119	+111.6° (ethanol)	109
Tetramethylmagnolamine	152		
Tetraethylmagnolamine	103		
Aztequine (XVIII)	176		115
Oxyacanthine (XXVI)	217	+279° ($CHCl_3$)	13, 14, 15
Oxyacanthine methiodide	250		
O-Methyloxyacanthine (XXV)	169		41
O-Methyloxyacanthine α-methine	153		15
Berbamine (XXXI)	172	+108.6° ($CHCl_3$) (t = 25)	22, 23
Berbamine tetrahydrate	156		
O-Methylberbamine (XXX)	182	+132° (t = 20)	18, 21
O-Ethylberbamine	188		21
O-Methylberbamine α-methine	172		18, 21
O-Methylberbamine β-methine	147		
Isotetrandrine (XXX)	182	+146° ($CHCl_3$) (t = 17)	23, 35
Isotetrandrine α-methine	172		
Tetrandrine (XXX)	217	+263.1° ($CHCl_3$) (t = 24)	25, 36
Tetrandrine picrate	242 (dec.)		
Tetrandrine α-methine	172		26
Tetrandrine β-methine	227 (dec.)		
Repandine (XXVI)	255	−106° ($CHCl_3$) (t = 15)	108
O-Methylrepandine dimethiodide	260 (dec.)	−95° (aq. ethanol) (t = 15)	
O-Methylrepandine methine dimethiodide	260 (dec.)		
Daphnandrine (XXIX)	280		111, 112
O,*N*-Dimethyldaphnandrine dimethiodide	256 (dec.)		
O,*N*-Dimethyldaphnandrine methine dimethiodide	260 (dec.)		
Fangchinoline	238	+255.1° ($CHCl_3$) (t = 18)	36

TABLE 1—(*Continued*)

Alkaloid and derivatives	M.p., °C.	$[\alpha]_D^t$	References
Fangchinoline picrate	224 (dec.)		
O-Methylfangchinoline (XXX)	217		
O-Ethylfangchinoline	117		
Pheanthine (XXX)	210	−278° ($CHCl_3$) (t = 30)	37
Pheanthine picrate	263		
Pheanthine α-methine	173		38
Trilobamine (Daphnoline) (XXVIII)	196	+356° (acetic acid) (t = 15)	40, 112
Trimethyltrilobamine (XXV)	169		40,41
Trimethyltriolabmine α-methine	152		41
O,O,N-Trimethyldaphnoline dimethiodide	260 (dec.)		112
Aromoline (XXVII)	175		112
O,O-Diethylaromoline dimethiodide	260 (dec.)		
O,O-Dimethylaromoline methine dimethiodide	240 (dec.)		
Epistephanine (XLIII or XLIV, R = CH_3)	198	+196° ($CHCl_3$) (t = 15)	100
Hydroepistephanine hydrochloride	260 (dec.)	+299° (H_2O) (t = 8)	128
Hydroepistephanine α-methine	110		
Hypoepistephanine (XLIII or XLIV, R = H)	257 (dec.)	175° (t = 27)	102
O-Methylhypoepistephanine (XLIII or XLIV, R = CH_3)	198		
Cehparanthine (XLVIII or XLIX)	155	+277° ($CHCl_3$) (t = 20)	42, 44
Cepharanthine α-methine	100 (hydrate)		44
Cepharanthine β-methine	184		
Isochondodendrine (LVII)	316 (dec.)	+120° (0.1*N* HCl) (t = 22)	104
Isochondodendrine dimethiodide	287 (dec.)		
O-Methylisochondodendrine (LXI)	273	−36.8° (ethanol)	55
O-Methylisochondodendrine α-methine	210		54, 55
O-Methylisochondodendrine β-methine	169		
d-Bebeerine (LXVI)	221	+332° (pyridine)	56, 71
l-Bebeerine (Curine) (LXVI)	221	−328° (pyridine)	71, 123
O-Methylbebeerine α-methine	122		76
Chondrofoline (LXVII)	135 (hydrate)	−281° (0.1*N* HCl) (t = 20)	68

TABLE 1—(*Continued*)

Alkaloid and derivatives	M.p., °C.	$[\alpha]_D^t$	References
Chondrofoline nitrate	225 (dec.)		
O-Methylchondrofoline methine methiodide	237, 190		
d-Tubocurarine chloride (LXVIII)	275	+215 (H_2O) (t = 25)	76, 123, 137
O-Dimethyltubocurarine iodide	267		
O-Methyltubocurarine methine methiodide	234, 230, 190		
Chondocurine	234	+200° (0.1*N* HCl) +105° (pyridine) (t = 24)	104
Chondocurine dimethiodide	280	+184° (methanol) (t = 24)	104, 137
O-Methylchondocurine dimethiodide	266		104
Neoprotocuridine (LXII)	232 (dec.)		82
O-Methylneoprotocuridine methiodide	>300		
O-Methylneoprotocuridine methine	>320		
Protocuridine	295		82
O-Methylprotocuridine dimethiodide	318 (dec.)		
Insularine (LXX)	160		83, 107
Insularine methiodide	300 (dec.)	+28° (t = 7)	
Hydroinsularine	135	+3.5°	
Insularine α-methine	115	(t = 10)	
Insularine β-methine	185		
Trilobine (LXXXVII)	235	+304° ($CHCl_3$) (t = 13)	85, 87, 88
Trilobine dimethiodide	276 (dec.)		
Trilobine methylmethine	218, 228		88
Isotrilobine (LXXXVIII)	215	+293° ($CHCl_3$) (t = 19.5)	86, 90
Isotrilobine dimethiodide	262 (dec.)		
Isotrilobine methylmethine	117, 122		
Micranthine (XCIV; R_5 = H; of R_1 and R_2 one is H, the other methyl; of R_3 and R_4 one is H, the other methyl)	196	−231 ($CHCl_3$) (t = 22)	113
Micranthine sulfate	310 (dec.)		
O,O,N-Trimethylmicranthine dimethiodide	260 (dec.)	−158° (H_2O) (t = 20)	
O,O,N-Trimethylmicranthine methine	115		

TABLE 1—*Continued*

Alkaloid and Derivatives	M.p. °C.	$[\alpha]_D^t$	References
Menisarine (XCVI or XCVII)	208	+149° ($CHCl_3$) (t = 12)	96, 98
Menisarine dimethiodide	270 (dec.)		
Dihydromenisarine	164	266° ($CHCl_3$) (t = 15)	
Methyldihydromenisarine methine	112		
Normenisarine	223	+190° (t = 21)	97
O-Methylnormenisarine (XCVI or XCVII)	208		

tures were proved by comparison with synthetic compounds (15). In order to locate the postions of the three phenolic groups in the molecule the Russian workers first ethylated (diazoethane) magnoline and then oxidized the triethylmagnoline as before. The oxidation products proved to be 4′,5-dicarboxy-2-ethoxydiphenyl ether (VIII, R = C_2H_5) and 1-oxo-6-methoxy-7-ethoxy-*N*-methyltetrahydroisoquinoline (IX, R = C_2H_5). These results showed that of the three phenolic groups in magnoline one is in the 4-position of the diphenyl ether and the other two in the 7-positions of the isoquinoline rings. Thus formula VI is assigned to magnoline.

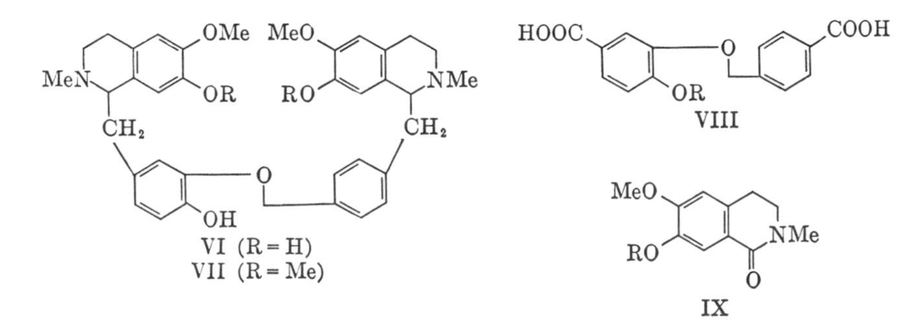

2. Dauricine

Closely related to magnoline is the alkaloid dauricine which has been found in *Menispermum dauricum* DC. by Kondo and Narita (3), and later by Manske (4) in the subterranean stems and roots of a woody liana, *Menispermum canadense* L., widely distributed throughout North America. It is a phenolic yellow resinous base soluble in most organic solvents. On the basis of the Rast molecular weight determination the Japanese workers (3) assigned to dauricine the empirical formula $C_{19}H_{23}O_3N$ and found it to possess one *N*-methyl, one phenolic, and two methoxyl groups. The alkaloid when treated with methyl iodide, then methylated with dimethyl sulfate, and the resulting *O*-methyldauricine methiodide subjected to a two-stage Hofmann degradation, yielded trimethylamine and a nitrogen-free substance (5, 6, 7). The latter on oxidation with potassium permanganate in acetone gave 4,5-dimethoxyphthalic acid (*m*-hemipinic) and 4′,5-dicarboxy-2-methoxydiphenyl ether (VIII, R = CH_3). On the basis of these degradation studies Kondo and Narita proposed that dauricine was identical with dimethylcoclaurine. However the degradation products from these two compounds were distinguishable. Faltis and Frauendorfer (52) suggested a biscoclaurine formula ($C_{38}H_{44}O_6N_2$), but the Japanese workers adhered to the dimethylcoclaurine formula because the results of Rast molecular weight determination of dauricine and of its derivatives agreed better with the simpler formula.

Five years later Kondo and Narita (8) redetermined the methoxyl values of a number of *O*-methyldauricine derivatives and found that these new values agreed better with the C_{38} formula. Finally they proved the structure of dauricine to be of the bisbenzylisoquinoline type by the synthesis of well-defined dauricine derivatives and by comparison with the natural products.

The starting materials for the synthesis were 4-methoxy-3,4′-diphenylether-1,1′-diacetic acid (X) and homoveratrylamine. The former (X) was obtained from 4′,5-dicarboxy-2-methoxydiphenyl ether (VIII, R = CH_3) by converting first to the acid chloride and then to the dialdehyde by the Rosenmund method, followed by side chain lengthening through the azlactone. The phenylacetic acid (X) and homoveratrylamine were condensed by heating in tetralin and the resulting amide (XI) ring-closed by means of phosphorus pentachloride in chloroform. This was then catalytically reduced to the scondary base (XII). The base (XII) was treated with dimethyl sulfate and the methyl methosulfate degraded according to the method of Hofmann. The resulting methine base (XIII) was identical with the α-methine base obtained from *O*-methyldauricine by Hofmann degradation. The position of the phenolic hydroxyl in dauricine was established by ethylation followed by a two-stage Hofmann degradation of *O*-ethyldauricine and oxidation of the resulting nitrogen-free compound. The fact that the oxidation product was 4′,5-dicarboxy-2-ethoxydiphenyl ether (VIII, R = C_2H_5) proved that the phenolic group was in the ortho position to the diphenyl ether linkage. Thus the structure of dauricine was shown to be that represented by VII.

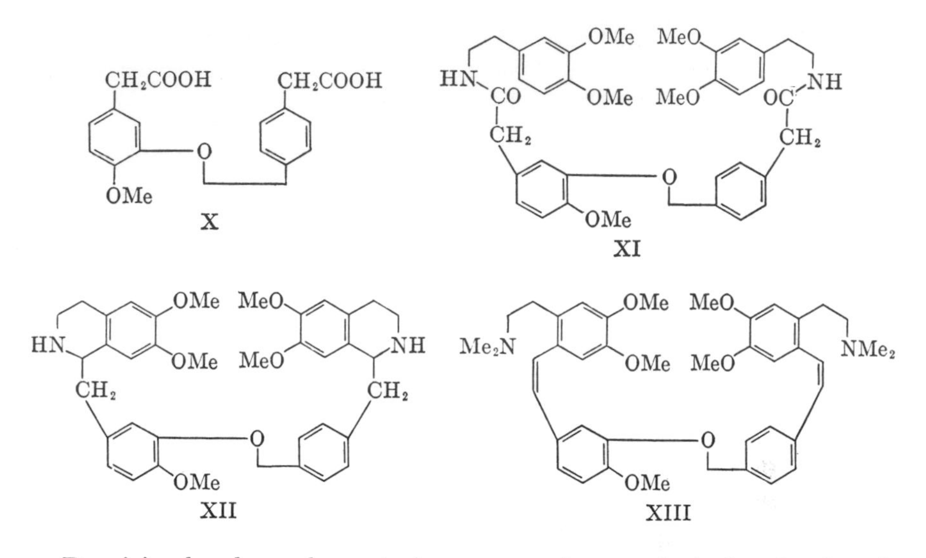

Dauricine has been shown to have some pharmacological action in animals (9). When administered as the hydrochloride to frogs, mice, and rabbits it provokes a mixed picture of paralysis and convulsions. Dauricine dimethiodide is curare-like in action but is only about one-seventh as potent as *d*-tubocurarine and is more toxic (114). It causes ataxis, respiratory depression, poor relaxation, and anoxic death at doses of 6 mg. per kilogram when administred to mice intraperitoneally.

3. MAGNOLAMINE

Magnolamine occurs together with magnoline in the leaves of *Michelia fuscata* Blume (*Magnolia fuscata*, Magnoliaceae). The two alkaloids can be separated by virtue of the difference of their solubility in chloroform. Magnolamine is a crystalline phenolic base with empirical formula $C_{32}H_{24}O(OH)_4(OCH_3)_2(NCH_3)_2$. In an attempt to elucidate the structure of magnolamine, Proskurnina (109) methylated it with diazomethane and oxidized the resulting tetramethyl ether with potassium permanganate in acetone solution. He obtained 1-oxo-2-methyl-1,2,3,4-tetrahydro-6,7-dimethoxyisoquinoline (IX, R = CH_3) and an acid (m.p. 280–281, $C_{16}H_{14}O_7$) which he named *magnolamic acid.* A similar oxidation of magnolamine tetraethyl ether yielded three products, one of which proved to be 1-oxo-2-methyl-1,2,3,4-tetrahydro-6-methoxy-7-ethoxyisoquinoline (IX, R = C_2H_5). This showed that magnolamine carries a hydroxyl group in the 7-position of each of the two isoquinoline nuclei.

Magnolamic acid was next examined in order to determine the structure of the diphenyl ether portions of the molecule of magnolamine. A study of the alkali fusion products of magnolamic acid pointed to the structure of a dimethoxydicarboxydiphenyl ether with both methoxyl groups on the same benzene nucleus. On this basis Proskurnina (109) proposed the structure XIV or XV for the alkaloid. This however proved to be incorrect when Tomita and coworkers (110, 135) synthesized a series of isomeric dimethoxydicarboxydiphenyl ethers and found that magnolamic acid was

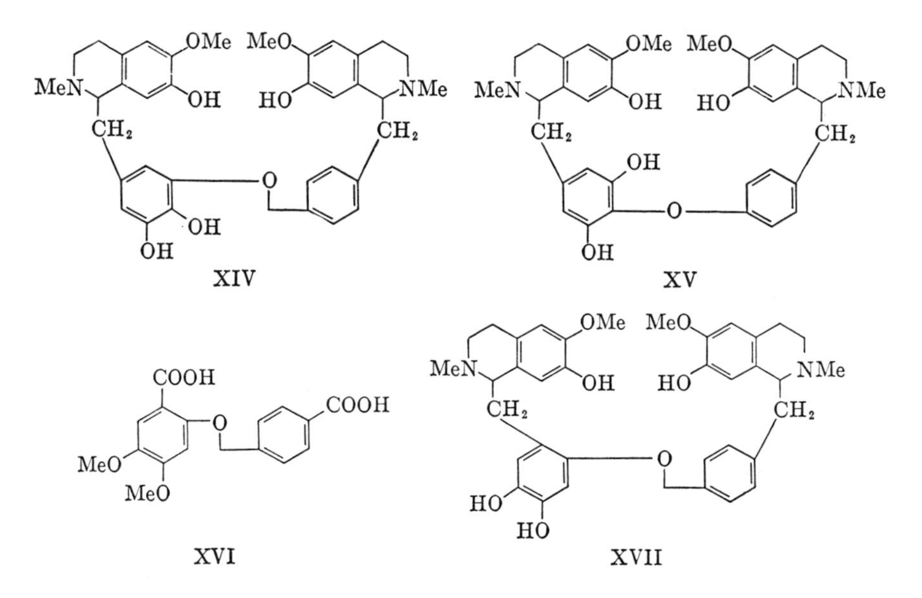

dentical with 2,4′-dicarboxy-4,5-dimethoxydiphenyl ether (XVI). The most probable structural formula for magnolamine is therefore XVII.

4. Aztequine

The alkaloid aztequine was isolated by Pallares and Garza (115) from the leaves of "Yoloxochitl," a plant belonging to the Mexican genus *Talauma* Juss. of the family Magnoliaceae. Analyses indicated the formula $C_{36}H_{40}O_7N_2$ and showed the presence of two methoxyl groups, four phenolic groups, and methylimino groups. A series of degradation studies indicated the structural formula XVIII for aztequine. The treatment of aztequine with hydriodic acid yielded two compounds, $C_{18}H_{21}O_4N$ and $C_{18}H_{20}O_3NI$. These were believed to be XIX and XX, respectively, arising from XVIII as a result of the diphenyl ether cleavage. When each of these fragments (XIX and XX) were further degraded 1-oxo-2-methyl-6-methoxy-7-hydroxy-1,2,3,4-tetrahydroisoquinoline (IX, R = H) and vanillic acid were formed.

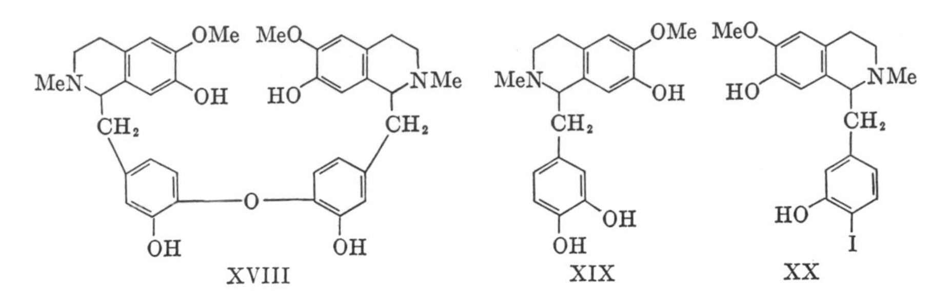

It is remarkable, if true, that hydriodic acid ruptures the diphenyl oxide linkage of XVIII and leaves intact methoxyl groups. Pallares and Garza did not report the melting points of XIX and XX, and the degradation products were identified only on the basis of their melting points, no mixed melting points with authentic samples being reported. It is therefore felt that further work is necessary in order to establish the structure of aztequine.

III. Alkaloids Containing Two Diphenyl Ether Linkages

This group of alkaloids is formed in the plant (Faltis theory) by a double enzymatic dehydrogenation of two molecules of norcoclaurine (II). It is necessary to perform this bimolecular dehydrogenation in three different ways in order to provide correct skeletal structures for the known bisbenzylisoquinoline alkaloids of this group. First, the two diphenyl ether linkages may be formed by the dehydrogenation occurring between the 12-hydroxyl of one molecule of II and the 11′-hydrogen of another molecule; and between the 7-hydroxyl of one molecule of II and the 8′-hydrogen of II. This can be done in two different ways and therefore two structural isomers (XXI and XXII) are evolved. Each of these structural isomers (XXI and XXII) possesses two asymmetric carbon atoms (at the 1-positions of the isoquinoline nuclei). Therefore there are four possible optical isomers for each structure. The alkaloids oxyacanthine, repandine, aromoline, berbamine, tetrandrine, isotetrandrine, pheanthine, fangchinoline, epistephanine, hypoepistephanine, and cepharanthine all possess the skeletal structures XXI or XXII. The differences between these eleven alkaloids lie in optical activity and the extent of alkylation (of the OH and NH groups). In two of these alkaloids (epistephanine and hypoepistephanine) one of the tetrahydroisoquinoline rings of the skeletal strucutres XXI and XXII is dehydrogenated to 3,4-dihydroisoquinoline.

Secondly, the bimolecular dehydrogenation of norcoclaurine (II) can take place between the 12-hydroxyl groups and the 8-hydrogens to form the symmetrical structure XXIII. The alkaloids isochondodendrine,

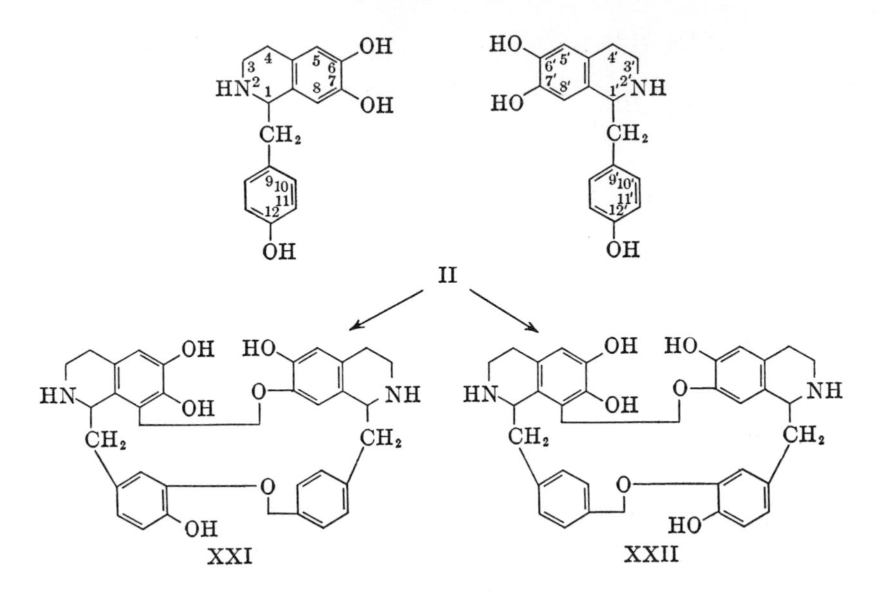

methylisochondodendrine, neoprotocuridine, protocuridine, and insularine possess the skeletal structure XXIII.

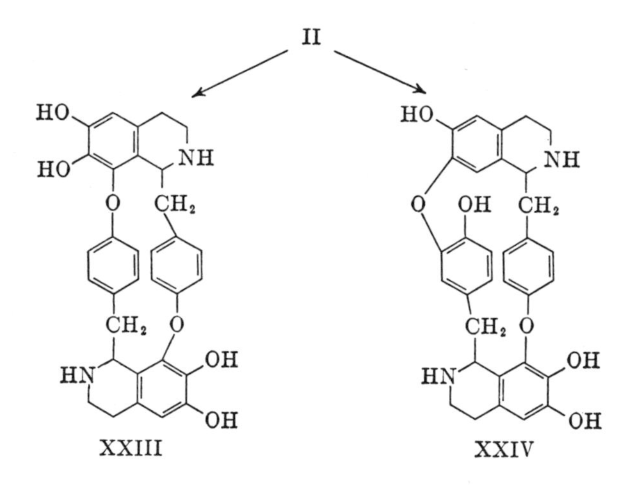

Thirdly, if the bimolecular dehydrogenation of II takes place between the 12-hydroxyl and 8′-hydrogen on the one hand and between the 7-hydroxyl and the 11′-hydrogen on the other the structure XXIV is formed. To this class belong the alkaloids bebeerine, chondrofoline, curine, tubocurarine chloride, and chondocurine.

1. OXYACANTHINE

The alkaloids oxyacanthine and berbamine found in the roots of *Berberis vulgaris* L., *B. aquifolium* Pursh (10–13), and in *B. thunbergii* DC. have been known for a long time, but exact knowledge of their constitutions has been acquired only recently. They are amorphous bases which solvate readily and then crystallize only with difficulty. The correct composition of oxyacanthine, $C_{37}H_{40}O_6N_2$, was determined by Späth and Kolbe (14), who were able to obtain the alkaloid in purer form than previous workers. Four of the oxygen atoms were accounted for by the presence of one phenolic and three methoxyl groups. The ease with which oxyacanthine underwent the Emde degradation to yield trimethylamine and a nitrogen-free compound suggested that two nitrogen atoms were bound in monocyclic rings. The structure was further elucidated by subjecting methylated oxyacanthine to a one-stage Hofmann degradation followed by permanganate oxidation of the resulting methine base (later proved to be XXXII) (15, 16). This yielded a dibasic acid (m.p. 313–314°) which was identical with 4′,5-dicarboxy-2-methoxydiphenyl ether (VIII, R = CH_3) synthesized by the Ullmann condensation of *p*-bromobenzoic acid ester and the sodium salt of isovanillic acid methyl ester. Oxyacanthine ethylated with diazoethane and degraded and oxidized similarly

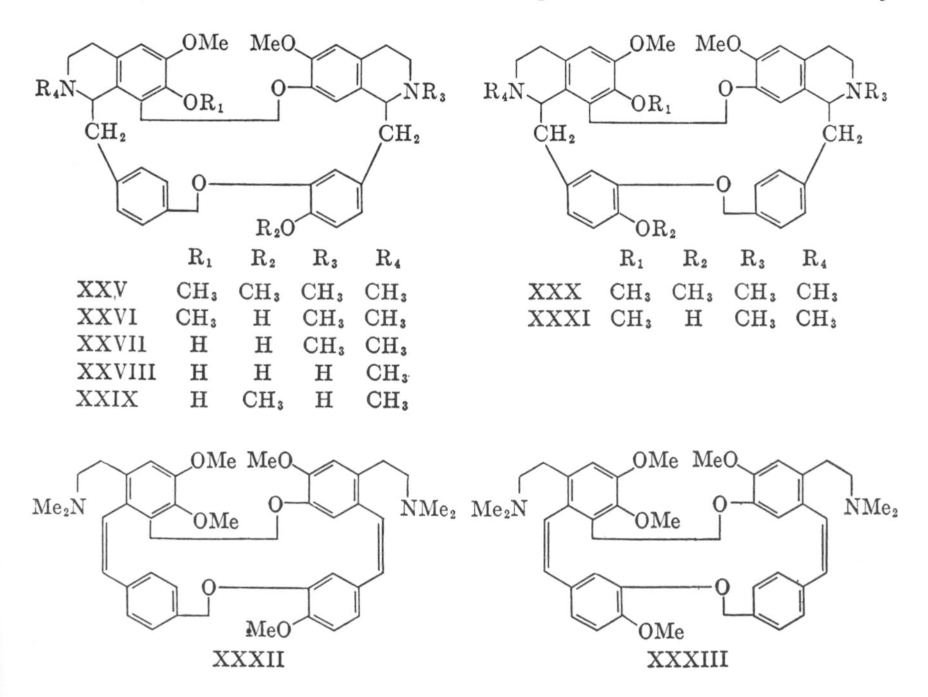

	R_1	R_2	R_3	R_4
XXV	CH_3	CH_3	CH_3	CH_3
XXVI	CH_3	H	CH_3	CH_3
XXVII	H	H	CH_3	CH_3
XXVIII	H	H	H	CH_3
XXIX	H	CH_3	H	CH_3

	R_1	R_2	R_3	R_4
XXX	CH_3	CH_3	CH_3	CH_3
XXXI	CH_3	H	CH_3	CH_3

XXXII

XXXIII

yielded 4′,5-dicarboxy-2-ethoxydiphenyl ether (VIII, R = C_2H_5), thus fixing the position of the phenolic group as ortho to the diphenyl ether linkage.

The structure of the nitrogenous half of the molecule of oxyacanthine was determined by von Bruchhausen and coworkers (17, 18). The methine base of oxyacanthine methyl ether (later proved to be XXXII) previously subjected to permanganate oxidation was now treated with ozone and two crystalline products were obtained in high yield. The nitrogen-free product was 4′,5-diformyl-2-methoxydiphenyl ether (XXXIV) whose constitution was easily shown by oxidation to VIII (R = CH_3). The nitrogen-containing degradation product formed a disemicarbazone, added bromine or hydrogen, and liberated trimethylamine when treated with alkali, observations which indicate the structure XXXV. This compound was next subjected to the Hofmann degradation to yield trimethylamine and the divinyl dialdehyde XXXVI, which on catalytic reduction produced 3,4′-diethyl-2,5′-diformyl-2′,5,6-trimethoxydiphenyl ether (XXXVII). Further reduction (Clemmensen) yielded 3,4,4′-trimethoxy-6,6′-diethyl-1,1′-dimethyl-2,3′-diphenyl ether (XXXVIII), which proved to be identical with a synthetic product obtained by the Ullmann condensation of 1,2-dimethoxy-4-ethyl-5-methyl-6-bromobenzene and the sodium salt of 2-methoxy-4-ethyl-5-methylphenol. Oxyacanthine therefore is composed of two benzyltetrahydroisoquinoline rings linked by two oxygen bridges and must have the formula XXVI or XXXI.

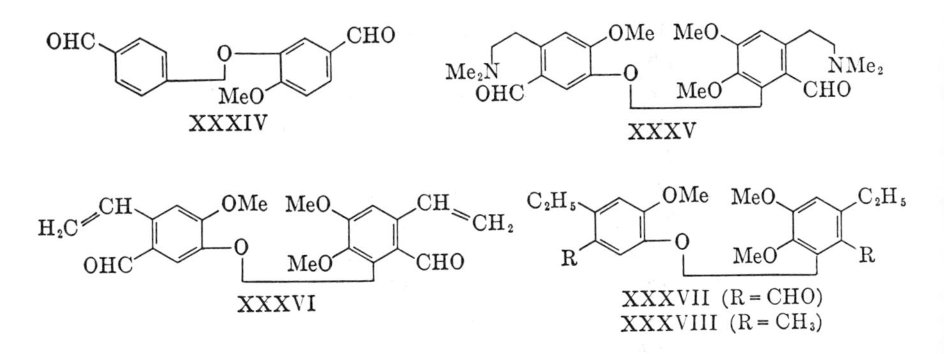

Tomita and coworkers (126) were able to prove (p. 215) that berbamine, which is the structural isomer of oxyacanthine, is represented by the formula XXXI. Therfore the structure of oxyacanthine must be XXVI.

Oxyacanthine is reported to have some sympathicolytic action (19). In dogs, after chloralose anesthesia, double vagatomy in the neck, and artificial respiration, this alkaloid counteracts the action of adrenaline on the blood pressure and renal constriction. When oxyacanthine hydrochloride is injected into the femoral artery of a dog it produces dilation of the blood vessels (20).

2. Berbamine

Berbamine occurs in *B. vulgaris*, *B. aquifolium* (12, 13), *B. thunbergii* (22), *Stephania cepharantha* Hayata (23), and in *B. swaseyi* Buckley (*Mahonia swaseyi* Fedde) to the extent of about 2% in the dried roots (24). Santos (21) found that berbamine was isomeric with oxyacanthine and that oxidation of berbamine methyl ether produced 4′,5-dicarboxy-2-methoxydiphenyl ether (VIII, R = CH_3), as in the case of oxyacanthine. The constitution of the isoquinoline portion of the molecule was determined by von Bruchhausen, Oberembt, and Feldhaus (18). The products obtained after a Hofmann degradation of *O*-methylberbamine followed by ozonization were the same two dialdehydes, XXXV and 4′,5-diformyl-2-methoxydiphenyl ether (XXXIV), as were obtained from *O*-methyloxyacanthine by similar treatment. On the basis of these facts von Bruchhausen and coworkers concluded that berbamine and oxyacanthine are structural isomers. If oxyacanthine is assigned the formula XXVI then berbamine must have the formula XXXI or vice versa.

The structural difference between these two alkaloids was obscure until Tomita and coworkers (126, 127, 132) began their study of the diphenyl ether cleavage products. When a solution of *O*-methylberbamine (isotetrandrine) in toluene was treated with sodium dissolved in liquid ammonia, two products were obtained. These were identified as *l*-1-(4′-methoxybenzyl)-*N*-methyl-6,7-dimethoxy-1,2,3,4-tetrahydroisoquinoline (XXXIX) and *d*-1-(4′-hydroxybenzyl)-*N*-methyl-6-methoxy-7-hydroxy-1,2,3,4-tetrahydroisoquinoline (XL) (132). If the two compounds XXXIX and XL are considered as hydrogenolysis products (XXX, dotted lines) there can be only one constitutional formula applicable to the structure of *O*-methylberbamine and that is XXX. Therefore the structure of berbamine must be that represented by XXXI, with the steric configurations at the two asymmetric centers levo- and dextrorotatory.

3. Isotetrandrine

Isotetrandrine, a crystalline base obtained from the alcoholic extract of *Stephania cepharantha*, is identical with *O*-methylberbamine and must therefore have the structure XXX (23, 35, 126, 127, 132). A two-stage Hofmann degradation of the methiodide of isotetrandrine yielded des-*N*-isotetrandrine (m.p. 220°), which did not depress the melting points of des-*N*-berbamine methyl ether. Final proof of the relation of these two alkaloids lies in the fact that berbamine methylated with diazomethane

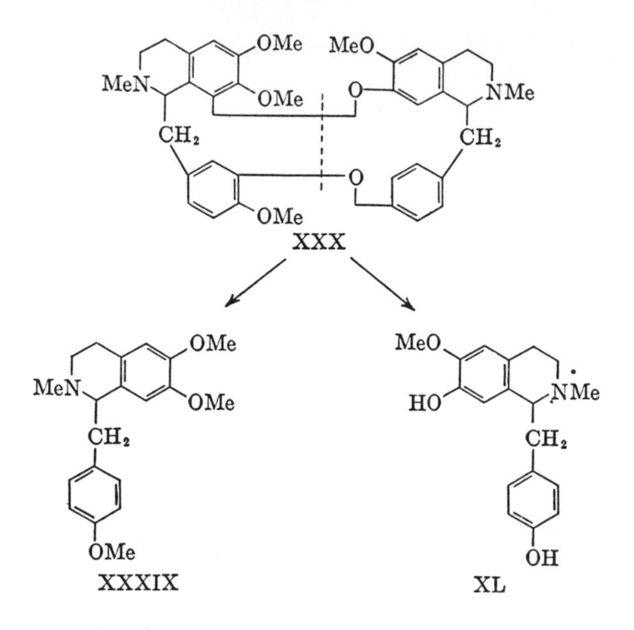

did not depress the melting point of isotetrandrine (23). The steric configuration of the two asymmetric centers in isotetrandrine are known to be *l*- and *d*- (127, 132). (See page 215).

4. Tetrandrine

The drugs known as han-fang-chi and mu-fang-chi, obtained from plants from the Mukden area and appearing on the Chinese market, contain the alkaloid tetrandrine (29, 31, 32, 34, 36), which was also isolated from *Stephania tetrandra* S. Moore of Japan and *Menispermum dauricum* (120). This alkaloid is a crystalline, dextrorotatory, ether-soluble base containing methoxy and *N*- methyl functional groups. It was at first mistaken for a benzylisoquinoline type (25, 26, 27) ($C_{19}H_{23}NO_3$) on the grounds of an erroneous molecular weight determination. However, the presence of 4′,5-dicarboxy-2-methoxydiphenyl ether (VIII, R = CH_3) in the oxidation products of the two-stage Hofmann degraded tetrandrine and a careful methoxyl determination of partially demethylated tetrandrine (28) indicated that a doubled formula ($C_{38}H_{42}N_2O_6$) like that of oxyacanthine was more probable. The extensive work of Kondo and Yano (28) elucidated the structure of tetrandrine further, and it was shown to be isomeric with *O*-methyloxyacanthine (XXV). These Japanese workers found that when the methiodide of tetrandrine was degraded according to the method of Hofmann and the resulting α-tetrandrine methylmethine ($C_{40}H_{46}N_2O_6$) (XXXIII) ozonized in acetic acid two products were formed, namely,

4′,5-diformyl-2-methoxydiphenyl ether (XXXIV) and the dialdehyde XXXV. These two compounds were found identical with the two dialdehydes obtained by a similar degradation of *O*-methyloxyacanthine (17, 18). Since the constitutions of these two compounds were proved by synthesis (von Bruchhausen and coworkers) there is little doubt that the structure of tetrandrine is either XXV or XXX.

Final proof of the structure of tetrandrine came when the alkaloid was subjected to the sodium in liquid ammonia reaction (127, 133). The two products *d*-1-(4′-methoxybenzyl)-*N*-methyl-6,7-dimethoxy-1,2,3,4-tetrahydroisoquinoline (XXXIX) and *d*-1-(4′-hydroxybenzyl)-*N*-methyl-6-methoxy-7-hydroxy-1,2,3,4-tetrahydroisoquinoline (XL) were isolated. It is thus evident that the structure of tetrandrine must be represented by XXX. However it was also proved (126) that isotetrandrine is represented by the same structure (XXX) and that its cleavage products are *l*-XXXIX and *d*-XL (127, 132). Therefore tetrandrine and isotetrandrine are optical isomers of the same structure (XXX), both the asymmetric centers of the former being in *d*-form (133).

Tetrandrine has a pharmacological action on animals (30, 33). Subcutaneous injection into mice, frogs, and cats showed lowering of blood pressure and paralysis of the respiratory and skeletal muscles. Respiration was first stimulated then depressed, and the animals died in convulsions. It has a quinine-like action on paramecia, and artificial fever induced in rabbits is reduced by its administration. Tetrandrine has the following additional effects on the rabbit: a marked irritative action on the mucous membrane; hyperglycemia; a reversal of the polymorphonuclear cells and lymphocytes. The minimum lethal doses of tetrandrine hydrochloride in mice, rats, guinea pigs, rabbits, and pigeons are 55, 55, 21, 17, and 125 mg. per kilogram, respectively.

5. Repandine

Bisbenzylisoquinoline alkaloids were first found in the plants of the family Monimiaceae when Bick and coworkers (108) isolated repandine from *Atherosperma repandulum* F. Muell. (*Daphnandra repandula* F. Muell.) in 1946. This alkaloid is a well-defined, optically active, crystalline, phenolic compound. Bick and Todd (108) found that when repandine was methylated with methyl iodide in methanolic sodium methoxide and the resulting *O*-methylrepandine dimethiodide subjected to the Hofmann degradation, an optically active *O*-methylrepandine methine was formed. This methine base (XXXII or XXXIII) when ozonized yielded 4′,5-diformyl-2-methoxydiphenyl ether (XXXIV) and the amino aldehyde XXXV. Both of these products were also obtained from oxyacanthine by an analogous series of reactions (17, 18). Furthermore, both *O*-ethyl-repandine (108) and *O*-ethyloxyacanthine (15) yielded the same compound, namely, 4′,5-dicarboxy-2-ethoxydiphenyl ether, on degradation. It is therefore evident that repandine is either identical or isomeric with oxyacanthine or with berbamine and must have the structure XXVI or XXXI.

Since in this series mixed melting points were not wholly satisfactory as a means of establishing the identity of compounds, Bick and Todd employed X-ray powder photography. They found that the powder photographs of *O*-methylrepandine methine dimethiodide and *O*-methyloxyacanthine methine dimethiodide were identical. This showed that repandine corresponds to oxyacanthine rather than berbamine in structure. An examination of the X-ray photographs and optical rotations revealed that repandine and oxyacanthine (XXVI) are optical isomers.

Finally Bick and Todd (108) were able to prove by direct comparison the identity of repandine and a base isolated by von Bruchhausen and Schulze (16) from impure oxyacanthine during an attempt to prepare the hydrochloride of the latter. The English workers do not believe that repandine arose from oxyacanthine through acid treatment (in the hydrochloride formation). Instead they believe that repandine actually occurs in small amounts along with oxyacanthine in at least one species of *Berberis*.

6. Daphnandrine

Daphnandrine occurs together with two other bisbenzylisoquinoline alkaloids (daphnoline and micranthine) in the bark of the Australian tree *Daphnandra micrantha* Benth. Pyman (111) recorded the isolation of the three alkaloids and observed their physical, chemical, and physiological properties. The chemical structures of these compounds were determined by Bick, Ewen, and Todd (112).

Daphnandrine is a weakly phenolic base insoluble in water, ethyl acetate, acetone, ether, or light petroleum, very sparingly soluble in boiling methanol, ethanol, or xylene, and fairly soluble in chloroform. Analyses showed that it contains three methoxyl groups and one methylimino group and has the empirical formula of $C_{36}H_{38}O_6N_2$. It was degraded in the same way as was oxyacanthine. Methylation with methyl iodide and methanolic sodium methoxide yielded *O,N*-dimethyldaphnandrine methiodide, which on Hofmann degradation gave *O,N*-dimethyldaphnandrine methine. This methine on ozonolysis yielded 2-methoxy-4′,5-diformyldiphenyl ether (XXXIV) and an amino aldehyde, the methiodide of which was converted by further Hofmann degradation to 2,2′,3-trimethoxy-5′,6-diformyl-4′,5-divinyldiphenyl ether (XXXVI). These two aldehydes were identified by comparison with specimens also obtained from oxyacanthine by an analogous series of reactions. An examination of the X-ray powder photographs of *O,N*-dimethyldaphnandrine dimethiodide and *O*-methyloxyacanthine dimethiodide showed that these two compounds are identical. The methine dimethiodides from them were also found identical. Thus it was established that *O*,*N*-dimethyldaphnandrine and *O*-methyloxyacanthine are the same and must be represented by formula XXV.

In an attempt to determine the position of the phenolic hydroxyl in daphnandrine, Bick, Ewen, and Todd (112) ethylated *N*-methyldaphnandrine dimethiodide with ethyl iodide and ethanolic sodium ethoxide and then subjected the resulting *N*-methyl-*O*-ethyldaphnandrine to the Hofmann degradation. A methine base was obtained which on ozonolysis yielded 2-methoxy-4′,5-diformyldiphenyl ether (XXXIV) as before. This showed that the phenolic group in daphnandrine must be attached to one of the tetrahydroisoquinoline nuclei and cannot occupy a position in the benzyl residue as it does in oxyacanthine and repandine (XXVI).

Working with structurally related alkaloids (*Chondrodendron* species) King (68, 82) showed that alkaloids containing phenolic groups in the 7-position of an isoquinoline residue or the 4-position of a benzyl residue gave a positive Millon reaction, whereas those with phenolic group in the 6-position of the isoquinoline nucleus gave no Millon reaction. Bick, Ewen, and Todd (112) found that daphnandrine gave a positive Millon reaction and on this basis concluded that daphnandrine contains a phenolic group in the 7-position of one of the tetrahydroisoquinoline nuclei. Daphnandrine is thus assigned the structure XXIX in which R_3 and R_4 are hydrogen and methyl, but not necessarily respectively.

7. Fangchinoline

A bisbenzylisoquinoline alkaloid was isolated (36) from the Chinese drug han-fang-chi and named fangchinolin. Fangchinoline and tetrandrine appear together in the alcoholic extract of the Chinese drug and are separated by fractional crystallization from acetone or by fractional crystallization of their picrates from acetone, tetrandrine picrate being the less soluble. Fangchinoline does not depress the melting point of tetrandrine. However, the two bases are not identical since fangchinoline possesses a phenolic group while tetrandrine does not. This phenolic group is abnormal in character for, although the alkaloid gives the ferric chloride color test and can be methylated with diazomethane, it is not soluble in aqueous alkali. Analysis and determination of molecular weight and functional groups revealed the fact that the difference between fangchinoline ($C_{37}H_{40}O_6N_2$) and tetrandrine ($C_{38}H_{42}O_6N_2$) is CH_2, and this led to the assumption that fangchinoline is a demethyltetrandrine, i.e., one of the methoxyl groups is demethylated. The correctness of this assumption was shown by methylation of fangchinoline with diazomethane to *O*-methylfangchinoline, which was identical with tetrandrine (XXX) in all respects. In an attempt to locate the position of the phenolic group, fangchinoline was ethylated with diazoethane and the *O*-ethylfangchinoline (m.p. 116–117°) oxidized with permanganate. From the oxidation products was isolated 4',5-dicarboxy-2-methoxydiphenyl ether (VIII, R = CH_3), which was also obtained from tetrandrine. This shows that the phenolic group is not on the diphenyl ether portion of the molecule of fangchinoline but must instead be attached to one of the isoquinoline rings. The above facts indicate that the structure of fangchinoline is XXX with one of the methoxyl groups on the isoquinoline rings demethylated.

8. Pheanthine

Pheanthus ebracteolatus (Presl) Merrill of the family Anonaceae contains a non-phenolic, ether-soluble tertiary base which was isolated by Santos (37) and named pheanthine. Santos observed that this alkaloid contained the same functional groups as tetrandrine and on Hofmann degradation followed by oxidation yielded 4',5-dicarboxy-2-methoxydiphenyl ether (VIII, R = CH_3) (38), as do tetrandrine, isotetrandrine, *O*-methylfangchinoline, *O*-methylberbamine, *O*-methyloxyacanthine, and *O*-methyldauricine. Santos (38) had assigned to pheanthine the formula $C_{37}H_{38}N_2O_6$, but analysis and methoxyl determination by Kondo and Keimatsu (39) on samples of pheanthine and its derivatives furnished by Santos agreed better with the $C_{34}H_{30}O_2N_2(OCH_3)_4$ of tetrandrine. A comparison of the physical constants of pheanthine and tetrandrine revealed that their optical rotations were equal and opposite and that their α-methine bases formed by Hofmann degradation) had the same melting points separately and in admixture, hence these two alkaloids are optical antipodes of the structure XXX. Absorption spectra of the two compounds agree with the above facts. Since it has been shown that both asymmetric centers of tetrandrine (133) are of the *d*-form those of pheanthine must be of the *l*-form.

9. Trilobamine (Daphnoline)

During the course of the study of alkaloids of the plant *Cocculus trilobus* DC., Kondo and Tomita (40) isolated, in addition to trilobine and isotrilobine which will be discussed later, a phenolic base which resembled closely the doubly oxygen-bridged bisbenzylisoquinoline alkaloids. The name trilobamine was assigned to it. Analytical figures agreed with either $C_{35}H_{36}N_2O_6$ or $C_{36}H_{38}N_2O_6$ and showed the presence of two phenolic, two methoxyl, and two *N*-methyl groups. Methylation with diazomethane and oxidation of the resulting trilobamine methyl ether with permanganate yielded 4',5-dicarboxy-2-methoxydiphenyl ether (VIII, R = CH_3). Application of the one-stage Hofmann degradation to trilobamine methyl ether gave the optically inactive crystalline (41) methyltrilobamine methylmethine which melted at 152° and did not depress the melting point of *O*-methyloxyacanthine methylmethine. A comparison of the trilobamine methyl ether and oxyacanthine methyl ether and their derivatives showed that they were identical. Trilobamine was then ethylated with ethyl iodide and alkali and the ethyl ether subjected to Hofmann degradation and oxidation. 4′,5-Dicarboxy-2-ethoxydiphenyl ether (VIII, R = C_2H_5) was isolated, thus establishing the position of one of the two phenolic groups as being in the diphenyl ether portion of the molecule. The position of the other phenolic group was not established until several years later.

Bick, Ewen, and Todd (112) examined the alkaloid called daphnoline which occurs in the bark of *Daphnandra micrantha* and *D. aromatica* F. M. Bailey previously isolated by Pyman (111). The physical and chemical properties of daphnoline and triolobamine were found to be the same and, although no mixed melting point was taken, these workers believed that the two alkaloids were identical. The alkaloid retains solvent of crystallization so tenaciously that it is not possible to remove it completely without causing some decomposition. It is this property which presumably prevented Kondo and Tomita (40) from obtaining satisfactory analytical results. Bick, Ewen, and Todd (112) discovered that daphnoline (trilobamine) possesses one methylimino group and one secondary amino group instead of two methylimino groups, and that *O,O,N*-trimethyldaphnoline is identical with *O*-methyloxyacanthine (XXV). Furthermore, one of the two phenolic groups in daphnoline could be selectively methylated with diazomethane to yield *O*-methyldaphnoline, which was found to be identical with daphnandrine (XXIX). Since *O,O,N*-trimethyldaphnoline has the structure XXV and *O*-methyldaphnoline (daphnandrine) the structure XXIX, the constitution of daphnoline (trilobamine) must be represented by XXVIII (of R_3 and R_4 one is H, the other CH_3).

10. Aromoline

Aromoline occurs in small amounts together with daphnoline in *Daphnandra aromatica.* Like daphnoline it retains solvent of crystallization very tenaciously and therefore is difficult to purify. Bick, Ewen, and Todd (112) showed that this alkaloid possesses two phenolic groups, two methoxyl groups, and two methylimino groups, and is represented by the formula $C_{36}H_{38}O_6N_2$. When it was methylated the resulting *O,O*-dimethylaromoline was found to be identical with *O,O,N*-trimethyldaphnoline (XXV). In the same way ethylation yielded *O,O*-diethylaromoline which was identical with *O,O*-diethyl-*N*-methyldaphnoline. Thus aromoline is *N*-methyldaphnoline and since daphnoline has been assigned the structure XXVIII (of R_3 and R_4 one is H, the other CH_3) then aromoline (*N*-methyldaphnoline) mus be reperesented by XXVII.

11. Epistephanine

This alkaloid occurs with a number of other alkaloids, including hypoepistephanine, in *Stephania japonica* Miers (99, 100). Earlier work (100–103, 118) indicated that the empirical formula of epistephanine was $C_{19}H_{21(23)}O_3N$ and that the alkaloid was of the aporphine type. A repetition of this work (128) showed that analytical figures agreed better with the formula $C_{32}H_{23(21)}(OMe)_4(NMe)O \cdot O \cdot (N=)$ which is of the biscoclaurine type. Oxidation of epistephanine with potassium permanganate yielded 4′,5-dicarboxy-2-methoxydiphenyl ether (VIII, R = CH_3). Reduction with zinc and sulfuric acid yielded two compounds, $C_{37}H_{40}O_6N_2 \cdot 2HCl \cdot 2H_2O$, $[\alpha]^8_D$ 299.3° (H_2O), and $C_{37}H_{40}O_6N_2 \cdot 2HCl \cdot 5H_2O$, $[\alpha]^{19}_D$ 92.0° (H_2O). Both of these products gave positive Liebermann secondary base reactions and yielded an identical optically inactive methine, $C_{40}H_{46}O_6N_2 \cdot 2H_2O$, so that they must have been diasterioisomers in which hydrogen atoms have been added to the double bond at the 1- and 2-positions of the dihydroisoquinoline nucleus. A second Hofmann degradation of the α-methine yielded the same nitrogen-free compound as was produced from methyltrilobamine by similar degradation. It was also shown that hydroepistephanine and *O*-methyloxyacanthine yield identical Emde degradation products (129). On the bases of these studies the structures XLI or XLII (R = CH_3) were proposed for the hydroepistephanine and XLIII or XLIV (R = CH_3) for epistephanine. Absorption spectrum studies

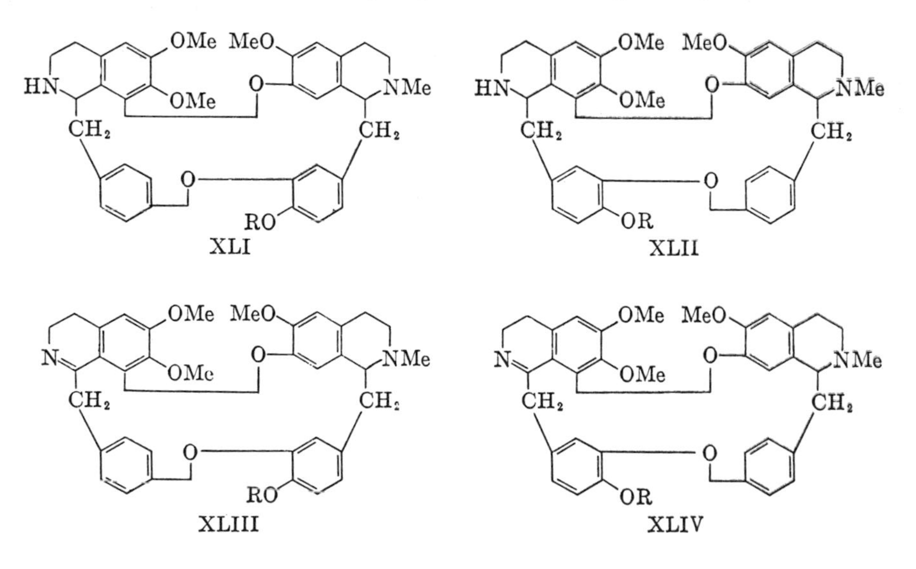

(106, 128) of both hydroepistephanine and epistephanine confirm the proposed structures of these compounds.

12. Hypoepistephanine

Another alkaloid of *Stephania japonica* is hypoepistephanine, which was originally known as ψ-epistephanine. It was studied by Kondo and his collaborators (102, 118, 119), who found it to be a bisbenzylisoquinoline alkaloid with the composition $C_{36}H_{36}O_6N_2$ or $C_{32}H_{23}(OCH_3)_3(OH)$-$(=NCH_3)(=N—)$. This compound when methylated with diazomethane yielded *O*-methylhypoepistephanine, which was identical with epistephanine (119). Ethylation of hypoepistephanine with diazoethane followed by permanganate oxidation of the resulting *O*-ethylhypoepistephanine yielded 2-ethoxy-4′,5-dicarboxydiphenyl ether (VIII, R = C_2H_5). This showed that the phenolic group in hypoepistephanine occupies the 4-position of one of the benzyl portions of the molecule, and the structure of hypoepistephanine must be XLIII or XLIV (R = H).

13. Cepharanthine

The only known biscoclaurine alkaloid containing a methylenedioxy group is cepharanthine, which occurs in the roots of *Stephania cepharantha* (42, 43, 47) and *S. sasakii* Hayata (45, 46, 105). Both of these plants are lianas native to the woods of southern Formosa. Cepharanthine is an ether-soluble, optically active, non-phenolic, amorphous tertiary base which can only be crystallized from benzene as the benzene adduct. It was earlier believed that this alkaloid ($C_{37}H_{38}O_6N_2$) contained three methoxyl groups and three oxygen bridges in the molecule, but recent careful functional group determination (44) showed that there are two methoxyl groups, two ether bridges, and one methylenedioxy group. Hofmann degradation of cepharanthine gave in the first stage the α-methine base, which on further degradation yielded trimethylamine and a nitrogen-free compound. From the oxidation products of the latter there was isolated 4′,5-dicarboxy-2 methoxydiphenyl ether (VIII, R = CH_3). In order to gain further knowledge regarding the structure of this alkaloid, the α-methine base was treated with ozone and the two products, 4′,5-diformyl-2-methoxydiphenyl ether (XXXIV) and the dimethylamino dialdehyde (XLV), separated. The dimethiodide of XLV on alkali treatment liberated trimethylamine and the divinyl dialdehyde XLVI. The vinyl groups could be catalytically reduced, and further reduction of the aldehyde groups (Clemmensen) yielded XLVII. This XLVII proved to be identical with the compound synthesized from 3-methyl-4-ethyl-6-methoxyphenol and 1-bromo-2-methyl-3-ethyl-5,6-methylenedioxybenzene by the Ullmann condensation. Kondo and Keimatsu therefore concluded that cepharanthine must have the structural formula XLVIII or XLIX. Attempts have been made to synthesize cepharanthine, but so far without success (125, 131).

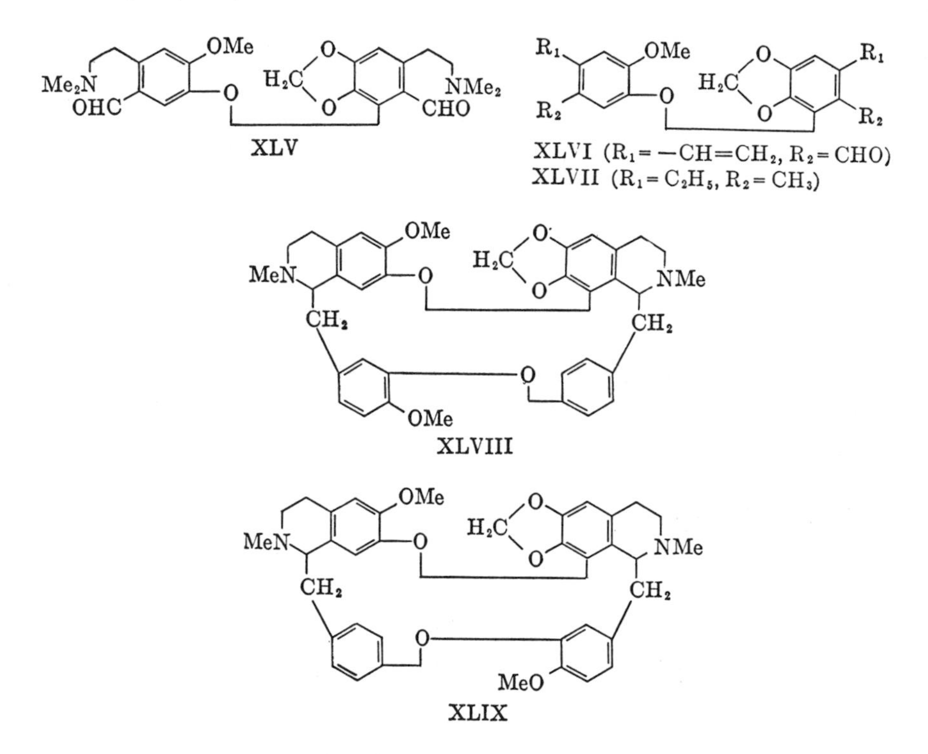

14. Isochondodendrine

Isochondodendrine, formerly known as isobebeerine, belongs to the symmetrical bisbenzylisoquinoline type of alkaloids. It occurs in the drug *Radix pareira bravae* of the English market, and in the plants of the genus *Chondodendron* Ruiz and Pav. (68), *Ch. platyphyllum* Miers, *Sychnosepalum microphyllum* Eichl. (*Ch. microphyllum* (Eichl.) Moldenke), and *Ch. tomentosum* Ruiz and Pav. (104), which grow in Brazil in the regions of Rio de Janeiro, Bahia, and the upper Amazon. It is also found in the plant *Pleogyne cunninghamii* Miers (Menispermaceae) (136). Isochondodendrine was at first assigned the formula $C_{18}H_{19}O_3N$ on the basis of analysis and Rast molecular weight determination and found to contain the functional groups methoxyl, phenolic hydroxyl, and *N*-methyl (48, 49). In a further study of structure, Faltis and Neumann (48) methylated the alkaloid with diazomethane, treated the isochondodendrine methyl ether with methyl iodide, and degraded the quaternary base according to Hofmann's method. Two methine bases were obtained to which the structures L and LI were assigned. The methine bases absorbed one mole of hydrogen

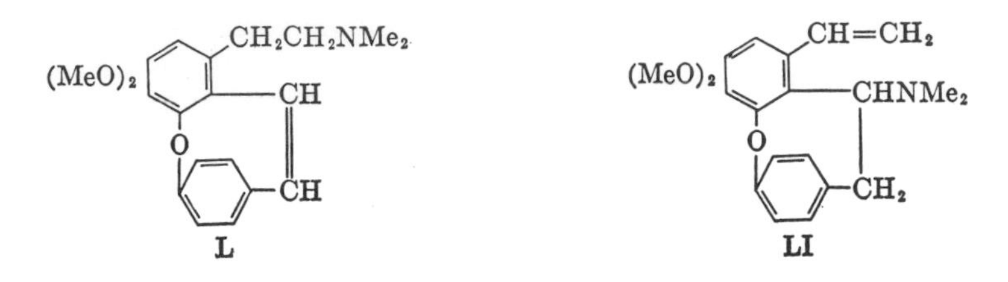

giving the hydromethine bases, which could also be obtained directly from *O*-methylisochondodendrine methochloride by reduction with sodium amalgam (Emde degradation).

The mixture of the two methine bases when treated with alcoholic alkali yielded a nitrogen-free compound which produced a tricarboxylic acid (m.p. 178°) on oxidation. For a number of years work was directed towards the identification of the tricarboxylic acid by degradative studies and by syntheses (50, 51, 52). Alkali fusion resulted in *p*-hydroxybenzoic acid, and on this basis it was concluded that the tricarboxylic acid must be one of the three isomeric acids LII, LIII, and LIV. All three were synthesized (50, 51, 52) by an Ullmann condensation of the appropriate compounds, and LIV (52) proved to be identical in all respects with that obtained from methylated isochondodendrine by degradation. Isochondodendrine was then assigned the structure LV or LVI.

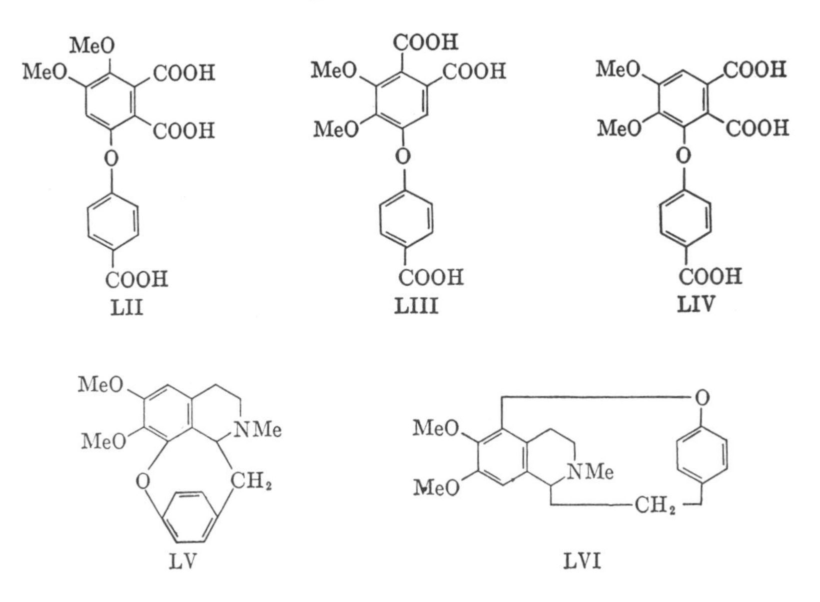

These structures are objectionable on steric grounds. The molecular weight of isochondodendrine determined in camphor according to the Rast method was rather high for this formula, but it was too low for twice this formula. However, when the molecular weights of a few derivatives of isochondodendrine were determined in pinene dibromide instead of in camphor the formula $C_{36}H_{38}O_6N_2$ was indicated instead of $C_{18}H_{19}O_3N$, and the structure LVII for isochondodendrine was advocated (53). This formula not only agreed with the Faltis belief that bisbenzylisoquinoline alkaloids are formed in the plant from two moles of coclaurine (I) through enzymatic dehydrogenations but also with all facts obtained from degrada-

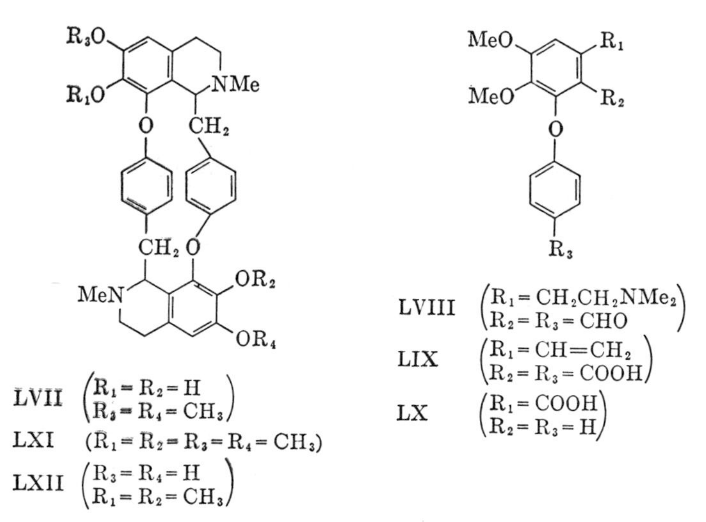

tive studies. Proof of this structure came when Faltis and Dietreich (54) subjected the inactive α-methine base obtained from isochondodendrine dimethyl ether by Hofmann degradation to ozone treatment in dilute sulfuric acid. A quantitative yield of the dimethylamino dialdehyde (LVIII) was obtained as the crystalline methiodide. The corresponding methochloride of LVIII when carefully oxidized with permanganate and then treated with alkali gave in 64 % yield pure 4′,6-dicarboxy-2,3-dimethoxy-5-vinyldiphenyl ether (LIX). This was then decarboxylated with quinoline and naturkupfer C to yield (55 %) a vinyldimethoxydiphenyl ether, which on oxidation with potassium permanganate in acetone yielded a compound identical with the synthetic 5-carboxy-2,3-dimethoxydiphenyl ether (LX). The positions of the two penolic groups in isochondodendrine are only assumed, the assumption being based on the belief that this alkaloid is formed from coclaurine (I).

15. Methylisochondodendrine (Cycleanine)

Recently Kondo, Tomita, and Uyeo (55) applied the technique of chromatographic adsorption on alumina to the separation of the alkaloids of *Cissampelos insularis* Makino and *Stephania cepharantha.* By this means they isolated, in addition to those known, a new, crystalline, ether-soluble alkaloid whose analysis agreed with that of a bisbenzylisoquinoline alkaloid. This same alkaloid was also found in *Chondodendron tomentosum* (104) and *Stephania capitata* Spreng (121). Through a comparison of its properties and that of its derivatives with samples of isochondodendrine dimethyl ether and derivatives provided by Faltis, the Japanese workers (55) established the structure of the new alkaloid as being fully methylated isochondodendrine (LXI). They suggested the names methylisochondodendrine or cycleanine. An attempt to synthesize this alkaloid was not successful (130). However, by means of sodium and liquid ammonia the compound has been bisected into only one phenolic base whose structure proved to be *l*-1-(4′-hydroxybenzyl)-6,7-dimethoxy-*N*-methyl-1,2,3,4-tetrahydroisoquinoline (134). This showed that cycleanine (methylisochondodendrine) has the structure (LXI) with both the asymmetric centers levorotatory.

16. Bebeerine (Chondodendrine)

In 1843 Maclagen (56) found two compounds of basic nature in *Nectandra* roots from British Guiana. One of these, an amorphous yellow powder, he named bebeerine (bebirine). Some time later a yellow powder was isolated from *Buxus sempervirens* L., whose fibers and leaves were used as a remedy for intermittant fever. This powder which was named buxin proved to be identical with bebeerine. Finally, the alkaloid known as pelosine which occurs in the roots of *Cissampelos pareira* L. and *Radix pareira bravae* was found to be identical with bebeerine (56, 59). Bebeerine also occurs in *Chondodendron platyphyllum, Ch. microphyllum, Abuta candicans* Rich. (*Ch. candicans* Sandwith) (68), and *Pleogyne cunninghamii* (136), as well as in the commerical powder known as bebeerum purum.

In 1936 Faltis and coworkers (67, 69) pointed out that the name bebeerine was not a desirable one because the original source of this alkaloid, the commercial powder bebeerum purum, was actually a preparation of *Chondodendron* species. They therefore renamed the alkaloid chondodendrine. However, other workers (68, 76, 77) adhered to the older name.

Scholtz first isolated bebeerine from the commercial powder in levorotatory form (56), but later he was able to isolate also the dextro form (60, 62) as well as a fraction claimed to be the racemic form on the basis that he could also obtain it by mixing chloroform solutions of the dextro- and levorotatory forms. Bebeerine is a crystalline base at first assigned the composition $C_{18}H_{21}NO_3$ (56, 61) and possessing the functional groups phenolic hydroxyl, methoxyl, and *N*-methyl (57, 58, 65, 66). Earlier work on the degradation of bebeerine, such as oxidation with potassium permanganate, chromic acid, nitric acid, potassium ferricyanide, and hydrogen peroxide (58) and alkali fusion, failed to elucidate the structure.

As in the case of isochondodendrine, the benzylisoquinoline type of structure (LV) for bebeerine was first proposed on the basis of an erroneous molecular weight determination. Such a structure was improbable on steric grounds, and a more careful analysis of bebeerine derivatives (72) showed that the double formula $C_{36}H_{38}O_6N_2$ agreed better with experimental facts. Bebeerine was next methylated, the dimethyl ether subjected to a two-stage Hofmann degradation, and the resulting nitrogen-free compound oxidized. This produced 4′,5,6-tricarboxy-2,3-dimethoxydiphenyl ether (LIV), which was identified by comparison with the synthetic compound (72). Thus, half the molecule of bebeerine was shown to be the same as half of the molecule of isochondodendrine.

Two years later King (77) repeated the work on the oxidative degradation of bebeerine, and from the mixture of degradation products, in addition to the tricarboxylic acid (LIV) which the previous workers isolated and identified, he isolated an unknown isomeric tricarboxylic acid. Although he did not synthesize this acid he assigned to it the structure LXV on the basis that on decarboxylation it yielded 2,2′-dimethoxydiphenyl ether. Consequently, King proposed the structure LXVI in which the phenolic groups are methylated for bebeerine dimethyl ether.

At the same time an important paper (67) appeared in which essentially the same conclusions with regard to the structure of bebeerine were arrived at by a different route. Faltis, Kadiera, and Doblhammer (67) treated the inactive α,α'-dimethylbebeerine methine, obtained by a one-stage Hofmann degradation of bebeerine dimethyl ether, with ozone and obtained a mixture of two dimethylamino dialdehydes. These were not isolated but were converted to the chloromethylate derivatives, oxidized with potassium permanganate to the acids, and boiled with dilute alkali to decompose the quaternary bases. Besides trimethylamine, a mixture of two vinyl carboxylic acids were obtained. One of these proved to be 4′,6-dicarboxy-2,3-dimethoxy-5-vinyldiphenyl ether (LIX). The other vinyl carboxylic acid, which was readily separated from LIX by virtue of its low solubility, was first decarboxylated by heating with quinoline and naturkupfer C and then oxidized with potassium permanganate in acetone. This yielded 4-carboxy-2,2′-dimethoxydiphenyl ether (LXIII), the structure of which was proved by direct comparison with the synthetic compound prepared by the Ullmann condensation of *o*-bromoanisole and vanillic acid.

The correctness of the assumption that the parent vinyl carboxylic acid of LXIII must have the structure LXIV was shown by the oxidation of LXIV to 4,5,5′-tricarboxy-2,2′-dimethoxydiphenyl ether (LXV) and comparison with the compound synthesized by the Ullmann condensation of 4-iodo-5-methoxyphthalic acid with isovanillic acid (69) or by the condensation of 3-methyl-4-acetyl-6-methoxyphenol with 3-bromoanisic acid followed by oxidation (69). The natural LXV and the synthetic compound were identical in all respects. When the three degradation products, LXIV, LIX and trimethylamine, were pieced together the structure LXVI for bebeerine was arrived at, the positions of the phenolic groups being assigned arbitrarily.

In order to mark the positions of the two phenolic groups in bebeerine King (79) applied the ethylating device. Bebeerine diethyl ether was converted through the quaternary methiodide to the methochloride, and

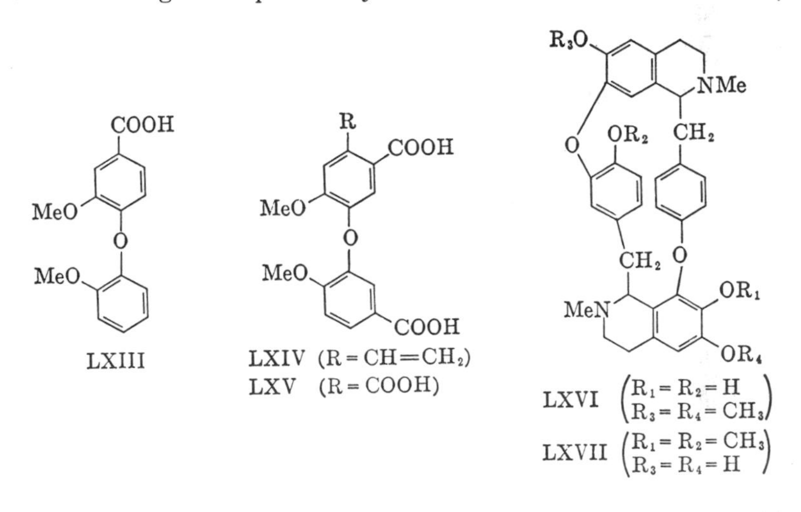

the latter subjected to a two-stage Hofmann degradation. The oxidation of the resulting nitrogen-free compound yielded two isomeric tricarboxylic acids. These were proved to be identical with 4,5,5′-tricarboxy-2′-ethoxy-2-methoxydiphenyl ether and 4′,5,6-tricarboxy-2-ethoxy-3-methoxy diphenyl ether, each of which was prepared by the Ullmann condensation of the appropriate compounds. This leaves little doubt as to the position of the phenolic groups, and therefore the structure of bebeerine (chondodendrine) must be LXVI.

In 1912 an amorphous base isomeric with crystalline bebeerine was isolated from Merck's *bebeerum sulfuricum amorphum* by precipitation with sodium carbonate and extraction with benzene and alcohol and purification by fractional solvent precipitation (63, 64). It was designated as β-bebeerine. Crystalline bebeerine and amorphous bebeerine differed widely in physical properties, and yet on acetylation they yielded the same acetyl derivatives and on Hofmann degradation they formed the same methine bases. These facts led Faltis and coworkers (67) to state that these two alkaloids are diastereoisomers. However, they were not able to confirm this view for, although they worked up three different shipments of *Radix pareirae*, they were not able to obtain any more of the amorphous β-bebeerine.

The physiological action of dextro, levo, and racemic forms of bebeerine has been studied (61, 62). Injections of solutions of their salts into animals brought results dependent upon the animal and upon the rotation of the alkaloid. The dextro form was found to be much more toxic to rabbits, cats, and white mice than the other forms, while in dogs it had little effect.

17. Chondrofoline

While examining alkaloids of the *Chondodendron* species King (68) encountered a new alkaloid present in *Chondodendron platyphyllum* only and named it chondrofoline. It had the composition $C_{35}H_{36}O_6N_2$, was phenolic in nature, and possessed three methoxyl groups. Complete methylation gave the amorphous *O*-methylchondrofoline methiodide and the methochloride. One-stage degradation of the methochloride yielded two crystalline *O*-methylchondrofoline methine methiodides. One of these proved to be identical with the inactive *O*-methylbebeerine methine methiodide obtained in an analogous degradation of *d*-bebeerine and the other an enantiomorph also obtained from *d*-bebeerine. Since chondrofoline did not give the Millon reaction and contained only one phenolic group, King proposed the structure LXVII for it in which the phenolic group is at OR_3 or OR_4.

18. Curine

Curare is the name given to the South American arrow poisons prepared from extracts of local plants by Indian tribes who dwell on the borders of Brazil, Peru, and Ecuador about the waters of the upper Amazon. The various curares are designated according to the containers into which they are packed. Tubo-curare, a dark red resinous mass is put into bamboo tubes, calabash-curare is packed in the gourd, and the pot-curare is brought to the market packed in tinted earthenware pots. The composition of the curare has been studied for a long time, but the amorphous nature of the constituents and the rarity of the crude native preparations have delayed progress in this field.

In 1897 Boehm (70) made a thorough study of the alkaloids present in curare. By extracting the tubo-curare with water, precipitating with aqueous ammonia, and extracting with alcohol he obtained the crystalline alkaloid called curine. This alkaloid also occurs in the stems of *Chondodendron platyphyllum* (68) and *Ch. tomentosum* (104), plants which are native of Brazil. Curine solvates with benzene or ethanol, and the product is so stable that heating at 180° is necessary in order to eliminate the solvent. The composition of curine as determined by Boehm (70) was $C_{18}H_{19}NO_3$ and possessed a phenolic, methoxyl, and an *N*-methyl group. Thirty-seven years later Späth and Kuffner (72) analyzed a number of curine derivatives and came to the conclusion that the formula should be doubled. The structural formula of this alkaloid was determined by Späth, Leithe, and Ladeck (71). Crystallographic examination showed that curine and *l*-bebeerine, isolated previously by Scholtz, were identical in morphological and optical properties. Scholtz (56) found that mixing equal parts of dextro and levo forms of bebeerine in chloroform solution produced the racemic form with melting point 300°. On mixing curine and *d*-bebeerine Späth and coworkers (71) obtained a compound melting at 300°. Further proof that curine and *d*-bebeerine (LXVI) are optical isomers was derived from the Hofmann degradation of curine dimethyl ether and bebeerine dimethyl ether. In the first stage of the degradation the methines obtained from the two compounds were identical, as also were the nitrogen-free compounds obtained in the second stage.

Curine is much less toxic than the other alkaloids of curare (73, 74, 78). It affects the conducting system and therefore has cardiac action. High concentrations of this alkaloid causes paralysis of the striated muscles and paralysis of the nerve end plates.

19. Tubocurarine Chloride

In addition to curine, Boehm (70) isolated from tubocurare the alkaloid tubocurarine, which is a water-soluble quaternary ammonium base. This alkaloid is best purified as tubocurarine chloride by crystallization from hydrochloric acid, and it exists in both dextro and levo forms. *d*-Tubocurarine chloride found application as an adjunct in surgical anesthesia, and in order to insure supplies of this drug it became necessary to find the plant which the Indians use in the preparation of tubocurare.

In 1939 King (123) obtained both the leaves and liana of the plant "amphi huasa" (poison rope) which is used by the Indians near Tarapoto in northern Peru for the preparation of curare. It was identified as *Chondrodendron tomentosum*, and chemical examination showed that it contained *l*-curine (*l*-bebeerine) and *l*-tubocurarine chloride and *not d*-tubocurarine chloride as expected. However Wintersteiner and Dutcher (81) examined similarly the curare prepared by Indians of the upper Amazon and also the plant used in the preparation. The plant was identified as *Chondrodendron tomentosum*, and the curare contained, among other alkaloids, *l*-curine and *d*-tubocurarine chloride. King attributed this discrepancy to the possible existence of two undifferentiated closely allied species of *Chondrodendron tomentosum*, one of which he had examined while Wintersteiner and Dutcher had examined the other. Several years later, King (124) again examined two lianas derived from *Chondrodendron tomentosum*, one of which grows in the region of the Madre de Dios river in Peru and the other near Sisa in the region of Tarapoto. Each of these plants contained *d*-tubocurarine chloride and not the *l*-form as found in a previous examination. Thus it was established that a liana growing in widely separated localities of Peru indistinguishable from *Ch. tomentosum* is a source of *d*-tubocurarine chloride. At the same time another liana of the same species contains *l*-tubocurarine chloride, which is an enantiomorph of inferior curariform activity. There is some evidence that *d*-tubocurarine also occurs in *Anomospermum grandifolium* Eichl. (124).

In the isolation of *d*-tubocurarine chloride from these plants a crude product is usually obtained which requires repeated crystallization from 0.1 *N* hydrochloric acid in order to purify it. The impurities are quaternary alkaloids among which is *d*-chondocurarine (a quaternary form of chondocurine) (137).

In 1935 King (75, 76) was able to elucidate the structure of tubocurarine chloride ($C_{38}H_{44}Cl_2N_2O_6$). On methylation with methyl iodide it gave the crystalline *O*-methyltubocurarine iodide, which when converted to the chloride and subjected to the Hofmann degradation yielded a mixture of four methines. These were converted into their methiodides and separated. Three of them were found to be identical in all respects with the three methine methiodides (two inactive and one dextrorotatory) obtained in a similar manner from *d*-bebeerine. In the second stage of the Hofmann degradation the mixed *O*-methyltubocurarine methine methochlorides gave trimethylamine and a nitrogen-free compound (m.p. 198–199°) which did not depress the melting point of the nitrogen-free compound obtained from *d*-bebeerine in a similar manner. These results indicate that *O*-methylbebeerine methochloride and *O*-methyltubocurarine chloride are diasterioisomeric. Since the constitution of bebeerine was proved to be LXVI (79), *O*-methylbebeerine methochloride and *O*-methyltubocurarine chloride must be represented by the formula LXVIII (76, 77, 79). However, the probability that the orientation of phenolic and methoxyl groups is different in the parent substances tubocurarine chloride and bebeerine methochloride could not be excluded.

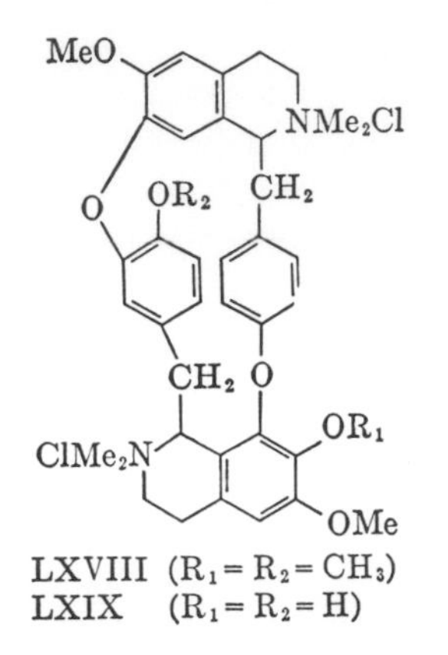

LXVIII ($R_1 = R_2 = CH_3$)
LXIX ($R_1 = R_2 = H$)

In order to settle this question King (122) ethylated *d*-tubocurarine chloride and then subjected the resulting *O*-ethyltubocurarine chloride to a two-stage Hofmann degradation. He obtained the same nitrogen-free compound as was obtained from bebeerine by an analogous series of reactions, and this proved that the two alkaloids also have the same orientation of phenolic and methoxyl groups. Therefore, *d*-tubocurarine chloride must have the structure LXIX. The optical rotations of the methines from *O*-methylbebeerine methochloride and *O*-methyltubocurarine chloride indicate that in *d*-bebeerine both asymmetric centers are dextrorotatory while in *d*-tubocurarine chloride one is dextro and the other levo.

Of the three alkaloids *d*-tubocurarine chloride, bebeerine, and curine (74, 76, 78, 80) the first has the strongest curarizing action. *d*-Tubocurarine chloride produces complete paralysis of the frog when doses of 0.5 mg. per kilogram are administered (76). It seems to cause typical respiratory paralysis in mammals. *l*-Tubocurarine chloride is many times weaker in curariform activity than its enantiomorph *d*-tubocurarine chloride (123).

20. *d*-Chondocurine

A sample of curare was prepared by Indians of the upper Amazon under the supervision of a botanist in order to insure the plant source. The plant species was *Chondodendron tomentosum* and the curare thus obtained was a black paste called Serpa which represented a concentrated aqueous extract of the stems and bark (81). The desiccated extract contained five alkaloids (104), *d*-isochondodendrine, methylisochondodendrine, *d*-tubocurarine chloride, curine, and a new base to which the name *d*-chondocurine was given.

This new base, $C_{36}H_{38}O_6N_2$, was shown to be of the bebeerine type by a study of the products of methylation. Treatment with methyl iodide and alkali methylated both the phenolic groups and the nitrogen atoms and yielded a crystalline product identical with the dimethyl ether of *d*-tubocurarine iodide. However, when the methylation was restricted to the nitrogen atoms, the resulting amorphous quaternary dimethochloride was not identical with tubocurarine chloride. Therefore, *d*-chondocurine methochloride (chondocurarine chloride) must differ from *d*-tubocurarine chloride only in the arrangement of free and methylated phenolic groups (104, 137). Chondocurarine chloride is three times as potent physiologically as *d*-tubocurarine chloride.

21. Neoprotocuridine and Protocuridine

Boehm (70) collected a number of pots of curare differing widely in physiological activity and yielding 250 g. of the crude drug. From this drug he isolated a quaternary and two non-quaternary bases. The latter two he named protocuridine (m.p. 276°) and protocurine (m.p. 306°), to which he assigned the formulas $C_{19}H_{21}O_3N$ and $C_{20}H_{23}O_3N$, respectively. In 1937 King (82) took up this work and carefully examined the contents of a small museum pot of curare. The crude drug was extracted with a 1 % tartaric acid solution at 100°, the non-alkaloidal impurities precipitated with lead acetate, and then the non-quaternary alkaloids precipitated by saturation with sodium bicarbonate. The amorphous non-quaternary bases so obtained constituted 38 % of the original curare and exhibited only a slight paralyzing action on frogs. From these King isolated two crystalline bases which were separated as hydrochlorides by fractional crystallization into the sparingly soluble neoprotocuridine hydrochloride and the much more soluble hydrochloride of protocuridine discovered by Boehm.

The optically inactive neoprotocuridine was assigned the formula $C_{36}H_{38}O_6N_2 \cdot 8H_2O$ and found to contain two phenolic and two methoxyl groups. Complete methylation of neoprotocuridine followed by Hofmann degradation yielded a methine methiodide which was indistinguishable from inactive α-methylisochondodendrine methine methiodide. Thus neoprotocuridine and isochondodendrine are different only in the orientation of phenolic and methoxyl groups, and since the former did not give a Millon reaction the structure LXII was assigned to it.

The second non-quaternary alkaloid of pot-curare, protocuridine, was crystallized from pyridine, and analysis showed that it was isomeric with neoprotocuridine. It differed from neoprotocuridine in that it gave the Millon reaction and was optically active. Complete methylation yielded *O*-methylprotocuridine methiodide (82), melting at 318° alone or in admixture with *O*-methylisochondodendrine methiodide. Thus, protocuridine differs from isochondodendrine (LVII) only in the orientation of the phenolic and methoxyl groups.

22. Insularine

The amorphous alkaloid insularine occurs together with methylisochondodendrine in *Paracyclea insularis* Makino. It was first isolated by Kondo and Yano (83) in 1927. Attempts to obtain insularine in crystalline form by purification through chromatographic absorption on alumina did not meet with success (55). The composition of insularine was first believed to be $C_{19}H_{21}NO_3$, with the presence of two methoxyls and one *N*-methyl group (83). However, later investigation (107) showed that a double formula of the bisbenzylisoquinoline type was in agreement with facts.

Insularine forms a methiodide which is easily converted with silver chloride to the methochloride. The latter when subjected to the Hofmann degradation yields two methine bases in the first stage and trimethylamine and des-*N*-insularine (LXXI) ($C_{36}H_{30}O_6$) in the second stage of the degradation. This crystalline nitrogen-free compound (LXXI) when treated with ozone and the resulting product oxidized with 1% aqueous potassium permanganate yielded three acids (107). Two of these, namely 4-methoxyisophthalic acid and 4′,5,6-tricarboxy-2,3-dimethoxydiphenyl ether (LIV) were identified by comparison with known compounds. The structure of the third, labelled insularinic acid (LXXII), was arrived at by degradation and identification of the fragments.

Catalytic reduction of methyl insularinate (LXXIII) in acetic acid in the presence of platinum oxide yielded a nonphenolic substance which was presumed to be hexahydrotoluic ester (LXXV) and a phenolic substance (LXXIV). This substance (LXXIV) proved to be dimethyl 3,4-dihydroxy-5-methoxyphthalate since it yielded dimethyl 3,4,5-trimethoxyphthalate (LXXVI) on methylation with diazomethane and 4-methoxy-5,6-diethoxyphthalic anhydride (LXXVII) on ethylation with diazoethane.

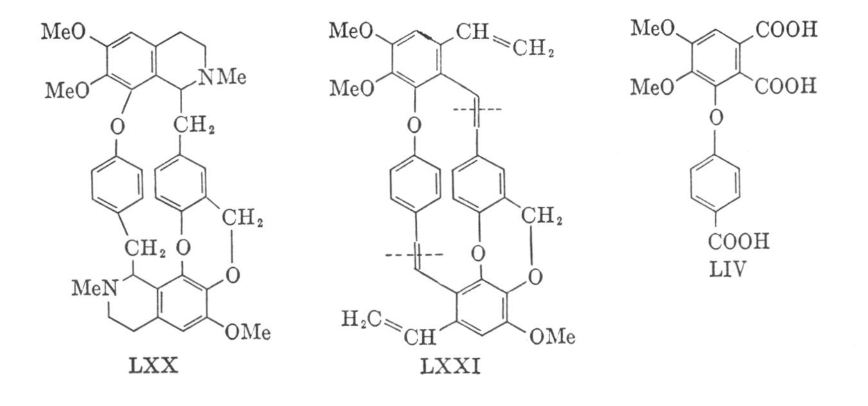

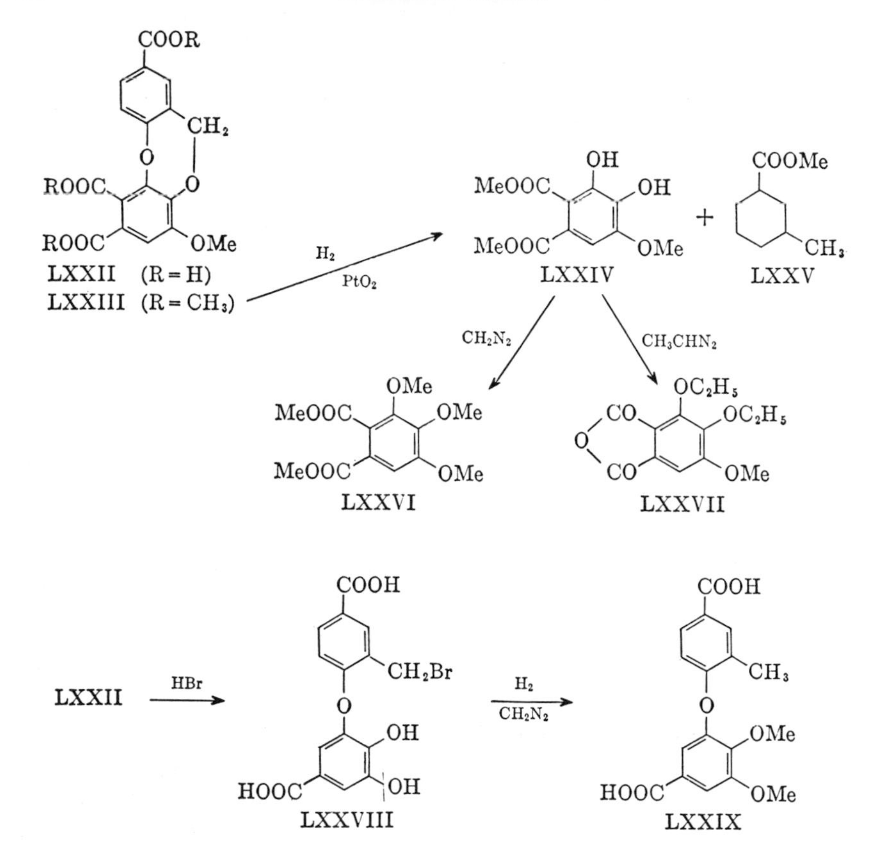

Further elucidation of the structure of insularinic acid came when it (LXXII) was heated at 130–145° in a sealed bomb with hydrogen bromide for one and one-half hours. The resulting product (LXXVIII) on catalytic reduction followed by methylation with diazomethane and saponification yielded 4,5′-dicarboxy-2′-methyl-2,3-dimethoxydiphenyl ether (LXXIX). This was synthesized from the potassium salt of methyl 4-hydroxy-3-methylbenzoate and methyl 3-bromo-4,5-dimethoxybenzoate by the Ullmann condensation.

Thus, the two main fragments resulting from the degradation of des-*N*-insularine are 4′,5,6-tricarboxy-2,3-dimethoxydiphenyl ether (LIV) and insularinic acid (LXXII). It is conceivable that these could arise from the des-*N*-insularine (LXXI) through the cleavage at the double bonds. On this basis Tomita and Uyeo (107) proposed the structure LXX for insularine. They also found support for this structure from absorption spectrum studies.

IV. Alkaloids Containing Three Diphenyl Ether Linkages

This group of bisbenzylisoquinoline alkaloids possesses a structure which includes three oxygen bridges consisting of one diphenyl ether linkage and a diphenylene dioxide ring. These alkaloids may be considered as the offsprings of coclaurine and of the oxyacanthine-berbamine series. Thus, a double dehydrogenation between two molecules of coclaurine (II) provides the structure LXXX of the oxyacanthine-berbamine type. A third oxygen bridge may be added to LXXX between the two isoquinoline portions of the molecule to form a diphenylene dioxide ring. This may be

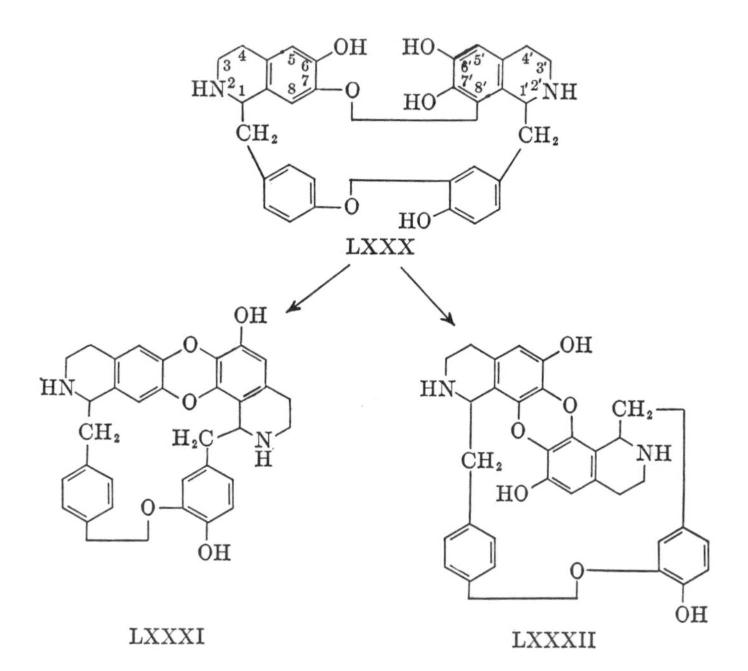

done in two ways: dehydrogenation between the 7′-hydroxyl and the 8-hydrogen of LXXX to provide the skeletal structure LXXXII for the alkaloids micranthine, menisarine, and normenisarine, and dehydration between the 6- and 7′-hydroxyl groups of LXXX to provide the skeletal structure LXXXI for trilobine and isotrilobine. However, the formation of a diphenyl ether linkage through dehydration of two phenolic groups is not considered biogenetically sound. A more plausible mechanism for the formation of LXXXI involves a triple dehydrogenation occurring between 1-(4-hydroxybenzyl)-6-hydroxytetrahydroisoquinoline and 1-(4-hydroxybenzyl)-6,7-dihydroxytetrahydroisoquinoline.

1. Trilobine and Isotrilobine

Trilobine and isotrilobine (formerly known as homotrilobine) occur in *Cocculus trilobus* DC. (85, 86) and in *Cocculus sarmentosus* Diels (88) and are isomeric. At first trilobine was believed to have the empirical formula $C_{19}H_{19}NO_3$ and two non-phenolic hydroxyl groups (87, 88, 90), but this belief was later disproved. Trilobine and isotrilobine have the composition $C_{36}H_{36}O_5N_2$ and contain two methoxyl and two *N*-methyl groups and a phenylene dioxide linkage. On oxidation with potassium permanganate they each yield 4′,5-dicarboxy-2-methoxydiphenyl ether (VIII, R = CH_3), which is also obtained from oxyacanthine (91, 92). The cleavage products of the methines obtained by Hofmann degradation of trilobine and isotrilobine are also identical.

Further knowledge regarding the constitution of the two alkaloids was obtained by subjecting their methines to ozonolysis. By this means Kondo and Tomita (92) split the molecule of trilobine (or isotrilobine)

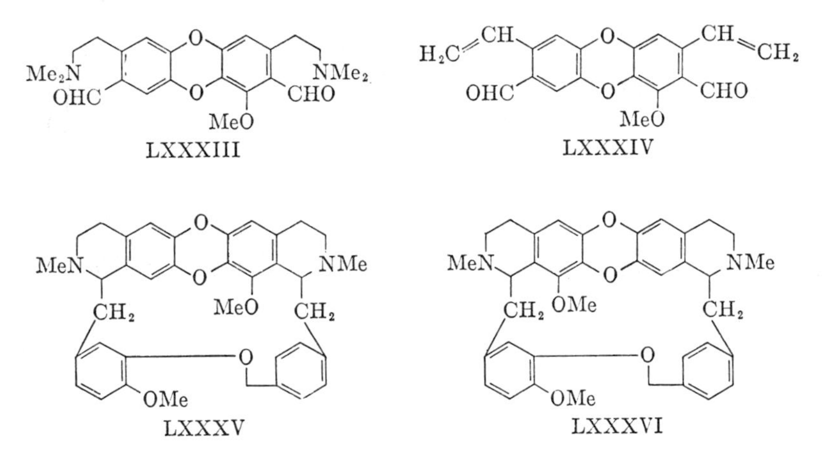

methylmethine into two parts, one of which was 4′,5-diformyl-2-methoxydiphenyl ether (XXXIV) (identified by oxidation to the diacid (VIII, R = CH_3)) and the other a dimethylamino dialdehyde at first believed to have the structure LXXXIII. This on Hofmann degradation yielded trimethylamine and a divinyl dialdehyde for which Kondo and Tomita then proposed the structure LXXXIV. This divinyl dialdehyde could be oxidized to a tetracarboxylic acid which on alkali fusion produced protocatechinic acid and a trace of gallic acid. The divinyl dialdehyde also formed an anil, the methiodide of which on digestion with dilute mineral acid yielded a small amount of a phenolic product. Since of the three methoxybenzaldehydes only the *o*-derivative under similar conditions loses its methyl group, it was concluded that the methoxyl group in the

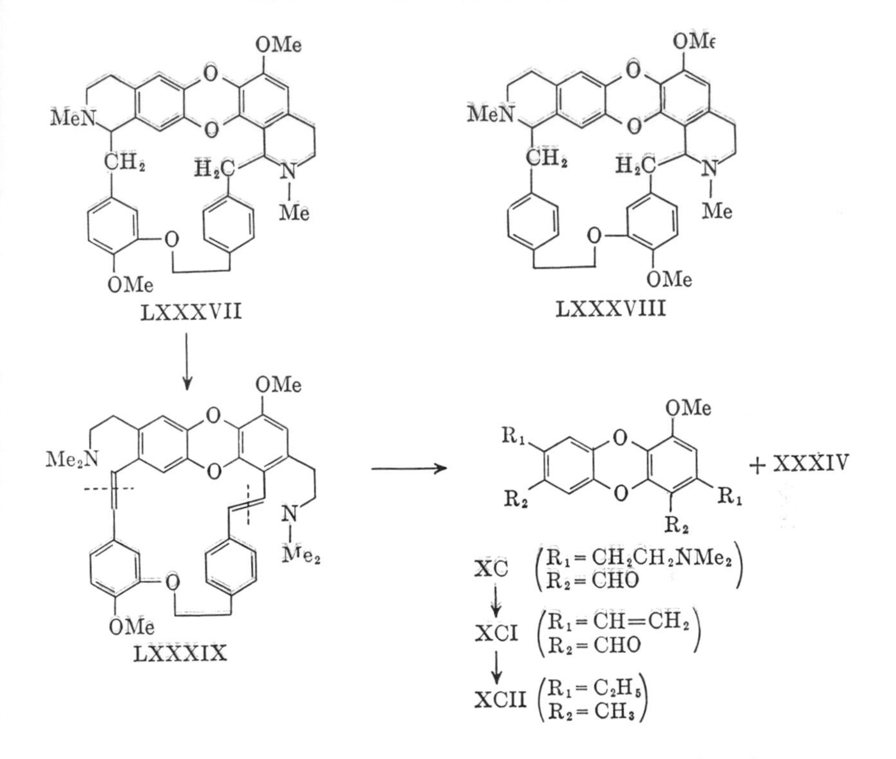

divinyl dialdehyde must occupy the position next to the aldehyde group as shown in the formula LXXXIV. On the basis of the above observations Kondo and Tomita (92) assigned to trilobine and to isotrilobine the structures LXXXV and LXXXVI.

On a purely theoretical basis Faltis (69, 94) proposed the alternate structures LXXXVII and LXXXVIII for trilobine and isotrilobine which also fit experimental facts. Experimental proof for these structures was provided several years later by Tomita and Tani (116, 117), who synthesized one of the degradation products of trilobine. The divinyl dialdehyde obtained from trilobine methylmethine by ozonolysis and degradation, previously believed to be the structure LXXXIV, was now hydrogenated first catalytically and then according to Clemmensen. A comparison of the resulting product with synthetic 1-methoxy-3,7-diethyl-4,6-dimethyl-diphenylene dioxide (XCII) (117) showed that they were identical. A reconstruction of the experimental facts showed that trilobine and isotrilobine must have structures LXXXVII and LXXXVIII. Thus, the Hofmann degradation of trilobine yielded trilobine methylmethine (LXXXIX), which on ozonolysis cleaved at the double bonds to give the dialdehyde XXXIV and the amino aldehyde XC. A further Hofmann degradation of

XC produced the *o*-vinylaldehyde (XCI) which on hydrogenation yielded the synthetic XCII.

Trilobine and its derivatives are toxic to frogs and mice when injected subcutaneously (89, 93), the minimum lethal dose being 500 mg. per kilogram. These compounds cause motor paralysis with occasional convulsions, and death is usually due to respiratory failure.

2. Micranthine

The alkaloid micranthine was first discovered by Pyman (111) in the bark of the Australian tree *Daphnandra micrantha* (Monimiaceae), together with two other bisbenzylisoquinoline alkaloids (daphnandrine and daphnoline). Although Bick and Todd (113) were unable to find either of the latter two in the bark of this plant, they found micranthine in much larger quantity (2% yield) than did Pyman. Analyses showed that micranthine contained one methoxy and one methylimino group, and the formula $C_{34}H_{32}O_6N_2$ was indicated (113). In a mixture of nitric and sulfuric acids this alkaloid gave a blue coloration (a specific test for the diphenylene dioxide system). The usual tests for phenolic groups gave negative or indecisive result, but the presence of two phenolic groups was indicated by other tests such as the presence of two active hydrogens (Zerewitinoff) and the solubility in Claisen's cryptophenol reagent. The presence of two phenolic groups was confirmed by methylation with methyl iodide in methanolic sodium methoxide to yield *O,O,N*-trimethylmicranthine dimethiodide, which on Hofmann degradation gave the optically inactive base *O,O,N*-trimethylmicranthine methine. This base now contained three methoxyl groups as compared to one present in the original alkaloid. Thus, two methoxyl groups must have been introduced through methylation.

In order to elucidate the structure of micranthine Bick and Todd (113) subjected *O,O,N*-trimethylmicranthine methine to ozonolysis and obtained two products. One proved to be 4′,5-diformyl-2-methoxydiphenyl ether (XXXIV). The other was an amino aldehyde which on further degradation (Hofmann) yielded a crystalline substance which from its analysis and properties appeared to be a diformyldimethoxydivinyldiphenylene dioxide. Bick and Todd deduced the structure of micranthine by recourse to the Faltis theory of the biogenesis of bisbenzylisoquinoline alkaloids.

First, the assumption was made that micranthine is unsubstituted at the 5-positions of the isoquinoline nuclei on the basis that no substituents are present in the 5-positions of all known bisbenzylisoquinoline alkaloids. Then, all the possible structures containing a diphenylene dioxide ring, one methoxyl and two phenolic groups that can be formed from two molecules of coclaurine (II) by enzymatic dehydrogenation or dehydration were considered. It became evident that only one structure, XCIII, met the requirements, and it could be formed by dehydrogenation occurring between the benzyl residues as in oxyacanthine and between the 7-hydroxyl groups and the 8-hydrogens of the isoquinoline nuclei. On this basis Bick and Todd (113) concluded that *O,O,N*-trimethylmicranthine must

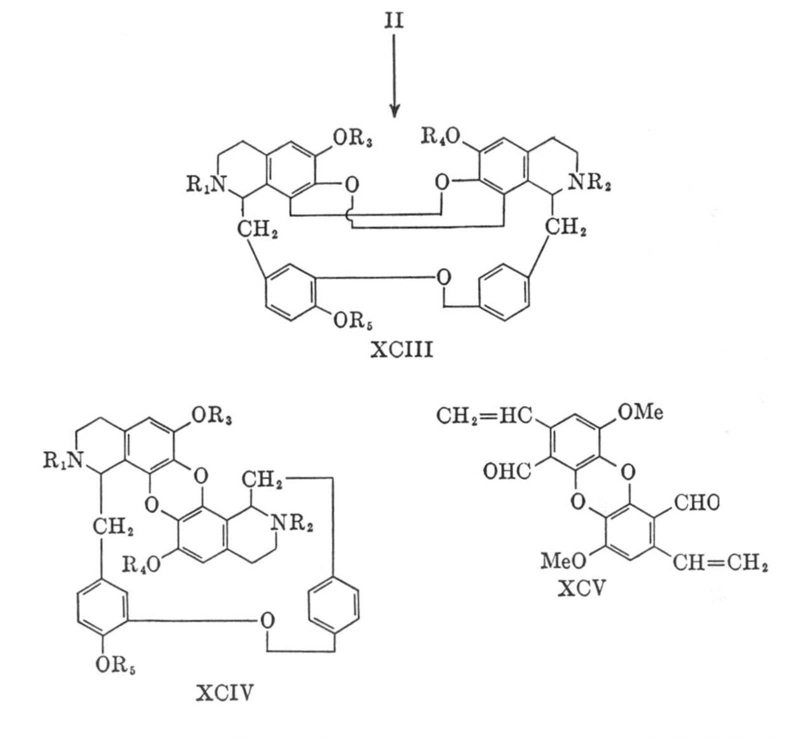

have the structure XCIV and that the dimethoxy divinyl dialdehyde obtained as the final degradation product is 4,9-diformyl-1,6-dimethoxy-3,8-divinyldiphenylene dioxide (XCV).

In an attempt to establish the position of the two phenolic groups in micranthine, Bick and Todd ethylated *N*-methylmicranthine dimethiodide and then subjected the resulting *N*-methyl-*O,O*-diethylmicranthine dimethiodide to the Hofmann degradation. The *N*-methyl-*O,O*-diethylmicranthine methine so obtained was ozonized, and the neutral product from the ozonolysis was identified as 4′,5-diformyl-2-ethoxydiphenyl ether by direct comparison with an authentic sample. Thus, one of the phenolic groups in micranthine must be located on the diphenyl ether portion of the molecule. Micranthine was thus given the structure XCIV in which R_5 = H, of R_1 and R_2 one is H and the other CH_3, and of R_3 and R_4 one is H, the other CH_3.

In a further study Bick and Todd (113) compared the properties of *O,O,N*-trimethylmicranthine methine and *N*-methyldihydromenisarine and of their derivatives. This comparison led them to believe that these two compounds were identical and that the parent bases from which the methines were derived, namely, *O,O,N*-trimethylmicranthine and *N*-methyldihydromenisarine are enantiomorphic.

The three *Daphnandra* alkaloids (micranthine, daphnoline, and daphnandrine) all appear to have the same physiological action, though daphnandrine is only very slightly active. Micranthine and daphnoline produce marked local action when injected hypodermically, causing great edematous infiltration of the subcutaneous tissues and loss of sensibility. They have also a depressent action on the central nervous system, causing anesthesia which seems to precede the loss of motor activity. There is also vasodilator circulating depression when given intravenously. Death from a fatal dose is due to respiratory paralysis.

3. Menisarine and Normenisarine

Two other alkaloids which contain the diphenylene dioxide ring as shown by the characteristic sulfuric–nitric acid color reaction are menisarine, occurring in *Cocculus sarmentosus* (97, 98), and normenisarine, present in *Cocculus trilobus* (97). Normenisarine is a phenolic alkaloid and when methylated it shows a gain of one methoxyl group. The methylated product, *O*-methylnormenisarine is identical in all respects with menisarine (97). Menisarine contains three methoxyl groups and one *N*-methyl group and has the formula $C_{36}H_{34}N_2O_6$. *Dihydromenisarine*, obtained by reduction of menisarine (zinc and acid) on oxidation with permanganate yielded 4′,5-dicarboxy-2-methoxydiphenyl ether (VIII, R = CH_3), a degradation product also of trilobine, oxyacanthine, and others. Kondo and Tomita (98) degraded dihydromenisarine according to the method of Hofmann and obtained an optically inactive methylmethine (m.p. 112°) which on ozonization gave two dialdehydes. One of these was 4′,5-diformyl-2-methoxydiphenyl ether (XXXIV) and the other a dimethylamino dialdehyde. The latter on heating with alkali produced trimethylamine and a compound which gave characteristic color reactions for an *o*-vinyl aldehyde and a diphenylene dioxide ring. The empirical formula and the nature of the degradation products of menisarine indicated a structure of the trilobine type.

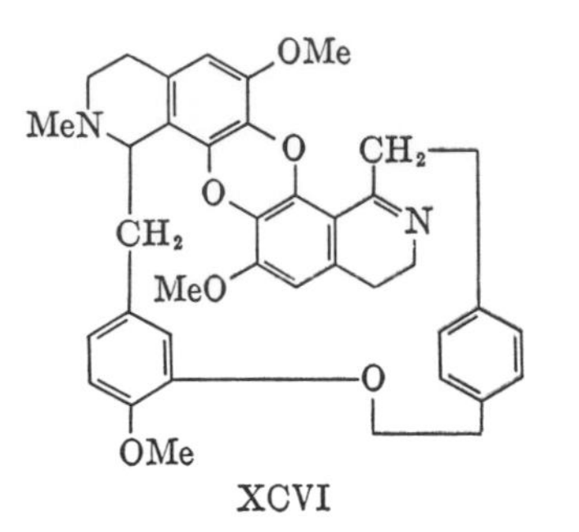

XCVI

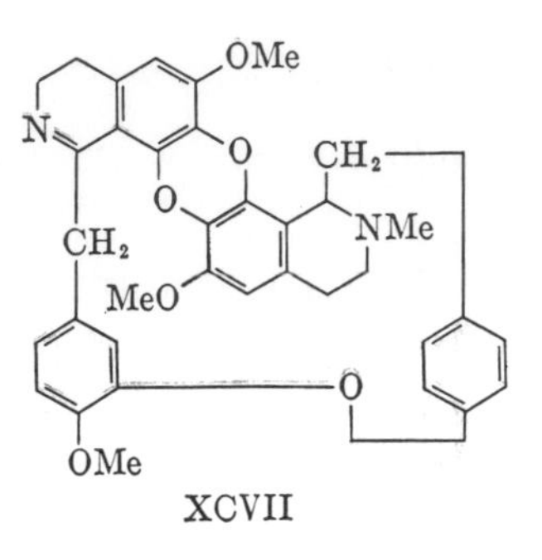

XCVII

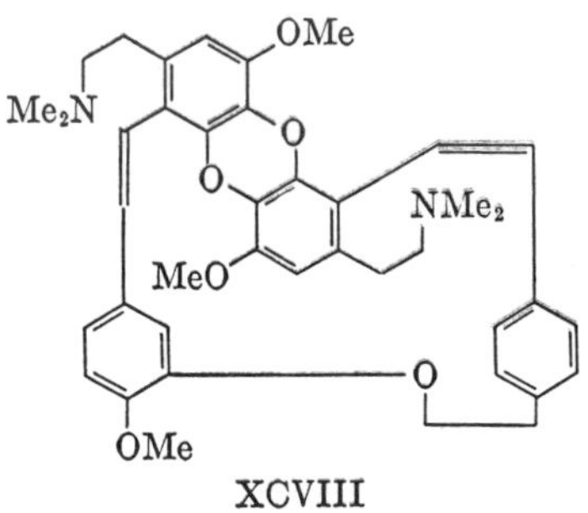

XCVIII

Recently Bick and Todd (113) compared the properties of *O,O,N*-trimethylmicranthine methine and *N*-methyldihydromenisarine methine and found them to be identical. They also found that the dimethiodides from which these methine bases were obtained by Hofmann degradation, namely, *N*-methyldihydromenisarine dimethiodide and *O,O,N*-trimethylmicranthine dimethiodide, were enantiomorphs. On the basis of these studies menisarine was assigned the structure XCVI or XCVII, and the methine basis *N*-methyldihydromenisarine methine and *O,O,N*-trimethylmicranthine methine the structure XCVIII.

V. References

1. N. F. Proskurnina and A. P. Orekhov, *Bull. soc. chim.*, **5,** 1357 (1938); *Chem. Abstr.*, **33,** 1439 (1939).
2. N. F. Proskurnina and A. P. Orekhov, *J. Gen. Chem. (U.S.S.R.)*, **10,** 707 (1940); *Chem. Abstr.*, **35,** 2520 (1941).
3. H. Kondo and Z. Narita, *J. Pharm. Soc. Japan*, **No. 542,** 279 (1927); *Chem. Abstr.*, **21,** 2700 (1927).
4. R. H. F. Manske, *Can. J. Research*, **21B,** 17 (1943).
5. H. Kondo and Z. Narita, *J. Pharm. Soc. Japan*, **49,** 688 (1929); *Chem. Abstr.*, **24,** 122 (1930).
6. H. Kondo and Z. Narita, *J. Pharm. Soc. Japan*, **50,** 589 (1930); *Chem. Abstr.*, **24,** 5301 (1930).
7. H. Kondo and Z. Narita, *Ber.*, **63B,** 2420 (1930).

8. H. Kondo, Z. Narita, and S. Uyeo, *Ber.*, **68B**, 519 (1935).
9. K. Horiuchi, *Mitt. med. Ges. Tokyo*, **45**, 740 (1931); *Chem. Abstr.*, **26**, 5347 (1932).
10. Polex, *Arch. Pharm.*, **6**, 271 (1836).
11. O. Hesse, *Ber.*, **19**, 3190 (1886):
12. C. Rüdel, *Arch. Pharm.*, **229**, 631 (1891).
13. H. Pommerehne, *Arch. Pharm.*, **233**, 127 (1895).
14. E. Späth and A. Kolbe, *Ber.*, **58**, 2280 (1925).
15. E. Späth and J. Pikl, *Ber.*, **62**, 2251 (1929).
16. F. von Bruchhausen and H. Schultze, *Arch. Pharm.*, **267**, 617 (1929).
17. F. von Bruchhausen and P. H. Gericke, *Arch. Pharm.*, **269**, 115 (1931).
18. F. von Bruchhausen, H. Oberembt, and A. Feldhaus, *Ann.*, **507**, 144 (1933).
19. R. Hamet, *Compt. rend.*, **197**, 1354 (1933); *Chem. Abstr.*, **28**, 1408 (1934).
20. R. Hamet, *Compt. rend. soc. biol.*, **136**, 112 (1942); *Chem. Abstr.*, **37**, 2812 (1943).
21. A. C. Santos, Dissertation, Westfälische Wilhelms-Univ., Münster, 1929, p. 5; *Chem. Abstr.*, **24**, 1647 (1930).
22. H. Kondo and M. Tomita, *J. Pharm. Soc. Japan*, **50**, 309 (1930); *Chem. Abstr.*, **24**, 3512 (1930).
23. H. Kondo, M. Tomita, M. Satomi, and T. Ikeda, *J. Pharm. Soc. Japan*, **58**, 920 (1938); *Chem. Abstr.*, **34**, 3752 (1940).
24. G. A. Greathouse and N. E. Rigler, *Plant Physiol.*, **15**, 563 (1940); *Chem. Abstr.*, **36**, 6202 (1942).
25. H. Kondo and K. Yano, *J. Pharm Soc. Japan*, **48**, 107 (1928); *Chem. Abstr.*, **22**, 2359 (1928).
26. H. Kondo and K. Yano, *J. Pharm. Soc. Japan*, **49**, 315 (1929); *Chem. Abstr.*, **23**, 4475 (1929).
27. H. Kondo and K. Yano, *J. Pharm. Soc. Japan*, **50**, 224 (1930); *Chem. Abstr.*, **24**, 3513 (1930).
28. H. Kondo and K. Yano, *Ann.*, **497**, 90 (1932).
29. S. Kubota, *Folia Pharmacol. Japon.*, **12**, No. 2, 328 (*Breviaria* 16) (1931); *Chem. Abstr.*, **25**, 5736 (1931).
30. S. Kubota, *Folia Pharmacol. Japon.*, **12**, No. 2, 338 (*Breviaria* 17) (1931); *Chem. Abstr.*, **25**, 5931 (1931).
31. S. Kubota and H. Takahashi, *Folia Pharmacol. Japon.*, **18**, No. 2–3, 143 (*Breviaria* 144) (1934); *Chem. Abstr.*, **28**, 7422 (1934).
32. K. K. Chen and A. L. Chen, *J. Biol. Chem.*, **109**, 681 (1935); *Chem. Abstr.*, **29**, 5223 (1935).
33. K. K. Chen, A. L. Chen, R. C. Andersen, and C. L. Rose, *Chinese J. Physiol.*, **11**, 13 24 (1937); *Chem. Abstr.*, **31**, 2688 (1937).
34. J. H. Chu, *Chinese J. Physiol.*, **14**, 315 (1939); *Chem. Abstr.*, **34**, 4739 (1940).
35. H. Kondo and I. Keimatsu, *J. Pharm. Soc. Japan*, **55**, 234 (1935); *Chem. Abstr.*, **29**, 5114 (1935).
36. Chang-Kong Chuang, Chi-Yi Hsing, Yee-Shang Kao, and Kuo-Jen Chang, *Ber.*, **72B**, 519 (1939).
37. A. C. Santos, *Rev. filipina med. y farm.*, **22**, No. 9, 11 (1931); *Chem. Abstr.*, **26**, 729 (1932).
38. A. C. Santos, *Ber.*, **65B**, 472 (1932).
39. H. Kondo and I. Keimatsu, *Ber.*, **68B**, 1503 (1935).
40. H. Kondo and M. Tomita, *J. Pharm. Soc. Japan.*, **51**, 452 (1931); *Chem. Abstr.*, **25**, 4887 (1931).
41. H. Kondo and M. Tomita, *J. Pharm. Soc. Japan*, **55**, 646 (1935); *Chem. Abstr.*, **33**, 627 (1939).

42. H. Kondo, Y. Yamashita, and I. Keimatsu, *J. Pharm. Soc. Japan*, **54**, 620 (1934); *Chem. Abstr.*, **31**, 105 (1937).
43. H. Kondo and I. Keimatsu, *J. Pharm. Soc. Japan*, **55**, 121 (1935); *Chem. Abstr.*, **29**, 7988 (1935).
44. H. Kondo and I. Keimatsu, *Ber.*, **71B**, 2553 (1938).
45. H. Kondo and M. Tomita, *J. Pharm. Soc. Japan*, **59**, 207 (1939); *Chem. Abstr.*, **34**, 7530 (1940).
46. H. Kondo and M. Tomita, *J. Pharm. Soc. Japan*, **59**, 542 (1939); *Chem. Abstr.*, **34**, 1023 (1940).
47. H. Kondo, S. Hasegawa, and M. Tomita, U. S. Patent, 2,206,407 (1940); *Chem. Abstr.*, **34**, 7542 (1940).
48. F. Faltis and F. Neumann, *Monatsh.*, **42**, 311 (1922); *Chem. Abstr.*, **16**, 2866 (1922).
49. F. Faltis and T. Heczko, *Monatsh.*, **43**, 377 (1923); *Chem. Abstr.*, **17**, 1480 (1923).
50. F. Faltis and A. Troller, *Ber.*, **61B**, 345 (1928).
51. F. Faltis and K. Zwerina, *Ber.*, **62B**, 1034 (1929).
52. F. Faltis and H. Frauendorfer, *Ber.*, **63B**, 806 (1930).
53. F. Faltis, S. Wrann, and E. Kühas, *Ann.*, **497**, 69 (1932).
54. F. Faltis and H. Dietreich, *Ber.*, **67B**, 231 (1934).
55. H. Kondo, M. Tomita, and S. Uyeo, *Ber.*, **70B**, 1890 (1937).
56. M. Scholtz, *Ber.*, **29**, 2054 (1896).
57. J. Herzig and H. Meyer, *Monatsh.*, **18**, 379 (1897).
58. M. Scholtz, *Arch. Pharm.*, **236**, 530 (1898).
59. M. Scholtz, *Arch. Pharm.*, **237**, 199 (1899).
60. M. Scholtz, *Arch. Pharm.*, **244**, 555 (1906).
61. H. Hildebrandt, *Arch. exptl. Pathol. Pharmakol.*, **57**, 279 (1907); *Brit. Chem. Abstr.*, **92**, 869 (1907).
62. M. Scholtz, *Pharm. Centralhalle*, **47**, 848; *Chem. Abstr.*, **1**, 222 (1907).
63. F. Faltis, *Monatsh.*, **33**, 873 (1911).
64. M. Scholtz, *Arch. Pharm.*, **250**, 684 (1912).
65. L. P. J. Palet, *Anales soc. quím. Argentina*, **6**, 156 (1918); *Chem. Abstr.*, **13**, 216 (1919).
66. H. Zeehuisen, *Arch. exptl. Pathol. Pharmakol*,. **86**, 342 (1920); *Chem. Abstr.*, **15**, 411 (1921).
67. F. Faltis, K. Kadiera, and F. Doblhammer, *Ber.*, **69B**, 1269 (1936).
68. H. King, *J. Chem. Soc.*, **1940**, 737.
69. F. Faltis, L. Holzinger, P. Ita, and R. Schwarz, *Ber.*, **74B**, 79 (1941).
70. R. Boehm, *Arch. Pharm.*, **235**, 660 (1897).
71. E. Späth, W. Leithe, and F. Ladeck, *Ber.*, **61B**, 1698 (1928).
72. E. Späth and F. Kuffner, *Ber.*, **67B**, 55 (1934).
73. F. Hauschild, *Arch. exptl. Pathol. Pharmakol.*, **174**, 742 (1934); *Chem. Abstr.*, **28**, 4787 (1934).
74. R. West, *Proc. Roy. Soc. Med.*, **28**, 565 (1935); *Chem. Abstr.*, **29**, 5927 (1935).
75. H. King, *Chemistry & Industry*, **1935**, 739.
76. H. King, *J. Chem. Soc.*, **1935**, 1381.
77. H. King, *J. Chem. Soc.*, **1936**, 1276.
78. R. West, *Arch. intern. pharmacodynamie*, **56**, 81 (1937); *Chem. Abstr.*, **31**, 6328 (1937).
79. H. King, *J. Chem. Soc.*, **1939**, 1157.
80. A. R. McIntyre and R. E. King, *Science*, **97**, 69 (1943); *Chem. Abstr.*, **37**, 1731 (1943).

81. O. Wintersteiner and J. D. Dutcher, *Science*, **97,** 467 (1943); *Chem. Abstr.*, **37,** 4205 (1943).
82. H. King, *J. Chem. Soc.*, **1937,** 1472.
83. H. Kondo and K. Yano, *J. Pharm. Soc. Japan*, **No. 548,** 815 (1927); *Chem. Abstr.*, **22,** 786 (1928).
84. E. Ochai, *J. Pharm. Soc. Japan*, **49,** 425 (1929); *Chem. Abstr.*, **23,** 5272 (1929).
85. H. Kondo and T. Nakazato, *J. Pharm. Soc. Japan*, **No. 511,** 691 (1924); *Chem. Abstr.*, **19,** 1708 (1925). M
86. H. Kondo and T. Nakazato, *J. Pharm. Soc. Japan.*, **No. 532,** 461 (1926); *Chem. Abstr.*, **21,** 2699 (1927).
87. H. Kondo and T. Nakazato, *J. Pharm. Soc. Japan*, **No. 532,** 465 (1926); *Chem. Abstr.*, **21,** 2699 (1927).
88. H. Kondo and M. Tomita, *J. Pharm. Soc. Japan*, **No. 542,** 265 (1927); *Chem. Abstr.*, **21,** 2699 (1927).
89. S. Tsuruta, *Folia Pharmacol. Japon.*, **3,** 280 (1926); *Ber. ges. Physiol. u. exptl. Pharmakol.*, **39,** 751; *Chem. Abstr.*, **21,** 3233 (1927).
90. H. Kondo and M. Tomita, *J. Pharm. Soc. Japan*, **48,** 659 (1928); *Chem. Abstr.*, **23,** 392 (1929).
91. H. Kondo and M. Tomita, *J. Pharm. Soc. Japan*, **50,** 1035 (1930); *Chem. Abstr.*, **25,** 2731 (1931).
92. H. Kondo and M. Tomita, *Ann.*, **497,** 104 (1932).
93. S. Fuse, *Japan. J. Med. Sci. IV. Pharmacol. Trans.*, **9,** 9 (1936); *Chem. Abstr.*, **31,** 8020 (1937).
94. F. Faltis, *Ann.*, **499,** 301 (1932).
95. H. King, *Ann. Repts. on Progr. Chem. (Chem. Soc. London)*, **30,** 242 (1933).
96. H. Kondo and M. Tomita, *J. Pharm. Soc. Japan*, **50,** 633 (1930); *Chem. Abstr.*, **24,** 5302 (1930).
97. H. Kondo and M. Tomita, *J. Pharm. Soc. Japan*, **55,** 911 (1935); *Chem. Abstr.*, **30,** 726 (1936).
98. H. Kondo and M. Tomita, *J. Pharm. Soc. Japan*, **55,** 637 (1935); *Chem. Abstr.*, **33,** 626 (1939).
99. H. Kondo and T. Sanada, *J. Pharm. Soc. Japan.*, **No. 514,** 1034 (1924); *Chem. Abstr.*, **19,** 1709 (1925),
100. H. Kondo and T. Sanada, *J. Pharm. Soc. Japan*, **No. 541,** 177 (1927); *Chem. Abstr.*, **21,** 2700 (1927).
101. H. Kondo and T. Sanada, *J. Pharm. Soc. Japan.*, **No. 549,** 930 (1927); *Chem. Abstr.*, **22,** 965 (1928).
102. H. Kondo and T. Sanada, *J. Pharm. Soc. Japan*, **48,** 1141 (1928); *Chem Abstr.*, **23,** 2978 (1929).
103. H. Kondo and T. Wotanabe, *J. Pharm. Soc. Japan*, **58,** 268 (1938); *Chem. Abstr.*, **32,** 5403 (1938).
104. J. D. Dutcher, *J. Am. Chem. Soc.*, **68,** 419 (1946).
105. M. Tomita, *J. Pharm. Soc. Japan*, **59,** 207 (1939); *Chem. Abstr.*, **34,** 7530 (1940).
106. M. Tomita, S. Uyeo, S. Sawa, K. Dai, and T. Miwa, *J. Pharm. Soc. Japan*, **69,** 22 (1949); *Chem. Abstr.*, **44,** 4476 (1950).
107. M. Tomita and S. Uyeo, *J. Chem. Soc. Japan*, **64,** 64, 70, 142, 147 (1943); *Chem. Abstr.*, **41,** 3803 (1947).
108. R. C. Bick and A. R. Todd, *J. Chem. Soc.*, **1948,** 2170.
109. N. F. Proskurnina, *J. Gen. Chem. (U.S.S.R.)*, **16,** 129 (1946); *Chem. Abstr.*, **41,** 460 (1947).

110. M. Tomita and E. Fujita, *J. Pharm. Soc. Japan*, **70,** 411 (1950).
111. F. E. Pyman, *J. Chem. Soc.*, **105,** 1679 (1914).
112. R. C. Bick, E. S. Ewen, and A. R. Todd, *J. Chem. Soc.*, **1949,** 2767.
113. R. C. Bick and A. R. Todd, *J. Chem. Soc.*, **1950,** 1606.
114. R. D. Coghill, Abbott Laboratories, Chicago, Ill., private communication.
115. E. Sodi Pallares and H. Martinex Garza, *Arch. Biochem.*, **16,** 275 (1948); *Chem. Abstr.*, **42,** 5036 (1948).
116. M. Tomita and C. Tani, *J. Pharm. Soc. Japan*, **62,** 468 (1942); *Chem. Abstr.*, **45,** 4728 (1951).
117. M. Tomita and C. Tani, *J. Pharm. Soc. Japan*, **62,** 481 (1942); *Chem. Abstr.*, **45,** 4729 (1951).
118. H. Kondo and T. Sanada, *J. Pharm. Soc. Japan*, **51,** 509 (1931); *Chem. Abstr.*, **25,** 4887 (1931).
119. H. Kondo and T. Nozoye, *J. Pharm. Soc. Japan*, **63,** 333 (1943); *Chem. Abstr.*, **45,** 3400 (1951).
120. H. Kondo, Z. Narita, and M. Murakami, *J. Pharm. Soc. Japan*, **61,** 117 (1941).
121. M. Tomita and H. Shirai, *J Pharm. Soc. Japan*, **62,** 381 (1942).
122. H. King, *J. Chem. Soc.*, **1948,** 265.
123. H. King, *J. Chem. Soc.*, **1947,** 936.
124. H. King, *J. Chem. Soc.*, **1948,** 1945.
125. H. Kondo, *Ann. Rept. ITSUU Lab.* (*Japan*), **No. 2,** 27, 43, 48, 50 (1951).
126. M. Tomita, E. Fujita, and F. Murai, *J. Pharm. Soc. Japan*, **71,** 226 (1951); *Chem. Abstr.*, **46,** 4554 (1952).
127. M. Tomita, E. Fujita, and F. Murai, *J. Pharm. Soc. Japan*, **71,** 301 (1951); *Chem. Abstr.*, **46,** 4555 (1952).
128. H. Kondo and K. Tanaka, *J. Pharm. Soc. Japan*, **63,** 267, 273 (1943); *Chem. Abstr.*, **45,** 3400 (1951).
129. K. Tanaka, *J. Pharm .Soc. Japan*, **64,** 27 (1944); *Chem. Abstr.*, **45,** 5173 (1951).
130. S. Kimoto and S. Honjo, *J. Pharm. Soc. Japan*, **64,** 258 (1944); *Chem. Abstr.*, **45,** 5137 (1951).
131. H. Kondo, H. Kataoka, and K. Nakagawa, *Ann. Rept. ITSUU Lab.* (*Japan*), **No. 3,** 49 (1952).
132. M. Tomita, E. Fujita, and F. Murai, *J. Pharm. Soc. Japan*, **71,** 1034 (1951); *Chem. Abstr.*, **46,** 5060 (1952).
133. M. Tomita, E. Fujita, and F. Murai, *J. Pharm. Soc. Japan*, **71,** 1039 (1951); *Chem. Abstr.*, **46,** 5060 (1952).
134. M. Tomita, E. Fujita, and F. Murai, *J. Pharm. Soc. Japan*, **71,** 1043 (1951); *Chem. Abstr.*, **46,** 5061 (1952).
135. M. Tomita, E. Fujita, and T. Nakamura, *J. Pharm. Soc. Japan*, **71,** 1075 (1951); *Chem. Abstr.*, **46,** 5060 (1952).
136. F. A. L. Anet, G. K. Hughes, and E. Ritchie, *Australian J. Sci. Research, Ser. A*, **3A,** 346 (1950); *Chem. Abstr.*, **45,** 822 (1951).
137. J. D. Dutcher, *J. Am. Chem. Soc.*, **74,** 2221 (1952).

CHAPTER 34

The Cularine Alkaloids

R. H. F. MANSKE

Dominion Rubber Research Laboratory, Guelph, Ontario

	Page
I. Introduction	249
II. Cularine	249
Structure	249
III. Cularimine	251
IV. Cularidine	252
V. References	252

I. Introduction

To date there have been found only cularine and several of its *O*- or *N*-desmethyl derivatives. The unique feature of this group is the presence of a seven-membered heterocycle containing an oxygen atom in a diphenyl ether linkage. The known occurrence of these alkaloids is restricted to the genera *Dicentra* and *Corydalis*.

II. Cularine

Cularine, $C_{20}H_{23}O_4N$, has been isolated from *Dicentra cucullaria* (L.) Bernh., *D. eximia* (Ker-Gawl.) Torr., *D. oregana* Eastwood, *D. formosa* (Andr.) Walp., and *Corydalis claviculata* (L.) DC. (1, 2). Only in the last-named plant does it constitute a major constituent, but its presence in very minute amounts can be ascertained by virtue of the fact that it forms an acid oxalate which is virtually insoluble in cold water or methanol. It is, therefore, readily isolated from mother liquors from which other alkaloids have been separated either as free bases or as salts other than oxalates. It is readily extractable as its hydrochloride from aqueous solutions by means of chloroform and thus separates along with dicentrine, glaucine, bicuculline, corlumine, etc.

The free base is moderately soluble in most organic solvents and crystallizes from hot methanol in large brilliant polyhedra which melt at 115°; $[\alpha]_D$ +285° (methanol). The hydrochloride is readily soluble in all hydrolytic solvents, can be crystallized from methanol–ethyl acetate, and melts at 207°.

Structure. Analytical data show the presence of three methoxyls in cularine. The fourth oxygen atom could not be recognized as a hydroxyl or carbonyl. The nitrogen is tertiary and is eliminated as trimethylamine in the second stage of the Hofmann degradation. Therefore, it is part of a ring and carries a methyl group. The non-nitrogenous compound, $C_{19}H_{18}O_4$ (m.p. 123°), resulting from the Hofmann degradation is doubly unsaturated and may be catalytically reduced to a tetrahydro compound, $C_{19}H_{22}O_4$ (m.p. 77°). Since the non-reactive fourth oxygen appeared to be present in ether linkage and since the known isoquinoline alkaloids with diphenyl ether linkages are constituted of two benzylisoquinoline nuclei, it was important to ascertain the molecular magnitude of cularine. Not only do the Rast values for cularine, but more important, the Rast values for the $C_{19}H_{18}O_4$ compound indicate the single formula. Evidently, therefore, cularine is a diphenyl ether in which the two phenyl nuclei of a benzylisoquinoline are joined by an ether bridge. The simplest such structure and the one involving the least strain is one in which the junction is at the 8- and 2′-positions as in I. This serves to explain the degradation

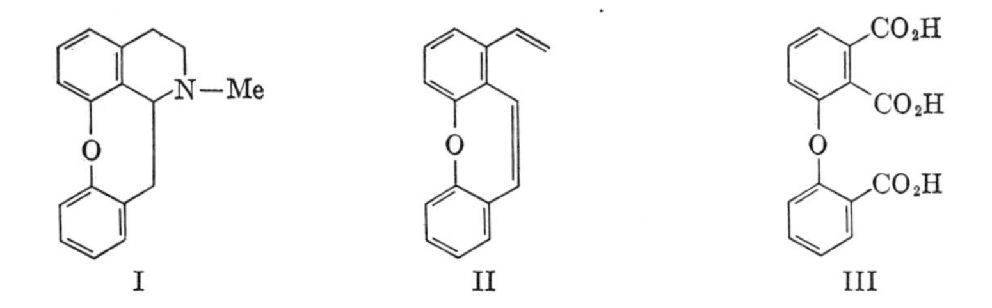

of cularine via the unsaturated compound (II) and the oxidation of the latter to a tribasic acid (III), $C_{18}H_{16}O_{10}$ (m.p. 187° when recrystallized from acetone-benzene; m.p. 113° when recrystallized from water; methyl ester melts at 152°). The positions of the three methoxyls not shown in the above formulas were determined by fission of the ether bridge by reacting cularine with metallic sodium in liquid ammonia (3). The resulting compound could have one of two possible structures or could, of course, be a mixture. Only one product, a phenolic base, was isolated, and this on oxidation with permanganate yielded 4-methoxyphthalic acid. Methylation of the hydroxyl and Hofmann degradation followed by oxidation also yielded 4-methoxyphthalic acid, as well as asaronic acid (2,4,5-trimethoxybenzoic acid), and therefore the phenolic base is IV and cularine must be V. Alternate positions of the ether bridge were discarded because of the impossibility of constructing the formula with atomic models (4).

The oxidation of the unsaturated compound II gives, in addition to the acid III already mentioned, a small amount of a monobasic acid, $C_{17}H_{14}O_7$ (m.p. 304°; methyl ester, m.p. 252°), which is regarded as 2,3,8-trimethoxyxanthone-5-carboxylic acid (VI). Its formation was considered to be analogous to the formation of fluorenone in the oxidation of phenanthrene

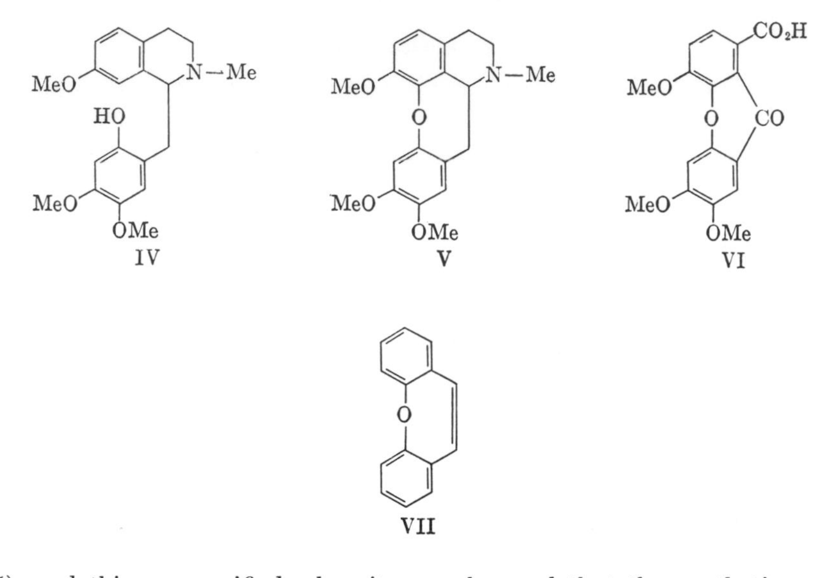

(5), and this was verified when it was observed that the synthetic compound VII on permanganate oxidation not only gave diphenylether-2,2′-dicarboxylic acid but also 6–7% of xanthone (6).

III. Cularimine

Cularimine, $C_{19}H_{21}O_4N$, has only been obtained from *D. eximia* (1). It crystallizes from ether in fine needles which melt at 102°. It was associated with cularine, from which it was separable by virtue of the fact that its acid oxalate is practically insoluble even in boiling water.

Cularimine contains three methoxyls and is a secondary base since it yields an insoluble *N*-nitroso derivative and a neutral benzoyl derivative (m.p. 174°). In the course of a Hofmann degradation of it there was obtained cularine methine, and the final non-nitrogenous compound on oxidation yielded the acids obtained from cularine. It was also possible to convert cularimine into cularine by methylation by means of formaldehyde and formic acid, and therefore it has structure VIII.

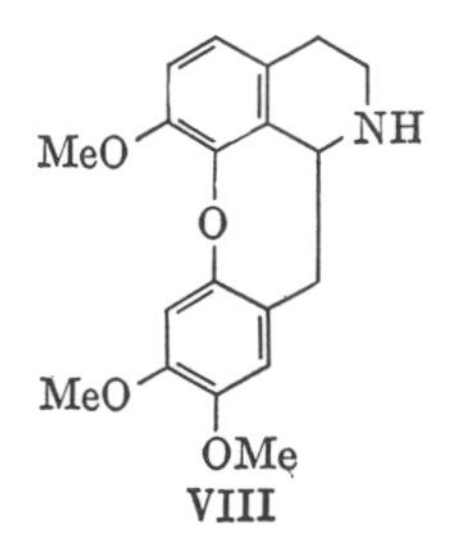

IV. Cularidine

Cularidine, $C_{19}H_{21}O_4N$, was found in very small amounts in *D. cucullaria* (1). It forms a hydrochloride that is only sparingly soluble in cold water or methanol. The free base is sparingly soluble in ether and when recrystallized from methanol–ether melts at 157°. It has two methoxyls and one phenolic hydroxyl. Its relation to cularine is shown by the fact that when methylated with diazomethane it yields cularine, but the position of the hydroxyl has not yet been determined.

The phenolic fractions from the alkaloids of *C. claviculata* (2) consist essentially of one or more *O*-desmethylcularines although it has not been possible to separate cularidine from the mixture. Although the mixture is amorphous it gives almost a quantitative yield of cularine on *O*-methylation with diazomethane.

V. References

1. R. H. F. Manske, *Can. J. Research,* **16B,** 81 (1938).
2. R. H. F. Manske, *Can. J. Research,* **18B,** 97 (1940).
3. P. A. Sartoretto and F. J. Sowa, *J. Am. Chem. Soc.*, **59,** 603 (1937).
4. R. H. F. Manske, *J. Am. Chem. Soc.*, **72,** 55 (1950).
5. R. Anschütz and F. R. Japp, *Ber.*, **11,** 211 (1878).
6. R. H. F. Manske and A. E. Ledingham, *J. Am. Chem. Soc.*, **72,** 4797 (1950).

CHAPTER 35

α-Naphthaphenanthridine Alkaloids

R. H. F. MANSKE

Dominion Rubber Research Laboratory, Guelph, Ontario

Page
I. Introduction 253
II. Occurrence 253
1. Chelidonine 253
2. Homochelidonine 254
3. Chelerythrine 254
4. Sanguinarine 255
5. Methoxychelidonine 255
6. Minor Alkaloids 255
III. Structure 256
IV. Pharmacology 261
V. References 262

I. Introduction

The α-naphthaphenanthridine (benzo[*c*]phenanthridine) alkaloids are derived from the tetracyclic system I in which the terminal nuclei are fully

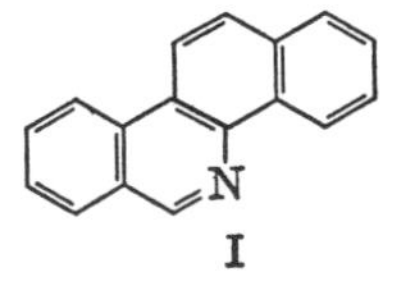

aromatic, each having at least two alkoxy groups. The two central nuclei are either aromatic or fully reduced, in which latter case there is a hydroxyl on the non-nitrogenous ring. The nitrogen always carries a methyl group.

These alkaloids, chelidonine, homochelidonine, methoxychelidonine, chelerythrine, and sanguinarine, are found in the Chelidonieae tribe of the Papaveraceae family as well as in the genus *Glaucium* of the same family (tribe—Papavereae). They are always accompanied by protopine, and sometimes by allocryptopine and the protoberberines.

II. Occurrence

1. CHELIDONINE

Chelidonine, $C_{20}H_{19}O_5N$, has been isolated only from *Chelidonium majus* L. (1), from *Dicranostigma franchetianum* (Prain) Fedde (2), and from *Stylophorum diphyllum* (Michx.) Nutt. (2, 3). It is always associated with protopine and this mixture can be freed of many of the admixed alkaloids by extracting them as their hydrochlorides from aqueous solution with chloroform. Protopine and chelidonine remain in the aqueous phase. The free bases are regenerated by the addition of alkali and extracted with chloroform.

The mixture is largely freed of solvent, and finally the chloroform is completely eliminated by repeated evaporation with methanol, which in turn is largely removed on a steam bath. The residue, which usually does not crystallize at this stage, is rapidly brought into solution in boiling ether and inoculated with a crystal of protopine. The latter crystallizes slowly but almost completely since crystalline protopine is virtually insoluble in ether, in which chelidonine is readily soluble.

When dealing with unpurified isolates it is not practical to attempt the direct crystallization of chelidonine from the ether mother liquor. It is best to convert the bases into their hydrochlorides and let the sparingly soluble chelidonine salt crystallize from an aqueous solution and recrystallize until it is colorless. Traces of protopine do not interfere in the next step. The regenerated free base is again taken up in ether, and the dried solution (potassium carbonate) is evaporated to a thin sirup. Hot methanol—about five milliliters per gram of residue—is added, the remaining ether is expelled, and the solution inoculated while hot. Chelidonine in large monoclinic tablets separates very rapidly, and since protopine is more soluble in methanol than in ether it is not a contaminant.

2. Homochelidonine

Homochelidonine, $C_{21}H_{23}O_5$, formerly α-homochelidonine, is known to occur only in *Ch. majus*, from which it was isolated by Schmidt and Selle (1). It crystallizes from ethyl acetate in colorless rhombohedra, but the salts are amorphous. The β- and γ-homochelidonines were shown to be closely related to cryptopine, and the now-accepted name of allocryptopine was suggested by Gadamer (4).

3. Chelerythrine

Chelerythrine, $C_{20}H_{17}O_4N \cdot H_2O$, has been isolated from *Ch. majus* (1, 5, 6), *Sanguinaria canadensis* L. (7, 8), *Bocconia arborea* Wats. (9), the roots but not the leaves of *B. cordata* Willd. (10, 11, 12), *B. pearcei* Hecht. (13), *Eschscholtzia californica* Cham. (14), and *Glaucium fimbrilligerum* Boiss. (15). Its reported occurrence in *Gl. flavum* Crantz (16) is doubtful. Its separation in a pure state is difficult except from the bark or wood of *B. arborea*, in which it occurs to the extent of 0.86 %. Its purification from this source is relatively easy because it is not contaminated with isolable amounts of sanguinarine. The hydrochloride is conveniently first crystallized from acetic acid and then from dilute hydrochloric acid. The free base crystallizes well if a hot concentrated solution in chloroform is treated with hot methanol. It is generally stated to melt at 207° but when sufficiently pure it melts at 210° (corr.). This is the melting point recorded by the writer (9) for alkaloid P61, which in a subsequent but unpublished examination proved to be an exceptionally pure specimen of chelerythrine. It was authenticated not only by a mixed melting point determination but also by the preparation of its ψ-cyanide.

4. Sanguinarine

Sanguinarine, $C_{20}H_{13}O_4N \cdot H_2O$, was the name given to an evidently impure preparation from *S. canadensis* (17). It was first obtained in a pure condition under the name of ψ-chelerythrine from chelidonine (18) and subsequently directly from *Ch. majus* (19). More recently it has been obtained from the roots of *Glaucium fimbrilligerum* (15). Its reported occurrence in *Bocconia cordata* (20) could not be confirmed (10).

The fraction of more soluble *Chelidonium* alkaloids from which most of the bases have been removed is treated in dilute acid solution with an excess of aqueous potassium cyanide. The precipitate is separated by filtration and washed thoroughly with dilute acetic acid. After drying it is repeatedly crystallized from acetone until most of the chelerythrine ψ-cyanide is recovered in the least soluble fractions. The more soluble product is then decomposed by boiling in ethanol with hydrochloric acid, and the free base is recovered and converted to its hydrogen tartrate. The tartrate crystallizing from the more soluble fractions is that of pure sanguinarine, does not have methoxyl, and is identical with ψ-chelerythrine (19).

5. Methoxychelidonine

Methoxychelidonine, $C_{21}H_{21}O_6N$, was obtained by Gadamer and Winterfeld (18) from *Ch. majus*. It has $[\alpha]_D$ +115.8° and forms a crystalline hydrochloride and aurichloride. In addition to the functional groups in chelidonine it contains an extra methoxyl. The presence of a hydroxyl is confirmed by the formation of an amorphous *O*-acetyl derivative. Although there are four unsubstituted positions in the two benzene nuclei only two (2 and 5, formula VI) are reasonable for the site of the methoxyl on biogenetic grounds. In either case the biogenetic precursors would be 3,4,5-trialkoxy derivatives, but a satisfactory choice between the two positions is not possible although von Bruchhausen and Bersch (21, 22) prefer position 5.

6. Minor Alkaloids

The following alkaloids whose structural relations are unknown have also been isolated from the plants which have yielded the α-naphthaphenanthridines. Base, $C_{19}H_{24}ON_2$ (m.p. 198–199°, $[\alpha]_D$ −40.7°; di-aurichloride, m.p. 122.4°), is ditertiary and phenolic and present in *Ch. majus* (23). Base a, m.p. 242–243°, and base b, m.p. 217°, neither further characterized from *Esch. californica* (14). The occurrence of sanguinarine in *Dicentra spectabilis* and in *St. diphyllum* could not be confirmed in later investigations (2, 24). *Bocconia arborea* has yielded three neutral nitrogenous compounds which were obtained from the water-insoluble fraction by digestion with alkali. They are: A, $C_{20}H_{17}O_4N$, m.p. 302°; B, $C_{20}H_{15}O_4N$, m.p. 191°; and C, $C_{31}H_{33}O_5N$, m.p. 332°. In view of the alkali treatment during their isolation they may be artifacts (9).

III. Structure

Gadamer (4) recognized that chelidonine and homochelidonine are closely related and that the latter probably differs from the former in the substitution of two methoxyls for a methylenedioxy. There is present in each alkaloid one non-phenolic hydroxyl and an *N*-methyl, and chelidonine carries two methylenedioxy groups.

When the alkaloids are treated at moderate temperatures with acetic anhydride, basic optically active *O*-acetyl derivatives are formed, but at the boiling point of the reagent dehydration takes place and optically inactive *N*-acetyl derivatives are formed as the result of ring scission. Mercuric acetate removes two hydrogen atoms (27) forming new colorless bases which yield intensely colored salts and which can be reduced to the original alkaloids without change of optical activity.

When the *O*-acetyl bases (25) are oxidized with mercuric acetate, colorless non-basic compounds are obtained which in contact with acids acquire basis properties and then form intensely colored salts (18, 26). Water and acetic acid are eliminated during this change, and the ultimate product from homochelidonine is identical with dihydrochelerythrine, which on exposure to air is oxidized to chelerythrine. Gadamer (27) attempted to correlate these results in structural formulas based upon an aporphine skeleton.

Von Bruchhausen and Bersch (21, 22) reinterpreted Gadamer's data in conjunction with the later findings of Kling (28) and of Schwarz (29), who subjected chelidonine to Emde and Hofmann degradations. When its methine is oxidized with permanganate there results a mixture of hydrastic acid (II) and a dimethylaminomethylmethylenedioxybenzoic acid. The latter was erroneously formulated by Schwarz, whose formula indicated

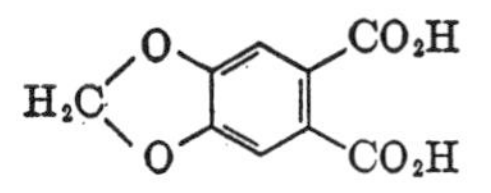

II

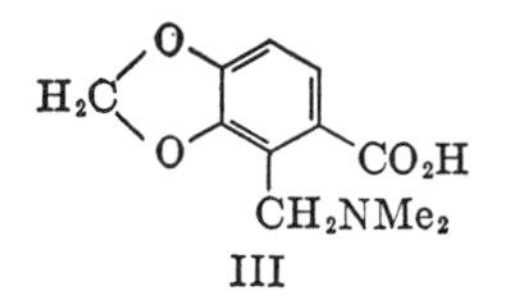

III

either that both benzene nuclei were similarly substituted or that both products resulted from the same nucleus. The correct structure (III) was arrived at by a synthesis from cryptopine by a route already traversed in part by Perkin (30). Anhydrocryptopine (XIX), p. 153) was first reduced catalytically to saturate the vinyl side chain and then with sodium amalgam to the fully saturated tetrahydroanhydrocryptopine (IV), which

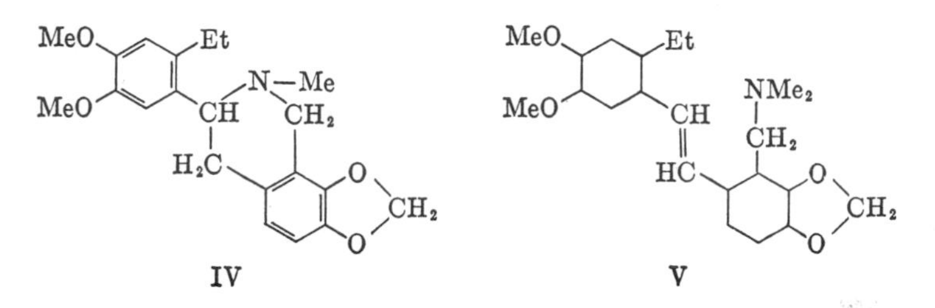

on Hofmann degradation yielded des-*N*-methyl-tetrahydroanhydrocryptopine (V). The latter on oxidation with permanganate or with ozone in acetic acid gave rise to 6-ethylveratric acid and the amino acid III which was isolated and characterized as its aurichloride and proved to be identical with Schwarz's acid.

It was therefore obvious that the methylenedioxy groups are not in the same relative positions on the two nuclei, and a biogenetic route to chelidonine from stylopine (tetrahydrocoptisine) was sought. This involved as a first step the migration of a hydroxyl from the quaternary nitrogen to an adjacent carbon, but the analogy to the cotarnine tautomerism is not valid in the writer's opinion (p. 171). By a series of further transformations formula VI for chelidonine was arrived at, and this structure was almost

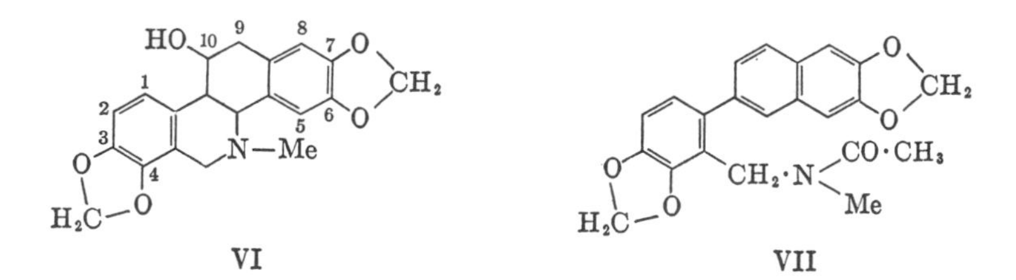

immediately confirmed by the independent work of Späth and Kuffner (31). These investigators sought evidence which would bear on Gadamer's aporphine structure by oxidation experiments. Chelidonine with permanganate gave rise to a separable mixture of hydrastic and 3,4-methylenedioxyphthalic acids. Furthermore, Gadamer's *N*-acetylanhydrochelidonine on nitric acid oxidation yielded benzene-1,2,4-tricarboxylic acid. Obviously a trisubstituted benzenoid ring is interposed between the two already known nuclei. A satisfactory expression for Gadamer's acetyl compound is VII when derived from structure VI for chelidonine, and these structures serve to explain the oxidation experiments. There remained, however, the unambiguous ordering of the four nuclei. Späth and Kuffner reexamined the base obtained by Gadamer and Stichel (32) when a mixture of chelerythrine and sanguinarine is subjected to distillation with zinc dust. An earlier erroneous formula for this base was corrected to $C_{17}H_{17}N$, and it was shown to be identical with α-naphthaphenanthridine (I) (33). Pure sanguinarine as well as chelidonine yielded the same base, and thus the sequence of the four nuclei is established with reasonable certainty. The exact location of the hydroxyl (34) was not determined, although the position indicated in formula VI was preferred on the grounds that Kling's (28) desmethyldihydromethine contains the fifth oxygen in ether linkage and can be satisfactorily formulated as VIII. Since the hydroxyl is secondary and can occupy only one of two possible

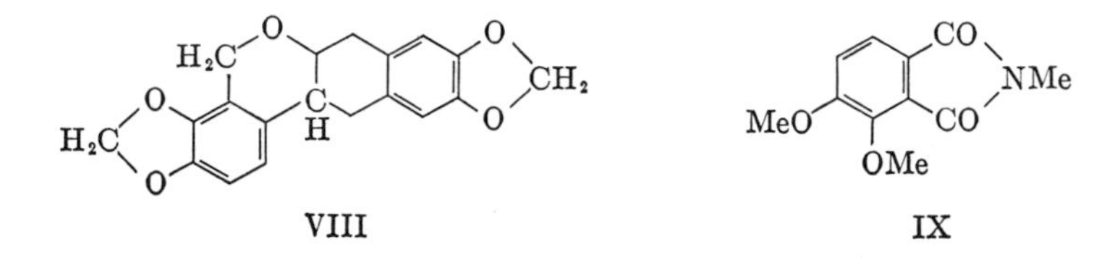

VIII IX

positions, the formation of the six-membered ether ring was regarded as more facile than a seven-membered one. It should be noted that the oxidation products obtained by Späth and Kuffner do not locate unequivocally the methylenedioxy groups but that the amino acid (III) of Schwarz and of von Bruchhausen and Bersch locates one such group, and hence the formation of hydrastic acid locates the other. The location of the methoxyls in homochelidonine was determined by Späth and Kuffner (35) by mild oxidation of chelerythrine which yielded the *N*-methylimide of hemipinic acid (IX). More drastic oxidation yielded hydrastic acid, and therefore homochelidonine is X.

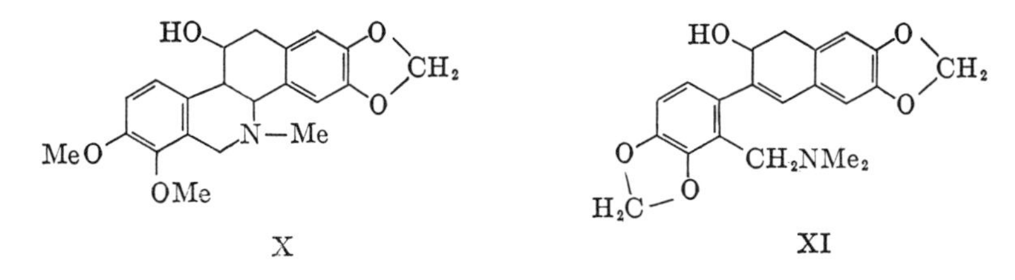

X XI

It is now possible to ascribe correct structures to some of Gadamer's compounds. Two methines are obtainable from chelidonine, and one of these must be XI. When this is heated with acetic anhydride it loses water and dimethylamine to yield the acetate XII, which on deacetylation yields

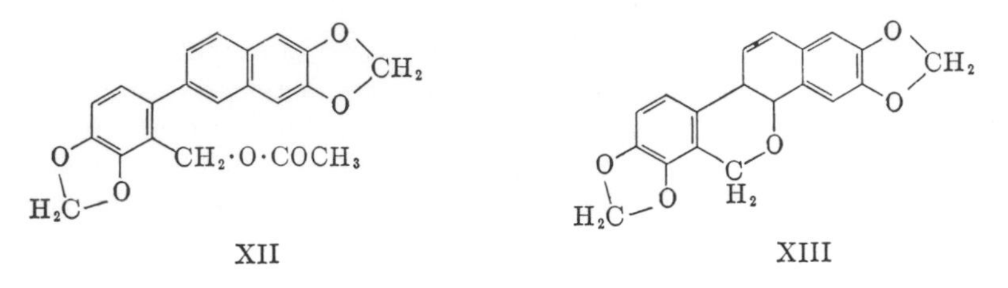

XII XIII

a substance $C_{19}H_{14}O_5$, probably represented by XIII, although Gadamer's suggested formulas have two extra hydrogens for both compounds. The compound obtained by boiling *N*-acetylanhydrochelidonine is ψ-anhydrochelidonine (XIV).

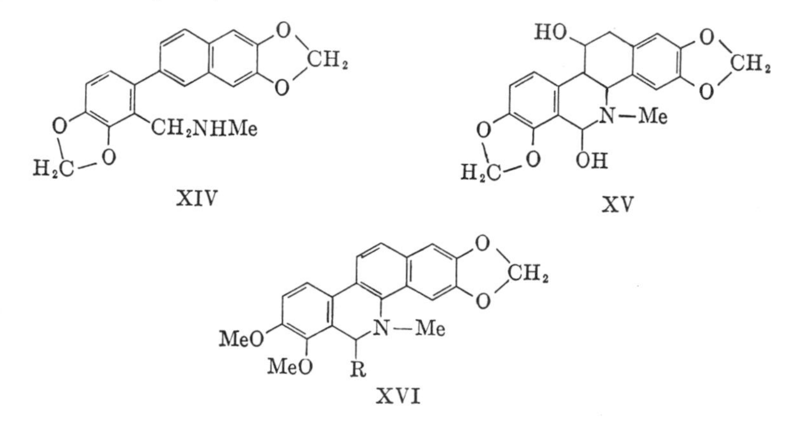

XIV XV

XVI

Didehydrochelidonine obtainable from *O*-acetylchelidonine by mercuric acetate oxidation (18) is evidently XV (carbinolamine formula) since reduction regenerates chelidonine and since it forms a neutral ψ-cyanide. The Grignard reaction products (36) of chelerythrine are alkyl (aryl) dihydrochelerythrines (XVI) (19).

The oxychelidonine of Gadamer and Theissen (37) which was obtained from some residues left from the preparation of chelidonine is also one of the products when the latter is oxidized with mercuric acetate. It was assumed that the methylene vicinal to the carbinol was oxidized in this reaction to a carbonyl, but such a formulation could not account for the non-basic nature of the compound. Such properties are consistent only with an amide structure (XVII), and its formation then is quite analogous

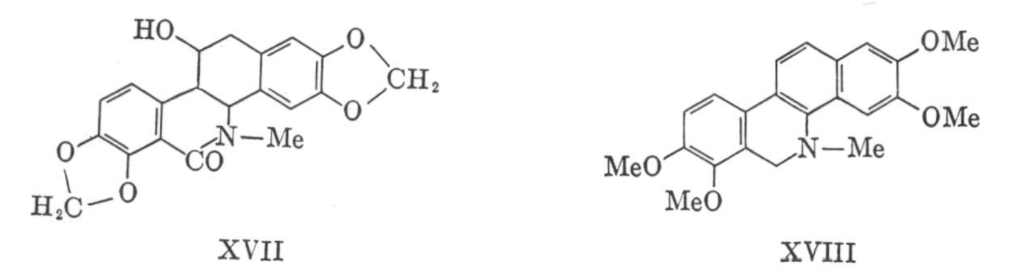

XVII XVIII

to the formation of 1-keto compounds from tetrahydroisoquinolines. Wintgen's (38) oxychelidonine is evidently chelidonine *N*-oxide.

Finally, Späth and Kuffner (39) succeeded in showing that the alkoxyl groups in chelerythrine and sanguinarine occupy the same positions. For this purpose the feebly basic dihydro bases of Karrer (36), who regarded them as non-basic, were demethylenated with sulfuric acid in the presence of phloroglucinol. The dihydroxy compound from chelerythrine and the tetrahydroxy compound from sanguinarine were methylated with diazomethane, and in both cases the same tetramethoxydihydro-*N*-methyl-α-naphthaphenanthridine (XVIII) was obtained.

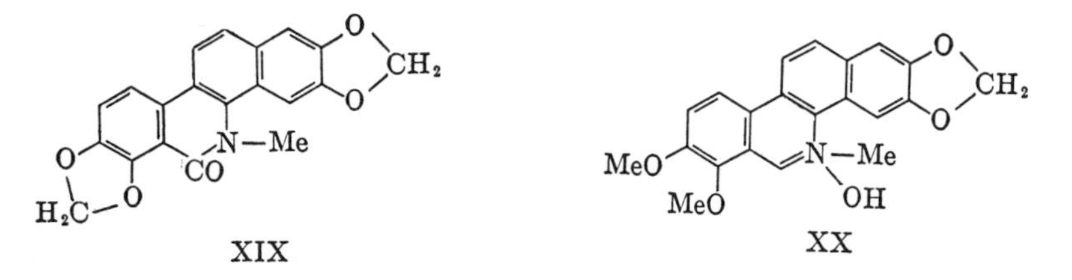

When sanguinarine nitrate is oxidized in alkaline solution with potassium ferricyanide it is converted into oxysanguinarine, a neutral compound whose structure is represented by XIX. It proved to be identical with a substance obtained from the crude mixture of *Sanguinaria* alkaloids (40) by a process involving chromatography.

Oxysanguinarine. One gram of sanguinarine nitrate in 200 cc. hot water is treated with a hot solution of 4 g. potassium ferricyanide and 2 g. potassium hydroxide in 100 cc. water. The mixture is then extracted with chloroform in a continuous extractor, the solvent removed from the extract, and the residue digested with 200 cc. 1% hydrochloric acid on the steam bath for 4 hours. The insoluble product (0.68 g.) is separated from the red-colored solution and purified by sublimation in a high vacuum. At 250–260° there is a forerun of unknown nature and the sought for compound subsequently sublimes at 290–310° in a yield of 74%. It is recrystallized from chloroform and then melts at 360–361° (corr.) when heated in an evacuated tube.

Chelerythrine uniformly crystallizes with some solvent of crystallization ($\frac{1}{2}H_2O$, C_2H_5OH, toluene), and in general this solvent is retained very tenaciously. Karrer's (36) results serve to explain this behaviour although they were wrongly interpreted in spite of the fact that the analogy with cotarnine was considered. The reaction with phenylhydrazine was thought to be due to hydrazone formation in consequence of a carbonyl, and since the hydrazone was no longer basic, the salt-forming property of chelerythrine was ascribed to the carbonyl oxygen. Gadamer (26) showed that these reactions, as well as those with Grignard reagents, active methylene compounds, and hydrogen cyanide, find a complete analogy in those of berberinium and cotarninium compounds and are explicable on the basis of a quaternary nitrogen reacting as a carbinolamine. Furthermore, the transformation of homochelidonine to chelerythrine indicates the correct structure (XX) for the latter regardless of the position of the hydroxyl in the former.

Sanguinarine. The first pure specimen of sanguinarine that had been obtained was probably that derived from chelidonine by Gadamer and Winterfeld (18) from the dehydration of didehydrochelidonine (XV). This is a feebly basic substance and proved to be dihydrosanguinarine although it was named dihydro-ψ-chelerythrine. When it is oxidized in chloroform solution with mercuric acetate it yields pure sanguinarine (ψ-chelerythrine, m.p. 239–242°) from which the authentic sanguinarine ψ-cyanide was first obtained.

IV. Pharmacology

Most of the older and scant literature on the pharmacology of these alkaloids was carried out on obviously impure preparations and tinctures and extracts. Extracts of *Ch. majus* given orally to humans are mildly narcotic, relieve bronchial spasms of cardiac origin, raise the blood pressure, dilate the coronary vessels of the heart, relax intestinal muscles, contract the uterus, and lower the blood sugar (41). However, Seel, Stieda, and Peplau (42) do not regard either chelidonium extracts or pure chelidonine as possessing true narcotic or hypnotic properties although their ingestion is followed by a demonstrable reduction in the sensation of pain. The rat uterus is stimulated by the plant extract but relaxes by chelidonine which, however, stimulated the isolated frog's heart in doses of 0.01 to 0.02 mg. but decreased the pulse rate. Doses exceeding 0.05 mg. produced arrythmia, heart block, and diastolic stoppage.

Hanzlik (43) had previously shown that chelidonine is comparatively non-toxic, and in some of its effects it resembles morphine except that its action is mainly peripheral. It abolishes the spontaneous contraction of the following excised organs: esophagus, fundus and pylorus of the frog stomach, intestine of cat and rabbit, and the pregnant uterus of the guinea pig. It is antagonistic to pilocarpine, pituitrin, histamine, and barium chloride, and its main effect is ascribed to its action on smooth muscle. Raymond-Hamet (44) observed its antagonism to adrenaline in dogs under chloralose anesthesia.

Sanguinarine at a concentration of 2.5 p.p.m. and chelerythrine at a somewhat higher concentration completely inhibit the root-rot fungus *Phymatotrichum omnivorum*. They were the most effective of 62 alkaloids (45, 46).

TABLE 1

PHYSICAL PROPERTIES OF α-NAPHTHAPHENANTHRIDINE ALKALOIDS AND SOME DERIVATIVES[a]

Compound	M.p., °C.	References
Chelidonine ([α]D + 115.4° (EtOH); + 117.4° ($CHCl_3$))	135–136	20 6
O-Acetyl-	161–163 and 184–186	18
O-Benzoyl-	210–211	38
N-Oxide (α) ([α]D 115° (*c* = 2, EtOH))		38
Methine A	145–146	25
Methine B	107–108	25
Methylanhydro-	152–153	25
ψ-Anhydrochelidonine	89	25
Hydrochloride	204–205	25
Bromochelidonine	230–231	18
O-Acetyl-	150–152	18
N-Acetylanhydro-	170–172	18
Didehydrochelidonine	Amorph.	18
ψ-Cyanide	194–195	18
Oxychelidonine ([α]D + 102.5°)	<285	37
Homochelidonine	182	1, 11
Methoxychelidonine	221	18
Aurichloride	237–238	18
Chelerythrine	207 (+ EtOH)	9
	263–264 ($2C_7H_7$)	8
	250 (½H_2O)	36
ψ-Cyano-	258	26
Phenylhydrazino-	158	36
Dihydro-	160–162	26
	166–167	39
Sanguinarine	239–242	18
ψ-Cyano-	237–238	18
Dihydro-	188–189	39
Oxysanguinarine	360–361	39

[a] The alkaloids are listed in the order in which they appear in the text and their derivatives follow the alkaloids. Salts are not listed unless they have a definite melting point.

V. References

1. E. Schmidt and F. Selle, *Arch. Pharm.*, **228,** 441 (1890).
2. R. H. F. Manske, *Can. J. Research*, **20B,** 53 (1942).
3. J. O. Schlotterbeck and H. C. Watkins, *Ber.*, **35,** 7 (1902).
4. J. Gadamer, *Arch. Pharm.*, **257,** 298 (1919).
5. Probst, Q. M. *Ann.*, **29,** 120 (1839).
6. M. Wintgen, *Arch. Pharm.*, **239,** 438 (1901).
7. E. Schmidt, G. König, and W. Tietz, *Arch. Pharm.*, **231,** 136 (1893).
8. R. Fischer, *Arch. Pharm.*, **239,** 409 (1901).

9. R. H. F. Manske, *Can. J. Research*, **21B**, 140 (1943).
10. P. Murrill and J. O. Schlotterbeck, *Ber.*, **33**, 2802 (1900).
11. E. Schmidt, *Arch. Pharm.*, **239**, 401 (1901).
12. K. Hopfgartner, *Monatsh.*, **19**, 179 (1898).
13. I. Maccio, *Arch. farm. y bioquím. Tucumán*, **3**, 27 (1946).
14. R. Fischer, *Arch. Pharm.*, **239**, 421 (1901).
15. R. A. Konovalova, S. Yunusov, and A. P. Orekhov, *J. Gen. Chem.* (*U.S.S.R.*), **9**, 1939 (1939).
16. R. Fischer, *Arch. Pharm.*, **239**, 426 (1901).
17. Dana, *Mag. Pharm.*, **23**, 125 (1829).
18. J. Gadamer and K. Winterfeld, *Arch. Pharm.*, **262**, 452 (1924).
19. J. Gadamer and A. Stichel, *Arch. Pharm.*, **262**, 452 (1924).
20. J. F. Eijkman, *Rec. trav. chim.*, **3**, 182 (1884).
21. F. von Bruchhausen and H. W. Bersch, *Ber.*, **63**, 2520 (1930).
22. F. von Bruchhausen and H. W. Bersch, *Ber.*, **64**, 947 (1931).
23. J. Gadamer and K. Winterfeld, *Arch. Pharm.*, **262**, 589 (1924).
24. R. H. F. Manske, *Can. J. Research*, **15B**, 274 (1937).
25. J. Gadamer, H. Dieterle, A. Stichel M. Theissen, and K. Winterfeld, *Arch. Pharm.*, **262**, 249 (1924).
26. J. Gadamer, *Arch. Pharm.*, **258**, 160 (1920).
27. J. Gadamer, *Arch. Pharm.*, **258**, 148 (1920).
28. Kling, Dissertation, Marburg, 1927.
29. Schwarz, Dissertation, Marburg, 1928.
30. W. H. Perkin, Jr., *J. Chem. Soc.*, **109**, 883 (1916).
31. E. Späth and F. Kuffner, *Ber.*, **64**, 370 (1931).
32. J. Gadamer and A. Stichel, *Arch. Pharm.*, **262**, 499 (1924).
33. C. Graebe, *Ann.*, **335**, 127 (1904).
34. L. Marion, D. A. Ramsay, and R. N. Jones, *J. Am. Chem. Soc.*, **73**, 305 (1951).
35. E. Späth and F. Kuffner, *Ber.*, **64**, 1123 (1931).
36. P. Karrer, *Ber.*, **50**, 212 (1917).
37. J. Gadamer and M. Theissen, *Arch. Pharm.*, **262**, 578 (1924).
38. M. Wintgen, *Arch. Pharm.*, **239**, 438 (1901).
39. E. Späth and F. Kuffner, *Ber.*, **64**, 2034 (1931).
40. E. Späth, F. Schlemmer, G. Schneck, and A. Gempp, *Ber.*, **70**, 1677 (1937).
41. H. Kreitmair, *E. Merck's Jaresber.*, **50**, 102 (1936).
42. H. Seel, H. Stieda, and G. Peplau, *Hippokrates*, **10**, 1281 (1939).
43. P. J. Hanzlik, *Zentr. Physiol.*, **28**, 551 (1914).
44. Raymond-Hamet, M. *Compt. rend. soc. biol.*, **112**, 31 (1933).
45. G. A. Greathouse, *Plant Physiol.*, **14**, 377 (1939).
46. G. A. Greathouse and N. E. Rigler, *Phytopathology*, **30**, 475 (1940).

CHAPTER 36

The Erythrophleum Alkaloids

G. DALMA

Research Laboratory, ATANOR S.A.M., Buenos Aires, Argentina

	Page
I. Isolation	265
II. Properties of the Alkaloids	266
1. Cassaine	266
2. Cassaidine	268
3. Erythrophleine	269
4. Erythrophlamine and Cassamine	269
5. Coumingine	270
6. Coumingidine	270
III. Pharmacology	271
IV. References	272

I. Isolation

The *Erythrophleum* alkaloids represent a clearly defined class, both as regards their chemical structure and pharmacological properties. They are alkamine esters of monocarboxylic acids of the diterpene series and possess remarkable cardiac activity of the digitalis type coupled with very intense local anesthetic action.

The genus *Erythrophleum* Afzel. belongs to the tribe Dimorphandreae, subfamily Caesalpinioideae, of the family Leguminosae. Well represented in the equatorial forests of West Africa, the species *E. guineense* G. Don is a widely distributed handsome tree with a number of ill-defined varieties or subspecies which have been the cause of some confusion. It is referred to by various names by the natives—cassa, ncassa, teli, burane, sassy, mançone, and others. The British colonists referred to it as red water tree.

The natives use the bark to prepare an intensely colored infusion, to poison their arrows, for medicinal purposes, as an ordeal drug, and in some regions of the Upper Congo as a tanning agent. The wood is very hard, not affected by termites, and finds important uses as structural timber. The hard sternutatory bark is richer in alkaloids than the other parts of the plant, all of which contain some alkaloids.

E. couminga Baill. is common in Madagascar and the Seychelles islands, is more toxic than *E. guineense*, and the leaves have been the cause of mass poisoning of livestock. *Cynometra densiflora* Elmer (*E. densiflora* Merrill) of the Philippines and *E. fordii* Oliver of Indo-China are devoid of toxic alkaloids. *E. laboucherii* F. Muell. (*E. chlorostachys* Baill.) of Australia contains alkaloids.

The name erythrophleine was applied by Gallois and Hardy (1) in 1875 to an uncharacterized alkaloid from *E. guineense* bark and from *E. couminga* leaves and seeds. They noted its powerful digitalis-like cardiac activity. Harnack and Zabrocky (2) in 1882 working with an amorphous erythrophleine from E. Merck of Darmstadt confirmed its cardiac activity and observed that the alkaloid suffers hydrolysis with hot hydrochloric acid to a nitrogen-free acid and a base of low molecular weight. Subsequently Harnack (3) examining an apparently different preparation, but from the same source, concluded that the empirical formula was $C_{28}H_{45}O_7N$, and that the hydrolytic acid, named erythrophleic acid, was $C_{27}H_{42}O_8$, and hence the basic fragment appeared to be methylamine. There followed a large number of reports of the presence of alkaloids in *Erythrophleum* species (4–9) without, however, reporting significant progress in the chemistry of the alkaloids until Dalma (10) succeeded in isolating three crystalline alkaloids (cassaine, cassaidine, and norcassaidine) and an amorphous one (homophleine) from *E. guineense*. Cassaine was characterized by the formation of a crystalline hydrochloride, hydrobromide, nitrate, and sulfate, and its empirical formula was established. Subsequently the same author (11) isolated the crystalline coumingine and the amorphous coumingaine from *E. couminga*, while Paris and Rigal (12) reported the following alkaloids along with their melting points from the bark of *E. guineense*: (*a*) 105–106° picrate, 332–334°; (*b*) 114–116°; (*c*) 105°; (*d*) 112°; and (*e*) 185–186°; picrate, 227–228°; acetyl derivative, 123–124°, from the seeds.

There followed a rapid succession of reports of the isolation and characterization of alkaloids: Schlittler (13) described the secondary coumingidine from *E. couminga;* Ruzicka, Plattner, and Engel (14) isolated coumingine and a new tertiary base, which was also found in *E. guineense* along with a second tertiary base by Engel and Tondeur (15); Paris (16) isolated cassaine from an unknown but botanically described *Erythrophleum* from Indo-China.

II. Properties of the Alkaloids

1. Cassaine

Cassaine, $C_{24}H_{39}O_4N$, crystallizes from ether in glossy flakes, belonging to the rhombic system. It melts at 142.5° and has $[\alpha]_D^{20}$ −113° (ethanol) and $[\alpha]_D^{20}$ −117° (*N*/10 hydrochloric acid) (10).

Isolation. The bark of *E. guineense* (5 kg.) in a finely ground condition was soaked with half its weight of 10% ammonia and extracted with ether. The combined extract was concentrated to 1.5 l. and washed repeatedly with 5% aqueous potash. The alkaloids were then extracted from the purified ether solution by means of $N/2$ hydrochloric acid containing sodium sulfite. The alkaloids were regenerated by alkali, the washed ether solution concentrated to 250 ml., and then treated with a solution of sulfuric acid in ether until no more precipitate was formed. The precipitate, from which the ether solution was easily decanted, was dissolved in 250 ml. of hot 90% ethanol, cooled, and treated with an equal volume of ether. The crystalline cassaine bisulfate which then separated was purified by a charcoal treatment in water and the regenerated base converted once more into its bisulfate which was again recrystallized. The base was regenerated from this and its solution in 500 ml. of ether left at $-10°$ when the free base gradually crystallized. The yield was about 5 g. (0.1%) (17).

Cassaine is a tertiary base that can be satisfactorily titrated with methyl red, bromophenol green, or iodoeosin as indicators; it gives a yellow-colored solution in sulfuric acid which in the presence of vanadium pentoxide becomes green. The bisulfate, $B \cdot H_2SO_4 \cdot 2H_2O$, melts with decomposition at 290° and the hydrochloride, $B \cdot HCl \cdot H_2O$, melts at 212–213° (17).

The presence of a hydroxyl and a carbonyl in cassaine are proved by the formation of a basic monoacetyl derivative (m.p. 123–124°) and of an oxime (m.p. 123–125°). The two remaining oxygen atoms are accounted for by an ester linkage which is hydrolyzed by acids as follows:

$$C_{24}H_{39}O_4N + H_2O \rightarrow C_{20}H_{30}O_4 + C_4H_{11}ON.$$

The resultant cassaic acid melts at 203° and has $[\alpha]_D^{20}$ $-126.3°$ (ethanol). It forms a methyl ester (m.p. 189–190°) and a monoacetyl derivative (m.p. 189–191°) which in turn yields a semicarbazone (m.p. 246–247°), and therefore the functions of the four oxygens are known. When cassaine is hydrolyzed in the presence of strong alkali there is obtained the same base, which has been shown to be dimethylaminoethanol (18), and the isomeric allocassaic acid which melts at 222–224° and has $[\alpha]_D^{20}$ $+81.8°$ (ethanol).

The absorption spectra of cassaic acid and of cassaine show that the double bond which is shown to be present by the ready reduction of the alkaloid to dihydrocassaine (m.p. 115–116°); $[\alpha]_D^{20}$ 0° in ethanol, $-6.5°$ in $N/10$ hydrochloric acid) is α,β- to the carboxyl rather than to the carbonyl. Dihydrocassaic acid melts at 253–255° and has $[\alpha]_D^{20}$ 0° (ethanol), $-5°$ ($N/10$ sodium hydroxide).

The hydroxyl in cassaic acid is secondary because oxidation of the acid with chromic acid generates a diketo acid (m.p. 238–239°, $[\alpha]_D^{20}$ $-164.5°$ in ethanol) which did not give positive reactions for aldehydes and which formed a methyl ester (m.p. 129–130°), a dioxime (m.p. 130–132°), and a disemicarbazone (m.p. 290°). Ruzicka and Dalma (19) have suggested that the saturated acid, free of oxygen-containing substituents, from which cassaic acid is derived, be named cassanic acid. The diketo acid obtainable from dihydrocassaic acid would thus be diketocassanic acid (m.p. 225°; methyl ester, m.p. 108°), and this on reduction by Clemmensen's method yields a monoketocassanic acid (m.p. 206°) (18) but on Wolff-Kischner reduction it forms cassanic acid (m.p. 224°, $[\alpha]_D^{20}$ +3° in chloroform) (20). When dihydrocassaic acid is reduced it gives rise to dihydroxycassanic acid (m.p. 262–265°; methyl ester, m.p. 172–174°), which when dehydrogenated with selenium at 340° affords 1,2,8-trimethylphenanthrene (m.p. 142–143°), thus accounting for seventeen of the twenty carbon atoms of cassaic acid. One of the lost carbons is evidently that of the carboxyl, and it is presumed that the other two are methyls from angular positions, so that cassaic acid is regarded as a diterpene derivative (19).

The position of the carboxyl has not yet been determined. Ruzicka and coworkers (21) converted the carboxyl into an isopropyl by reacting the methyl ester of cassanic acid with excess methylmagnesium iodide and dehydrating the intermediate carbinol (m.p. 132–133°) and then dehydrogenating with selenium at 350°. The resultant hydrocarbon, $C_{20}H_{22}$ (m.p. 131–132°), was regarded as a trimethylisopropylphenanthrene but was not identical with a synthetic specimen of the 1,7,8,2-derivative. Subsequent comparison of the UV-spectra of a number of synthetic phenanthrenes with that obtained from cassanic acid led the authors to the conclusion that their hydrocarbon was not a tetraalkylphenanthrene but one containing only three substituents, and therefore that the carboxyl is in the side chain.

2. Cassaidine

Cassaidine, $C_{24}H_{41}O_4N$, isolated by Dalma (10), crystallizes from acetone–ether in hard translucent prisms which melt at 139.5° and have $[\alpha]_D^{20}$ −98° (ethanol) and −104° (*N*/10 hydrochloric acid). It was separated from the mother liquors from the crystallization of cassaine sulfate and obtained in about 0.1% yield. The sulfate melts at 228° and the hydrochloride at 251° (22).

Cassaidine is a tertiary base and like cassaine may be titrated with the same indicators. It is easily differentiated by color reactions from cassaine. With sulfuric acid it yields an orange-colored solution and with sulfovanadic acid the color is raspberry red. With the Keller-Kiliani-Cloetta reagent (ferric chloride in a mixture of sulfuric and acetic acids) it gives an intense red solution (cassaine—golden yellow). It is much less soluble in the usual organic solvents than is cassaine.

A Zerewitinoff determination showed the presence of two hydroxyls, but crystalline acetyl or benzoyl derivatives could not be prepared. The UV-spectrum indicates no carbonyl but a double bond apparently in conjugation with the carboxyl. Acid hydrolysis of cassaidine generates dimethylaminoethanol and a crystalline acid, cassaidic acid, $C_{20}H_{32}O_4$, which melts at 275–277° (methyl ester, m.p. 162–163°). Mild oxidation with chromic acid converts the two hydroxyls into carbonyls. The resulting acid is identical with the oxidation product of cassaic acid, and therefore the two acids, and consequently the two alkaloids, cassaine and cassaidine, differ only in that the latter has a secondary hydroxyl in the place of the carbonyl in the former.

Dihydrocassaidine, melting at 96–97°, is readily prepared by catalytic reduction of cassaidine, and when hydrolyzed with alcoholic potash it gives rise to dihydroxycassanic acid identical with that obtainable from cassaine (22).

3. Erythrophleine

Erythrophleine, as the free base and in the form of its salts, has only been obtained in the amorphous condition. A Merck preparation was examined by Blount, Openshaw, and Todd (23), and analysis of the sulfate indicated that the base was $C_{24}H_{39}O_5N$ with one methoxyl. One mole of hydrogen is taken up rapidly (ethylene) on catalytic hydrogenation, and a second is taken up much more slowly (carbonyl). The base furthermore showed a positive carbonyl reaction with 2,4-dinitrophenylhydrazine. Hydrolysis with either acid or alkali generated the crystalline erythrophleic acid, $C_{21}H_{32}O_5$ (m.p. 218°, $[\alpha]_D^{20}$ $-40°$ in chloroform), and methylaminoethanol, C_3H_9ON, characterized as its picrate (m.p. 148°). The methyl ester (amorphous) of erythrophleic acid forms a crystalline 2,4-dinitrophenylhydrazone, thus confirming the presence of the carbonyl. The UV-spectra of the alkaloid and its hydrolytic acid fragment indicate that the double bond is α,β- to the carboxyl. Selenium dehydrogenation of the acid generates 1,2,8-trimethylphenanthrene, thus indicating a close relation to the other alkaloids of this group.

4. Erythrophlamine and Cassamine

Erythrophlamine, $C_{25}H_{39}O_6N$, and cassamine, $C_{25}H_{39}O_5N$, were obtained by Engel and Tondeur (24) from a specimen of *E. guineense* bark originating at Yangamhi, Stanleyville Province, Belgian Congo, which also contained cassaine and cassaidine (15). The separation of the alkaloids was a tedious one involving several salts in a number of solvents, and chromatography.

Erythrophlamine crystallizes from ether–hexane and melts at 149–151° with $[\alpha]_D^{20}$ $-62.5°$ (ethanol). The bisulfate, the hydrochloride, the hydrobromide, and the perchlorate are amorphous, but the picrate crystallizes from dilute ethanol and melts at 184–187°. Acid hydrolysis converts this alkaloid into erythrophlamic acid, $C_{21}H_{30}O_6$ (m.p. 218–220°, $[\alpha]_D^{22}$ $-63°$ in ethanol; methyl ester, m.p. 177–178°) and dimethylaminoethanol. The erythrophlamic acid contains one methoxyl and a double bond in conjugation with the carboxyl. It also has a hydroxyl and a carbonyl because the methyl ester yields an acetate (m.p. 103°) and an oxime (m.p. 182–184°) (14, 24).

Cassamine crystallizes from pentane and then melts at 86–87° with $[\alpha]_D^{19}$ $-56°$ (ethanol). The perchlorate crystallizes from dilute acetone, the bisulfate from ethanol–ether, and the hydrochloride from acetone, but the salts do not have sharp melting points. The hydrobromide and the picrate were obtained in the amorphous state. When heated with 2*N* hydrochloric acid cassamine generates dimethylaminoethanol and cassamic acid, $C_{21}H_{30}O_5$, (m.p. 217–218°, $[\alpha]_D^{20}$ $-62°$ in ethanol). This acid yielded a noncrystalline methyl ester which formed a crystalline *p*-nitrophenylhydrazone (m.p. 227–228°) and an oxime (m.p. 96–98°). The *p*-phenylphenacyl ester of cassamic acid crystallizes readily and melts at 127–131°. One methoxyl and a double bond conjugated with the carboxyl are present in the acid, so that the function of only one oxygen remains to be determined.

5. Coumingine

Coumingine, $C_{29}H_{47}O_6N$, crystallizes from ether in brilliant needles which melt at 142° and have $[\alpha]_D^{20}$ $-70.8°$ (ethanol) (11, 25). The hydrochloride crystallized from ethanol–ether melts at 195°.

Coumingine is a tertiary base, somewhat weaker than cassaine or cassaidine. It is readily soluble in most organic solvents except hexane and ether. It does not give a color reaction with sulfuric acid, but with sulfovanadic acid it gives a pale green solution. It does not form an acetyl derivative, but a monoxime (m.p. 165°) can be obtained. A readily reducible double bond is in conjugation with the carboxyl, and dihydrocoumingine melts at 95–96° ($[\alpha]_D^{20}$ $-8°$ (ethanol)) and forms a crystalline hydrochloride (m.p. 160–162°).

The hydrolysis of coumingine or its dihydro derivative with either acid or alkali is somewhat more complicated than that of cassaine and those already mentioned although dimethylaminoethanol represents the basic fragment. There is obtained cassaic acid and in addition β-hydroxyisovaleric acid. Since the only hydroxyl in cassaine is in the cassaic acid moiety coumingine must be β-hydroxyisovalerylcassaine, and it is possible to hydrolyze coumingine with *N*/2 sulfuric acid to dimethylaminoethanol and coumingic acid, $C_{25}H_{38}O_6$ (m.p. 200°, $[\alpha]_D^{20}$ $-81°$ in ethanol), which is β-hydroxyisovalerylcassaic acid (26).

6. Coumingidine

Coumingidine, $C_{28}H_{45}O_6N$, when crystallized from ether melts at 160–161° It is a secondary base and forms an *N*-acetyl derivative (m.p. 155°), an *N*-nitroso derivative (m.p. 174°), and a phenylthiocarbamate (m.p. 146°). The nitroso derivative upon treatment with cuprous chloride in hydrochloric acid (27) regenerated coumingidine, and its hydrochloride thus purified melted at 217–219°. A double bond in coumingidine is readily saturated, and the resultant dihydro base forms a sparingly soluble perchlorate (m.p. 166–168°) as well as a crystalline acetyl derivative (m.p. 115–116°). Acid hydrolysis of coumingidine generates methylaminoethanol, thus confirming the secondary nature of the alkaloid, together with coumingidic acid, $C_{25}H_{38}O_6$, which was difficult to purify but its methyl ester, $C_{26}H_{40}O_6$ (m.p. 204–206°), on alkaline hydrolysis formed an acid identified as cassaic acid. Evidently coumingidic acid is an acylcassaic acid, but the nature of the acid fragment concerned in this acylation was not determined (13). When the methyl ester of dihydrocoumingidic acid was heated with selenium to 340° there was formed 1,2,8-trimethylphenanthrene.

In conclusion, it may be pointed out that a number of structural formulas have been suggested for cassanic acid, but they are speculative except for the phenanthrene nucleus.

III. Pharmacology

The use of infusions of *Erythrophleum* bark by natives and the results of early pharmacological study have already been noted. The individual alkaloids constitute a rather homogeneous group as regards the type of response, but they differ somewhat as to intensity of action and sometimes as to detail. The poisoning shows the following common features—typical digitalis-like cardiac action, paralysis of the respiratory center, strong adrenaline-like blood pressure increase, emetic action, diarrhea with bloody stools, strong salivation, dyspnoea, uncertainty of movements, trembling of the extremities, thirst, headache, visual and general sensual disturbance, and depressing action on the cortex (except cassaine which has an exciting action) with temporary periods of excitation accompanied by tonic and clonic cramps. Death is due to cardiac and respiratory paralysis. The alkaloids also induce intense and long-lasting local anesthesia accompanied in most cases by irritation of the tissues concerned.

Chen and his associates (28, 29, 30) studied the relative potencies of erythrophleine, coumingine, coumingaine, cassaidine, homophleine, cassaine, and acetylcassaine and concluded that coumingine was the most potent cardiac stimulant, its effect being about equal to that of scillaren A. The local anesthetic effects of all the alkaloids were observed on the cornea of the rabbit and on the skin of the guinea pig, together with the previously noted irritant action. The alkaloids caused an increase of the blood pressure and stimulated the isolated rabbit intestine and guinea pig uterus.

Santi and Zweifel (31) determined the minimum lethal dose for cassaidine, cassaine, homophleine, erythrophleine, and coumingine by injection into the ventral sack of the frog and by subcutaneous injection into white mice. The toxicity increased in the order given, and the last showed observable responses on the isolated frog heart at a dilution of 1 to 5 million.

Cacciavillani (32) noted that with these alkaloids the diastolic effect persisted even with very small doses whereas with the digitalis glycosides it is the systolic effects which are noted at corresponding levels. The response can be observed with the rabbit heart at a dilution of 1 to 150 million.

Trabucchi (33) noted that these alkaloids have their most powerful anesthetic effect on mucosa, the action being characterized by a slow onset of symptoms and a high intensity of long duration. They are generally more potent than cocaine—erythrophleine, homophleine, and coumingine surpassing the potency of percaine. The irritating action of homophleine is so low that it shows promise of use in medicine.

Other investigators have also studied these alkaloids (34, 35). In the main they confirmed or only slightly extended previous knowledge, but Krayer and his associates (36, 37) demonstrated that these alkaloids elicit a well-defined inotropic response. Ruzicka, Plattner, and Engel (38) prepared a series of esters of dimethylamino- and diethylaminoethanol with bile acids. The compounds showed a slight but uncharacteristic digitalis-like action, and some showed mild local anesthetic effects with marked local irritation.

The characteristic effects caused by these alkaloids disappear almost entirely when the double bonds in them are saturated.

IV. References

1. N. Gallois and E. Hardy, *Compt. rend.*, **80**, 1221 (1875); *J. pharm. chim.*, **24**, 25 (1876); *Bull. soc. chim.*, [2]**26**, 39 (1876).
2. E. Harnack and R. Zabrocky, *Arch. exptl. Pathol. Pharmakol.*, **15**, 404 (1882).
3. E. Harnack, *Arch. Pharm.*, **234** 561 (1896).
4. Jacobson, "Untersuchungen Uber Muavin," Thesis, Dorpat, 1892.
5. M. Laborde, *Ann. musée colonial Marseille*, [2]**5**, 305 (1907).
6. F. B. Power and A. H. Salway, *Am. J. Pharm.*, **84**, 333 (1912).
7. J. M. Petrie, *Proc. Linnean Soc. N. S. Wales*, **46**, 337 (1921).
8. C. W. Maplethorpe, *Pharm. J.*, **111**, 85 (1923).
9. P. Kamerman, *S. African J. Sci.*, **23**, 179 (1926).
10. G. Dalma, *Ann. chim. appl.*, **25**, 569 (1935).
11. G. Dalma, *Atti congr. intern. chim., 10th Congr., Rome*, (May 19) **1938**.
12. R. Paris and M. Rigal, *Bull. sci. pharmacol.*, **47**, 79 (1940).
13. E. Schlittler, *Helv. Chim. Acta*, **24/E**, 319 (1941).
14. L. Ruzicka, P. A. Plattner, and B. G. Engel, Exper., **1**, 160 (1945).
15. B. G. Engel and R. Tondeur, *Experientia*, **4**, 430 (1948).
16. R. Paris, *Ann. Pharm. franç.*, **6**, 501 (1948).

17. G. Dalma, *Helv. Chim. Acta*, **22,** 1497 (1939).
18. F. Faltis and L. Holzinger, *Ber.*, **72,** 1443 (1939).
19. L. Ruzicka and G. Dalma, *Helv. Chim. Acta*, **22,** 1516 (1939).
20. L. Ruzicka, G. Dalma, and E. W. Scott, *Helv. Chim. Acta*, **24/E,** 179 (1941).
21. L. Ruzicka, B. G. Engel, A. Ronco, and K. Berse, *Helv. Chim. Acta*, **28,** 1038 (1945).
22. L. Ruzicka and G. Dalma, *Helv. Chim. Acta*, **23,** 753 (1940).
23. B. K. Blount, H. T. Openshaw, and A. R. Todd, *J. Chem. Soc.*, **1940,** 286.
24. B. G. Engel and R. Tondeur, *Helv. Chim. Acta*, **32,** 2364 (1949).
25. L. Ruzicka, G. Dalma, and W. E. Scott, *Helv. Chim. Acta*, **24,** 63 (1941).
26. L. Ruzicka, G. Dalma, B. G. Engel, and W. E. Scott, *Helv. Chim. Acta*, **24,** 1449 (1941).
27. E. C. S. Jones and J. Kenner, *J. Chem. Soc.*, **1932,** 711.
28. K. K. Chen, A. L. Chen, and R. C. Anderson, *J. Am. Pharm. Assoc.*, **25,** 579 (1936).
29. K. K. Chen, C. C. Hargreaves, and W. T. Winchester, *J. Am. Pharm. Assoc.*, **27,** 9 (1938).
30. K. K. Chen, C. C. Hargreaves, and W. T. Winchester, *J. Am. Pharm. Assoc.*, **27,** 307 (1938).
31. R. Santi and B. Zweifel, Boll. soc. ital. biol. sper., **11,** 758 (1936).
32. R. Cacciavillani, *Boll. soc. ital. biol. sper.*, **12,** 339 (1937).
33. E. Trabucchi, *Arch. farmacol. sper.*, **64,** 97 (1937).
34. R. Santi, *Arch. exptl. Pathol. Pharmakol.*, **193,** 152 (1939).
35. E. Rothlin and M. Raymond-Hamet, *Arch. intern. pharmacodynamie*, **63,** 10 (1939).
36. H. M. Maling and O. Krayer, *J. Pharmacol. Exptl. Therap.*, **86,** 66 (1946).
37. O. Krayer, A. Farah, and F. C. Uhle, *J, Pharmacol. Exptl. Therap.*, **88,** 277 (1946).
38. L. Ruzicka, P. A. Plattner, and B. G. Engel, *Helv. Chim. Acta*, **27,** 1553 (1944).

CHAPTER 37

The Aconitum and Delphinium Alkaloids

E. S. STERN

J. F. Macfarlan and Co. Ltd., Edinburgh, Scotland

Page

I. Introduction 275
II. The Chemistry of the Atisines 278
1. Atisine 280
2. The Minor Alkaloids of *Aconitum heterophyllum:* Hetisine, Heteratisine, and Benzoylheteratisine 284
3. Lucidusculine, Kobusine, and Pseudokobusine 287
4. Staphisine 289
5. Talatisine, Songorine, and Napelline 291
6. Ajaconine and Delatine 292
7. Miyaconitine and Miyaconitinone 292
III. The Chemistry of the Aconitines 292
1. The Alkaloids Derived from Aconine and Mesaconine 297
2. Alkaloids Derived from Hypaconine, Neoline, Bikhaconine, and Pseudaconine 305
3. Delphinine 309
IV. The Monoester Alkaloids Derived from Methoxyl-rich Amino Alcohols Analogous to the Aconines 320
1. Lycoctonine and the Alkaloids Derived Therefrom 320
2. Isotalatisidine and Condelphine 326
3. Lappaconitine and Septentrionaline 326
V. "Miscellaneous" Alkaloids Isolated from *Aconitum* and *Delphinium* Species 328
VI. References 330

I. Introduction

The two genera *Aconitum* and *Delphinium*, which belong to the family Ranunculaceae, produce several series of closely related monobasic alkaloids. In fact, the same alkaloid may be found in different species of the two genera: thus, isotalatisidine and its acetyl ester condelphine occur in *A. talassicum* and in *D. confusum*, respectively, and esters of lycoctonine occur in *A. lycoctonum* and in several *Delphinium* species. On the other hand, closely similar plant species (e.g., *A. septentrionale* and *A. lycoctonum*, and a series of East Asian *Aconitum* species) may be differentiated by their content of related but different bases.

This occurrence in related plant species of mixtures of chemically related alkaloids is of considerable genetic interest and has stimulated research in recent years. Another reason why *Delphinium* alkaloids have received increasing attention is their great toxicity which makes some of the widely occurring larkspur species serious stock poisons. In spite of their intrinsic interest and although raw material is often available in abundance, the elucidation of structures of *Aconitum* and *Delphinium* alkaloids has not so far been possible because of the considerable practical difficulties attending the investigations.

Since related alkaloids frequently form mixtures that are not readily separable, purification of the bases obtainable has been assured only by careful application of modern techniques. For this reason much of the early work, some of which dates back to the first half of the nineteenth century, is now of historical rather than chemical interest. The examination by many early workers of impure material caused confusion and impeded, rather than aided, later chemical work. Whilst no structure has been established for any alkaloid discussed in this chapter, recently tentative formulations (1, 2) have been put forward as a basis for the review of the properties of atisine. In spite of the lack of structural formulas, a great deal of information is available about the properties and chemical behavior of the *Aconitum* and *Delphinium* alkaloids, and the close interrelation of some alkaloids of the two species has been fully elucidated.

It is now clear that these alkaloids are derived from complex polyhydric amino alcohols, probably based on the formula $C_{19}H_{28} \cdot NH$, and that they are thus related, formally at least, to the diterpenes (3). It is not clear, however, whether all the alkaloids have the same polycyclic skeletal structure: some of the simpler bases are definitely pentacyclic, and the substituted $C_{19}H_{28} \cdot NH$ nucleus contains one unsaturated center. In most of the more complex alkaloids, however, no definite chemical proof has been given that such unsaturation is present; however, the ultraviolet absorption spectra exhibit end-absorption in the region 2200–2600 A., and the presence of one inert unsaturated center may thus be presumed. It is likely, therefore, that all the bases have pentacyclic skeleta.

From a consideration of their properties, (30) the alkaloids can be broadly divided into several groups, largely on the basis of the substituents present, which apparently affect both the chemical and the pharmacological behavior. One group comprises the comparatively simple and nontoxic amino alcohols, e.g., atisine, staphisine, kobusine, etc., generally called the atisines, which are not extensively oxygenated and contain one methoxyl group at most. A second group of alkaloids, called the aconitines, is very much more toxic and more heavily substituted, particularly by methoxy groups of which three or four generally occur; in this group, two of the alcoholic hydroxyl groups are esterified, one by acetic acid, the other by an aromatic acid (benzoic acid or, frequently, the *p*-methoxy- or 3,4-dimethoxy derivative thereof). Hydrolysis of the aconitines gives the corresponding parent amino alcohols, the relatively nontoxic aconines: the aconines are more heavily substituted than the atisines, but otherwise comparable to them in several ways. Several alkaloids intermediate in toxicity and substitution between the atisines and aconitines are known: these are generally methoxyl-substituted monoesters of the alkaloidal amino alcohol with benzoic acid or anthranilic acid derivatives. These monoesters, particularly those derived from lycoctonine, are widely distributed in nature and are receiving increasing attention.

It has not hitherto proved possible to correlate the structures of the separate groups of alkaloids, i.e., of the atisines, the aconitines, and the lycoctonines, and the possibility that their differences in chemical behavior (particularly in ease of dehydrogenation) may be due to considerable structural differences cannot be excluded at the present time.

The general approach to the elucidation of the structure of the *Aconitum* and *Delphinium* alkaloids follows that practised in many other groups of naturally occurring complex bases. The initial characterization usually provides an empirical formula and the recognition of some, at least, of the functional groups; but, some of the inadequate early work has resulted in repeated revision of several empirical formulas, and it is probably safe to assume that further work, particularly on the many minor and little studied alkaloids (see Section V), will necessitate more revisions and possibly prove the identity of some of the alkaloids mentioned in the present review, which is confined to well-characterized bases.

The heavy substitution of many of the molecules makes an early determination of the nature of the functional groups imperative. Among the oxygenated functions, besides the ester groupings present in the aconitines and lycoctonines, free hydroxyl groups and methoxyl groups occur frequently. The basic nitrogen atom is almost always tertiary and usually substituted by a group that reacts analytically either like a methyl or like an ethyl group. The nature of the *N*-substituent provides a valuable check on the empirical formula derived for the alkaloid: generally the total number of carbon atoms in the molecule is given by the sum of the skeletal carbon atoms (i.e., the nineteen carbons of the $C_{19}H_{28} \cdot NH$ nucleus), the methoxyl substituents, the ester groupings, and the *N*-alkyl group. Moreover, unsaturation is found in many of the alkaloids, and quantitative hydrogenation has lately become a routine procedure in this field. The recent application of physico-organic methods, particularly ultraviolet absorption spectroscopy, has also greatly aided investigations by disclosing the presence of "inert unsaturation," already discussed.

Further progress has been achieved with only a few of the *Aconitum* and *Delphinium* alkaloids and is based largely on the dehydrogenation to phenanthrene derivatives and on oxidative studies; little success has attended several attempts at Hofmann degradation. The complexity of the mixtures encountered in the chemical degradation of the alkaloids limits the usefulness of a general summary and necessitates detailed discussion of each group of alkaloids, relations between which have been ascertained or seem likely.

As already mentioned, the complex alkaloids present in *Aconitum* and *Delphinium* species are highly toxic (their lethal dose for man being of the order of 2–5 mg.); this property has long been known and aconite was used in ancient times as an arrow poison. Because of their great toxicity, the aconitines are now rarely used therapeutically, but previously "tincture of aconite" had been used for the local relief of neuralgia and toothache, and systemically for hypertension, gout, and rheumatism. These uses are based on the peripheral and central action on the nervous system, respectively. The peripheral action, due to absorption through the skin or mucosa, first produces an intense and characteristic tingling sensation and warmth, and later anesthesia of the sensory nerves. Centrally, aconitine and the related alkaloids stimulate the medullary vagal centers and cause a slowing of the heart rate and lowering of the blood pressure. Although somewhat difficult to detect by classical methods, the presence of aconitine and related alkaloids in biological material can readily be demonstrated by paper-chromatographic methods.

II. The Chemistry of the Atisines

For the purposes of the present discussion, the atisines are defined as those *Aconitum* and *Delphinium* alkaloids that contain not more than one methoxyl group. This definition groups together fourteen of the simpler bases (cf. Table 1), all of which contain a tertiary nitrogen atom, though in three of them no simple alkyl group is attached to the basic nitrogen. Only three of the bases, those of highest molecular weight, contain one ester grouping, in each case the acetoxy group (although one benzoate, benzoylheteratisine, is also found in nature).

The atisines generally occur in small amounts (0.05–1%) in plant material, freqently accompanying one of the aconitines; the atisines remain in the mother liquors after the preliminary extraction of the aconitines, and many of these minor alkaloids no doubt still remain to be isolated and characterized. Their common occurrence strongly suggests a chemical relationship between the aconitines and the atisines.

On the assumption that the simpler bases, with fewer substituents, might lend themselves more readily to degradative studies, attention has concentrated in recent years on the examination of some of the atisines, and particularly on the readily available atisine itself. These studies have permitted a tentative formulation (I) of atisine in terms of a pentacyclic structure; for the present the related atisines are therefore assumed to have similar pentacyclic structures based on the skeletal formula $C_{19}H_{28}\cdot NH$ (cf. Table 1): the empirical formulas so far established (with the exception of

TABLE 1

FORMULAS, PROPERTIES, AND OCCURRENCE OF THE ATISINES

Base	Empirical formula	M.p., °C.	$[\alpha]_D$	Occurrence	Functional groups	Part-formulas based on pentacyclic $C_{19}H_{28}\cdot NH$	Δ req.	Δ found	Ref
? Delatine	$C_{19}H_{25}O_3N$	264	+13°	*D. elatum*					4
				A. fischeri					
Kobusine	$C_{20}H_{27}O_2N$	268	+84°	*A. kamtschaticum*	1·OH; 1 epoxy; =N; C=C	$C_{19}H_{22}(OH)(\cdot O\cdot)(Me)(:N)$	1	1	5, 6
				A. sachalinense					
				A. lucidusculum					
Pseudokobusine	$C_{20}H_{27}O_3N$	272	+50°	*A. yezoense*	2 OH; 1 epoxy; =N; C=C	$C_{19}H_{22}(OH)_2(\cdot O\cdot)(Me)(:N)$	1	1	7
				A. lucidusculum					
Hetisine	$C_{20}H_{27}O_3N$	256	+14°	*A. heterophyllum*	3 OH(?); tert. N; C=C	$C_{19}H_{21}(OH)_3(Me)(:N\cdot)$	1	1	8
Talatisine	$C_{20}H_{29}O_3N$	246	+38°	*A. talassicum*	3 OH; $N\cdot CH_3$; C=C	$C_{19}H_{23}(OH)_3(NMe)$	2	1	3
Songorine	$C_{21}H_{29}O_3N$	203	−140°	*A. soongoricum*	2 OH; 1·C=O; $N\cdot C_2H_5$; C=C	$C_{19}H_{22}(OH)_2(:O)(NEt)$	2	1	9
Staphisine	$C_{21}H_{31}ON$	208	−159°	*D. staphisagria*	$N\cdot CH_3$; C=C(1 or 2?); OH(?)	$C_{19}H_{24}(OH)(Me)(NMe)$	2	?	10
Ajaconine	$C_{21}H_{31}O_3N$	165	−133°	*D. ajacis*	$N\cdot CH_3$; C=C	$C_{19}H_{22}(?OH)_3(Me)(NMe)$	2	—	11
	$C_{22}H_{33}O_3N$	172	−119°			$C_{19}H_{21}(OH)_3(Me)_2(NMe)$	2	1	12
						$C_{19}H_{22}(OH)_3(Me)(NEt)$	2		
Atisine	$C_{22}H_{33}O_2N$	57–60		*A. heterophyllum*	2 OH; $N\cdot C_2H_5$; 2 C=C	$C_{19}H_{23}(OH)_2(Me)(NEt)$	2	2	13
				A. anthora					
Napelline	$C_{22}H_{33}O_3N$	85–88		*A. napellus*	3 OH; $N\cdot C_2H_5$; C=C(1 or 2)	$C_{19}H_{22}(OH)_3(Me)(NEt)$	2	?	14, 15
Heteratisine	$C_{22}H_{33}O_5N$	267	+40°	*A. heterophyllum*	2 OH; 1 OCH_3; $N\cdot C_2H_5$; lactone; C=C	$C_{19}H_{23}(OH)_2(:O\cdot O\cdot)(OMe)(NEt)$	1	0	8, 16
Miyaconitinone	$C_{23}H_{27}O_6N$	285	−28°	*A. miyabei*	1 $O\cdot CO\cdot CH_3$; 4 C=O; $N\cdot C_2H_5$	$C_{19}H_{19}(OAc)(:O)_4(NEt)$	1	0	33
Miyaconitine	$C_{23}H_{29}O_6N$	218	−88°	*A. miyabei*	1 OH; 1 $O\cdot CO\cdot CH_3$; 3 C=O; $N\cdot C_2H_5$	$C_{19}H_{20}(OH)(OAc)(:O)_3(NEt)$	1	0	33
Lucidusculine	$C_{24}H_{35}O_4N$	171	−95°	*A. lucidusculum*	2 OH; 1 $O\cdot CO\cdot CH_3$; $N\cdot C_2H_5$; C=C	$C_{19}H_{22}(OH)_2(OAc)(Me)(NEt)$	2	1	27, 5

delatine which is probably erroneously formulated) can readily be derived from a pentacyclic $C_{19}H_{28} \cdot NH$, though this leads to the postulation of a hindered (unreactive) ethylenic linkage in some of the bases. Whether these particular bases are, in fact, penta- or hexacyclic remains to be ascertained.

1. Atisine

Atisine is the alkaloid long known (17) to be present (to the extent of about 0.5–1 %) in the roots of atis (*Aconitum heterophyllum* Wall.) and appears to be identical with anthorine (18), the alkaloid isolated from *A. anthora* L. The fact that atisine is more readily accessible and also less complex than many of the other *Aconitum* alkaloids has stimulated interest in its investigation since its structure may provide a guide to that of the related alkaloids. In recent years the older formulation for atisine (19) has been corrected (20) and its properties have been studied intensively, so that it has proved possible (2) to postulate a tentative structural formula (I), on the basis of which the reactions may be discussed.

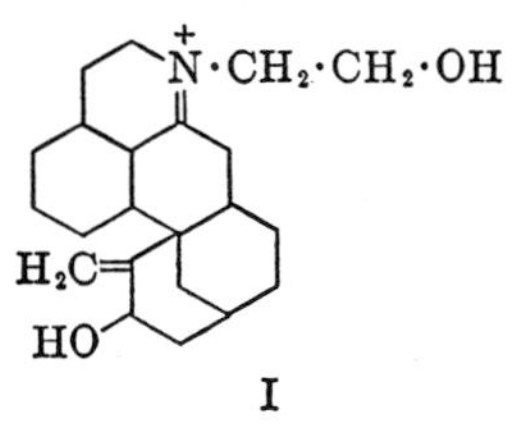

I

Atisine is generally isolated as the hydrochloride, from which the base cannot be readily prepared in crystalline form; a melting point can, however, be determined on the condensate from the molecular distillation of this resinous material.

Ground root (13 kg.) of *A. heterophyllum* is extracted twice with 70% ethanol (39 l.), the root being pressed (13). After vacuum-evaporation of the solvent, the aqueous syrup is treated with 10% sulfuric acid (25% of its volume) and extracted with chloroform. The aqueous phase is then rendered just alkaline to litmus with sodium carbonate and extracted with benzene to remove other bases. Atisine is then liberated by adding sodium hydroxide to the aqueous phase until strongly alkaline and immediately extracting exhaustively with benzene. Concentration of the benzene extracts gives a resinous alkaloid mixture which is dissolved in ethanol and converted into the hydrochlorides by addition of hydrochloric acid (*d* 1.19) until barely acid to Congo red. Concentration of the liquors gives crude atisine hydrochloride (46 g. in all) as crystalline precipitate, whilst the mother liquors retain the hydrochlorides of heteratisine and hetisine.

Atisine contains two unsaturated centers since, on hydrogenation over platinum oxide, a tetrahydro derivative can be isolated (in about 30%

yield). On vigorous alkaline treatment atisine affords dihydroatisine (21) by a remarkable disproportionation, but under milder conditions a molecular rearrangement takes place to isoatisine. Since tetrahydroatisine is stable to alkali, the rearrangement may be assumed to be connected with one of the unsaturated centers. Both isomers give the same tetrahydro derivative, which is also obtained from dihydroatisine on hydrogenation.

Atisine hydrochloride (1.2 g.) with methanol (20 ml.) saturated with sodium hydroxide at 100° for 90 hr. (sealed tube) gives, on dilution and ether-extraction, dihydroatisine (75%).

Atisine hydrochloride (1 g.) in boiling methanol (40 ml.) containing sodium hydroxide (3 g.) for 3.5 hr. gives, on dilution and extraction with chloroform, isoatisine (almost quantitatively).

Atisine, moreover, is a stronger base than are isoatisine and tetrahydroatisine, and it is probable, therefore, that at least one of the unsaturated centers is associated with the nitrogen atom; in the weaker base, isoatisine, this center is assumed to have moved (2), as demonstrated in the part-formula (II).

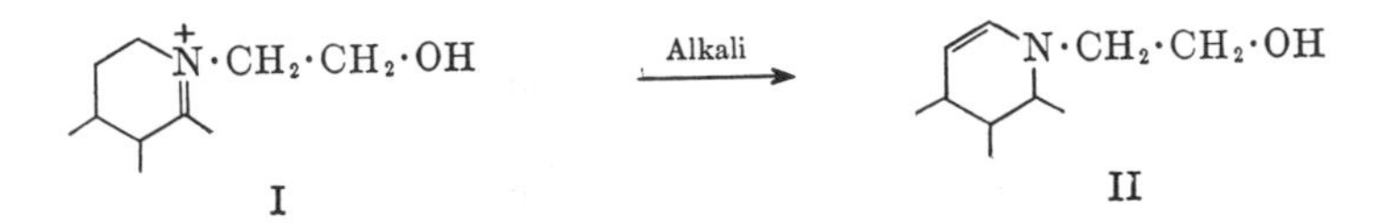

Some further evidence in favor of this formulation may be adduced from the ultraviolet absorption curves of the isomers. Neither of these shows any well-defined maximum between 2200 and 2800 A., and a conjugated system of unsaturated bonds may thus be excluded. However, both isomers exhibit rising "end-absorption" over this wide spectral region, and the curve is moved by changes in pH of the aqueous media: thus the absportion data suggest a close association between one unsaturated and the basic center of the molecule.

The other outstanding features of the atisine molecule are the two oxygen atoms; since the base and its tetrahydro derivative both contain two reactive hydrogen atoms and give diacetates, both oxygen atoms are accounted for as hydroxyl groups (13) and not as a methylenedioxy group as had been thought previously (20). Physical constants of the simple derivatives of atisine are collected in Table 2.

The presence of an *N*-alkyl group in atisine was established by Lawson and Topps (20), but their results which led to the conclusion that this was a methyl group were erroneous. Later work (22) has, in fact, shown that the material obtained on determination of the *N*-alkyl group is largely tetraethylammonium iodide, and that the group attached to the nitrogen

TABLE 2

SIMPLE DERIVATIVES OF ATISINE

Compound	Base		Hydrochloride		Hydrobromide		Hydriodide	
	M.p., °C.	$[\alpha]_D$	M.p., °C.	$[\alpha]_D$	M.p., °C.	$[\alpha]_D$	M.p., °C.	$[\alpha]_D$
Atisine	57–60		311–312	+28°	273	+24°	279 (d.)	+27°
Diacetylatisine			241–243 (d.)					
Dihydroatisine	156–158	−45°	261–263	−16°				
Tetrahydroatisine	171–174	−33°						
Isoatisine	150–151	−16°	295–299 (d.)	−4°				

atom thus has two carbon atoms; the low recoveries of the quarternary salt may be cited in support of a modified *N*-ethyl group.

Further insight into the structure of atisine was obtained (13) by dehydrogenation over selenium, when 1-methylphenanthrene and 6-ethyl-1-methylphenanthrene were identified in the complex mixture of products (23, 24). The latter substance had not previously been encountered, and its presence in the dehydrogenation mixture is of considerable interest.

The oxidative degradation of atisine and isoatisine has also yielded most interesting results which may most conveniently be discussed (2) on the basis of the tentative formulas (I) and (II) postulated for atisine and isoatisine. Although atisine (I) ($C_{22}H_{33}O_2N$) is not attacked under mild conditions by potassium permanganate in acetone containing acetic acid, isoatisine (II) on such gentle oxidation yields a neutral oxoisoatisine (III) ($C_{22}H_{33}O_3N$) which contains the same number of hydrogen atoms but one more oxygen atom than does isoatisine. Hydrogenation of the lactam oxoisoatisine to a dihydro derivative (IV) confirms that the oxidation saturates one of the ethylenic linkages and leads to the tentative formulations outlined in the reaction scheme below

Oxidation of atisine (I) with an excess of alkaline permanganate at low temperature proceeds by a different route and affords a lactamdicarboxylic acid (V) ($C_{21}H_{29}O_6N$) which is unsaturated, since, on hydrogenation, it readily absorbs one molar proportion of hydrogen. The dihydro acid (VI) is identical with the lactamdicarboxylic acid (VI) obtained analogously from isoatisine (II) and from oxoisoatisine (III) through dihydroxyoxoisoatisine (VII): both lactamdicarboxylic acids contain one tertiary carboxyl group and a primary hydroxyl group. This hydroxyl is attacked by further oxidation and two lactamtricarboxylic acids (VIII) and (IX) are obtained, from V and VI, respectively, or directly from atisine and isoatisine, respec-

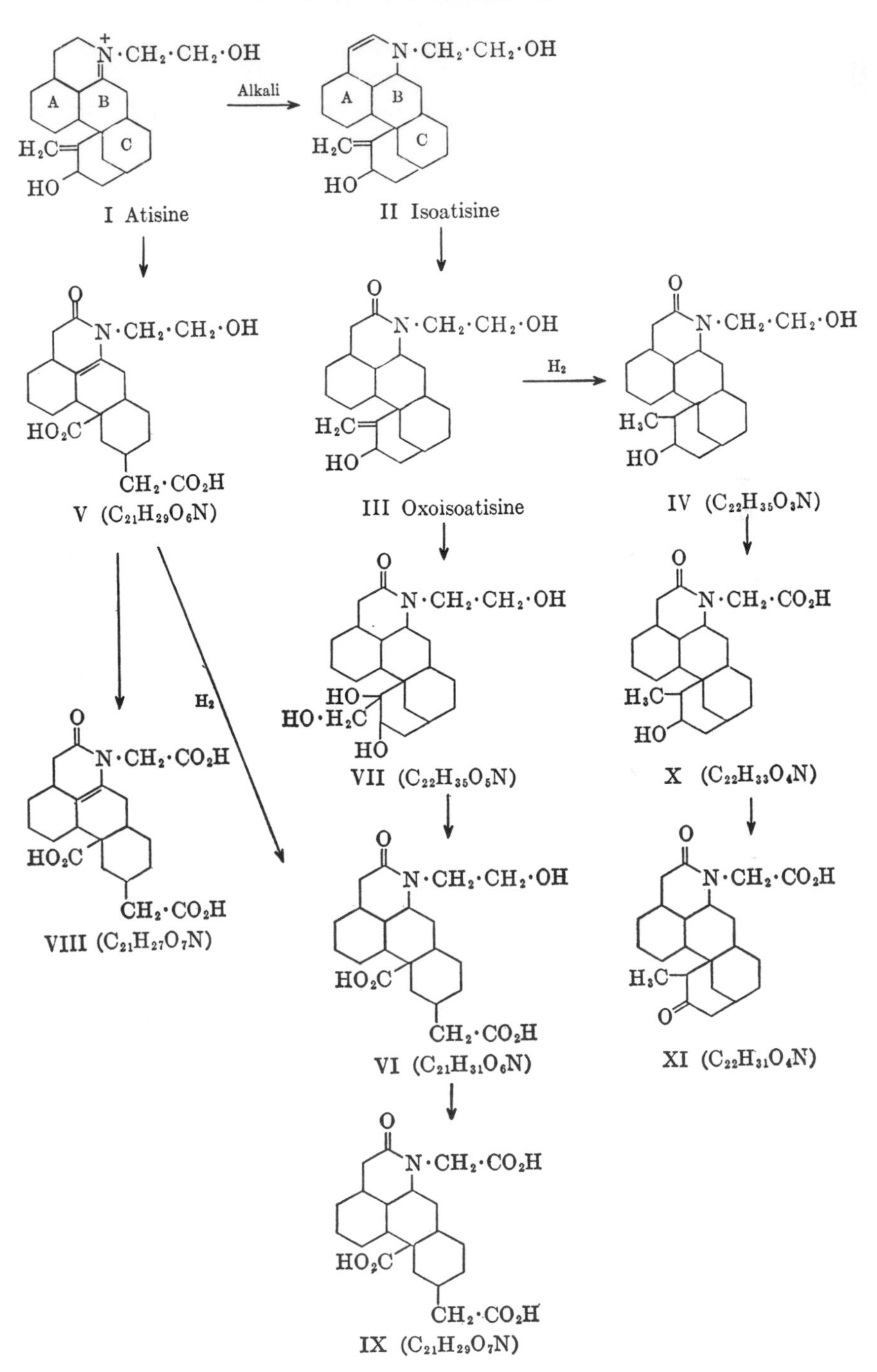
N·CH₂·CH₂·OH
A
B
C
H₂C=
HO
Alkali
I Atisine
II Isoatisine
H₂
V (C₂₁H₂₉O₆N)
III Oxoisoatisine
IV (C₂₂H₃₅O₃N)
VII (C₂₂H₃₅O₅N)
X (C₂₂H₃₃O₄N)
VIII (C₂₁H₂₇O₇N)
VI (C₂₁H₃₁O₆N)
XI (C₂₂H₃₁O₄N)
IX (C₂₁H₂₉O₇N)

tively. The two tricarboxylic acids differ in that VIII retains one ethylenic linkage, and IX is thus the dihydro derivative of VIII.

Dehydrogenation of the saturated tricarboxylic acid (IX) gives 1,6-dimethylphenanthrene, whereas the characteristic product of dehydrogenation of atisine, tetrahydroatisine, and oxoisoatisine is 6-ethyl-1-methylphenanthrene. Since the lactamdicarboxylic acid (VI) derived from isoatisine also affords 1,6-dimethylphenanthrene, the 6-ethyl group must arise from a structural feature lost in the later oxidative stages.

Whilst on oxidation of oxoisoatisine (III) the ethylenic linkage in the allyl position to the secondary hydroxyl group is attacked, such reaction is not possible with dihydrooxoisoatisine (IV); instead, the primary hydroxyl group suffers initial oxidation (though slowly) and a monocarboxylic acid (X) results which may be further oxidized to a ketocarboxylic acid (XI), the ketonic group of which is readily detected by its ultraviolet absorption.

The formulation proposed (2) for atisine therefore serves to explain the properties of the alkaloid, if it is assumed (*a*) that the 6-ethyl-1-methylphenanthrene isolated from its dehydrogenation products represents the major portion of the carbon skeleton of atisine, and is not an artifact, and (*b*) that the molecule contains no unsaturated centers resistant to hydrogenation. With this formulation the way is now open to preliminary synthetic studies and to a critical review of the chemistry of the related simpler aconitum alkaloids.

2. The Minor Alkaloids of *Aconitum heterophyllum*: Hetisine, Heteratisine, and Benzoylheteratisine

The mother liquors from the isolation of atisine from *A. heterophyllum* contain three alkaloids, of which one, heteratisine, may be an artifact obtained during the isolation by hydrolysis of its benzoyl ester (25); although heteratisine appears to be more abundant than hetisine it is more complex (cf. Table 4) and the latter has therefore been more closely investigated.

In view of their occurrence with atisine it may be assumed that these minor alkaloids are genetically and also structurally related to atisine, but evidence to this end is lacking. In the case of heteratisine and benzoylheteratisine chemical work is confined to the elucidation of the functional groups present (8, 25) (cf. Table 1), and these alkaloids appear to be more complex than most of the "atisines."

Heteratisine contains a lactone grouping, a structural feature rare in these alkaloids. Of the twenty-two carbon atoms, three are accounted for as the methoxyl and the *N*-ethyl substituents, and the remaining nineteen presumably form the usual polycyclic nucleus: the lactone grouping must therefore take the place of a methyl or of a hydroxymethyl group present in the related alkaloids.

TABLE 3

OXIDATION PRODUCTS OF ATISINE AND ISOATISINE (2, 22)

Oxidation products	Formula	M.p., °C.	$[\alpha]_D$	Derivative	Formula	M.p., °C.	$[\alpha]_D$
Derivatives of isoatisine (II)							
Oxoisoatisine (III)	$C_{22}H_{33}O_3N$	*ca.* 240–250	−39° ($CHCl_3$)	Dibromide hydrobromide	$C_{22}H_{33}O_2NBr_2$, HBr	212–215	
				Dihydro derivative (IV)	$C_{22}H_{35}O_3N$	219–223	−38° ($CHCl_3$)
Dihydroxyoxoisoatisine (VII)	$C_{22}H_{35}O_5N$	253–258	−33° (EtOH)				
Lactamdicarboxylic acid (VI)	$C_{21}H_{31}O_6N$	255–257	−17° (EtOH)	Methyl ester	$C_{22}H_{33}O_6N$	129.5–131	
				Dimethyl ester	$C_{23}H_{35}O_6N$	non-cryst.	
Lactamtricarboxylic acid (IX)	$C_{21}H_{29}O_7N$	258–261	+9° (MeOH)	Methyl ester	$C_{22}H_{31}O_7N$	210–215	+2° (EtOH)
				Dimethyl ester	$C_{23}H_{33}O_7N$	240–245	+15° (EtOH)
				Trimethyl ester	$C_{24}H_{35}O_7N$	non-cryst.	+9° (EtOH)
				Anilide (Phenylimide)	$C_{27}H_{32}O_5N_2$	299–302	
				Anilide dimethyl ester	$C_{29}H_{38}O_6N_2$	235–238	
Derivative of acid (IX) by action of thionyl chloride							
Lactamdicarboxylic acid	$C_{19}H_{27}O_5N$	220–223		Methyl ester	$C_{20}H_{29}O_5N$	301–309	
				Dimethyl ester	$C_{21}H_{31}O_5N$	non-cryst.	
Derivatives of dihydrooxoisoatisine (IV)							
Lactamcarboxylic acid (X)	$C_{22}H_{33}O_4N$	240–244		Methyl ester	$C_{23}H_{35}O_4N$	228–231	
Ketolactamcarboxylic acid (XI)	$C_{22}H_{31}O_4N$	223.5–229		Methyl ester	$C_{23}H_{33}O_4N$	non-cryst.	
Derivatives of atisine (I)							
Lactamdicarboxylic acid (V)	$C_{21}H_{29}O_6N$	323–326	−23.5° (EtOH)	Methyl ester	$C_{22}H_{31}O_6N$	229–232	
				Dimethyl ester	$C_{23}H_{33}O_6N$	193–195	
				Dihydro derivative (VI)	$C_{21}H_{31}O_6N$	256–258	−22° (EtOH)
Lactamtricarboxylic acid (VIII)	$C_{21}H_{27}O_7N$	310–315	+39° (EtOH)				

TABLE 4

PROPERTIES OF THE MINOR ALKALOIDS FROM *A. HETEROPHYLLUM*

Name	Base			Hydrochloride	
	Formula	M.p., °C.	$[\alpha]_D$	M.p., °C.	$[\alpha]_D$
Heteratisine	$C_{22}H_{33}O_5N$	265–267	+40° (MeOH)	265–270 (d.)	
Benzoylheter-atisine	$C_{29}H_{37}O_6N$	213–214	+73° (EtOH)	218–221 (d.)	
Hetisine	$C_{20}H_{27}O_3N$	253–256	+14° (EtOH)	*ca.* 325 (d.)	+12.5° (EtOH)

Hetisine carries less complex substitution, but its structural features have not been completely explained, as yet, and no systematic oxidative studies exploring its relation to atisine are on record. Hetisine readily affords a dihydro compound and is thought to contain three reactive hydrogen atoms (presumably as hydroxyl groups) although no crystalline acetyl derivative has been obtained. The nitrogen atom is tertiary; in view of the C_{20} formulation, and the presumed presence of the usual C_{19} nucleus, the only possible alkyl substituent at the nitrogen atom is a methyl group. The presence of an *N*-methyl group is, however, excluded by analysis (8), and the twentieth carbon atom must be attached to the nucleus as a methyl or methylene substituent.

Dehydrogenation of hetisine gives (26) 1,7-dimethylphenanthrene, a distinct difference from atisine, the characteristic dehydrogenation product of which is 1,6-dimethylphenanthrene. Since 1,7-dimethylphenanthrene is also obtained (31) from abietic acid and from another *Aconitum* alkaloid, staphisine, the relationship between some, at least, of the *Aconitum* alkaloids and the diterpenes may be more than formal.

Attempts to degrade hetisine to a nitrogen-free polycyclic substance by exhaustive methylation are unsuccessful, since at the second degradative cycle methanol (instead of water) is split off and the methine produced in the first degradative step is regenerated. One interesting feature of this work is the isolation of dihydrodesmethylhetisine by hydrogenation of this methine base obtained from hetisine methiodide. As hetisine itself contains one unsaturated center (cf. Table 1) and the methine contains a new double bond, formation of a tetrahydro derivative would be expected; the reason for the inertness of one of the unsaturated centers in desmethylhetisine is obscure.

Oxidation of the dihydrodesmethylhetisine with permanganate proceeds smoothly with loss of two hydrogen atoms and affords a well-crystallized

TABLE 5

DERIVATIVES OF HETISINE

Compound	Formula	M.p., °C.	Hydrochloride M.p., °C.	Methiodide M.p., °C.	Metho-chloride M.p., °C.
Hetisine	$C_{20}H_{27}O_3N$	253–256	*ca.* 325 (d.)	320–325 (d.)	
Dihydrohetisine	$C_{20}H_{29}O_3N$	250–255	333		
Desmethylhetisine	$C_{21}H_{29}O_3N$	122–124	303–305	246–250	285–290
Dihydrodesmethyl-hetisine	$C_{21}H_{31}O_3N$		315–318 (subl.)	249–251	
Oxidation product from dihydrodes-methylhetisine	$C_{21}H_{29}O_3N$	139–141			

base, isomeric with the methine desmethylhetisine. This smooth oxidation lends support to the view that oxidative degradation of hetisine may yield valuable results.

3. Lucidusculine, Kobusine, and Pseudokobusine

The East Asian species *A. lucidusculum* Nakai contains three alkaloids that are generally classed as atisines. Lucidusculine (27) appears to be characteristic of this species, but kobusine also occurs (29) in *A. sachalinense* F. Schmidt and in *A. fischeri* Reichb. (*A. kamtschaticum* Pall.) and pseudokobusine was first isolated (7) from *A. yezoense* Nakai. Some properties and derivatives of kobusine and of pseudokobusine resemble those of hetisine (8), which has the same molecular formula as pseudokobusine. A comparison of products of further reactions, particularly of dehydrogenation and Hofmann and oxidative degradations, would be of interest and of value for the elucidation of the possible relationships or even identities, but unfortunately chemical studies, particularly on the recently discovered pseudokobusine, are too scanty to permit this.

In contrast to most of the other alkaloids commonly classed as atisines, lucidusculine (27) is an ester, namely, the monoacetate, of a trihydric amino alcohol "luciculine" containing no methoxyl group: since luciculine is unsaturated, its original formulation has been revised (8, 28). The presence of a second ethylenic linkage may be expected if lucidusculine is derived from a pentacyclic $C_{19}H_{28}\cdot NH$ nucleus. Both lucidusculine and luciculine form well-crystallized salts, and the former also readily yields a methiodide. Reaction of either base with acetyl chloride results in acetylation of the reactive hydroxyl group(s); lucidusculine diacetate is identical with luciculine triacetate (6).

Hofmann degradation of luciculine methiodide gives (28) a new base,

TABLE 6

THE SIMPLER ALKALOIDS OF *A. LUCIDUSCULUM*, THEIR SALTS, AND METHIODIDES

Alkaloid	Formula	M.p., °C.	$[\alpha]_D$
Luciduseuline	$C_{24}H_{37}O_4N$	170–171	−95° ($CHCl_3$)
Hydrochloride		245–265 (dec.)	
Hydrobromide		248–250 (dec.)	−63° (H_2O)
Perchlorate		260–265	−70° (EtOH)
Picrate		173–176	
Methiodide		197	−65° (EtOH)
Kobusine	$C_{20}H_{27}O_2N$	268	+84° ($CHCl_3$)
Hydrochloride		300 (dec.)	+41° (H_2O)
Hydrobromide		285 (dec.)	+41° (H_2O)
Perchlorate		220 (dec.)	
Picrate		277	
Chloroplatinate		262 (dec.)	
Nitrite		242 (dec.)	
Methiodide		287	
Pseudokobusine	$C_{20}H_{27}O_3N$	271–272	+50° ($CHCl_3$)
Hydrochloride		307	+29° (H_2O)
Hydrobromide		300 (dec.)	+23° (H_2O)
Perchlorate		260	
Picrate		260	
Chloroplatinate		255	
Methiodide		287	

called mesoluciculine, the methiodide of which cannot be degraded further: thus Hofmann degradation of luciculine, like that of hetisine (26), can only be carried through one cycle. Dihydroluciculine methiodide, which is very hygroscopic, cannot be successfully submitted to Hofmann degradation (28).

Determination of the functional groups of kobusine has occasioned some difficulty, and an early report (5) has had to be corrected (6): it appears (6) that kobusine gives a mono- (not characterized) and a diacetyl derivative, and, on hydrogenation, dihydrokobusine, characterized as diacetate. Hydrogenation was previously (5) thought to proceed with absorption of two molar proportions of hydrogen, when, after acetylation, "triacetyltetrahydrokobusine" was obtained: the melting point of this is the same as that now given for diacetyldihydrokobusine. Further confirmation of all the formulas derived is probably desirable.

The ready formation of the methiodide proves the presence of a tertiary nitrogen atom, which does not, however, carry a simple alkyl group. The methiodide, on attempted Hofmann degradation (28), splits off water and gives methylanhydrokobusine ($C_{21}H_{29}O_2N$, m.p. 168–170°) in good yield; a crystalline methiodide (m.p. 221–222°) of this is described, but the dihydro derivative is non-crystalline.

Pseudokobusine, like kobusine but unlike hetisine, gives a crystalline diacetyl derivative, and like both kobusine and hetisine, a dihydro compound; the properties of this and of its hydrochloride correspond so well to those of dihydrohetisine and its hydrochloride that the possibility of identity of the substances will have to be examined. Dihydropseudokobusine, however, may be characterized as a triacetyl derivative, a reaction not hitherto recorded for dihydrohetisine. In boiling thionyl chloride. two hydroxyl groups of pseudokobusine are replaced and a dichloro compound results.

4. Staphisine

Staphisine accompanies delphinine, from the mother liquors of which it has been isolated (10), in *Delphinium staphisagria* L. Although purified by modern techniques, including chromatography, samples of staphisine give fluctuating analyses and have varying molecular weights: the material is therefore thought to be an equilibrium mixture of a simple base and its dimolecular condensation product, but the exact reasons and conditions for this equilibration have not been established.

$$C_{21}H_{31}ON \rightleftarrows C_{42}H_{60}ON_2 + H_2O$$

A C_{22} formulation has also been considered, but now appears to be unlikely because of dehydrogenation experiments (10, 31) which yield, among other products, 1,7-dimethylphenanthrene and 7-isopropyl-1,3-dimethylphenanthrene. The latter product appears to indicate a close relationship between staphisine and diterpenoid structures, and on the basis of a diterpenoid formulation a C_{20} skeleton can (but a C_{21} skeleton cannot) readily be envisaged; since it has an *N*-methyl group, one staphisine unit is likely to contain twenty-one carbon atoms in all.

The uncertainty surrounding its molecular formula has made recognition of its functional groups difficult in spite of the fact that staphisine contains less oxygen than any other related alkaloid. The molecule, on hydrogenation, absorbs hydrogen, but the exact degree of unsaturation has not yet been established: two forms (differing in melting point) of a tetrahydro derivative of the dimolecular form appear to result. In this connection the ultraviolet absorption curve of staphisine is of interest: it exhibits a maximum at 2670 A. (ϵ *ca.* 10,000), which may indicate the presence of two homoannular conjugated ethylenic linkages in one of the equilibrium forms. On the assumption that staphisine (like other atisines) is derived from the pentacyclic $C_{19}H_{28}\cdot NH$ nucleus, it may be considered likely that the "monomeric" form $C_{21}H_{31}ON$ contains two ethylenic linkages: of these two (if present), one appears to be resistant to hydrogenation and it is unlikely therefore that the ethylenic linkages of the monomeric form are conjugated; conjugation, moreover, would probably produce absorption of

TABLE 7

DERIVATIVES OF LUCICULINE, KOBUSINE, AND PSEUDOKOBUSINE

Compound	Formula	Base		Hydrochloride		Methiodide	Diacetate		Other derivative	
		M.p., °C.	$[\alpha]_D$	M.p., °C.	$[\alpha]_D$	M.p., °C.	M.p., °C.	$[\alpha]_D$	M.p., °C.	$[\alpha]_D$
Luciculine	$C_{22}H_{33}O_3N$	148–150 (?anhyd.) 115–117 (+1 H_2O)	−12° (EtOH)	198–203 (d.)	−9.5° (H_2O)	267 (d.)	153–157	−76° ($CHCl_3$)	Triacetate (m.p. 157°) [hydrochloride 139–144	−50° (H_2O)]
Dihydroluciculine	$C_{22}H_{35}O_3N$	50–100		187–200 (d.)						
Mesoluciculine	$C_{21}H_{31}O_3N$	199–200	−13° (3% alkali)	157–159 (d.)		276 (d.)			Picrate 205–206	
Kobusine	$C_{20}H_{27}O_2N$	268	+84° ($CHCl_3$)	300 (d.)	+41° (H_2O)	287	139–140			
Dihydrokobusine	$C_{20}H_{29}O_2N$	not reported					183–184 (d.)			
Methylanhydrokobusine	$C_{21}H_{29}O_2N$	168–170	+74° (EtOH)			221–222 (d.)				
Pseudokobusine	$C_{20}H_{27}O_3N$	271–272	+50°($CHCl_3$)	307	+29° (H_2O)	287	145–146			
Dihydropseudokobusine[a]	$C_{20}H_{29}O_3N$	248–249		>310					Triacetate 231	
Dichloropseudokobusine	$C_{20}H_{25}ONCl_2$	>320								

[a] Other salts of dihydropseudokobusine: hydrobromide, m.p. 310°; perchlorate, m.p. 138°; picrate, m.p. 260°; chloroplatinate, m.p. 263–264°.

higher intensity than is observed. The conjugated system may thus be characteristic of the dimolecular form, and the ultraviolet absorption may ultimately provide a useful means of studying the equilibration of the two forms.

5. Talatisine, Songorine, and Napelline

These three alkaloids have been isolated from different *Aconitum* species: talatisine (3) from the rare *A. talassicum* Popov, songorine (9) from *A. soongoricum*, and napelline (14, 15) from *A. napellus* L. (the main alkaloid of which is aconitine). Whilst the empirical formulas and main functional groups of these alkaloids may be considered to be firmly established, none of them has yielded degradation products or other derivatives that throw light on the nuclear structures.

None of the three alkaloids carries any methoxyl substituent. In the case of talatisine all three oxygen atoms are present as hydroxyl groups as shown by conversion into the triacetate (by acetic anhydride–pyridine) and into a trichloro compound (by boiling thionyl chloride). Presence of one ethylenic linkage is confirmed by hydrogenation to a dihydro derivative.

In the case of songorine, only two of three oxygen atoms are present as hydroxyls and convertible into acetoxy or chloro groups. The third oxygen is present as a carbonyl group, and songorine yields a semicarbazone. Again, presence of one ethylenic linkage is readily confirmed by hydrogenation in the usual manner.

Both talatisine and songorine, if pentacyclic, may contain a second ethylenic or other unsaturated linkage, resistant to hydrogenation. In addition to the difference in one of the oxygenated substituents, talatisine differs from songorine in carrying an *N*-methyl group; songorine has an *N*-ethyl group. The two alkaloids may be quite closely related: considerable interest would attach to the Meerwein-Ponndorf reduction of the carbonyl group of songorine, since the triol so produced may differ from talatisine only in the *N*-alkyl group (a relationship obtaining between aconitine and mesaconitine).

Napelline (15), like songorine, carries an *N*-ethyl (16) and, like talatisine, three hydroxyl groups. On hydrogenation, however, an indefinite mixture is produced from which a dihydro derivative has been isolated. The presence of one ethylenic linkage is thus confirmed, and that of a second not excluded; two unsaturated centers would be expected if napelline is pentacyclic. On dehydrogenation (14, 15) napelline gives a complex mixture of phenanthrene hydrocarbons and a basic fraction ($C_{17}H_{17}N$), but none of the dehydrogenation products has hitherto been identified.

6. Ajaconine and Delatine

These two bases have not been submitted to extensive chemical study. Ajaconine has long been known (32) to occur in *Delphinium ajacis* L., but its empirical formula (11, 12) cannot be considered to be established with certainty. Ajaconine absorbs one molar proportion of hydrogen on hydrogenation (12), and at least one ethylenic linkage must therefore be present. Formation of a methiodide (11) establishes the presence of a tertiary nitrogen atom; results of *N*-methyl determinations are very low, however, and the nature of the *N*-alkyl is thus uncertain.

Delatine, which has been isolated comparatively recently (4) from *Delphinium elatum* L., cannot readily be related to the pentacyclic $C_{19}H_{18} \cdot NH$ nucleus on the basis of the empirical formula given. If the base described is pure, it may be erroneously formulated; alternatively, it may not belong to the group of alkaloids here considered (although the general resemblance to the atisines makes this unlikely). Chemical evidence as to its constitution is lacking.

7. Miyaconitine and Miyaconitinone

These two remarkable bases have recently (33) been isolated from the East Asian species *Aconitum miyabei* Nakai, and may form a link between the atisines and the aconitines. The new bases miyaconitine and (the less soluble) miyaconitinone are highly oxygenated but contain no methoxyl groups; instead, they have one acetoxy group and several carbonyl groups: in miyaconitinone there are four of these (two of them adjacent, as shown by formation of a quinoxaline derivative on reaction with *o*-phenylenediamine), whilst miyaconitine has three (two of them adjacent) and one hydroxyl group. Evidently one of the carbonyl groups of miyaconitinone is present in the reduced form in miyaconitine, which is, moreover, converted into miyaconitinone on oxidation with chromic–acetic acid.

The two new alkaloids, on hydrolysis, afford the corresponding alcohols miyaconine (containing two hydroxyl and three carbonyl groups) and miyaconinone (with one hydroxyl group and four carbonyl groups), respectively. Hydrolysis and subsequent hydrogenation yield a non-crystalline pentahydric alcohol that may be considered a precursor of the lower aconitines (which, however, contain both hydroxyl and methoxy groups). No evidence has been reported that an ethylenic linkage is present, although the two bases, if pentacyclic, would be expected to have one.

III. The Chemistry of the Aconitines

The aconitines comprise the highly toxic and highly oxygenated tertiary bases that contain generally three or four methoxyl substituents and two esterified hydroxyl groups: one of the ester groupings is the acetate group,

TABLE 8

SALTS AND DERIVATIVES OF STAPHISINE, TALATISINE, SONGORINE, NAPELLINE, AJACONINE, AND DELATINE

Alkaloid	M.p., °C.	$[\alpha]_D$
Staphisine		
Hydrochloride	260–265 (dec.)	
Hydrobromide	255–258 (dec.)	
Methiodide, Mono-	255 (dec.)	
Di-	250 (dec.)	
Dihydro-(a)	205–209	
(b)	252–254	
Talatisine		
Hydrochloride	256–257	
Perchlorate	222 (dec.)	
Picrate	247–250 (dec.)	
Hydriodide	265 (dec.)	
Dihydro-	262–263	
Picrate	230–231	
Triacetyl-	213–214	
Perchlorate	165–166	
Methiodide	253–254	
Trichloro-	175–176	+8.6° (MeOH)
Songorine		
Hydrochloride	257–258	−114° (H_2O)
Hydrobromide	261	
Perchlorate	234–235 (dec.)	
Nitrate	230–231	
Methiodide	213–214 (dec.)[a]	
Dihydro-	205–206	
Hydrochloride	286–287 (dec.)	
Methiodide	207 (dec.)	
Diacetyl	132–134	
Hydrochloride	155–156	
Diacetyl-	180–182	
Hydrochloride	239–240	
Dichloro-	237–238	
Semicarbazone	247–248	
Napelline		
Hydrochloride	222	−94° (H_2O)
Hydrobromide	237–240 (dec.)	
Dihydro-	? 145–165	
Hydrobromide	256–258	
Ajaconine		
Picrate	95–98	
Acid oxalate	234–235 (dec.)	
Methiodide	134 (dec.)	
Delatine		
Hydrochloride	274–277	+13° (H_2O)

[a] The Hofmann degradation product des-*N*-methylsongorine has m.p. 215° (hydrochloride, m.p. 285°; methiodide, m.p. 255–256°).

TABLE 9

DERIVATIVES OF MIYACONITINE AND MIYACONITINONE

(All m.p. are with decomposition)

Compound	Formula	M.p., °C.	$[\alpha]_D$
Miyaconitine	$C_{23}H_{29}O_6N$	218	−88° ($CHCl_3$)
Hydrochloride		253	−60° (EtOH)
Hydrobromide		270	−50° (H_2O)
Perchlorate		286–290	
Chloroplatinate		252	
Monoxime		296–297	
Semicarbazone		>300	
Quinoxaline derivative		233–235	
Miyaconine	$C_{21}H_{27}O_5N$	253	−8.6° ($CHCl_3$)
Hydrochloride		292	
Hydrobromide		286	
Perchlorate		274–280	
Diacetate		151	+47° (EtOH)
Miyaconitinone	$C_{23}H_{27}O_6N$	285	−27.6° (AcOH)
Perchlorate		255–256	
Chloroplatinate		256–258	
Semicarbazone		255	
Quinoxaline derivative		295–300	
Miyaconinone	$C_{21}H_{25}O_5N$	242	−41° (AcOH)
Hydrochloride		252	
Monoacetate		285	

the other an aromatic group, generally the benzoate group or a methoxyl derivative thereof. Hydrolysis of the diesters affords the parent amino alcohols: several of these amino alcohols have been characterized, and two groups of ester-alkaloids have been recognized in which more than one alkaloid is derived from the same amino alcohol (see Table 10).

The chemical investigations of the aconitines can be summarized under three headings: first, the establishment of the number and the nature of the peripheral substituents; secondly, those reactions such as hydrolysis and esterification, that involve only the functional groups; and, finally, the more complex reactions in which substituents at two or more nuclear positions are involved. The last category of more complex reactions includes the mild pyrolysis, alcoholysis, and oxidation of the alkaloids and of the parent amino alcohols. Although some alkaloids, such as mesaconitine, pseudaconitine, hypaconitine, and particularly aconitine and delphinine, have been studied more intensively than the remaining aconitines, it seems clear that all the alkaloids of this group undergo similar changes when submitted to these reactions, which will therefore be outlined very briefly before the chemistry of individual examples is discussed in detail.

Hydrolysis of the diester-alkaloids proceeds in two stages: the aliphatic

TABLE 10

THE ACONINES AND DERIVED ACONITINES: FORMULAS AND OCCURRENCE

Parent amino alcohol	Formula	Part-formula based on pentacyclic $C_{19}H_{28}\cdot NH$			Derived ester-alkaloid	Ester group		Formula	Occurrence
			Δ req.	Δ found		Aliphatic	Aromatic		
Delphonine	$C_{24}H_{39}O_7N$	$C_{19}H_{21}(OH)_3(OMe)_4(NMe)$	1	—	Delphinine	OAc	Benzoate	$C_{33}H_{45}O_9N$	*D. staphisagria*
Hypaconine	$C_{24}H_{39}O_8N$	$C_{19}H_{20}(OH)_4(OMe)_4(NMe)$	1	—	Hypaconitine	OAc	Benzoate	$C_{33}H_{45}O_{10}N$	*A. napellus* etc.
Mesaconine	$C_{24}H_{39}O_9N$	$C_{19}H_{19}(OH)_5(OMe)_4(NMe)$	1	—	Mesaconitine	OAc	Benzoate	$C_{33}H_{45}O_{11}N$	*A. fauriei* *A. napellus* *A. excelsum* *A. ibukiense*
Neoline	$C_{23}H_{37-39}O_6N$ $C_{24}H_{39-41}O_6N$	$C_{19}H_{20-22}(OH)_3(OMe)_3(NMe)$ $C_{19}H_{19-21}(OH)_3(OMe)_3(NEt)$	?		Neopelline	OAc	Benzoate	$C_{32}H_{43-45}O_8N$ $C_{33}H_{45-47}O_8N$	*A. napellus*
Bikhaconine	$C_{25}H_{41}O_7N$	$C_{19}H_{21}(OH)_3(OMe)_4(NEt)$	1	—	Bikhaconitine	OAc	3,4-Dimethoxybenzoate	$C_{36}H_{51}O_{11}N$	*A. spicatum*
Pseudaconine	$C_{25}H_{41}O_8N$	$C_{19}H_{20}(OH)_4(OMe)_4(NEt)$	1	—	Indaconitine	OAc	Benzoate	$C_{34}H_{47}O_{10}N$	*A. chasmanthum*
					α-Veratroylpseudaconitine	—	3,4-Dimethoxybenzoate	$C_{34}H_{49}O_{11}N$	*A.* from Nepal
					Pseudaconitine	OAc	3,4-Dimethoxybenzoate	$C_{36}H_{51}O_{12}N$	*A. balfourii* *A. deinorrhizum*
					α-Pseudaconitine	OAc	3,4-Dimethoxybenzoate	$C_{36}H_{51}O_{12}N$	*A.* from Nepal
Aconine	$C_{25}H_{41}O_9N$	$C_{19}H_{19}(OH)_5(OMe)_4(NEt)$	1		Aconitine	OAc	Benzoate	$C_{34}H_{47}O_{11}N$	*A. napellus*, etc.
					Jesaconitine	OAc	*p*-Methoxybenzoate	$C_{35}H_{49}O_{12}N$	*A. subcuneatum* *A. yezoense*

ester grouping is split first and the "half-ester" containing the aromatic ester grouping may be isolated; further hydrolysis then affords the ester-free amino alcohol. On acetylation with acetyl chloride all the free hydroxyl groups react (a pentaacetate being obtained from aconine): it may be assumed that all the hydroxyl groups are primary or secondary.

On mild pyrolysis, at or just above the melting point, the aconitines lose one molecule of acetic acid and give the corresponding "pyro-compounds" (e.g., pyraconitine, pyropseudaconitine, etc.). The mechanism by which this pyrolysis proceeds is by no means clear and may, in fact, differ in the different compounds: thus, pyraconitine has been assumed to contain either an epoxy group formed by elimination of acetic acid between the ester grouping and an adjacent hydroxyl (34, 35), or an ethylenic linkage (37); in pyropseudaconitine all the hydroxyl groups present in pseudaconitine appear to be preserved (36) and either an "inert" ethylenic linkage or an additional ring must be formed on pyrolysis; finally, pyrolysis of α-oxodelphinine, which also proceeds with loss of acetic acid, gives pyro-α-oxodelphinine which definitely contains (37) and ethylenic linkage.

Alcoholysis of the aconitines proceeds in the alcohol at elevated temperatures (*ca.* 125°) with replacement of the acetate group by the alkoxy group (38, 39): thus, in methanol a methyl ether results, which is a methyl ether of the benzoate (or other monoester) of the parent amino alcohol. On hydrolysis (39) methanol is split off as well as the acyl grouping and the parent amino alcohol is obtained: the ready fission of the new ether grouping is noteworthy.

Oxidation of the aconitines has been studied in only a few cases: no deep-seated cleavage of the molecule results under the conditions used; instead, the methylene group adjacent to the basic nitrogen may be oxidized (by potassium permanganate in acetone) to a carbonyl group, the product being a lactam which readily loses the *N*-alkyl group on further oxidation. The secondary nitrogen atom in the presence of nitrous acid, or if nitric acid is the oxidizing agent, is nitrosated, and nitric acid also introduces one or more nitro groups into the molecule (both into the aromatic ester part and into the aconine skeleton): thus nitric acid affords the nitro-*N*-nitroso derivative of a lactam. Both nitric acid and chromic acid also specifically oxidize one secondary hydroxyl group present in aconitine and pseudaconitine (but not in hypaconitine) to a carbonyl group: the resulting ketone contains a labile methoxyl group, presumably in the β-position to the carbonyl group, which is lost as methanol on heating. The final product of oxidation with chromic acid in these cases is thus an α,β-unsaturated ketone and of oxidation with nitric acid in these cases an α,β-unsaturated keto lactam further substituted by a nitro and an *N*-nitroso group. These oxidative steps are considered in more detail in the discussion of the chemistry of aconitine and delphinine.

Finally, it must be pointed out that none of the reactions outlined above throws any light on the polycylic skeleton of the aconitines. The aconitines do not form quaternary salts readily, and attempts at Hofmann degradation have therefore met no success. Moreover, in contrast to the atisines, the aconitines give intractible mixtures on dehydrogenation over selenium, and the presence of a phenanthrene nucleus has not been established so far. On the contrary, some evidence has been obtained (37) (from the dehydrogenation of "hexahydrobenzoyloxodedelphonine") that a di*cyclo*pentenobenzene fragment forms part of the delphinine molecule: the full significance of this finding is not yet apparent.

1. The Alkaloids Derived from Aconine and Mesaconine

Aconine, the amino alcohol, is the parent of two ester-alkaloids, aconitine (the acetate benzoate) and jesaconitine (the acetate *p*-methoxybenzoate), and differs from mesaconine, the parent of mesaconitine (the acetate benzoate), only in the *N*-alkyl substituent. Aconine carries an *N*-ethyl (40, 49) and mesaconine an *N*-methyl group; these two compounds thus yield the same nitro-*N*-nitroso derivative, and aconitine and mesaconitine give the same oxidation product, oxonitine (41), with elimination of the *N*-alkyl group. It is convenient, therefore, to combine the discussion of these closely related alkaloids.

Aconitine and mesaconitine occur together abundantly in the blue aconite (*Aconitum napellus*) and in a number of other *Aconitum* species (29), particularly the East Asian *A. fauriei* Léveillé and Vaniot, *A. grossedentatum* Nakai, *A. hakusanense* Nakai, *A. ibukiense* Nakai, *A. majimai* Nakai, *A. mokchangense* Nakai, and *A. zuccarini* Nakai; mesaconitine also occurs (29) as a chief alkaloid in *A. fischeri* (*A. kamtschaticum*), in *A. manchurikum* Nakai, and in *A. excelsum* Reichb. (9). Jesaconitine is somewhat rarer and is encountered in the East Asian species (29) *A. sachalinense* and *A. yezoense*, and together with aconitine in *A. subcuneatum* Nakai.

Aconitine, identical with some fractions of japaconitine (a mixture), is the most readily accessible of the *Aconitum* alkaloids. It has long been known (42) and can be separated from amorphous material as the insoluble perchlorate. The confusing and contradictory studies on aconitine reported before 1900 have been fully and critically reviewed (39). This review and the accompanying repetition and extension of earlier work (39) first corroborated the now-accepted formulation of aconitine as $C_{34}H_{47}O_{11}N$ (43) and of aconine as $C_{25}H_{41}O_9N$. Aconine is obtained from aconitine by hydrolysis either with water at 160–170° or with boiling alcoholic alkali. More careful hydrolysis, with boiling water, results in removal of acetic acid only and in the isolation of the intermediate benzoylaconine (picraconitine).

Hydrolysis of Aconitine: Benzoylaconine (cf. 44). Aconitine (4 g.) is neutralized with dilute sulfuric acid and the solution, after dilution to 80 ml., is refluxed for 12 hr. The acetic acid split off is removed by steam-distillation and the residue treated with ammonia: the unchanged aconitine thus precipitated is collected by filtration, and the filtrate is saturated with ammonium sulfate and extracted with chloroform. The organic phase on vacuum-evaporation affords benzoylaconine (*ca.* 3 g.).

Complete Hydrolysis of Aconitine (cf. 41, 44). (*a*) Aconitine (3 g.) is heated with water (60 ml.) in a sealed tube at 160–170° for 5.5 hr. The cool mixture is filtered and the filtrate treated with dilute hydrochloric acid (3 ml.). The liquid is concentrated to about 10 ml., freed from benzoic acid by extraction with ether, decolorized with carbon, again evaporated, and finally kept in a desiccator over sulfuric acid. Aconine hydrochloride (*ca.* 1.5 g.) crystallizes.

(*b*) A solution of the alkaloid (7.5 g.) in alcohol (180 ml.) is refluxed for 45 minutes in a stream of nitrogen while *N*-potassium hydroxide (2 equiv.) in alcohol is added during 15 minutes. After removal of solvent (inert atmosphere) the residue is treated with chloroform which dissolves the aconine. After evaporation the base is taken up in little dilute hydrochloric acid and kept in a desiccator until aconine hydrochloride crystallizes.

Hydrolysis of jesaconitine (45) proceeds similarly, yielding aconine and acetic and *p*-methoxybenzoic acids or *p*-methoxybenzoylaconine and acetic acid. Analogously, mesaconitine (41) gives mesaconine and acetic and benzoic acids or benzoylmesaconine and acetic acid.

All three alkaloids, aconitine, jesaconitine, and mesaconitine, give triacetates, and the parent amino alcohols, aconine and mesaconine, give pentaacetates: of the eleven oxygen atoms in aconitine, four are therefore present in the two ester groupings and three as free hydroxyl groups. Because they can readily be esterified, all these groups may be assumed to be primary or secondary.

The remaining four oxygen atoms of aconitine and mesaconitine have been accounted for (46), by Zeisel determination, as methoxyl groups; jesaconitine carries a fifth methoxyl substituent in the aromatic ester grouping. The peripheral substituents of these alkaloids can thus be considered to be firmly established. No direct evidence has, however, been obtained hitherto for the presence of any nuclear unsaturated linkage: the alkaloids do not add bromine and are inert to the acidic permanganate test for unsaturation (39); moreover, no hydrogenated derivative of aconine has been reported in spite of attempted hydrogenation (1), and aconitine only yields a hexahydro derivative (47) by reduction of the benzoate to the hexahydrobenzoate group. On the other hand, the ultraviolet absorption spectrum of aconine exhibits pronounced "end-absorption" (1): whilst this cannot be due to a conjugated system, for which a clear absorption maximum would be expected, it may indicate the presence of an ethylenic linkage, especially in the vicinity of the auxochromic nitrogen atom; the presence of an ethylenic linkage near the nitrogen atom would also explain the unusually high basic dissociation constant of aconine (47). Thus, the presence of an "inert" ethylenic linkage cannot be excluded, and the nuclear skeleton of aconitine may be either pentacyclic (as is that of atisine) or, less probably, hexacyclic.

Three types of reaction involving only the peripheral functional groups of aconitine have been described. The hydrolysis and esterification received early attention (cf. 39) and acetylation products in particular have been examined. In spite of original statements to the contrary, it is now clear (39) that the hydroxyl groups of aconitine and benzoylaconine are "equivalent" and that aconitine triacetate is identical with benzoylaconine tetraacetate.

Secondly, the pyrolysis of aconitine at or above its melting point results in the internal loss of a molecule of acetic acid, giving pyraconitine (34). Little is known about the mode of elimination of acetic acid, and it was assumed that epoxide-formation occurred between the acetoxy group and an adjacent hydroxyl. More recently (1, 37), however, it has been suggested that a new ethylenic linkage is introduced by this pyrolysis, and the position is now in urgent need of clarification. On hydrolysis pyraconitine loses its benzoate grouping in the usual manner and yields pyraconine.

Thirdly, alcoholysis of aconitine proceeds at 120–130° (sealed tubes) with loss of the acetyl grouping (38) and introduction of a new alkoxy group. Thus, the product of the reaction of aconitine and methanol is methylbenzoylaconine. As remarkable as its formation is the hydrolysis of methylbenzoylaconine (39), during which it splits off benzoic acid and methanol giving aconine: the great ease with which the new ether group is eliminated is noteworthy.

Preparation of Methylpicraconitine (Methylbenzoylaconine) (39). Aconitine (4 g.) is heated with methanol (30 ml.) at 120–130° for 2 hr. in a sealed tube. The resulting mixture is evaporated and the residue dissolved in water containing a few drops of acetic acid. Filtration, treatment of the filtrate with a slight excess of sodium hydroxide, and extraction with ether give, from the organic phase, methylbenzoylaconine (3 g.).

Alternatively (and preferably), the base may be crystallized directly from the alkaline aqueous solution by warming gently for some time. The product is recrystallized from ether-light petroleum.

Oxidation of aconitine with potassium permanganate in acetone and acetic acid yields a variety of products, among which acetaldehyde was recognized at an early date (39). It did not appear until much later (40) that the acetaldehyde arises from the *N*-ethyl group. The neutral, sparingly soluble oxidation product oxonitine obtained (48) in this reaction has been much studied. Since the same oxonitine arises from mesaconitine

TABLE 11

SIMPLE DERIVATIVES OF ACONITINE, JESACONITINE, AND MESACONITINE

Compound	Formula	Base		Hydro-chloride		Hydro-bromide		Hydr-iodide	Chlo-roau-rate	Perchlorate		Acetate			Pyroderiv.			Other derivatives:		
		M.p., °C.	$[\alpha]_D$	M.p., °C.	$[\alpha]_D$	M.p., °C.	$[\alpha]_D$	M.p., °C.	M.p., °C.	M.p., °C.	$[\alpha]_D$		M.p., °C.	$[\alpha]_D$		M.p., °C.	$[\alpha]_D$		M.p., °C.	$[\alpha]_D$
Aconitine	$C_{34}H_{47}O_{11}N$	205	+19°	195	−31°	210	−31°	226	158	222	−19°	Tri	208			171	−112°	Hexahydroaconitine perchlorate	210	
Jesaconitine	$C_{35}H_{49}O_{12}N$	131							209	232	−17°	Tri	232		Perchlorate	273	−27°	Perbromide	182	
Aconine	$C_{25}H_{41}O_{9}N$	132	+23°	176	−8°	225						Penta	242	−34°	Amorph.		−91°			
															Hydrochloride	154	−125°			
Benzoylaconine	$C_{32}H_{45}O_{10}N$	130	+6°	217	−21°	273		205										Methylbenzoyl-aconine	211	
				270																
p-Methoxybenzoyl-aconine	$C_{35}H_{47}O_{11}N$	—		210	−19°															
Mesaconitine	$C_{33}H_{45}O_{11}N$	209	+26°			173	−25°		226	225	−15°	Tri			Perchlorate	287		γ-Pyromesaconitine	170	−107
															Hydrobromide	215	−38°	hydrobromide	241	−102
Mesaconine	$C_{24}H_{39}O_{9}N$	—										Penta	229	−19°						
Benzoylmesaconine	$C_{31}H_{43}O_{10}N$	—		257	−24°	246	−22°													

ACONITINE AND ITS SIMPLE DERIVATIVES ($R = C_{25}H_{36}O_4N$)

$R(OBz)(OAc)_4$

$R(OBz)(OAc)(OH)_3$ —Hydrolysis→ $R(OBz)(OH_4)$ —Hydrolysis→ $R(OH)_5$

Aconitine — Benzoylaconine — Aconine

Aconitine: alcoholysis (MeOH) → $R(OBz)(OMe)(OH)_3$ Methylbenzoylaconine

Aconitine: pyrolysis (−AcOH) → $R{=}(OBz)(OH)_3$ Pyraconitine —Hydrolysis→ $R{=}(OH)_4$ Pyraconine

(41), it seems clear that the N-alkyl group is either removed or degraded by this oxidative attack: the neutral nature of oxonitine, moreover, indicates (49) that it is a lactam, presumably formed by oxidation of a methylene group adjacent to the nitrogen atom; the formulation $C_{32}H_{41}O_{12}N$ is therefore proposed for oxonitine (49). The oxidation does not, however, proceed cleanly, and other oxidation products, notably oxoaconitine, $C_{34}H_{45}O_{12}N$, have been isolated (47). Some doubt, in fact, exists as to the correct formulation of oxonitine: a formula, $C_{33}H_{43}O_{12}N$, containing one additional methylene grouping has been proposed (47) although this would not explain the copious evolution of acetaldehyde which requires a loss of a two-carbon unit from aconitine. The C_{32} formulation for oxonitine has therefore been retained in the present discussion.

Preparation of Oxonitine (57; but see also 47). Aconitine (5 g.) in pure acetone (250 ml.) is oxidized at room temperature with powdered potassium permanganate (11 g.) in acetic acid (12.5 ml.), added during 5–7 days. When all permanganate has reacted, the precipitated oxonitine and manganese dioxide are collected, washed with acetone, and suspended in water. A current of sulfur dioxide is passed to remove the manganese dioxide: this leaves oxonitine (65%) as precipitate in a pure condition. Evaporation of the liquors gives further oxonitine which may best be recrystallized from acetic acid–acetone.

Oxonitine, like aconitine, on hydrogenation under slightly increased pressure gives hexahydrooxonitine (47), the benzoate grouping being converted into hexahydrobenzoate. Pyrolysis under reduced pressure converts (50) oxonitine into pyroxonitine, by elimination of acetic acid. Both oxonitine

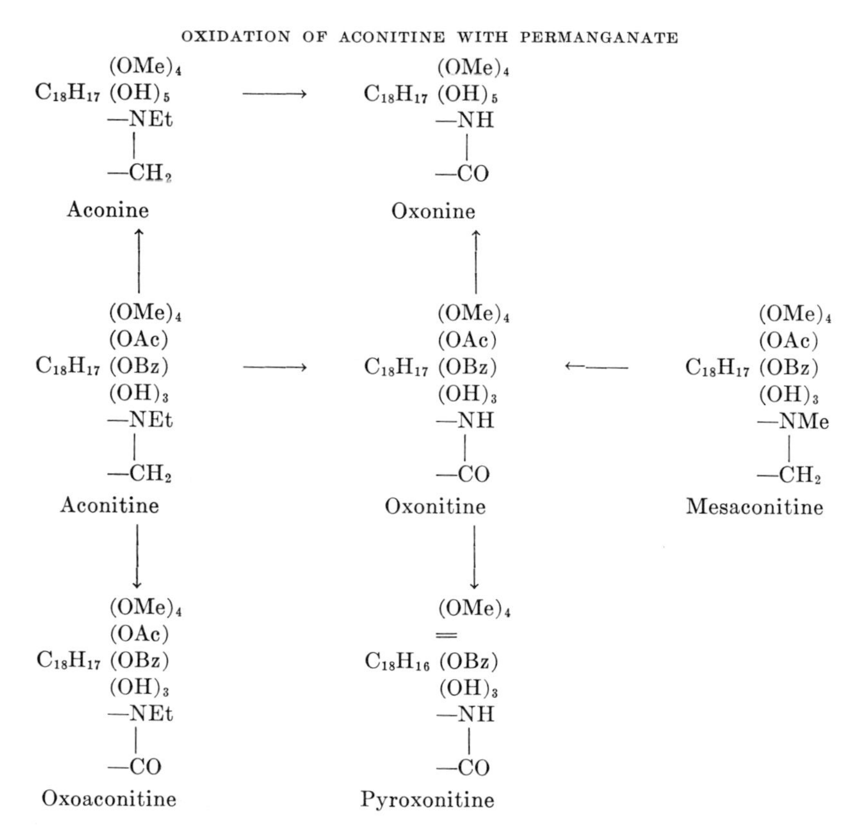

and pyroxonitine may be hydrolyzed and thus give oxonine and pyroxonine, respectively. Oxonine pentaacetate may be obtained directly from aconine pentaacetate. Cleavage of oxonitine with methanolic hydrogen chloride proceeds under vigorous conditions with loss of carbon dioxide, but the base produced (47) has not been investigated further.

Oxidation with chromic acid in acetone as oxidizing agent proceeds differently (51, 52): one of the secondary hydroxyl groups of aconitine is oxidized to a highly enolized ketone group, the product being called aconitinone. This, on heating, readily splits off methanol to give a new base, aconitoline, which retains both the ester groups of aconitine; its hydrolysis product (containing four hydroxyl groups) is also obtainable by direct oxidation of aconine (53, 39) and readily affords a methiodide; aconitoline itself, however, does not react readily with methyl iodide. Pyrolysis of aconitoline in the usual manner gives acetic acid and pyroaconitoline.

Preparation of Aconitinone and Aconitoline (51). Aconitine (3 g.) is dissolved in pure acetone (180 ml.) and cooled in ice and salt. To the cold solution is added a solution of chromic anhydride (3 g.) and water (1.5 g.) in cooled acetone (30 ml.). After 10 days in the cold the solvent is vacuum-evaporated, and the residue is dissolved in sulfurous acid and extracted with ether: neutral by-products are thus removed. The aqueous layer is rendered alkaline, and the base precipitated is collected. The precipitate is extracted with acetone, and the acetone is vacuum-evaporated. On addition of a trace of ether the base crystallizes and may be recrystallized from ethyl acetate, or purified as perchlorate by crystallization from ethanol. Yield of aconitinone: 2.4 g.

Recrystallization of aconitinone base from methanol results in partial conversion into the desmethanol compound aconitoline, which is obtained from the mother liquors.

The remarkable lability of the methoxyl group of aconitinone which is eliminated as methanol is clearly due to the newly formed carbonyl group and has been explained (51) as due to the presence in one ring in aconitine of a 1,3-diol monoether, converted by oxidation into a β-methoxyketone (aconitinone), and thence into the α,β-unsaturated ketone (aconitoline).

OXIDATION OF ACONITINE WITH CHROMIC ACID (51)

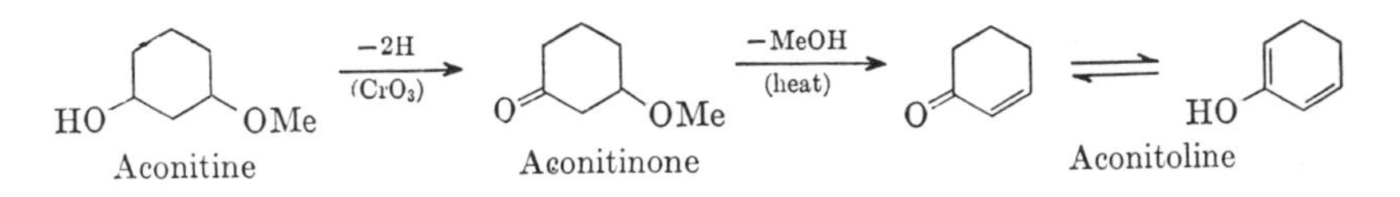

Aconitine Aconitinone Aconitoline

The formulation of aconitoline as an α,β-unsaturated ketone should be capable of direct proof, since such ketones and their derivatives generally have characteristic ultraviolet absorption spectra: unfortunately, the absorption spectrum of aconitoline is not on record, and such direct evidence in support of the reaction scheme outlined (51) is therefore not yet available. It is clear, however, that the oxidation according to the above scheme cannot proceed unless the hydroxyl group in the β-position to the methoxyl is free: some indirect evidence may be adduced for the reaction scheme since triacetylaconitine (53) in which this group is esterified is not attacked whilst mesaconitine (51) is. Moreover, of the two alkaloids, hypaconitine and pseudaconitine, containing one hydroxyl group less than aconitine, the latter (54) is, but hypaconitine (51) is not, oxidized by chromic acid: it appears, therefore, that the hydroxyl group which hypaconitine lacks is that in the β-position to one of the methoxyls, that specifically attacked by chromic acid.

Vigorous oxidation of aconitine with nitric acid yields (55, 53) a neutral nitro-*N*-nitroso derivative ($C_{31}H_{35}O_{13}N_3$) containing only three methoxyl groups; this is also the end-product of the oxidation with nitric acid of oxonitine, mesaconitine (56), aconitoline, and oxoaconitine (53). In spite of earlier statements to the contrary, the nitro-*N*-nitroso derivative does not carry a carboxylic acid function (53) and is insoluble in sodium carbonate; its alkali-solubility may thus be ascribed to a tautomeric change to an aciform. The nitro-N-nitroso compound is produced from aconitine by loss of the N-alkyl group (replaced by the N-nitroso group) and of one methoxyl group. Since it is obtainable from aconitoline and from oxonitine, the nitro-N-nitroso compound must clearly contain both the ketone group of the former and the lactam carbonyl of the latter. Oxidation with nitric acid thus goes one stage further than the other oxidation processes, and the nitro-N-nitroso compound appears to be the final oxidation product of aconitine obtainable under conditions which do not disrupt the polycyclic system.

Oxidation of Aconitine with Nitric Acid (47). Aconitine (0.75 g.) with nitric acid (5 ml.) of sp. gr. 1.42 on the steam bath for 1 hr. (55) or aconitine (1.1 g.) with nitric acid (10 parts) of sp. gr. 1.2 at 100° for 2 hr. (52) gives, on dilution, a precipitate comprising the nitro-N-nitroso derivative, $C_{31}H_{35}O_{13}N_3$. This may be recrystallized from alcohol, after initial purification by dissolution in chloroform or acetone and vacuum-evaporation of the solvent.

Under milder conditions intermediate nitro compounds are formed (53) which carry no N-nitroso group but may be further oxidized to the nitro-N-nitroso compound. Hydrolysis of this latter compound under acid conditions results in splitting off of the nitroso group and produces a secondary base; under alkaline conditions the two acyl residues are lost. Action of nitrous acid on aconitine (52, 53) gives a nitroso derivative ($C_{34}H_{44}O_{13}N_2$) which does not appear to have an N-alkyl group but retains all four methoxyl groups.

The action of nitric acid on aconitine can thus be resolved into several steps (53) of which the first appear to be the oxidative removal of two hydrogen atoms, the loss of a methoxyl group, and the substitution of a nitro group. Attack at and near the nitrogen atom appears to be more complex and to occur later.

The oxidation of jesaconitine and of its triacetate with permanganate in dilute sulfuric acid (49) proceeds in close analogy to that of aconitine, and acetaldehyde and triacetyljesoxonitine have been isolated (49).

Mesaconitine, the lower N-alkyl homologue of aconitine, behaves similarly, giving oxonitine and formaldehyde (50), and pentaacetylmesaconine, like pentaacetylaconine, gives pentaacetyloxonine. The oxidation of mesaconine with chromic acid and with nitric acid (51), too, proceeds analogously to that of aconine.

2. Alkaloids Derived from Hypaconine, Neoline, Bikhaconine, and Pseudaconine

Of the seven ester-alkaloids obtained from *Aconitum* species and derived from the above four amino alcohols (cf. Table 10) one, the amorphous neopelline, which has been isolated (58) from the amorphous basic residue remaining after extraction of aconitine from *A. napellus*, has received little study, and its homogeneity and formula are not established with certainty. The high toxicity of neopelline and the presence therein of at least three methoxyl groups appear to indicate, however, that neopelline, if homogeneous, is a true aconitine. The formula ($C_{32}H_{45}O_8N$) originally suggested (58) for neopelline would indicate the presence of a saturated pentacyclic nucleus, substituted by three methoxyl two ester, and one *N*-methyl groups; the last oxygen function has not been characterized as no well-defined acetate could be obtained from neopelline or its parent amino alcohol, the amorphous neoline ($C_{23}H_{39}O_6N$). Neoline has also been found (14) in the "free" (unesterified) state in the amorphous bases from *A. napellus*, though it is not clear whether it is an artifact. The formula ($C_{24}H_{41}O_6N$) suggested by this later work (14) requires the presence of an additional methyl group as compared with the first formulation: both sets of analytical figures fit the C_{24} formulation. In analogy with the other aconitines, neopelline and neoline may well have two hydrogen atoms less (cf. 5) and incorporate an inert unsaturated linkage or, possibly, a hexacyclic nucleus.

Bikhaconitine, obtained (59) from *A. spicatum* Stapf, has also received but little attention. Its functional groups (cf. Table 10) have been established (59) and its hydrolysis to 3,4-dimethoxybenzoylbikhaconine and thence to bikhaconine described; both these bases are amorphous, though they give crystalline salts. Pyrolysis of bikhaconitine proceeds at 180° in the usual manner with elimination of acetic acid, but its other reactions have not been investigated. In the absence of oxidative experiments, no information is available about the relationship, if any, between bikhaconine and delphonine, which have the same number of hydroxyl and methoxyl substituents: should these occupy the same nuclear positions, the two amino alcohols would differ only in the *N*-alkyl substituent (as do aconine and mesaconine) and should thus give the same product on oxidation with potassium permanganate.

The possibility of a similar relationship between hypaconine and pseudaconine is disproved by the different reactivities of their esters towards chromic acid and nitric acid (see above): whilst hypaconitine is inert towards these reagents, presumably because none of the hydroxyl groups is in an "activated" position, pseudaconitine is oxidized in a manner closely analogous to that of aconitine. Thus, apart even from the difference in the *N*-alkyl group (3), the substituents at the polycylcic nucleus are attached at different positions.

Hypaconitine accompanies aconitine in *A. napellus* (60) and also occurs in several East Asian species (29), such as *A. ibukiense*, *A. fischeri* (*A. kamtschaticum*), *A. senanense* Nakai, *A. tortuosum* Willd., *A. grosseden-*

TABLE 12

OXIDATION PRODUCTS OF ACONITINE, MESACONITINE, HYPACONITINE, AND PSEUDACONITINE

Product from	Oxonitine type			Aconitoline type								Nitro-*N*-nitroso derivative type					
							Salts			Hydrolysate					Hydrolysate		
	Formula	M.p., °C.	$[\alpha]_D$	Formula	M.p., °C.	$[\alpha]_D$	Salt	M.p., °C.	$[\alpha]_D$	Hydrolysate	M.p., °C	Formula	M.p., °C.	$[\alpha]_D$	Formula	M.p., °C.	$[\alpha]_D$
Aconitine[a]	$C_{32}H_{41}O_{12}N$	282 (d.)	−45°	$C_{33}H_{41}O_{10}N$	222					$C_{24}H_{35}O_8N$		$C_{31}H_{35}O_{13}N_3$	279 (d.)	−31°	$C_{31}H_{36}O_{12}N_2$	253 (d.)	
										Hydrochloride	224 (d.)						
										Methiodide	225 (d.)						
Mesaconitine[b]	$C_{32}H_{41}O_{12}N$	282 (d.)	−45°	$C_{32}H_{39}O_{10}N$			Hydrobromide	212		$C_{23}H_{33}O_8N$	252 (d.)	$C_{31}H_{35}O_{13}N_3$	279 (d.)	−31°	$C_{31}H_{36}O_{12}N_2$	253 (d.)	
										Hydrochloride	267 (d.)						
							Perchlorate	226									
Hypaconitine	$C_{32}H_{41}O_{11}N$	268 (d.)	−63°	—													
Pseudaconitine				$C_{35}H_{45}O_{11}N$	255	+68°	Hydrochloride	180	+40°	$C_{24}H_{35}O_7N$	177	$C_{33}H_{38}O_{16}N_4$	276 (d.)		$C_{22}H_{29}O_{10}N_3$	215	+31°
							Picrate	229									

[a] Other derivatives: Hexahydrooxonitine has m.p. 253°
Oxoaconitine: $C_{34}H_{45}O_{12}N$; has m.p. 261°; $[\alpha]_D$ −99°
Pyroxonitine: $C_{30}H_{37}O_{10}N$; has m.p. 180°; $[\alpha]_D$ −127°
(?Hexahydro-derivative: m.p. 163°)
Aconitinone: $C_{34}H_{45}O_{11}N$; has m.p 212°(d.)
Aconitine *N*-nitroso derivative: $C_{34}H_{44}O_{13}N_2$; has m.p. 281°(d.).

[b] Other derivatives: Mesaconitinone: $C_{33}H_{43}O_{11}N$; m.p. 173°(d.); $[\alpha]_D$ −35°
(Perchlorate, m.p. 215°(d.); chloroaurate, m.p. 226°(d.); semicarbazone, m.p. 214°(d.); diacetate, m.p 215°(d.) isonitroso deriv. m.p. 236°(d.), $[\alpha]_D$ −99°).
Anhydromesaconitoline: $C_{32}H_{37}O_9N$; has m.p. 194° $[\alpha]_D$ +26°
(Diacetate, m.p. 157°(d.); $[\alpha]_D$ +57°; dihydro diacetate, m.p. 204°; $[\alpha]_D$ −31°).

tatum, *A. hakusanense* and *A. callianthum* Koidz. The alkaloid is in many ways closely related to mesaconitine but, as stated above, lacks the "activated" hydroxyl group present in the latter which is specifically oxidized by chromic acid. Hydrolysis (60) in the usual manner gives, first, the amorphous benzoylhypaconine and thence hypaconine. Pyrolysis under reduced pressure yields acetic acid and pyrohypaconitine, and oxidation with permanganate in acetone containing acetic acid affords hypoxonitine. All these reactions parallel those reported for aconitine, and may be formulated analogously. Hypoxonitine should therefore differ from oxonitine only by having one hydroxyl group less: the original formula (60) for hypoxonitine ($C_{24}H_{29}O_9N$) should therefore be revised to $C_{32}H_{41}O_{11}N$, on the assumption that the oxidation proceeds with loss of the *N*-methyl group as formaldehyde (49) and with oxidation of the methylene group adjacent to the nitrogen atom to carbonyl: in fact, the C_{32} formulation fits the analytical figures for hypoxonitine better than does the original C_{24} formulation.

Pseudaconine is the parent of four ester-alkaloids found in nature: two of these, pseudaconitine (54) and α-pseudaconitine (61), are certainly isomeric since on hydrolysis they both yield acetic acid, 3,4-dimethoxybenzoic acid, and pseudaconine. The physical properties of the two isomeric alkaloids and their salts are very similar (cf. Table 13), and it appears (61) that they may differ only in the position of attachment of the 3,4-dimethoxybenzoyl group since the difference between the 3,4-dimethoxybenzoylpseudaconines (the intermediate hydrolysis products) is much greater than that between the diesters.

Pseudaconitine occurs in *A. balfourii* Stapf, and in *A. deinorrhizum* Stapf (cf. 54, 59), and its oxygenated functions have been characterized (54, 62) by Zeisel determination and by acetylation (to a diacetate); the low analytical figures obtained for the methylimino grouping together with the evolution of acetaldehyde during oxidation with permanganate (41, 54) suggest the presence of an *N*-ethyl group (3), though this has not been proved directly. Hydrolysis of pseudaconitine proceeds in the usual way first to the monoester, 3,4-dimethoxybenzoylpseudaconine (veratroylpseudaconine) and thence to pseudaconine. Pyrolysis and alcoholysis of pseudaconitine proceed normally (36), pyropseudaconitine and 3,4-dimethoxybenzoylpseudaconine alkyl ethers, respectively, being obtained.

Pyrolysis of the fully acetylated pseudaconine tetraacetate also proceeds with elimination of one molecule of acetic acid only: the pyropseudaconine triacetate produced, on hydrolysis gives pyropseudaconine. Thus one acetate residue must be uniquely activated and different from the other four ester groupings; isolation (61) of a minor amount of a second pyrolysis product (m.p. 284°) has not so far helped to elucidate the environment of this group. Similarly, alcoholysis of pseudaconine tetraacetate proceeds with replacement of only one of the acetate groups.

Quite apart from the interest attaching to these considerations of environmental effects on the reactivity of different ester groups, the elimination of acetic acid from pseudaconine tetraacetate has an important bearing on the possible mechanisms of this pyrolysis: in this particular instance no free hydroxyl group is present to permit formation of an epoxide, yet pyrolysis proceeds with normal ease. Since no epoxide can be formed, it must be deduced that either a new ethylenic linkage or an additional ring is introduced during the reaction (36). Of these alternatives the former is much more likely, despite the failure of attempts at catalytic hydrogenation. This reaction may thus provide further evidence that the pyro compounds of the aconitines contain one ethylenic linkage more than do their parent compounds (see also 1, 37).

Pseudaconine appears not only to have the labile acetyl group common to all the aconitines, but also to have a labile methyl group which has not been reported so far in these alkaloids. Thus pseudaconine in boiling 10*N*-sulfuric or 65% phosphoric acid loses methanol and a methyl group so that the product "des-*O*-methyldemethoxydehydropseudaconine" (61) carries only two methoxyl substituents. Closely related to this unusual reaction may be the finding (36) that acetylation of pyropseudaconitine gives a triacetate ("triacetyldemethylpyropseudaconitine") formed by replacement of a methyl by an acetyl group and by acetylation of the two free hydroxyls; hydrolysis of this triacetate gives demethylpyropseudaconine.

Oxidation of pseudaconitine apparently proceeds in close analogy to that of aconitine. Action of potassium permanganate liberates (48) acetaldehyde and affords a substance (m.p. 235°) which may, in the light of present knowledge, be regarded as pseudoxonitine. Chromic acid also oxidizes pseudaconitine (54) giving a product which may now be regarded as pseudaconitoline (53) and formulated as $C_{35}H_{45}O_{11}N$ (a reasonable fit to the analytical data); hydrolysis of this gives the corresponding trihydroxy ketone together with acetic acid and 3,4-dimethoxybenzoic acid.

Action of nitric acid on pseudoaconitine gives two products, one of which appears to be the "normal" nitro-*N*-nitroso derivative (analogous to that obtained from aconitine) with an additional nitro group, substituted in the aromatic ester grouping: on hydrolysis this yields 6-nitro-3,4-dimethoxybenzoic acid, acetic acid, and the nitro-*N*-nitroso compound derived from pseudaconine. The original formula ($C_{33}H_{40}O_{16}N_4$) proposed (54) for dinitro-*N*-nitrosopseudaconitine has therefore been revised (53) to $C_{33}H_{38}O_{16}N_4$. The other product obtained by oxidation with nitric acid contains the *N*-nitroso group, but only one nitro group, and on hydrolysis also gives 6-nitro-3,4-dimethoxybenzoic acid (54) and acetic acid; it is possible that this product may be the analogue of the dinitro-*N*-nitroso compound lacking the second nitro group, but the analytical data do not fit well to the formula ($C_{33}H_{39}O_{14}N_3$) thus derived.

α-Pseudaconitine has been isolated from commercial "Nepaul Aconite Root" (61) which, surprisingly, contained no aconitine; the half-hydrolysis product, α-3,4-dimethoxybenzoylpseudaconine (α-veratroylpseudaconine) is also present in this natural material (though possibly an artifact). It is this half-hydrolysis product that provides the main evidence for the difference between the two naturally occurring isomers. Like pseudaconitine, α-pseudaconitine is readily pyrolyzed with loss of acetic acid, but, in contrast to pyropseudaconitine, the α-pyropseudaconitine thus obtained is noncrystalline.

Indaconitine, isolated (59) from *A. chasmanthum* Stapf, is the fourth naturally occurring ester-alkaloid derived from pseudaconine. It is the acetate benzoate, as shown by its hydrolysis to pseudaconine and acetic and benzoic acids. Pyrolysis of indaconitine proceeds, as usual, with elimination of acetic acid, but two isomeric pyroindaconitines have been described (59), the α-isomer derived from the alkaloid itself, and the β-isomer from indaconitine hydrochloride. No oxidative studies are on record.

3. Delphinine

Delphinine is the main alkaloid present in *Delphinium staphisagria*; it was first isolated in 1819 and summaries of the early investigations on it are available (63, 64). It is now clear that, although quite readily accessible, delphinine is not readily purified, and as late as 1950 the empirical formula now accepted and first proposed (63) in 1938 was in dispute (65). The hydrolysis of delphinine rapidly gives (66) benzoic acid and (63) acetic acid and the amorphous parent amino alcohol, called delphonine (in analogy to aconine). The remaining oxygen atoms are present (67) as four methoxyl groups and one hydroxyl group that can be acylated; the nitrogen atom carries a methyl group (or its analytical equivalent). Delphinine may thus be considered as a true member of the aconitines, especially since the ultraviolet absorption spectra and basic dissociation constants of aconine and delphonine are similar.

The chemical behavior of delphinine also confirms this view. Pyrolysis of delphinine proceeds at 200° with elimination of acetic acid (68) giving pyrodelphinine which on hydrogenation consumes approximately four molecular proportions of hydrogen: the non-crystalline hydrogenated material, however, appears to be only a hexahydro derivative (the benzoate radical being reduced): clearly these contradictory observations require

TABLE 13

SALTS AND SIMPLE DERIVATIVES OF THE ACONITINES DERIVED FROM NEOLINE, BIKHACONINE, HYPACONINE, PSEUDACONINE, AND DELPHONINE

Compound	Formula	M.p., °C.	$[\alpha]_D$
Neopelline	? $C_{33}H_{45-47}O_8N$	*ca.* 80	
Neoline	? $C_{24}H_{39-41}O_6N$	154	+10°
Hydrobromide		215	−4°
Monoacetate aurichloride		145	
Bikhaconitine	$C_{36}H_{51}O_{11}N$	123	+12°
Hydrochloride		161	−9°
Hydrobromide		175	−12°
Aurichloride		233	
Pyrobikhaconitine			
Aurichloride		123	
Bikhaconine	$C_{25}H_{41}O_7N$		+34°
Hydrobromide		150	
Nitrate		128	+15°
Aurichloride		188	
Veratroylbikhaconine	$C_{34}H_{49}O_{10}N$	125	+30°
Hydriodide		190	
Aurichloride		148	
Hypaconitine	$C_{33}H_{45}O_{10}N$	198	+23°
Hydrobromide		179	−20°
Perchlorate		180	−11°
Aurichloride		245	
Pyrohypaconitine		120	+22°
Hypaconine	$C_{24}H_{39}O_8N$		
Tetracetate		184	
Benzoylhypaconine	$C_{31}H_{43}O_9N$		
Hydrochloride		244	−6°
Pseudaconitine	$C_{36}H_{51}O_{12}N$	213	+17°
Hydrochloride		182	−18°
Hydrobromide		199	−18°
Hydriodide		230	
Perchlorate		239	
Nitrate		198	
Aurichloride		233	
Diacetate		229	+24°
Pyropseudaconitine		135	+175°
Demethyl-, triacetate		228	+28°
α-Pseudaconitine	$C_{36}H_{51}O_{12}N$	206	+25°
Perchlorate		246	
Indaconitine	$C_{34}H_{47}O_{10}N$	203	+18°
Hydrobromide		{218 187	−17°
Hydriodide		230	
Aurichloride		152	
α-Pyroindaconitine		133	+92°
Hydrobromide		198	+55°

TABLE 13—(*Continued*)

Compound	Formula	M.p., °C.	[α] D
β-Pyroindaconitine			
Hydrobromide		250	+28°
Pseudaconine	$C_{25}H_{41}O_8N$	95 (solvated)	+39°
Tetraacetate		228	−8°
Des-*O*-methyldemethoxydi-hydro-		133	+18°
Veratroylpseudaconine	$C_{34}H_{49}O_{11}N$	199	−38°
Nitrate		232	
Methyl ether		207	+30°
α-Veratroylpseudaconine	$C_{34}H_{49}O_{11}N$	211	+55°
Hydrobromide		247	
Perchlorate		233	
Hydriodide		246	
Benzoylpseudaconine	$C_{32}H_{45}O_9N$	133	+34°
Hydrochloride		244	−8°
Hydrobromide		247	
Aurichloride		182	
Delphinine	$C_{33}H_{45}O_9N$	200	+25°
Hydrochloride		214	
Acid oxalate		168	
Triacetate		235	
Benzoate		173	
Hydroxy-		182	+7°
Hexahydro-		193	
Nitroso-		241	
Pyrodelphinine		212	
Delphonine	$C_{24}H_{39}O_7N$	78	+38°
Methiodide		165	
des-*N*-methyl-		143	
Pyrodelphonine		amorph.	
Benzoyldelphonine	$C_{31}H_{43}O_8N$		
Methyl ether		175	+27°

clarification. Delphinine itself also gives the hexahydro derivative expected, and any ethylenic linkage present in the nucleus thus resists hydrogenation. Alcoholysis, as in the other aconitines, readily replaces the acetyl group and yields the benzoyldelphonine alkyl ether (68).

Delphonine, rather surprisingly, affords a methiodide quite readily (1, 65), and this quaternary salt has been submitted to Hofmann degradation. Distillation of the methiodide with aqueous sodium hydroxide gives the methine containing the same number of carbon atoms and an ethylenic linkage: the nitrogen atom is thus in a hydroaromatic ring (probably six-membered, since zinc-dust distillation of delphinine affords piperidine among other products) which is opened at this stage. The

TABLE 14

OXIDATION PRODUCTS OF DELPHININE AND DERIVATIVES

Starting material	Substance	Substance			Hydrogenated derivative			Other derivatives	
		Formula	M.p., °C.	$[\alpha]_D$		M.p., C.	$[\alpha]_D$	Deriv.	M.p., °C.
Simple oxidation products of delphinine:								Hexahydro	195
Delphinine	α-Oxodelphinine[a]	$C_{33}H_{43}O_{10}N$	221	−62°				Demethyl	273
	β-Oxodelphinine[a]	$C_{33}H_{43}O_{10}N$	229	+31°					
	γ-Oxodelphinine	$C_{33}H_{43}O_{10}N$	229	+40°					
	Benzoyloxodelphinine	$C_{40}H_{47}O_{11}N$	187						
Substances derived from α-oxodelphinine:									
α-Oxodelphinine	Pyro-α-oxodelphinine (XV)	$C_{31}H_{39}O_8N$	262	+173°	Hexa	242	+209°	Demethyl	310
					Octa	189	−15°		
	Isopyro-α-oxodelphinine (XVI)	$C_{31}H_{39}O_8N$	296	−13°	Octa	216	−72°		
	Isopyro-α-oxodelphonine (XXII)	$C_{24}H_{35}O_7N$	219		Di(XXIII)	198			
	Monochloro compound (XIII)	$C_{32}H_{40}O_9NCl$	243	−60°	Hexa	229			
	Dichloro compound (XIV)	$C_{32}H_{39}O_8NCl_2$	227						
Substances derived from pyro-α-oxodelphinine (XV) by chlorine substitution, etc.:									
Pyro-α-oxodelphinine	Monochloro compound (XVII)	$C_{30}H_{36}O_7NCl$	320						
	Dichloro compound (XVIII)	$C_{29}H_{33}O_6NCl$	265		Hexa	218			
	Diacetoxy compound from XVIII	$C_{33}H_{39}O_{10}N_6$	280						

	Octahydro compound (XIX) from dechlorinated XVIII	$C_{31}H_{45}O_8N$	187						
	Oxodedelphonine (XX)	$C_{22}H_{33}O_6N$	312						
Substances prepared from isopyro-α-oxodelphinine by demethylation, etc.:									
Octahydro-XVI	Dimethylanhydrooctahydroisopyro-α-oxodelphinine	$C_{29}H_{41}O_7N$	275						
XVI	Methylanhydroisopyro-α-oxodelphinine	$C_{28}H_{31}O_7N$	170	−52°	Octa	147			
XVI	Desmethylanhydroisopyro-α-oxodelphinine (XXI)	$C_{27}H_{29}O_7N$	301	−49°				Ketone (oxime	194 248)
XXI	Desmethylanhydroisopyro-α-oxodelphonine (XXII)	$C_{20}H_{25}O_6N$	173		Di	292			
XXII	Desmethylanhydrodiketo acid	$C_{20}H_{21}O_7N$	304		Di	223			
Substances prepared from isopyro-α-oxodelphonine by oxidation, etc.:									
XXII	Unsaturated acid (XXVI)	$C_{24}H_{33}O_8N$	200–245	+48°				Methyl ester	205
XXVI	Keto lactone (XXVII)	$C_{24}H_{33}O_8N$	235	+74°				Methyl ester oxime	178
XXIII	Saturated acid (XXIV)	$C_{24}H_{35}O_8N$	166	+7°				Methyl ester oxime	142
XXIV	Dimethylanhydroketo acid	$C_{22}H_{29}O_7N$	277						
XXIV	1,3-Diketone (XXV)	$C_{24}H_{33}O_7N$	142						
XXV	β-Hydroxy ketone	$C_{24}H_{35}O_7N$	213						

[a] Derived methylbenzoyloxodelphonine: of α-oxodelphinine: m.p. 237°; $[\alpha]_D$ −47°.
of β-oxodelphinine: m.p. 185°; $[\alpha]_D$ + 27°.

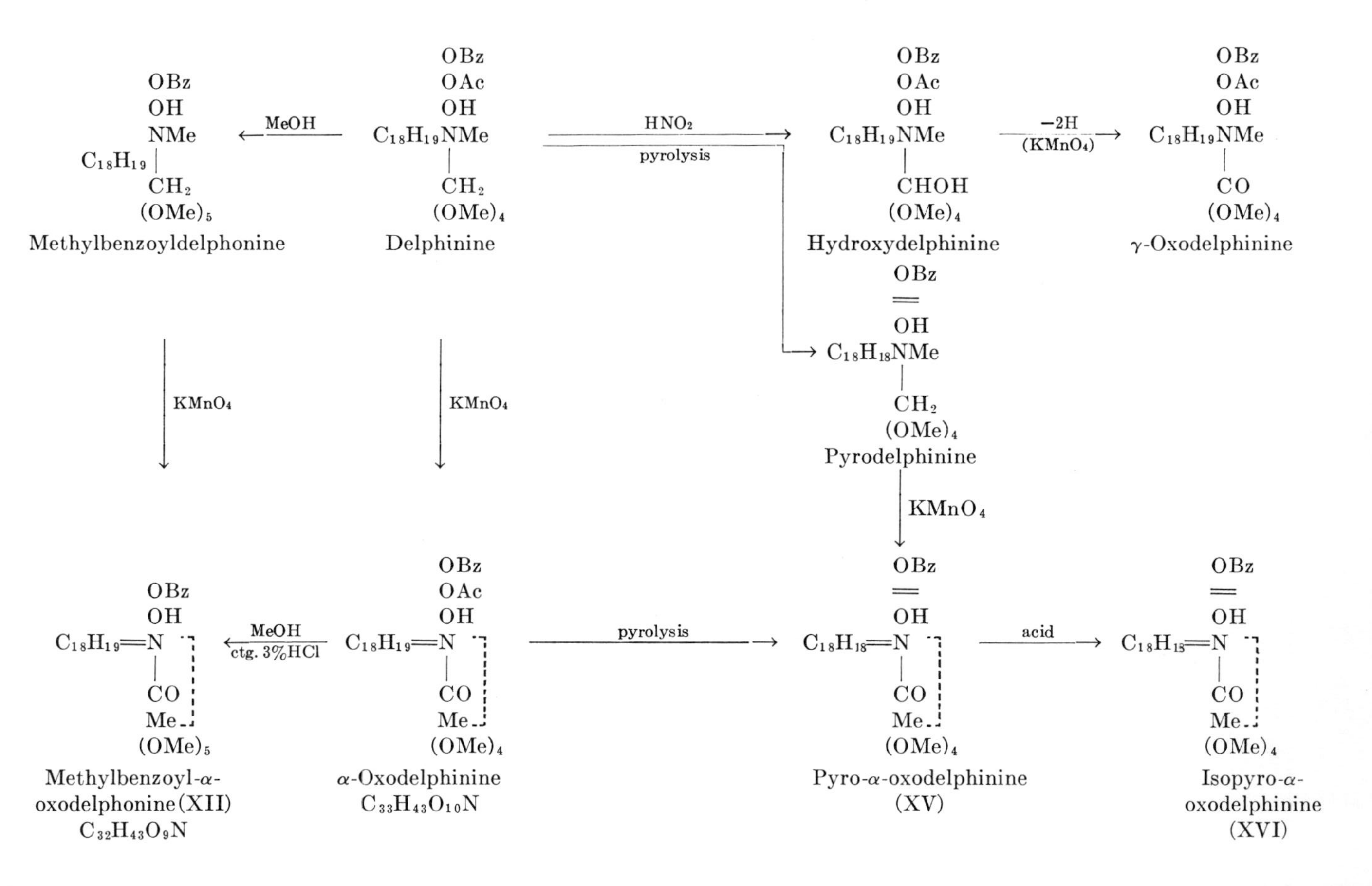
Methylbenzoyldelphonine
MeOH
Delphinine
HNO$_2$
pyrolysis
Hydroxydelphinine
−2H (KMnO$_4$)
γ-Oxodelphinine
Pyrodelphinine
KMnO$_4$
MeOH ctg. 3%HCl
Methylbenzoyl-α-oxodelphonine(XII) $C_{32}H_{43}O_9N$
α-Oxodelphinine $C_{33}H_{43}O_{10}N$
Pyro-α-oxodelphinine (XV)
acid
Isopyro-α-oxodelphinine (XVI)

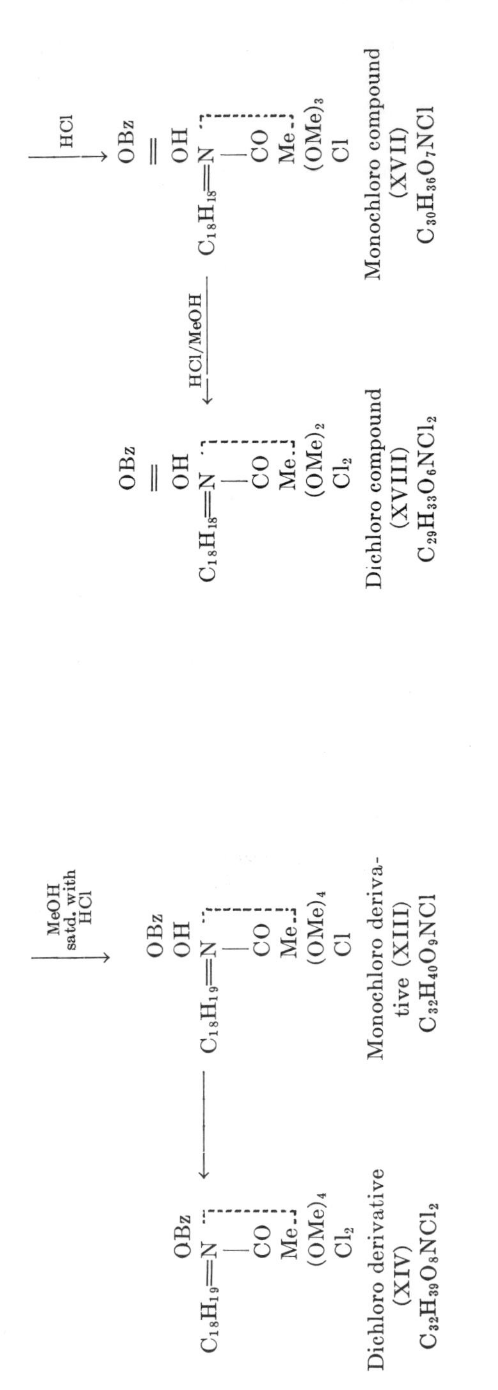

HCl
MeOH satd. with HCl
HCl/MeOH
Monochloro compound (XVII) C30H36O7NCl
Dichloro compound (XVIII) C29H33O6NCl2
Monochloro derivative (XIII) C32H40O9NCl
Dichloro derivative (XIV) C32H39O8NCl2

methine, too, forms a methiodide, which may be degraded to a nitrogen-free compound: oxidation of this nitrogen-free material, however, gives an intractable resin, approximating to $C_{20}H_{24}O_{12}$, which is assumed to be a tricarboxylic acid (65).

The oxidation of delphinine with permanganate (63, 68) gives two isomeric oxodelphinines (designated α and β); the α-isomer is produced in better yield and was recognized at an early date (69). The oxodelphinines correspond to oxoaconitine in that no carbon atom is lost during the oxidation which converts the methylene group next to the nitrogen atom into a carbonyl group, giving a neutral lactam. The isomeric oxodelphinines differ in the grouping attached at the nitrogen atom: whilst β-oxodelphinine carries the usual *N*-methyl (or equivalent) group, the α-isomer does not appear to have an *N*-methyl group: it must be concluded that during oxidation to α-oxodelphinine the *N*-methyl (or equivalent) group suffers such modification that it eludes the usual determination thereafter. The oxodelphinines (particularly the α-isomer) and their derivatives have been much studied since they may provide a guide to the polycylic skeleton of delphinine, carrying relatively few substituents and thus more amenable to further degradation.

Besides α- and β-oxodelphinine, a third (γ-) isomer has been described (70); delphinine with sodium nitrite in acetic acid at 100° gives a nitroso derivative (10%) which retains all the oxygenated groups but has no *N*-methyl, and a hydroxydelphinine: the new hydroxy group on oxidation with permanganate in acetone affords the neutral γ-oxodelphinine (which has an *N*-methyl) and which is superficially indistinguishable from the β-isomer except in specific rotation.

Alcoholysis of the oxodelphinines with methanol containing hydrogen chloride (3%), but not with methanol alone, yields the corresponding methylbenzoyl-α-(or β- or γ-)oxodelphonine (XII). The α-isomer XII is also obtained directly by oxidation of methylbenzoyldelphonine with permanganate. The isomeric oxodelphinines differ in their reactivity towards methanolic hydrochloric acid: whilst the β-isomer is unattacked, α-oxodelphinine reacts rapidly first with replacement of one methoxyl group by chlorine to give the monochloro derivative (XIII), and on prolonged reaction with further introduction of chlorine in place of the free hydroxyl group, giving the dichloro derivative (XIV). Attempts to eliminate these chloro substituents by hydrogenation (in the endeavor to attain a less heavily substituted molecule) were unsuccessful and merely resulted in production of the hexahydrobenzoates instead of benzoates.

Attention has therefore turned to α-oxodelphinine, which is readily pyrolyzed to pyro-α-oxodelphinine (XV): this, on hydrogenation, absorbs four molecular proportions of hydrogen and is thus the first pyrolysis product for which the presence of an unsaturated linkage (introduced by the pyrolysis) has been proved; it has been suggested (37) that the elimination of acetic acid may always in this series introduce such an olefinic linkage.

Pyro-α-oxodelphinine undergoes a remarkable isomerization in acidic solution to isopyro-α-oxodelphinine; further action of concentrated aqueous hydrochloric acid results in replacement of one methoxyl group by chlorine, while in methanolic hydrogen chloride two methoxyl groups are replaced by chlorine. This dichloro compound (XVIII) when heated with methanol regenerates isopyro-α-oxodelphinine and with sodium acetate in acetic acid gives the diacetate, but with zinc dust in acetic acid one of the chlorine atoms is removed completely and the other replaced by acetoxyl; hydrogenation thence affords a compound (XIX) containing two functional groups less than does α-oxodelphinine. Alkaline hydrolysis of this compound (XIX) affords a simpler base (XX), called "oxodedelphonine" (70),

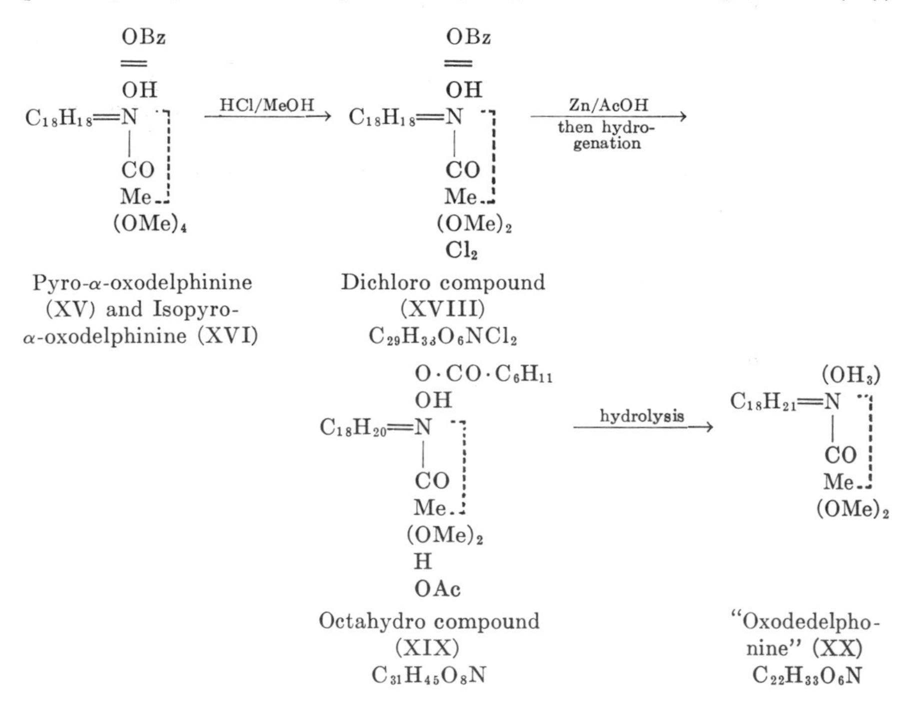

Pyro-α-oxodelphinine (XV) and Isopyro-α-oxodelphinine (XVI)

Dichloro compound (XVIII) $C_{29}H_{33}O_6NCl_2$

Octahydro compound (XIX) $C_{31}H_{45}O_8N$

"Oxodedelphonine" (XX) $C_{22}H_{33}O_6N$

which differs from α-oxodelphinine in having hydrogen atoms replacing the original acetoxy and one methoxy group and in having hydroxyl groups in place of the original benzoyloxy and another methoxy group.

The octahydro compound (XIX) ("hexahydrobenzoyloxodedelphonine acetate") on dehydrogenation over selenium gives, among other (intractable) products, a benzenoid hydrocarbon, $C_{17}H_{24}$, which is resistant to further dehydrogenation and may be a dicyclopentenobenzene of undetermined origin: if this assumption proves correct and if this substance represents a major fragment of the delphinine skeleton, it may prove difficult to construct a "diterpenoid" formula for delphinine.

Another approach to the preparation of a less heavily substituted delphonine skeleton involves the demethylation of isopyro-α-oxodelphinine (XVI) with zinc chloride (71). Whilst nitric acid will readily remove one methoxyl group from α-oxodelphinine and isopyro-α-oxodelphinine (70) and whilst in hydrochloric acid partial exchange of methoxyl for chloro substituents can be effected (70), a saturated solution of zinc chloride in 5% aqueous hydrochloric acid is a most potent demethylating agent even at 40°; it converts octahydroisopyro-α-oxodelphinine ($C_{31}H_{47}O_8N$) with loss of two methyl groups and of one molecule of water, into a dimethylanhydro derivative ($C_{29}H_{41}O_7N$) which is resistant to hydrogenation. Under similar conditions pyro-α-oxodelphinine is first isomerized to isopyro-α-oxodelphinine (see above) and then demethylated to a mixture comprising the monomethylanhydro compound ($C_{28}H_{31}O_7N$) (with loss of three methyl groups and one molecule of water), and the completely demethylated desmethylanhydroisopyro-α-oxodelphinine (XXI) ($C_{27}H_{29}O_7N$). At higher temperatures (60°) the latter (XXI) is accompanied by a monochloro compound ($C_{27}H_{28}O_6NCl$) in which one hydroxyl group is replaced by chlorine. The completely demethylated ester (XXI) on hydrogenation absorbs four molar proportions of hydrogen, and on hydrolysis (XXI) gives the water-soluble desmethylanhydroisopyro-α-oxodelphonine (XXII), which on hydrogenation absorbs only one molecule of hydrogen: since presumably the "pyro" ethylenic linkage is thus saturated, the loss of water during demethylation may thus either cause epoxide-formation or introduce an olefinic link resistant to hydrogenation.

```
          OBz                          OBz
          =                            2 = (?)                          2 = (?)
$C_{18}H_{18}$ OH      ——→   $C_{18}H_{17}$ =N ┐      ——→   $C_{18}H_{17}$ =N ┐
          =N ┐                          |  :                            |  :
          |  :                          CO :                            CO :
          CO :                        Me ..┘                          Me ..┘
          Me ..┘                       (OH)4                           (OH)5
          (OMe)4
```

Isopyro-α-oxodelphinine (XVI)	Desmethylanhydro compound (XXI)	Desmethylanhydro-isopyro-α-oxo-delphonine (XXII)
	$C_{27}H_{29}O_7N$	$C_{20}H_{25}O_6N$

Whilst the corresponding monomethylanhydro compound is inert to chromic acid (71), desmethylanhydroisopyro-α-oxodelphinine (XXI) is oxidized by chromic acid in acetic acid to a monoketone ($C_{27}H_{27}O_7N$): it may therefore be concluded that the methoxyl group most resistant to demethylation is secondary. The hydrolysis product, desmethylanhydroisopyro-α-oxodelphonine, is similarly oxidized to an unsaturated desmethylanhydrodiketo acid ($C_{20}H_{21}O_7N$) which gradually and incompletely lactonizes to the isomeric saturated desmethylanhydrodiketo lactone, $C_{20}H_{21}O_7N$.

Some insight into the environment of the functional groups of these oxidation products has been attained by carrying out analogous experiments on isopyro-α-oxodelphonine (XXII) and on dihydropyro-α-oxodelphonine (XXIII). This last, apparently saturated diol (XXIII) (containing, at most, the resistant nuclear ethylenic linkage) is converted by chromic acid into the apparently saturated keto acid (XXIV) ($C_{24}H_{35}O_8$), the four methoxyl groups remaining unaffected: the remaining oxygen atoms are accounted for as the carboxyl, ketonic carbonyl, and lactam carbonyl groups. This keto acid (XXIV) on sublimation loses one molecule of water and gives a neutral product (XXV), thought to be a 1,3-diketone ($C_{24}H_{33}O_7N$), which is labile to alkali.

The oxidation of the unsaturated isopyro-α-oxodelphonine (XXII) proceeds similarly to an unsaturated keto acid (XXVI) ($C_{24}H_{33}O_8N$) which, however, isomerizes completely in acidic solution or on sublimation to an apparently saturated lactone (XXVII) ($C_{24}H_{33}O_8N$). Thus, the two keto acids behave differently on sublimation: the unsaturated acid (XXVI) isomerizes to a lactone (XXVII), whilst the saturated acid (XXIV) dehydrates and may yield a 1,3-diketone (XXV). This "diketone" (XXV) on hydrogenation in methanol absorbs one molecule of hydrogen, presumably giving a β-hydroxy ketone (XXVIII) ($C_{24}H_{35}O_7N$) that cannot be saponified; hydrogenation in acetic acid eliminates one of the carbonyl groups giving a monoketone (XXIX) ($C_{24}H_{37}O_6N$).

Some very tentative conclusions have been drawn as to the structural features of isopyro-α-oxodelphinine (though it is impossible to extend these directly to pyro-α-oxodelphinine). Since chromic acid attack occurs readily only on isopyro-α-oxodelphonine (i.e., after saponification of the benzoate group), it is suggested that the benzoyl group is attached to a secondary hydroxyl group, adjacent to a tertiary hydroxyl (see part-formulas above).

Oxidation may then be assumed (71) to give the keto acid, in which the ethylenic linkage is conjugated with the carbonyl group: this placing of the ethylenic linkage is purely speculative and not fully corroborated by the ultraviolet absorption spectrum (which, instead of the high-intensity maximum near 2350 A. expected for an isocyclic α,β-unsaturated ketone,

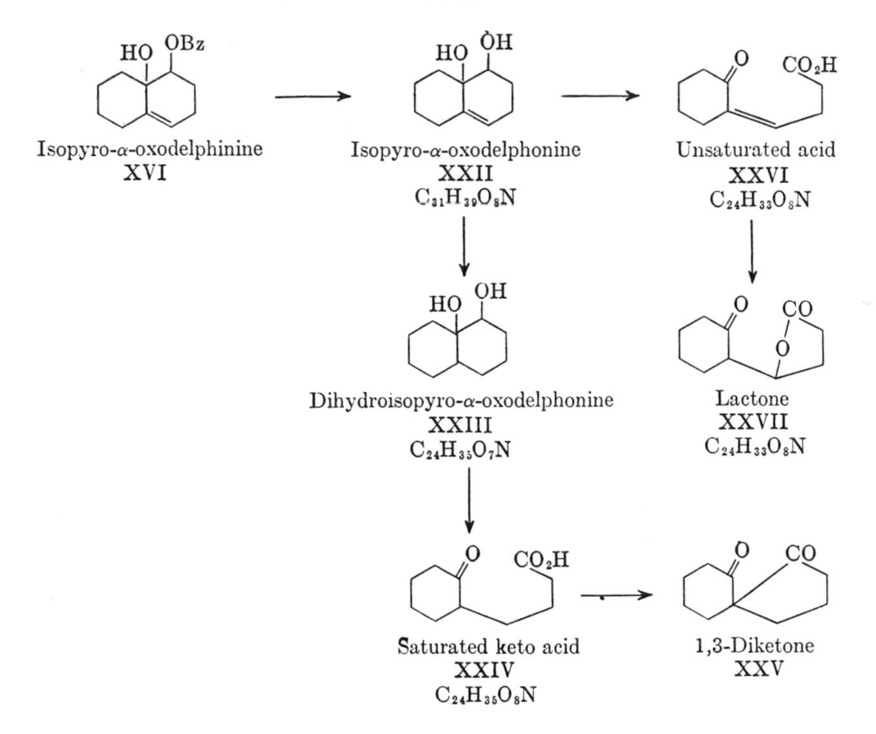

exhibits a broad inflection of lower intensity in this region); however, for the reaction sequence proposed any "activated" ethylenic linkage at a suitable distance from the carboxyl group will do. Lactonization of the unsaturated acid (XXVI), but not, of course, of the saturated acid (XXIV), is then assumed to occur by addition across the "activated" ethylenic linkage; the saturated keto acid (XXIV) would condense internally on the activated methylene group next to the carbonyl group with the production of a 1,3-diketone. There is no evidence that any other functional groups (lactam or methoxyl) participate in these transformations.

IV. The Monoester Alkaloids Derived from Methoxyl-rich Amino Alcohols Analogous to the Aconines

1. Lycoctonine and the Alkaloids Derived Therefrom

Whilst most of the aconines and related amino alcohols have been isolated from alkaloids present in plants of either one or the other of the genera *Aconitum* and *Delphinium*, lycoctonine is remarkable in that its derivatives occur in species of both these genera (cf. Table 15). Not only is it widely distributed in the *Delphinium* genus, but it was originally isolated (72) from *A. lycoctonum* L.

In spite of much early work, which has been critically reviewed (73),

TABLE 15

THE MONOESTER ALKALOIDS DERIVED FROM METHOXYL-RICH AMINO ALCOHOLS

Amino alcohol	Formula	Ref.	Ester-alkaloid	Formula	Acid component	Natural source	Ref.
Lycoctonine	$C_{25}H_{41}O_7N$	73	Anthranoyllycoctonine	$C_{32}H_{46}O_8N_2$	Anthranilic acid	*D. consolida*	78
						D. barbeyi	75
			Ajacine	$C_{34}H_{48}O_9N_2$	*N*-Acetylanthranilic acid	*D. ajacis*	32, 77, 81
			Lycaconitine	$C_{36}H_{48}O_{10}N_2$	*N*-Succinylanthranilic acid	*A. lycoctonum*	73
						A. gigas Léveillé and Vaniot (*lycoctonum gigas* Nakai)	76
			Delartine	$?C_{36}H_{53}O_{11}N_2$	*N*-Acylanthranilic acid	*D.* species	80
			Methyllycaconitine (Delsemidine)	$C_{37}H_{50}O_{10}N_2$	*N*-L-Methylsuccinylanthranilic acid	*D. elatum*	79
						D. brownii	74
						D. semibarbatum	87
			Delsemine	$C_{37}H_{53}O_{10}N_3$	*N*-L-Methylsuccinylanthranilic acid half-amide	*D. semibarbatum* Bien.	87
						D. oreophilum Huth	87
Isotalatisidine	$C_{23}H_{37}O_5N$	3	Condelphine	$C_{25}H_{39}O_6N$	Acetic acid	*D. confusum*	82
						A. talassicum	3
Lappaconine	$C_{23}H_{37}O_6N$	84, 86	Lappaconitine	$C_{32}H_{44}O_8N_2$	*N*-Acetylanthranilic acid	*A. septentrionale*	83–86
Base (unnamed)	$?C_{25}H_{41}O_7N$	85	Septentrionaline	$?C_{33}H_{46}O_9N_2$	?Acylanthranilic acid	*A. septentrionale*	85

little is known about the chemistry of lycoctonine, and even its empirical formula is still open to some doubt. Nor is it known whether lycoctonine occurs as such in plants or whether it is produced during extraction and working up: when found, lycoctonine is always accompanied by one of its esters and it is therefore probably an artifact. Support for this conclusion can be drawn from the fact that these esters are very labile in aqueous solutions, even near neutrality (73).

Four formulas proposed for lycoctonine have been considered in recent years. One formula (74), $C_{20}H_{33}O_5N$, obviously excludes the possibility of a $C_{19}H_{28}\cdot NH$ cyclic skeleton for lycoctonine and may be discarded. The earlier established $C_{25}H_{39}O_7N$ (73) and the very recent $C_{24}H_{41}O_7N$ (75) and $C_{25}H_{41}O_7N$ (76) remain to be discussed, since they correspond quite well to the analytical figures published (cf. Table 16). It is possible to differentiate between these formulas by considering the structural features known to be present in the molecule and deriving part-formulas (cf. Table 17) on the basis of a pentacyclic skeleton analogous to that assumed to be present in the aconines.

In lycoctonine, six of the seven oxygen atoms have been characterized: four methoxyl and two hydroxyl groups are known to be present. No evidence bearing on the seventh oxygen atom has been substantiated, and, since a carbonyl group appears to be excluded by the absorption spectrum, it may be assumed that either an epoxide-ether linkage or a hydroxyl group not detectable by "active" hydrogen determinations is present (see also 76).

Great importance attaches to the nature of the *N*-alkyl group since this determines the number of carbon atoms in the lycoctonine formula. In the early (73) and some recent work (75) it was assumed that the nitrogen atom bears a methyl group, and this led naturally to a C_{24} formulation (see Table 17); in fact, it has been proved (76, 77) that an *N*-ethyl group is present, as trimethylethylammonium iodide may be isolated during the *N*-alkyl determination.

Resolution of the formulas considered (Table 17) shows that the C_{20} formulation (*a*) is untenable and that the C_{24} formulation (*b*) is incompatible with the presence of an *N*-ethyl group. Moreover, the formula (*b*), $C_{24}H_{41}O_7N$, would require the presence of a saturated pentacyclic skeleton: this is unlikely to be correct, since the ultraviolet absorption spectrum of lycoctonine (75) is similar to that of aconine between 2200 and 2600 A. and exhibits a maximum near 2200 A. This maximum, not hitherto established in aconine (the absorption of which has not been examined below 2200A.), may be ascribed to an ethylenic linkage in the α,β-position to the nitrogen atom (C═C—N chromophore), analogous to that assumed to be present in aconine and delphonine.

These considerations lead to a C_{25} formulation for lycoctonine and

TABLE 16

THE EMPIRICAL FORMULA OF LYCOCTONINE

Base		Required for			Found					
		$C_{24}H_{41}O_7N$	$C_{25}H_{39}O_7N$	$C_{25}H_{41}O_7N$		Ref.		Ref.		Ref.
Anhyd.	C	63.27	64.47	64.21	64.12		64.10			
	H	9.07	8.44	8.84	8.71	73	8.52	76		
	N	3.07	3.01	3.00	3.05					
With 1 H_2O	C	60.86	62.10	61.84	61.45		61.65		62.61	
	H	9.15	8.55	8.93	8.75	75	8.73	76	8.84	74
	N	2.96	2.90	2.89	2.95		3.15		3.54	

TABLE 17

EMPIRICAL FORMULAS CONSIDERED FOR LYCOCTONINE

Formula	Ref.	Part-formula based on pentacyclic $C_{19}H_{28}\cdot NH$	Δ req.
(*a*) $C_{20}H_{33}O_5N$	74	—	—
(*b*) $C_{24}H_{41}O_7N$	75	$C_{19}H_{21}(OH)_2(OMe)_4(NMe) + OH + H_2$	None
(*c*) $C_{25}H_{39}O_7N$	73	$C_{19}H_{20}(OH)_2(OMe)_4(NEt) + O<$	1
(*d*) $C_{25}H_{41}O_7N$	76	$C_{19}H_{21}(OH)_3(OMe)_4(NEt)$	1

indicate the presence of at least one unsaturated center in the molecule. Both formulas (*c*) and (*d*) do this. However, the formula (*c*), $C_{25}H_{39}O_7N$, is deficient by four hydrogen atoms as compared with a saturated pentacyclic $C_{19}H_{28}\cdot NH$ system: the "missing" two hydrogen atoms are unlikely to be due to a normal ethylenic linkage since lycoctonine resists hydrogenation (76) and gives a perbromide, not a normal dibromide (73). Formula (*c*), therefore, can only represent lycoctonine if the seventh oxygen atom forms an epoxide-ether linkage. If, however, it forms part of a hydroxyl group, which seems more likely (76), then formula (*d*), $C_{25}H_{41}O_7N$, correctly represents lycoctonine. Clearly a final choice between formulas (*c*) and (*d*) cannot be made by considering analytical figures (cf. Table 16) but only on the basis of such further studies as may confirm the presence of an epoxide or of a third hydroxyl group. In the present review the formula (*d*) is adopted for lycoctonine and literature formulations are amended accordingly.

Lycoctonine forms a monoacetate (76) when kept at room temperature with acetyl chloride, and is remarkable in that it yields a most labile methiodide (76) which is reconverted into lycoctonine even by dilute

TABLE 18

SIMPLE DERIVATIVES OF LYCOCTONINE AND ITS ESTERS

	Base		Hydrochloride		Hydro-bro-mide	Hydriodide		Perchlorate		Picrate	Chloro-aurate	Other derivatives	
	M.p., °C.	$[\alpha]_D$	M.p., °C.	$[\alpha]_D$	M.p., °C.	M.p., °C.	$[\alpha]_D$	M.p., °C.	$[\alpha]_D$	M.p., °C.	M.p., °C.		M.p., °C.
Lycoctonine[a]	143	+53°	152		190	175		215		161	115	Acetate "Methiodide"	133 187
Anthranoyllycoctonine	{135 165	+54°	182	+24°	185	183	+33°	207	+29°	160	159	N-acetyl (see ajacine)	
Ajacine	154	+53°								167			
Lycaconitine	—	+42°						>235					
{Delartine	130	+45°						190					
{Methyllycaconitine	128	+52°				201		195					
Delsemine	125	+43°											

[a] Hydroxylcoctonine $C_{25}H_{41}O_8N$ has m.p. 151°; $[\alpha]_D$ +39° and gives a monomethyl ether, m.p. 185° (methiodide, m.p. 189°).

aqueous ammonia: this substance, unsuitable for Hofmann degradation, may, in fact, be the hydrodide and not the methiodide. With moist silver oxide, lycoctonine "methiodide" gives hydroxylycoctonine (28), which is also obtained by direct oxidation of lycoctonine with this reagent (76): hydroxylycoctonine with methanolic hydrogen chloride yields a monomethyl ether (76).

The alkaloids derived from lycoctonine are monoesters formed with anthranilic (*o*-aminobenzoic) acid or *N*-acyl derivatives thereof. It is noteworthy that where the *N*-acyl group is dibasic (i.e., succinyl in lycaconitine and methylsuccinyl in methyllycaconitine) the *N*-acylanthranilic acid residue esterifies two of the hydroxyl groups of the alkaloid.

The esters of lycoctonine with anthranilic acid and its *N*-acyl derivatives are highly toxic, and the *Delphinium* species in which they occur are sources of cattle poisoning; these alkaloids are, therefore, of considerable economic importance, and it is to be hoped that the long period during which their chemistry has been neglected is now coming to an end. The studies on record now show that purification of these labile alkaloids is troublesome, and only small quantities of the bases have been isolated hitherto. Chemical work has therefore been confined to the characterization of the alkaloids and the elucidation of their relation to lycoctonine by identification of the acid fragment obtained on hydrolysis. Properties of the bases and their simple derivatives are recorded in Table 18.

The two melting points recorded in the literature for anthranoyllycoctonine are obtained on the same crystalline sample (75) from *D. barbeyi* Huth under different conditions; this material is obviously identical with that from *D. ajacis* (77). Non-crystalline anthranoyllycoctonine is obtained from *D. consolida* L. (78) and *D. brownii* Rydb. (74) and may be either isomeric with or less pure than the crystalline base. Ajacine is the *N*-acetyl (77) and lycaconitine the *N*-succinyl derivative (73) of anthranoyllycoctonine, the amino group of the anthranilic acid residue being acylated. Methyllycaconitine (79) is the L-methylsuccinyl derivative of anthranoyllycoctonine and the optically active methylsuccinic acid is readily isolated on hydrolysis. On vigorous hydrolysis delsemine (87) yields the same products as methyllycaconitine, but mild hydrolysis proves that it is, in fact, the derivative of the half-amide of L-methylsuccinic acid.

Delartine (80), isolated from an unidentified Central Asian *Delphinium* species (cf. Table 15), is obviously wrongly formulated. On hydrolysis it gives lycoctonine and an unidentified *N*-acylanthranilic acid (m.p. 160–164°), which, in turn, is hydrolyzed to anthranilic acid and to a "new" acid, m.p. 170–172°, that is not fully characterized. Delartine may be identical with methyllycaconitine (87).

2. Isotalatisidine and Condelphine

Although isotalatisidine was first found in *A. talassicum* and condelphine in *D. confusum* Popov, these two alkaloids are closely related, condelphine being the monoacetate of isotalatisidine, to which it can readily be hydrolyzed (82). The fact that two so closely related alkaloids occur in plants of different genera (cf. Table 15) makes them of considerable genetic interest; the inaccessibility of these rare Central Asian plants has, however, prevented fuller investigation of the two bases.

Isotalatisidine is not a true aconine, since it carries only two (instead of the usual four) methoxyl groups; but it appears to be derived from the $C_{19}H_{28}\cdot NH$ skeleton, and its formula has been resolved into $C_{19}H_{23}(OH)_3(OMe)_2(NEt)$. Condelphine diacetate and isotaladisidine triacetate are identical.

3. Lappaconitine and Septentrionaline

Lappaconitine (crystalline) and septentrionaline (amorphous) are the two alkaloids isolated (83) from *A. septentrionale* Koelle that have been examined in some detail (84, 85, 86). Both alkaloids are monoesters of the parent amino alcohols with derivatives of anthranilic acid, but whilst the acid esterifying the parent lappaconine has been firmly identified as *N*-acetylanthranilic acid (85), that (m.p. 126°) forming part of septentrionaline has been erroneously formulated (85) as $C_8H_9O_3N$ (see also below): its constitution is therefore unknown.

The difficulties encountered in the purification of these alkaloids are amply illustrated by the fact that the first three investigations of lappaconitine led to three different empirical formulas: $C_{34}H_{48}O_8N_2$ (83), $C_{32}H_{44}O_8N_2$ (84), and $C_{32}H_{42}O_9N_2$ (85). The most recent work (86), in the course of which the alkaloid was purified by chromatography on kieselguhr and its homogeneity established by paper-chromatography, has substantiated the formula $C_{32}H_{44}O_8N_2$ for lappaconitine, and hence of $C_{23}H_{37}O_6N$ for lappaconine. The presence of three methoxyl groups (85) and of an *N*-methyl group (84) may be taken as established, and, on the assumption that the three remaining oxygen atoms form hydroxyl groups, a "resolved" part-formula for lappaconine may be postulated (cf. Table 19) from which it appears that lappaconine is analogous to delphonine but contains one methoxyl group less.

Lappaconitine on acidic hydrolysis (84) affords acetic acid and anthranoyllappaconine (picrolappaconine); alkaline hydrolysis (85) splits off *N*-acetylanthranilic acid and produces the parent amino alcohol lappaconine.

The amorphous septentrionaline has received even less attention (85),

TABLE 19

PART-FORMULAS DERIVED FOR ISOTALATISIDINE, LAPPACONINE, AND THE PARENT ALCOHOL OF SEPTENTRIONALINE

Compound	Formula	Part-formula based on pentacyclic $C_{19}H_{28} \cdot NH$	Δ req.
Isotalatisidine	$C_{23}H_{37}O_5N$	$C_{19}H_{23}(OH)_3(OMe)_2NEt$	1
Lappaconine	$C_{23}H_{37}O_6N$	$C_{19}H_{22}(OH)_3(OMe)_3NMe$	1
Base from septentrionaline	?$C_{25}H_{41}O_7N$	$C_{19}H_{21}(OH)_3(OMe)_4NEt$	1

TABLE 20

PROPERTIES OF ISOTALATISIDINE, LAPPACONINE, AND THE BASE FROM SEPTENTRIONALINE AND OF THEIR SIMPLE DERIVATIVES

Compound	Formula	Base		Chloroplatinate	Acetyl deriv.
		M.p., °C.	$[\alpha]_D$	M.p., °C.	M.p., °C.
Isotalatisidine	$C_{23}H_{37}O_5N$	142	±0°		Tri: 134
Condelphine[a]	$C_{25}H_{39}O_6N$	158	+27°		Di : 134
Lappaconine[b]	$C_{23}H_{37}O_6N$	96	+22°		
Anthranoyllappaconine	$C_{30}H_{42}O_7N_2$	216	+22°	310	
Lappaconitine	$C_{32}H_{44}O_8N_2$	227	+34°		
Base from septentrionaline	$C_{25}H_{41}O_7N$	131	+33°		
Septentrionaline	$C_{33}H_{46}O_9N_2$	89	+30°		

[a] Other derivatives of condelphine: perchlorate, m.p. 210°; oxalate, m.p. 162°; $[\alpha]_D$ −24°; methiodide, m.p. 205°.

[b] Other derivatives of lappaconine: hydrochloride, m.p. 247°; hydrobromide, m.p. 240°; chloroaurate, m.p. 127°.

and its formula cannot be considered as established with certainty. On alkaline hydrolysis it yields an unidentified acid (the potassium salt of which is soluble in alcohol) that may be further hydrolyzed to anthranilic acid; the basic hydrolysis product is the hitherto unnamed parent amino alcohol which has not yet been purified and may be isomeric, or even identical, with lycoctonine. Like lycoctonine, the alkaloid contains four methoxyl groups (85), and if its parent amino alcohol is, in fact, isomeric with lycoctonine the presence of an *N*-ethyl group would be expected. Since *A. lycoctonum* and *A. septentrionale* are very similar, considerable interest attaches to the relation between septentrionaline and lycoctonine: its elucidation awaits evidence based on modern work.

TABLE 21

MISCELLANEOUS ALKALOIDS ISOLATED FROM ACONITUM AND DELPHINIUM SPECIES

Alkaloid	Formula[a]	Natural source	Ref.	Extended part-formula[a]
Talatisamine	$C_{22}H_{35}O_4N$	*A. talassicum*	3	$C_{19}H_{24}(OH)(OMe)_3(NH)$
Talatisidine	$C_{23}H_{37}O_5N$	*A. talassicum*	3	$C_{19}H_{23}(OH)_3(OMe)_2(NEt)$
Ajacinine	$C_{22}H_{35}O_6N$	*D. ajacis*	81	
Ajacinoidine	$C_{38}H_{56}O_{12}N_2$	*D. ajacis*	81	
Alkaloid "B"	$C_{26}H_{39}O_8N$	*D. ajacis*	77	$C_{19}H_{19}(OH)_3(OAc)(OMe)_3NEt$
Alkaloid "C" }	{ $C_{24}H_{37}O_7N$	*D. ajacis*	77	$C_{19}H_{19}(OH)_4(OMe)_3NEt$
Delphamine }	{ $C_{25}H_{41}O_7N$	D. species (unnamed)	82	$C_{20}H_{23}(OH)_4(OMe)_3NEt$
Delcosine	$C_{22}H_{37}O_6N$	*D. consolida*	78	$C_{19}H_{22}(OH)_3(OMe)_3NH$
Delsoline	$C_{25}H_{43}O_7N$	*D. consolida*	78	$C_{19}H_{23}(OH)_3(OMe)_4NEt$
Delsonine	$C_{24}H_{41}O_6N$	*D. consolida*	78	
Consolidine	$C_{33}H_{49}O_9N$	*D. consolida*	78	$C_{19}H_{22}(OH)_2(OBz)(OMe)_3NR + C_4H_8$
Delpheline	$C_{25}H_{39}O_6N$	*D. elatum*	79	$C_{19}H_{22}(OH)(O_2CH_2)(OMe)_3NEt$
Deltaline	$C_{21}H_{33}O_6N$	*D. occidentale* S. Wats.	88	$C_{19}H_{23}O(OH)_3(OMe)_2NH$
Lucaconine	$C_{21}H_{33}O_6N$	*A. luciduscululm*	89	$C_{19}H_{22}(OH)_4(OMe)_2NH$
Unnamed base	$C_{20}H_{29}O_5N$	*D. staphisagria*	90	
Delphatine	$C_{27}H_{41-45}O_7N$	*D. biternatum* Huth	93	$C_{19}H_{21}(OH)_2(OMe)_5NEt$
Delbine	$C_{24}H_{39}O_7N$	*D. biternatum*	93	

[a] These formulations cannot be considered firmly established.

V. "Miscellaneous" Alkaloids Isolated from Aconitum and Delphinium Species

Besides the alkaloids discussed in the preceding sections of this review, several bases have been reported as constituents of different *Aconitum* or *Delphinium* species (see Table 21). These bases are grouped here under the heading "miscellaneous," since they have received little chemical study and are not fully characterized so that their purity is not assured and their empirical formulas are probably, in most cases, in need of amendment. Several of the bases reported by early workers are amorphous and clearly grossly impure; these are not reviewed.

Remarkable in this assortment of bases is the appearance of four formulas which, if correct, indicate the presence of alkaloids carrying a secondary (instead of the usual tertiary) amino group. Of these four bases, lucaconine (89) is definitely stated to be a secondary amine, although this function has not been characterized. Talatisamine (3), although formulated as a secondary amine, does not yield a crystalline *N*-acyl derivative with acetic anhydride or with benzoyl chloride, and fails to react with methyl iodide: since only the base itself has been analyzed, the

TABLE 22

PROPERTIES OF THE "MISCELLANEOUS" ALKALOIDS AND OF THEIR SIMPLE DERIVATIVES

Compound	Base		Hydrochloride		Perchlorate		Other salts			Other derivative		
	M.p., °C.	[α] D	M.p., °C.	[α] D	M.p., °C.	[α] D	Salt	M.p., °C.	[α] D	Deriv.	M.p., °C.	[α] D
Talatisamine	141	±0°	196									
Talatisidine	221	−20°	189		220		Picrate	164				
Ajacinine	211	+52°					Hydrobromide	160				
							Hydriodide	170				
							Acid oxalate	195				
							Picrate	103				
Ajacinoidine	126	+46°					Picrate	130				
Alkaloid "B"	195	+34°					Chloroaurate	205				
Alkaloid "C"	206	+57°					Chloroaurate	171				
Delphamine	200	+67°					Acid tartrate	160		Methiodide	180	
							Nitrate	160	+33°	Diacetate	121	+29°
Delcosine	204	+57°	89 (solvated)		218	+32°	Hydrobromide	103 (+MeOH)		Triacetate	203	
Delsonine	—	—			216	+23°	Hydriodide	202		Isodelsonine	111	
Delsoline	216	+52°			193	+28°	Hydrobromide	83 (+MeOH)				
Consolidine	157	+64°										
Delpheline	227	−26°	219	−43°			Nitrate	193	−41°	Monoacetate	125	−35°
Deltaline	181	−28°					Chloroaurate	125		Triacetate	272	
Lucaconine	200	+57°			213							
Unnamed Base	290	−19°					Acid oxalate	305		Dihydrocompound	238	
Delphatine	106	+39°			221	+8°				Methiodide	198	
Delbine	158	+34°										

formulation may be in error. Deltaline (88) gives analytical values in close agreement with the formula $C_{21}H_{33}O_6N$: three hydroxyl groups have been characterized and two methoxyl groups established, and on the basis of a $C_{19}H_{28} \cdot NH$ skeleton, the nitrogen atom apparently cannot carry a simple alkyl group; this remarkable anomaly requires confirmation. Delcosine, the fourth of the "secondary" bases, is one of the group of minor alkaloids isolated from *D. consolida* the formulas of which are as yet the subject of controversy (78, 91, 92): further work on more highly purified material is required before the correctness of present formulations can be ascertained.

Another group of minor alkaloids, the formulation of which is in doubt, has been obtained from *D. ajacis* (77, 81); these bases have, perhaps, received more attention than some of the other alkaloids listed in Table 21, but little agreement has been reached between the different workers, who have, in fact, found different minor alkaloids in different plant specimens. It is clear (77) that alkaloid "B" is a monoester, the acetate of alkaloid "C;" it has been suggested (82) that, since their properties are similar, the latter amino alcohol and delphamine may be identical, although the formulas so far assigned to these two bases differ. The possibility that some of the following bases, alkaloid "C" (77), delphamine (82), ajacinine (81), delsonine, and delcosine (78), and perhaps lucaconine (89) as well, may represent different states of purity of one base cannot be dismissed at the present time. A similar relationship might exist between talatisidine and delpheline.

The most important experimental fact, however, reported for any of the "miscellaneous" bases concerns the unnamed base recently (90) isolated, which accompanies delphinine and staphisine in *D. staphisagria*. This base, which may not be correctly formulated, on dehydrogenation over selenium yields a crystalline hydrocarbon ($C_{18}H_{16}$), the ultraviolet absorption spectrum of which indicates the presence of a phenanthrene structure. The fact that the presence of a phenanthrene system can be established both in this new base and in staphisine, i.e., in both minor alkaloids accompanying delphinine, whilst delphinine itself does not readily yield a phenanthrene derivative on dehydrogenation (70), should stimulate further research in this field. If the reason for this difference in behavior can be ascertained, it should permit a better understanding of the nature of the polycyclic skeleton present in the atisines and in the aconitines and result in a great advance towards the complete elucidation of the structures of the *Aconitum* and *Delphinium* alkaloids.

VI. References

1. L. C. Craig, Leonor Michaelis, S. Granick, and W. A. Jacobs, *J. Biol. Chem.*, **154**, 293 (1944).

2. W. A. Jacobs, *J. Org. Chem.*, **16,** 1593 (1951).
3. R. Konowalowa and A. Orékhoff, *Bull. soc. chim. France*, **7,** 95 (1940).
4. J. A. Goodson, *J. Chem. Soc.*, **1943,** 139.
5. H. Suginome and F. Shimanouti, *Ann.*, **545,** 220 (1940).
6. H. Suginome and S. Umezawa, *J. Fac. Sci., Hokkaido Univ., Ser. III. Chem.*, **4,** 14 (1950); H. Suginome, S. Kakimoto, and J. Sonoda, *ibid.*, **4,** 25 (1950).
7. H. Suginome, T. Koyama, and Y. Kunimatsu, *Proc. Japan Acad.*, **22,** No. 5, 120 (1946); *J. Fac. Sci., Hokkaido Univ., Ser. III. Chem.*, **4,** 16 (1950).
8. W. A. Jacobs and L. C. Craig, *J. Biol. Chem.*, **143,** 605 (1942).
9. S. R. Yunusov, *J. Gen. Chem. (U.S.S.R.)*, **18,** 515 (1948).
10. W. A. Jacobs and L. C. Craig, *J. Biol. Chem.*, **141,** 67 (1942).
11. M. V. Hunter, *Quart. J. Pharm. and Pharmacol.*, **17,** 302 (1944).
12. J. A. Goodson, *J. Chem. Soc.*, **1945,** 245.
13. W. A. Jacobs and L. C. Craig, *J. Biol. Chem.*, **143,** 589 (1942).
14. W. Freudenberg and E. F. Rogers, *J. Am. Chem. Soc.*, **59,** 2572 (1937); *Science*, **87,** 139 (1938).
15. L. C. Craig and W. A. Jacobs, *J. Biol. Chem.*, **143,** 611 (1942).
16. C. F. Huebner and W. A. Jacobs, *J. Biol. Chem.*, **170,** 515 (1947).
17. J. Broughton, Blue Book, East India Cinchona Cultivation, 1877, p. 133.
18. A. Goris and M. Métin, *Compt. rend.*, **180,** 968 (1925); A. Goris, *Compt. rend.* **205,** 1007 (1938).
19. H. A. D. Jowett, *J. Chem. Soc.*, **69,** 1518 (1896).
20. A. Lawson and J. E. C. Topps, *J. Chem. Soc.*, **1937,** 1640.
21. W. A. Jacobs and L. C. Craig, *J. Biol. Chem.*, **147,** 567 (1943).
22. C. F. Huebner and W. A. Jacobs, *J. Biol. Chem.*, **170,** 515 (1947); **174,** 1001 (1948).
23. L. C. Craig and W. A. Jacobs, *J. Biol. Chem.*, **152,** 651 (1944).
24. C. F. Huebner and W. A. Jacobs, *J. Biol. Chem.*, **170,** 203 (1947).
25. W. A. Jacobs and L. C. Craig, *J. Biol. Chem.*, **147,** 571 (1943).
26. W. A. Jacobs and C. F. Huebner, *J. Biol. Chem.*, **170,** 189 (1947).
27. R. Majima and S. Morio, *Proc. Imp. Acad. (Tokyo)*, **7,** 351 (1931); *Ber.*, **65,** 599 (1932).
28. H. Suginome and S. Umezawa, *J. Fac. Sci., Hokkaido Univ., Ser. III. Chem.*, **4,** 44 (1950).
29. H. Suginome and S. Imato, *J. Fac. Sci., Hokkaido Univ., Ser. III. Chem.*, **4,** 33 (1950).
30. W. R. Dunstan and T. A. Henry, *J. Chem. Soc.*, **87,** 1650 (1905).
31. L. C. Craig and W. A. Jacobs, *J. Biol. Chem.*, **152,** 645 (1944); C. F. Huebner and W. A. Jacobs, *ibid.*, **169,** 211 (1947).
32. O. Keller and O. Völker, *Arch. Pharm.*, **251,** 207 (1913).
33. H. Suginome, S. Furusawa, Y. Chiba, and S. Kakimoto, *Proc. Japan Acad.*, **22,** No. 5, 117 (1946); *J. Fac. Sci., Hokkaido Univ., Ser. III. Chem.*, **4,** 1 (1950).
34. W. R. Dunstan and F. H. Carr, *J. Chem. Soc.*, **65,** 178 (1894).
35. H. Schulze and A. Liebner, *Arch. Pharm.*, **251,** 453 (1913); **254,** 567 (1916).
36. T. M. Sharp, *J. Chem. Soc.*, **1928,** 3094.
37. W. A. Jacobs and C. F. Huebner, *J. Biol. Chem.*, **170,** 209 (1947).
38. W. R. Dunstan, T. Tickle, and D. H. Jackson, *J. Chem. Soc.*, **P., 1896,** 159.
39. H. Schulze, *Arch. Pharm.*, **244,** 136, 165 (1906).
40. W. A. Jacobs and R. C. Elderfield, *J. Am. Chem. Soc.*, **58,** 1059 (1936).
41. R. Majima and H. Suginome, *Ber.*, **58,** 2048 (1925); S. Morio, *Ann.*, **476,** 181 (1929).
42. P. L. Geiger (with Hesse), *Ann.*, **7,** 269 (1833); J. Morson, *Arch. Pharm.*, **18,** 87 (1839); T. Groves, *Pharm. J.*, **8,** 121 (1868).

43. M. Freund and P. Beck, *Ber.*, **27,** 433 (1894).
44. R. Majima and H. Suginome, *Ber.*, **57,** 1466 (1924); R. Majima, H. Suginome, and S. Morio, *Ber.*, **57,** 1456 (1924).
45. R. Majima and S. Morio, *Ber.*, **57,** 1472 (1924).
46. A. Ehrenberg and C. Purfürst, *J. prakt. Chem.*, **45,** 604 (1892).
47. W. A. Jacobs, R. C. Elderfield, and L. C. Craig, *J. Biol. Chem.*, **128,** 439 (1939).
48. F. H. Carr, *J. Chem. Soc.*, **101,** 2241 (1912).
49. R. Majima and K. Tamura, *Ann.*, **526,** 116 (1936).
50. K. Tamura, *Ann.*, **533,** 183 (1938).
51. R. Majima and K. Tamura, *Ann.*, **545,** 1 (1940).
52. A. Lawson, *J. Chem. Soc.*, **1936,** 80.
53. W. A. Jacobs and L. C. Craig, *J. Biol. Chem.*, **136,** 323 (1940).
54. T. A. Henry and T. M. Sharp, *J. Chem. Soc.*, **1928,** 1105.
55. O. L. Brady, *J. Chem. Soc.*, **103,** 1821 (1913).
56. H. Suginome, *Ann.*, **533,** 172 (1938).
57. G. Barger and Ellen Field, *J. Chem. Soc.*, **107,** 231 (1915).
58. H. Schulze and G. Berger, *Arch. Pharm.*, **262,** 553 (1924).
59. W. R. Dunstan and A. E. Andrews, *J. Chem. Soc.*, **87,** 1636 (1905).
60. R. Majima and S. Morio, *Ann.*, **476,** 171 (1929).
61. L. Marion and O. E. Edwards, *J. Am. Chem. Soc.*, **68,** 2565 (1946).
62. M. Freund and R. Niederhofheim, *Ber.*, **29,** 852 (1896).
63. W. A. Jacobs and L. C. Craig, *J. Biol. Chem.*, **127,** 361 (1939).
64. W. Schneider, *Pharm. Zentralhalle*, **90,** 151 (1951).
65. W. Schneider, *Arch. Pharm.*, **283,** 86, 281 (1950).
66. J. Katz, *Pharm. Zentralhalle*, **41,** 618 (1900).
67. T. Walz, *Arch. Pharm.* **260,** 9 (1922).
68. W. A. Jacobs and L. C. Craig, *J. Biol. Chem.*, **128,** 431 (1939).
69. O. Keller, *Arch. Pharm.*, **263,** 274 (1925).
70. W. A. Jacobs and L. C. Craig, *J. Biol. Chem.*, **136,** 303 (1940); W. A. Jacobs and C. F. Huebner, *ibid.*, **170,** 209 (1947).
71. W. A. Jacobs and Y. Sato, *J. Biol. Chem.*, **180,** 133, 479 (1949).
72. F. Hübschmann, *Schweiz. Wochschr. Pharm.*, **3,** 269 (1865).
73. H. Schulze and E. Bierling, *Arch. Pharm.*, **251,** 8 (1913).
74. R. H. F. Manske, *Can. J. Research*, **16B,** 57 (1938); L. Marion and R. H. F. Manske *ibid.*, **24B,** 1 (1946).
75. W. B. Cook and A. O. Beath, *J. Am. Chem. Soc.*, **74,** 1411 (1952).
76. H. Suginome and K. Ohno, *J. Fac. Sci., Hokkaido Univ., Ser. III. Chem.*, **4,** 36 (1950).
77. J. A. Goodson, *J. Chem. Soc.*, **1944,** 108; **1945,** 245.
78. L. Marion and O. E. Edwards, *J. Am. Chem. Soc.*, **69,** 2010 (1947).
79. J. A. Goodson, *J. Chem. Soc.*, **1943,** 139.
80. M. S. Rabinovich and R. A. Konovalova, *J. Gen. Chem. (U.S.S.R.)*, **19,** 1387 (1949).
81. M. V. Hunter, *Pharm. J..* **150,** 82 (1943); *Quart. J. Pharm. and Pharmacol.*, **17,** 302 (1944).
82. M. S. Rabinovich and R. A. Konovalova, *J. Gen. Chem. (U.S.S.R.)*, **12,** 321, 329 (1942).
83. v. Schroff, *Jahresber. Pharm.*, **6,** 102 (1871); H. V. Rosendahl, *Arb. Pharmak. Inst., Dorpat*, **11,** 1 (1895).
84. H. Schulze with F. Ulfert, *Arch. Pharm.*, **260,** 230 (1922).
85. G. Weidemann, *Arch. exptl. Pathol. Pharmakol.*, **95,** 166 (1922).

86. A. Jermstad and K. B. Jensen, *Pharm. Acta Helv.*, **26,** 33 (1951); *Norg. Apoteker-foren. Tidsskr.*, **16,** 1 (1951).
87. S. Yunusov and N. K. Abubakirov, *J. Gen. Chem. (U.S.S.R.)*, **19,** 269 (1949); **21,** 967 (1951); **22,** 1461 (1952).
88. J. F. Couch, *J. Am. Chem. Soc.*, **58,** 684 (1936).
89. H. Suginome, S. Kakimoto, J. Sonoda, and S. Noguchi, *Proc. Japan Acad.*, **22,** No. 5, 122 (1946).
90. G. R. Clemo and B. Nath, *J. Chem. Soc.*, **1952,** 1751.
91. E. Cionga and C. Iliescu, *Ber.*, **74,** 1031 (1941).
92. L. N. Markwood, *J. Am. Pharm. Assoc.*, **13,** 696 (1924).
93. S. Yunusov and N. K. Abubakirov, *J. Gen. Chem. (U.S.S.R.)*, **19,** 869 (1949).

General References

94. T. A. Henry, The Plant Alkaloids, 4th ed., Churchill, London, 1949, pp. 673–700.
95. H.-G. Boit, Fortschritte der Alkaloidchemie seit 1933, Akademie-Verlag, Berlin, 1950, p. 351–361.
96. F. E. Hamerslag, The Technology and Chemistry of Alkaloids, Van Nostrand, New York, 1950, pp. 26–43.
97. L. F. Fieser and Mary Fieser, Natural Products Related to Phenanthrene, Reinhold, New York, 1949, pp. 611–619.

Author Index

Numbers in parentheses are reference numbers and are included to assist in locating references where the author's name is not mentioned in the text. Numbers in italics refer to the page of the article on which the reference is listed.

A

Abderhalden, E., 190 (292), *198*
Abe, T., 85 (116a, 117a), *115*
Abubakirov, N. K., 322 (87), 325 (87), 328 (93), *333*
Adamson, D. C. M., 184 (136), *193*
Addinal, C. R., 179 (72), *192*
Adkilen, P., 79 (11), *113*, 157 (35), *165*
Adler, E., 138, 139 (93), *144*
Adler, L., 189 (270), *197*
Ahluwalia, G. S., 170 (10), *190*
Albricht, Marianne, 189 (273), *197*
Allen, A. H., 31 (5), *71*
Alles, G. A., 159 (79), *166*
Almgren, H., 87 (200), *117*
Alyavdina, L. A., 31 (8), *72*
Amorosa, M., 23, *27*
Andant, A., 186 (176), *194*
Andersen, R. C., 217 (33), *244*, 271 (28), *273*
Anderson, T., 38 (47a), *73*, 170 (7), *190*
Ando, Y., 83 (105), *115*, 158 (76), 160 (76), *166*
Andrews, A. E., 305 (59), 307 (59), 309 (59), *332*
Anet, F. A. L., 224 (136), 227 (136), *247*
Anneler, E., 184 (137, 138), *193*
Annett, H. E., 184 (139, 149), *193*, *194*
Anschütz, R., 251 (5), *252*
Arata, 85 (114), *115*
Arens, J. F., 37, *73*
Arima, A., 183 (98), *192*
Armit, J. W., 37 (34), *73*
Arnolt, R. I., 24 (34, 35), *27*
Aron, J., 45 (66b), *73*
Asahina, Y., 80 (38), 82 (70), 93 (38), *114*, 126, 133 (71), *143*, *144*, 158 (48, 64), *165*
Ashford, W. R., 113 (272), *118*, 122 (16), *143*
Aston, B. C., 138 (94), *145*
Athanasescu, B., 51 (76), 55 (76), 60 (76), *74*
Awe, W., 36 (28), 55 (28), *72*, 79 (22), 83 (89), 84 (196), *113*, *115*, *117*

B

Babich, S., Kh., 17, *21*
Bacialli, L., 189 (241), *196*
Baggesgaard-Rasmussen, H., 184 (144), 186 (185, 186, 187), *194*, *195*
Baghwat, V. K., 52 (80), *74*
Balakhovskii, S. D., 20 (62), *21*
Barger, G., 2 (17), *6*, 86 (148), *116*, 121 (10), 125, 132, 134, 137 (76), 138 (76), 139, 140, 142, *143*, *144*, *145*, 154, *165*, 301 (57), *332*
Barlow, O. W., 189 (244, 248), *196*
Barthel, W. F., 87 (178), *117*
Battandier, J. A., 79 (15), *113*, 157 (39), 158 (39), *165*
Baumgarten, G., 185 (160), 187 (160), *194*
Bayerle, H., 1 (9), *6*, 16, 18 *21*, 71, *75*
Bayle, E., 184 (156, 157), 186 (157, 181), *194*, *195*
Beal, G. D., 87 (201), *117*, 187 (201), *195*
Beath, A. O., 321 (75), 322 (75), 323 (75), 325, (75), *332*
Beauquesne, L., 86 (153), 93 (153), *116*
Baccari, E., 9 (3), *20*
Beck, H., 90 (214), 105 (214), *117*
Beck, P., 297 (43), *332*
Beck, W. C., 45 (68), *73*
Becke, F., 9, 10, 14 (12, 13), 15, *20*, 23, 24, *26*
Becker, F., 170 (15), *191*
Becker, P., 175 (50), *191*
Beckmann, H., 184 (124), *193*
Beckurts, H., 186 (173), *194*
Belloni, E., 186 (168), *194*
Berger, F., 42, 70, *73*, 132, 141, *144*
Berger, G., 304 (58), 305 (58), *332*
Bernhauser, E., 59 (96), *75*
Bernier, M., 25 (67), *28*
Bersch, H. W., 255 (21, 22), 256, 258, *263*
Berse, K., 268 (21), *273*

Bezssonoff, N., 190 (283), *197*
Bezuglyĭ, D. V., 17, *21*
Bick, R. C., 204 (108, 112), 205 (112), 206 (113), 217, 218 (108), 219, 221, 240, 241, 242, 243, *246*, *247*
Bierling, E., 320 (73), 321 (73), 322 (73), 323 (73), 325 (73), *332*
Billek, G., 67, *75*
Blache, P., 149 (10), *164*
Blount, B. K., 269, *273*
Blyth, J., 187 (211), *195*
Boedecker, F., 44 (64), *73*
Boehm, R., 230, 231, 234, *245*
Boit, H. G., *333*
Boschan, F., 14, *20*, 24 (46), *27*
Both, E., 183 (97), *192*
Bourgouin, E., 123, *143*
Bradshaw, H. H., 45 (70), 46 (70), 47 (70), *74*
Brady, O. L., 303 (55), 304 (55), *332*
Britton, N. L., 15, 23, 24, 25, *27*
Brochmann-Hansen, E., 84 (198), *117*
Broughton, J., 280 (17), *331*
Brown, D. G., 187 (208, 209), *195*
Brown, D. R., 150 (14), *164*
Bruchhausen, F. von, 85 (128), 105, 106, 108, *116*, *118*, 162, 163, 164, *166*, 204 (18), 213 (16, 17, 18), 215, 217, 218, *244*, 255 (21, 22), 256, 258, *263*
Bruck, J., 12, *20*, 24 (47–49), *27*
Bruckner, V., 48 (72d), *74*
Brüggemann, J., 190 (287), *197*
Brunner, H., 186 (194), *195*
Brunner, K., 84 (193, 194), *117*, 186 (171), *194*
Bruns, D., 107 (259, 260), 108, *118*
Brustier, V., 184 (140), *193*
Buchner, C. A., 84 (180), *117*
Buchner, J. A., 84 (180), *117*
Buck, J. S., 32 (13a, b), 33 (13a, b), 35 (13a, b, 23), 40 (13b, 23), 70 (13a), *72*, 95 (228), 98, *118*
Büchi, J., 32 (12), *72*
Burger, A., 34 (19), 35 (19), 36 (29), 40 (19), 53 (29, 83) 55 (29, 83), 57 (83), 58, 59, 61 (83), 62 (29, 83), 63 (83), *72*, *74*
Burger, G., 97 (232), 109 (232), *118*
Busse, S. and V., 31 (8), *72*

C

Cacciavillani, R., 272, *273*
Callow, R. K., 136 (83), *144*
Capellmann, R., 24 (23), *27*
Carr, F. H., 186 (174), *194*, 296 (34), 299 (34, 48), 308 (48), *331*, *332*
Castelli, F., 31 (7), *72*
Castrillón, J. A., 10, *21*, 24 (36), 25, 26 (71), *27*, *28*
Castro, E. R., 86 (134) 93, (134), 95 (134), *116*
Chaigneau, M., 184 (120), 186 (120), *193*
Change, Kuo-Jen, 204 (36), 216 (36), 219 (36), *244*
Charlesworth, E. H., 122 (16), *143*
Chasonikova, K. A., 183 (100), *192*
Chatterjee, R., 63 (99, 102, 103), 64 (100, 101), *75*, 85 (117, 119, 124, 130–133), 86 (131, 133), 111 (117, 119), *115*, *116*, *118*
Chen, A. L., 216 (32), 217 (33), *244*, 271 (28), *273*
Chen, K. K., 216 (32), 217 (33), *244*, 271, *273*
Chentsova, M. G., 19, *21*
Chernoruzkii, H., 190 (299), *198*
Chevalier, M., 84 (177), *117*
Chiba, Y., 279 (33), 292 (33), *331*
Child, R., 86 (157), *116*
Chodoff, R. J., 45 (70), 46 (70), 47 (70), *74*
Chopra, R. N., 189 (240, 243), *196*
Chou, T. Q., 78 (1), 79 (25), 93 (25), 105 (2), *113*
Christ, W., 185 (160), 187 (160), *194*
Christensen, B. V., 87 (166), *116*
Chu, J. H., 216 (34), *244*
Chuang, Chang-Kong, 204 (36), 216 (36), 219 (36) *244*
Ciamician, G., 189 (276), *197*
Cionga, E., 330 (91), *333*
Claus, A., 37 (36, 38, 39), *73*
Clayson, D. B., 18, *21*
Clemo, G. R., 328 (90), 330 (90), *333*
Coghill, R. D., 209 (114), *247*
Cole, H. H., 45 (68), *73*
Cole, H. I., 87 (199), *117*, 187 (207), *195*
Collier, H. O., 57 (90), *74*
Collins, D. C., 45 (68), *74*
Cook, W. B., 321 (75), 322 (75), 323 (75), 325 (75), *332*

Cooper, N., 184 (315), 189 (315), *198*
Costa, O. de A., 85 (118), *115*, 186 (164, 165, 166), *194*
Couch, J. F., 328 (88), 330 (88), *333*
Couerbe, 173 (25), *191*
Craig, L. C., 276 (1), 279 (8, 10, 13, 15), 280 (13), 281 (2, 13, 21), 282 (13, 23), 284 (8, 25), 286 (8, 31), 287 (8), 289 (10, 13), 291 (15), 298 (1, 47), 299 (1, 47), 301 (47), 302 (47, 53), 303 (53), 304 (47, 53), 308 (1, 53), 309 (63, 68), 311 (1, 68), 316 (63, 68, 70), 317 (70), 318 (70), 319 (71), 330 (70), *330*, *331*, *332*
Craig, L. E., 34 (18), 41 (18), 55 (18), *72*
Cromwell, B. T., 85 (116), *115*
Csókan, P., 184 (152), 186 (152), *194*
Cuénod, C. L., 45 (66b), *73*
Cumming, W. M., 187 (208, 209), *195*
Cunningham, R. W., 48 (72f), *74*

D

Dai, K., 223 (106), *246*
Dalma, G., 266, 267 (17), 268 (20, 22), 269 (22), 270 (11, 25, 26), *272*, *273*
Dalmer, O., 183 (102), 190 (102), *192*
Dana, 255 (17), *263*
Danckwortt, P. W., 82 (71), *114*, 149, 157, 158, *164*, 184 (155), *194*
da Silva, R. D., 85 (118), *115*, 186 (164, 165), *194*
Davis, L., 84 (195), *117*
De, S., 101 (237), *118*
Decker, H., 36 (31), 37 (31, 32, 37), 38 (47d), 51 (77), 62 (31, 32), *72*, *73*, *74*, 171, 175 (50), *191*
de Haan, H., 183 (108), *193*
DeLanghe, J., 159 (80), *166*
Deleano, N. T., 189 (274), *197*
Dellepiane, G., 189 (259–261), *197*
Delphaut, J., 57 (88, 89), *74*, 149 (10), *164*
Demole, V., 45 (66a), *73*
Dengel, F., 17, *21*, 24 (50), *27*
Denigès, G., 187 (199), *195*
Denk, W., 45 (70), 46 (70), 47 (70), *74*
Derosne, C., 183, *192*
de Takats, G., 45 (68), *73*
Détri, J., 183 (110), 184 (141), *193*
Deulofeu, V., 159 (80), *166*
de Waal, J. W., 184 (133, 134), *193*
Dey, B. B., 87 (175), *117*
Diehl, H. S., 45 (68), *74*
Dieterich, H., 205 (54), 226, *245*
Dieterle, H., 186 (190), *195*, 256 (25), 262 (25), *263*
Dietzel, R., 184 (127), 186 (192), *193*, *195*
Dikshit, B. B., 189 (243, 271), *196*, *197*
Dille, J. M., 190 (295), *198*
Dirner, Z., 47 (72a), *74*
Dittmer, O., 135, 136, *144*
Djerassi, C., 25, *28*
Dobbie, J. J., 50, 57, (75), *74*, 81 (54), 104 (246), 107 (261), *114*, *118*, 130 *144*, 172 (19), 174 (41), 186 (175), *191*, *194*
Doblhammer, F., 227 (67), 228 (67), 230 (67), *245*
Dobrowsky, A., 35 (22b), 41, 45 (70), 46 (22b, 70), 47 (70), 49 (22b), 50 (73), 58 (22b, *72*, *74*, 104 (247), 107, 108 (247), *118*, 177 (66), *192*
Dobson, B., 40, *73*, 83 (96), *115*
Dombrowski, Anna, 184 (125), *193*
Dopffel, O., 45 (70), 46 (70), 47 (70), *74*
Dorfman, M., 32 (12), *72*
Dott, D. B., 185 (322), 186, *194*, *198*
Dragendorff, G., 30 (1a), *71*
Dunant, G., 36 (31), 37 (31), 62 (31), *72*
Dunstan, W. R., 296 (34, 38), 299 (34, 38), 305 (59), 307 (59), 309 (59), 276 (30), *331*, *332*
Duquénois, P., 187 (203), *195*
Durand, 186, *194*
Dutcher, J. D., 205 (104), 206 (104, 137), 224 (104), 227 (104), 231 (104), 232, 233 (81, 104), 234 (104, 137), *246*, *247*
Dutt, S., 170 (12), *190*

E

Eddy, N. B., 44, *73*
Eder, R., 184 (118), 186 (118), *193*
Edinger, A., 37 (38), *73*
Edwards, G. A., 173 (28), *191*
Edwards, O. E., 307 (61), 308 (61), 309 (61), 322 (74, 78), 328 (78), 330 (78), *332*
Ehrenberg, A., 298 (46), *332*
Eichler, T., 36 (32), 62, *72*
Eiderman, E. M., 186 (189), *195*
Eijkman, J. F., 79 (13), 86 (136), 109, *113*, *116*, 173, 186 (30), *191*, 255 (20), 262 (20), *263*
Eisenbrand, J., 126 (26), *143*

Eisenbrand, L., 126 (26), *143*

Ekkert, L., 187 (221), *196*

Elderfield, R. C., 297 (40), 298 (47), 299 (40, 47), 301 (47), 302 (47), 304 (47), *331*, *332*

Elek, S. R., 45 (68), *73*

Eliel, E. E., 35 (22c), 58 (22c), *72*

Ellert, M., 187 (203), *195*

Engel, B. G., 266, 268 (21), 269, 270 (14, 24, 26), *272*, *273*

Epstein, H., 37 (33, 42), 54 (33), 55 (33), 60 (33), 61 (42), 62 (33, 42), *72*, *73*

Evers, N., 185 (159), *194*

Ewell, E. E., 23, *27*

Ewen, E. S., 204 (112), 205 (112), 218 219, 221, *247*

F

Fabre, R., 184 (115, 156, 157), 186 (157, 179, 181), 190 (308, 309), *193*, *194*, *195*, *198*

Faiveley, J., 24 (63), *28*

Falco, F., 24 (64), *28*

Faltis, F., 138, 139, *144*, 200 (69), 203, 205 (54), 208 (52), 211, 224, 225 (50–52), 226 (53, 54), 227, 228 (67), 229 (63), 230, 239, 240, *245*, *246*, 267 (18), 268 (18), *273*

Farah, A., 272 (37), *273*

Feist, K., 84 (197), 86 (159), 92, 93, 95 (159), *116*, *117*, *118*

Feldhaus, A., 204 (18), 213 (18), 215, 217 (18), *244*

Fellows, E. J., 48 (72f), *74*

Fenn, G. K., 45 (68), *73*

Ferguson, J. W., 35 (26), 43, *72*

Field, Ellen, 301 (57), *332*

Fieser, L. F., *333*

Fieser, Mary, *333*

Filippo, J. D., 125, *143*

Finkelstein, J., 67 (108), *75*

Finkelstein, Marie, 35 (22a), 40 (22a), 56, 58 (22a), *72*

Fischer, R., 82 (75, 76), 83 (80), 84 (76), *114*, 120, 121 (2), *143*, 158 (67), 159 (67), *165*, 186 (197), *195*, 254 (8, 14, (16), 256 (14), *262*

Fitch, T. B., 45 (68), *74*

Fleischer, K., 38 (*45*), *73*, 106, *118*, 164, *166*

Fleitman, T., 84, *117*

Fodor, G., 18, *21*, 47 (72c, d), 48 (72d, e), 71 (119), *74*, *75*

Foote, P. A., 79 (9), *113*

Foster, G. C., 170 (8), 183, *190*, *192*

Foster, G. E., 31 (6b), *72*

Frank, H., 186 (197), *195*

Frankforter, G. B., 179 (71), *192*

Frauendorfer, H., 208 (52), 225 (52), *245*

Frerichs, G., 109, *118*

Freudenberg, K., 184 (147), *194*

Freudenberg, W., 279 (14), 291 (14), 305 (14), *331*

Freund, M., 2 (14), *6*, 14, *21*, 38 (45), *73*, 81 (52), 83 (94), 87 (170), 88 (206, 207), 90 (214), 104, 105 (214), 106, 107, (258), *114*, *115*, *116*, *117*, *118*, 132, *144*, 162 (84), 155 (24), 162, *165*, *166*, 170 (15), 173 (26, 34), 174 (39, 43), 175 (39, 56), 179 (71, 73), 186 (31), *191*, *192*, 297 (43), 307 (62), *332*

Frick, N., 25, *28*

Fritsch, P., 173, 174, *191*

Frommel, E., 45 (66b), *73*

Fujita, E., 4 (22), *6*, 210 (110, 135), 214 (126), 215 (126, 127, 132), 216 (127, 132), 217 (126, 127, 132, 133), 220 (133), 227 (134), *247*

Furusawa, S., 279 (33), 292 (33), *331*

Fuse, S., 240 (93), *246*

G

Gadamer, J., 2 (15), *6*, 33 (14), 37, 38 (48), 52, *72*, *73*, *74*, 79 (19, 20), 81 (53, 55, 59, 61), 83 (19, 87), 84 (184), 89, 90, 91 (211, 218), 92 (211), 93, 94 (224), 96 (59), 104 (245), 105, 106 (250), 107 (260), 108, *113*, *114*, *115*, *117*, *118*, 120, 121, 127, 129, 130 (51, 52, 61), 131, 133, 134 (73), 135, 136, *143*, *144*, 151 (17), 158 (58, 77), 160, 162, 163, 164, *165*, *166*, 254, 255 (18, 19), 256, 257, 258, 259, 260, 261, 262 (18, 25, 26, 37), *262*, *263*

Gaebel, G. O., 162, *166*

Galat, A., 44, *73*

Gallatty, L., 51 (77), *74*

Galleis, F., 184 (129), *193*

Gallois, N., 266, *272*

Galotti, M., 186 (170), *194*

Gams, A., 39 (51a, b), *73*, 92, 98, *117*

Gangl, J., 14, 15 (25), *20*, 24 (51), *27*
Gareet, S., 48 (73a), *74*
Garza, H. Martinex, 210, 211, *247*
Gaubert, P., 183 (112), *193*
Gaudin, O., 189 (264), *197*
Geiger, P. L., 297 (42), *331*
Geller, L. E., 25, *28*
Gempp, A., 84 (111), *115*, 260 (40), *263*
George, H., 184 (157), 186 (157), *194*
Gerichten, E. von, 172 (20), *191*
Gericke, P. H., 213 (17), 217 (17), *244*
Ghose, T. P., 127, *143*
Girardet, A., 2 (17), *6*, 134 (77, 78), 137 (76), 138 (76), *144*
Gisvold, O., 79 (10), *113*
Glycart, C. K., 184 (123), *193*
Gnesin, Yu, D., 187 (210), *195*
Go, J., 81 (50), 91 (50), 102, *114*, 120 (4), 129 (4), 130 (4), 131, *143*, *144*, 158 (56), *165*
Goldschmiedt, G., 32 (9), 34 (9), *72*
Goodson, J. A., 279 (4, 12), 292 (4, 12), 321 (77), 322 (77, 79), 325 (77, 79), 328 (77, 79), 330 (77), *331*, *332*
Gordin, H. M., 84 (187, 189, 190), *117*, 186 (193), *195*
Gori, G., 184 (316), *198*
Goris, A., 280 (18), *331*
Gorter, K., 125, *143*
Goto, K., 38 (46), *73*, 86 (161, 162), 98, *116*, 136, 137, *144*, 154 (20), *165*
Govindachari, T. R., 140 (97, 98), *145*
Graebe, C., 258 (33), *263*
Granick, X., 276 (1), 298 (1), 299 (1), 308 (1), 311 (1), *330*
Grant, R. L., 190 (285), *197*
Grassie, V., 141, *145*
Greathouse, G. A., 85 (121, 122), *115*, 215 (24), *244*, 261 (45, 46), *263*
Greshoff, M., 125, *143*
Groenewoud, P. W. G., 182, 183 (86), *192*
Groves, T., 297 (42), *331*
Gruber, W., 39 (53), *73*
Gruterink, Alide, 187 (213), *195*
Günzel, E., 86 (160), 92 (160), 95 (160), *116*
Guérin, G., 184 (314), *198*
Guggenheim, M., 1 (4), *6*
Guha, M. P., 63 (102, 103), 64 (100, 101) *75*, 85 (130–133), 86 (131, 133), *116*
Gulland, J. M., 131, 134, 136, *144*
Gurgel, L., 85 (118), *115*, 186 (164), *194*
Guyot, H., 189 (254), 190 (254), *197*
Gvishiani, G. J., 20, *21*

H

Haagen-Smit, A. J., 24 (62), 25 (62), *28*
Haars, O., 79 (30), 81 (30), *113*, 133 (72), *144*, 158 (55), *165*
Haffner, F., 189 (245), *196*
Hahn, G., 1, *6*, 39 (52), 70, *73*, *75*
Hamerslag, F. E., *333*
Hamet, R., 214 (19), 215 (20), *244*
Handysyde, F. P., 184 (136), *193*
Hantzsch, A., 172 (18), *191*
Hanzlik, P. J., 189 (267), *197*, 261, *263*
Harder, M., 184 (147), *194*
Hardy, E., 266, *272*
Hargreaves, C. C., 271 (29, 30), *273*
Harlay, V., 41, *73*
Harnack, E., 266, *272*
Hasegava, S., 223 (47), *245*
Hatcher, R. A., 184 (315), 189 (315), *198*
Hauschild, F., 231 (73), *245*
Haworth, R. D., 32 (13 b), 33 (13 b), 35 (13b), 40 (13b), 65 (105), *72*, *75*, 92, 95 (221), 98, 102, *117*, *118*, 127 (33, 34), 131, 134, 136 (83), *143*, *144*, 156, 157 (29, 31, 32), 160, 161, *165*, *166*, 182 (85), 183 (85), 187 (85, 198), *192*, *195*
Hayashi, M., 189 (266), *197*
Heathcote, R. S. A., 149 (8), *164*
Heczko, T., 224 (49), *245*
Heffter, A., 8, 9, 10, 19, *20*, *21*, 24, 26, *27*
Heiduschka, A., 184 (119), 187 (200), *193*, *195*
Henderson, V. E., 190 (310), *198*
Henry, T. A., 23, *27*, 303 (54), 307 (54) 308 (54), 309 (54), 276 (30), *331*, *332*, *333*
Herrero Ducloux, E., 24, 25 (26, 27, 29, 30), *27*
Herzig, J., 228 (57), *245*
Herzig, P., 184 (128), *193*
Hess, K., 58 (92), *74*, 175, *191*
Hesse, O., 18, *21*, 31 (4a, b), 38 (47b, c), 48, 56 (74b), 57, 58 (93a), 59, 60, *71*, *73*, *74*, *75* 83 (91, 97, 98, 99, 103), 85 (125), *115*, 157, *165*, 183, 185 (93, 321), 187 (92), *192*, *198*, 213 (11), *244*, 297 (42), *331*

Heyl, G., 9, 15, 20 (27), *21*, 24, 25, 26, *27*, 79 (31), *113*, 126, 127, *143*
Heymans, A., 44 (64), *73*
Hilburg, S., 24 (64), *28*
Hildebrandt, H., 228 (61), 230 (61), *245*
Hinterberger, F., 183 (90, 91), 187 (216), *192*, *196*
Hirano, S., 189 (256), *197*
Hirsch, A., 32 (9), 34 (9), *72*
Hobschette, A., 23, *26*
Hodgson, H. W., 184 (136), *193*
Hönigschmidt, O., 32 (9), 34 (9), *72*
Holló, Z., 184 (154), *194*
Holmes, H. L., 68 (112), *75*, 78 (3), 101 (3), *113*
Holter, H., 108, *118*, 134, *144*
Holzinger, L., 200 (69), 203 (69), 227 (69), 229 (69), *245*, 267 (18), 268 (18), *273*
Honjo, S., 227 (130), *247*
Hooper, D., 87 (168), *116*
Hope, E., 174 (42), 176 (42), 181, 185 (81), 186 (84), 187 (84), *191*, *192*
Hopfgartner, K., 254 (12), *263*
Horiuchi, K., 209 (9), *244*
Houssay, B. A., 190 (304), *198*
Hromatka, O., 131, *144*
Hsing, Chi-Yi, 204 (36), 216 (36), 219 (36), *244*
Huang-Minlon. 79 (26), 93 (26), 102 (26), *113*
Huber, H. U., 86 (147), *116*, 130 (60), 132, *144*
Huebner, C. F., 279 (16), 281 (22), 282 (24), 285 (22), 286 (26, 31), 288 (26), 289 (31), 291 (16), 296 (37), 297 (37), 299 (37), 308 (37), 316 (70), 317 (37, 70), 318 (70), *331*, *332*
Hübschmann, F., 320 (72), *332*
Hüetlin, E., 37 (36), *73*
Hughes, G. K., 224 (136), 227 (136), *247*
Hummel, J. J., 87 (173), *117*
Hunter, M. V., 279 (11), 292 (11), 322 (81), 328 (81), 330 (81), *331*, *332*
Husemann, A., 187 (214), *196*

I

Ikeda, T., 204 (23), 215 (23), 216 (23), *244*
Iliescu, C., 330 (91), *333*
Imato, S., 287 (29), 297 (29), 305 (29), *331*
Inaba, R., 137 (89), *144*
Inubushi, Y., 86 (135), *116*
Ionesco, I., 189 (274), *197*
Ishii, S., 86 (135), *116*
Issekutz, K. V., 47 (72a), *74*
Ita, P., 200 (69), 203 (69), 227 (69), 229 (69), *245*
Iwakawa, K., 109, *118*
Iwakiri, M., 183 (98), *192*

J

Jackson, D. H., 296 (38), 299 (38), *331*
Jacobs, W. A., 276 (1, 2), 279 (8, 10, 13, 15, 16), 280 (2, 13), 281 (2, 13, 21, 22), 282, (2, 13, 23, 24), 284 (2, 8, 25), 285 (2, 22), 286 (8, 26, 31), 287 (8), 288 (26), 289, (10, 31) 291 (15, 16), 296 (37), 297 (37, 40), 298 (1, 47), 299 (1, 37, 40, 47), 301 (47), 302 (47, 53), 303 (53), 304 (47, 53), 308 (1, 37, 53), 309 (63, 68), 311 (1, 68), 316 (63, 68, 70), 317 (37, 70), 318 (70, 71), 319 (71), 330 (70), *330*, *331*, *332*
Jacobson, 266 (4), *272*
Jäckh, I., 42 (60), *73*
Janot, M. M., 25 (67), *28*, 184 (120), 186 (120), *193*
Japp, F. R., 251 (5), *252*
Jensen, K. B., 322 (86), 326 (86), *333*
Jermstad, A., 183 (99), *192*, 322 (86), 326 (86), *333*
Joachimoglu, G., 19, *21*
Joachimowitz, Marianne, 84 (192), *117*, 186 (169), *194*
Jones, E. C. S., 271 (27), *273*
Jones, E. G., 180 (79), *192*
Jones, R. N., 186 (177), *194*, 258 (34), *263*
Jordan, C. B., 186 (180), *194*
Josephi, W., 2 (14), *6*, 81 (52), 104, 107 (258), *114*, *118*, 132, *144*, 162 (84), *166*
Josephson, K., 169 (3), *190*
Jowett, H. A. D., 87 (176), 92, *117*, 159, *166*, 280 (19), *331*
Julian, P. L., 18, *21*, 24 (52), *27*, 81 (56), 91 (56), 102, 103 (56), *114*

K

Kabachnik, M. I., 32 (10), *72*
Kadiera, K., 227 (67), 228 (67), 230 (67), *245*
Kakemi, K., 46 (71e), 57 (71c), *74*

Kakimoto, S., 279 (6, 33), 287 (6), 288 (6), 292 (33), 328 (89), 330 (89), *331*, *333*
Kako, H., 190 (296), *198*
Kalb, M., 172 (18), *191*
Kamerman, P., 266 (9), *272*
Kan, I., 86 (140), *116*, 128, *143*
Kao, Yee-Shang, 204 (36), 216 (36), 219 (36), *244*
Karrer, P., 259 (36), 260, 262 (36), *263*
Karstendieck, H., 45 (70), 46 (70), 47 (70), *74*
Kassner, O., 37 (39), *73*
Kataoka, H., 224 (131), *247*
Katz, J., 309 (66), *332*
Katz, L. N,, 45 (68), *73*
Kauder, E., 9, 10, *20*, 26, 58 (93b), 60, *75*
Kaufman, E., 35 (22c), 58 (22c), *72*
Keenan, G. L., 186 (182), *195*
Keeser, E., 19, *21*
Keimatsu, I., 204 (35), 205 (42, 44), 215 (35), 220, 223 (42, 43, 44), *244*, *245*
Keller, O., 292 (32), 316 (69), 322 (32), *331*, *332*
Kenner, J., 271 (27), *273*
Kerstein, W., 173 (36), *191*
Kesztler, F., 2 (10), *6*, 12, 14, 15 *20*, 24 (53, 54), *28* 70, *75*
Kimoto, S., 227 (130), *247*
Kin, K., 189 (265), *197*
Kindler, K., 35 (25), 41, 43, *72*
King, F. E., 52 (81a, b,), *74*
King, H., 67 (107), *75*, 200 (95), 203 (95), 205 (68, 76, 123), 206 (76, 82, 123), 219, 224 (68), 227 (68, 76, 77), 229, 230, 231 (68), 232, 233, 234, *245*, *246*, *247*
King, R. E., 233 (80), *245*
Kipperman, E. C., 169 (2), *190*
Kipple, Helen M., 190 (295), *198*
Kirpal, A., 32 (9), 34 (9), *72*
Kiselev, V. V., 83 (83a), *114*, 136, *144*
Kitasato, Z., 37 (35), 38 (46), 39, *73*, 86 (137, 138, 139, 164, 165), 93 (164), 98, 102 (165), 103, 109, 110 (164), *116*, *118*, 128 129 *143*, 154 (20), *165*, 184 (153), 186 (153), *194*
Klauser, O., 37 (37), *73*
Klee, W., 3 (18), *6*, 83 (88), 104 (245), *115*, *118*, 135, 136, *144*, 158 (74), *166*
Kley, W., 39 (52), *73*
Klein, G., 186 (167, 183), 187 (167), *194*, *195*
Kling, 256, 258, *263*
Kljatchkina, B., 183 (109), 184 (109), *193*
Klyachkina, B. A., 184 (142, 143), 187 (206), *193*, *194*, *195*
Knoch, F., 37, *73*, 130, *143*
Knörck, K. F., 96, 97, *118*
Knowles, R., 189 (240), *196*
Kobayashi, S., 61 (98), *75*
Kocak, H., 184 (145), *194*
Koch, W., 136, *144*
Kochhar, B. D., 170 (10), *190*
Kocsis, E. A., 184 (154), *194*
König, G., 84 (110), *115*, 158 (75), 160 (75), *166*, 254 (7), *262*
Koenigs, W., 38 (43), *73*, 107 (256), *118*
Koepfli, J. B., 106, *118*, 161, *166*
Kofler, A., 184 (122), *193*
Kofler, L., 184 (122), *193*
Kohei, K., 83 (105), *115*, 158 (76), 160 76), *166*
Kohlmayer, H., 45 (70), 46 (70), 47 (70) *74*
Kolbe, A., 85 (127), *116*, 204 (14), 213, *244*
Kolthoff, M., 184 (114), *193*
Kondo, H., 65, *75*, 85 (123), 93 (123), 95 (123), *115*, 204 (3, 22, 23, 25, 26, 35, 41), 205 (40–42, 44, 55, 100, 102, 128), 206 (82, 85–88, 90), 207 (3, 96–98), 208 (5–8), 215 (22, 23, 35), 216 (23, 25–28, 120), 220, 221 (41), 222 (99–103, 118, 128), 223 (42–47, 128), 224 (125, 131), 227 (55), 235, 238 (85–88, 90–92), 239, 242 (97, 98), *243*, *244*, *245*, *246*, *247*
Kondo, R., 52, *74*
Kondo, T., 52 (78), 65, *74*, *75*
Konovalova, A. A, 17, *21*
Konovalova, R. A., 17, *21*, 68 (110, 111), *75*, 83 (78, 82, 83a, 84), 84 (107–109), *114*, *115*, 120 (5), 130 (5), 136, 141 (100, 102), *143*, *144*, *145*, 158 (68), 159 (68), *166*, 254 (15), 255 (15), *263*, 276 (3), 279 (3), 291 (3), 305 (3), 307 (3), 322 (3, 80, 82), 325 (80), 326 (82), 328, (3, 82), 330 (82), *331*, *332*
Konson, B. L., 83 (83), *114*
Kostanecki, S. von, 175 (54), *191*
Kovàcs, Ö., 18, *21*, 71 (119), *75*

Koyama, T., 279 (7), 287 (7), *331*
Kramers, G. H., 31 (6a), 63 (98a), *72*, *75*, 149, *164*
Kratzl, K., 67, *75*
Krayer, O., 272 (36, 37), *273*
Kreitmair, H., 46 (72b), 47 (72b), *74*, 261 (41), *263*
Kremann, R., 183 (113), *193*
Krishna, S., 127, *143*
Kropf, F., 176 (57), *191*
Krueger, H., 44, *73*
Kruta, E., 78 (1), 94 (227), 106 (227), 112 (227), *113*, *118*
Kruysse, A., 187 (218), *196*
Kubly, M., 184 (318), *198*
Kubota, S., 216 (29, 31), 217 (30), *244*
Kühas, E., 226 (53), *245*
Küssner, W., 183 (101), *192*
Kuffner, F., 15, 17, 18, *21*, 24 (55, 56), *28*, 70, *75*, 79 (21), *113*, 228 (72), 231, *245*, 257, 258, 260, 262 (39), *263*
Kunimatsu, Y., 279 (7), 287 (7), *331*
Kuntze, F., 133, 134 (73), *144*
Kutschera-Aichbergen, H., 45 (70), 46 (70), 47 (70), *74*

L

La Barre, J., 189 (258), *197*
Labat, M. A., 187 (222, 224), *196*
Laborde, M., 266 (5), *272*
Labriola, R., 159 (80), *166*
Lachmann, S., 88 (207), *117*
Ladeck, F., 205 (71), 231, *245*
LaForge, F. B., 87 (178), *117*
Laland, P., 183 (104, 106), 189 (106), *192*, *193*
Lampe, V., 175 (54), *191*
Lang, N., 58, *75*, 104 (248), *118*
Lauder, A., 50, 57 (75), 81 (54), 104 (246), 107 (74, 261), *114*, *118*, 130, *144*, 172 (19), 186 (175), *191*, *194*
Lawson, A., 280 (20), 281 (20), 302 (52), 304 (52), *331*, *332*
L'Ecuyer, P., 52 (81b), *74*
Ledingham, A., 158 (71), 160 (71), *166*
Ledingham, A. E., 83 (81), *114*, 251 (6), *252*
Leete, E., 2 (12), *6*
Leiner, G., 45 (70), 46 (70), 47 (70), *74*
Leinzinger, M., 47 (72a), *74*
Leithe, W., 56 (87), 60 (87), *74*, 94 (225) 110, *118*, 205 (71), 231, *245*
Lelièvre, J. L., 184 (141), *193*
Lemay, L., 68 (111a), *75*
Leonard, N. J., 176 (58), *191*
Leprince, M., 87 (179), *117*
Lettré, H., 189 (273), *197*
Leubner, G. W., 176 (58), *191*
Levi, R., 31 (7), *72*
Levy, J., 45 (67), *73*
Lévy, Jeanne, 189 (264), *197*
Lewin, L., 9, 12, *20*, 24, *27*
Lewis, J. T., 24 (61), *28*
Liebermann, C., 89 (209, 210), *117*, 132 (68), *144*, 176 (57), 180, *191*, *192*
Liebner, A., 296 (35), *331*
Linde, O., 84 (188), *117*
Litterschied, F., 187 (215), *196*
Loufti, M., 45 (66b), *73*
Lucas, V., 186 (166), *194*
Ludueña, F. P., 24 (35, 61, *27*, *28*, 149 (11), *164*
Lungberg, H., 190 (313), *198*
Lutz, R. E., 31

M

McCall, M. L., 45 (68), *74*
Maccio, I., 79 (16), *113*, 254 (13), *263*
McDavid, J. W., 91 (217), *117*
McGeogh, Sarah N., 174 (40), *191*
Machiguchi, E., 30 (1b), *71*, 83 (102), *115*
Macht, D. I., 189 (253, 255, 257), 190 (301), *196*, *197*, *198*
McIntyre, A. R., 233 (80), *245*
McMillian, A., 83 (95), *115*, 179 (76), 185 (76), *192*
Mahla, F., 173, 186 (32), *191*
Majima, R., 279 (27), 287 (27), 297 (41, 49), 298 (41, 44, 45), 301 (41, 49), 302 (51), 303 (51), 304 (49, 51), 305 (60), 307 (41, 49, 60), *331*, *332*
Major, A. T., 179 (72), *192*
Makkert, Laura, 184 (147), *194*
Makoshi, K., 79 (24), 80 (39), 103 (24), 107 (24), *113*, *114*, 158 (41), *165*
Maling, H. M., 272 (36), *273*
Malinowski, S., 39 (50), *73*, 105 (249), *118*
Mancini, M. A., 184 (319), *198*
Maniwa, H., 86 (140), *116*, 128, *143*
Mannich, C., 41, *73*
Manske, R. H. F., 2 (16), 3 (20), 4 (16,

23, 24), 5 (25), *6*, 18, *21*, 68 (112, 113), *75*, 78 (3–6), 79 (5, 7, 12, 17, 27–29), 80 (6, 29, 32–37, 40–43), 81 (28, 34, 44–49, 51, 60, 62, 63), 82 (28, 64–69, 72–74, 77), 83 (72, 79, 81), 84 (72), 86 (149), 91 (6, 33), 93 (5, 28, 32, 37, 40), 94 (29, 41, 43, 45, 46), 95 (6, 32, 33, 43, 51, 69), 96 (32, 40, 41, 43, 46), 97 (5, 28, 29, 32, 37, 42, 47, 49, 72, 77, 79, 233), 98 (34, 47, 49, 77, 233), 99 (6, 34), 100 (5, 29, 37, 45), 101 (3), 102 (3, 4, 29, 33, 35, 36, 40, 41, 45, 46, 51, 62, 72, 77), 103 (28, 29, 46, 243), 107 (46), 108 (51, 265), 110 (72, 233), 113, *113*, *114*, *116*, *118*, 120 (6–9), 121 (11), 122 (7–9, 16), 123 (20), 127 (7–9), 129 (7–9, 50), 130 (50, 53–57, 63), 133 (50), 139 (96), 141, *143*, *144*, *145*, 148, 149 (2–7), 155 (4, 7, 25–28), 156 (27), 157 (34, 36), 158 (2, 3, 4, 6, 7 25–27, 42–47, 49–54, 57, 59–63, 65, 66, 69, 70, 71), 159 (3, 6, 27, 31, 34, 36, 42, 43, 44, 59, 63), 160 (71), 161 (6), *164*, *165*, *166*, 177 (61–64), 178 (62, 64, 67–69), 187 (64, 67, 69, 225–236), 188 (68, 225, 230, 232, 233, 238), 189 (62, 64, 227, 232, 234, 239), *192*, *196*, 207, *243*, 244 (1, 2), 250 (4), 251 (1, 6), *252*, 253 (2), 254 (1, 9), 255 (9), 256 (2, 9, 24), *262*, *263*, 321 (74), 322 (74), 323 (74), *332*

Maplethorpe, C. W., 185 (159), *194*, 266 (8), *272*

Marañon, J. M., 86 (145), *116*, 130 (58), *144*

Marion, L., 2 (12), *6*, 68 (111a), *75*, 83 (81), *114*, 140, 141, *145*, 155 (28), 158 (71), 160 (71), *165*, *166*, 186 (177), *194*, 258 (34), *263*, 307 (61), 308 (61), 309 (61), 321 (74), 322 (74, 78), 323 (74), 325 (74, 78), 328 (78), 330 (78), *332*

Markees, S., 45 (66a), *73*

Markwood, L. N., 330 (92), *333*

Marshall, M. A., 181, 182 (82), 185 (82), *192*

Maruyama, S., 190 (290, 291), *198*

Matsuoka, T., 190 (288, 289), *198*

Matthissen, A., 170 (8), 183, *190*, *192*

Mayrhoffer, A., 184 (121), 186 (121), *193*

Meisner, N. J., 184 (119), *193*

Meissner, R., 189 (249), *196*

Menon, K. N., 32 (11), *72*

Mercier, F., 57 (88), *74*, 149 (9, 10), *164*, 183 (110), 190 (297, 298, 300, 307), *193*, *198*

Merck, E., 46 (71f), 57 (71f), *74*, 123, 129, *143*, *144*

Merck, F., 175, *191*

Merck, G., 30 (2), *71*

Merlis, V. M., 17, 20, *21*

Métin, M., 280 (18), *331*

Meyer, H., 228 (57), *245*

Meyer, T. M., 86 (142), *116*, 142 (108), *145*

Michaelis, Leonor, 276 (1), 298 (1), 299 (1), 308 (1), 311 (1), *330*

Midzuno, T., 19, *21*

Miller, E. R., 157 (38), 159 (38), *165*

Miller, G. H., 189 (262), *197*

Miller, M. R., 80 (32), 95 (32), 96 (32), 97 (32), *113*, 158 (43), 159 (43), *165*

Miller, W. von, 179 (77), *192*

Milliken, W., 35 (26), 43, *72*

Mirza, R., 176 (59), *192*

Mitter, P. C., 101 (237), *118*

Miwa, T., 223 (106), *246*

Möhrke, W., 189 (246), *196*

Mogilewa, A., 20 (48), *21*

Mohunta, L. M., 102, 104 (238), *118*

Molinelli, E. A., 190 (304), *198*

Moll, T., 183 (102), 190 (102), *192*

Mollett, C. E., 87 (166), *116*

Moore, D. K., 52 (80), *74*

Mori, N., 52 (78), *74*

Morio, S., 279 (27), 287 (27), 297 (41), 298 (41, 44, 45), 305 (60), 307 (60), *331*, *332*

Morson, J., 297 (42), *331*

Mosettig, E., 81 (58, 59), 93, 95, 96 (58, 59, 230), 97 (58), 98, 105, *114*, *118*, 154 (21), *165*

Moss, A. R., 1 (2), *6*

Mothnagel, Margarethe, 41, *73*

Motigase, S., 80 (38), 93 (38), 103, *114*, 133 (71), *144*, 158 (48), *165*

Müller, A., 32 (12), *72*

Müller, J., 3 (19), *6*, 136 (85), *144*

Müller, W., 186 (173), *194*

Mukherjee, B., 189 (243), *196*

Murai, F., 213 (126), 214 (126), 215 (126, 127, 132), 216 (127, 132), 217 (126, 127, 132, 133), 220 (133), 227 (134), *247*

Murakami, M., 216 (120), *247*
Murayama, Y., 86 (163), 87 (163, 174), 93 (163), 95 (163), *116*, *117*
Murphy, F. D., 45 (68), *73*
Murrill, P., 79 (14), *113*, 157 (37), 159 (37), *165*, 254 (10), 255 (10), *263*

N

Nakada, T., 12, 16, *21*
Nakagawa, K., 224 (131), *247*
Nakamura, T., 4 (22), *6*, 210 (135), *247*
Nakazato, T., 206 (85–87), *246*
Narita, Z., 204 (3, 8), 207 (3), 208 (5–8), 216 (120), *243*, *244*, *247*
Nath, B., 328 (90), 330 (90), *333*
Nathanael, W. R. N., 86 (157), *116*
Neppach, 85 (120), *115*
Neugebauer, H., 84 (193, 194), *117*, 186 (171), *194*
Neugebauer, N., 186 (191, 194), *195*
Neumann, F., 224, *245*
Neuweiler, W., 190 (286), *197*
Niccolini, Maria P., 189 (241), *196*
Niederhofheim, R., 307 (62), *332*
Niedfeld, H. A., 24 (60), 25, *28*
Nishihara, K., 12, 16, *21*
Noguchi, S., 328 (89), 330 (89), *333*
North, E. O., 87 (201), *117*, 187 (201), *195*
Nozaki, H., 137 (89), *144*
Nozoye, T., 223 (119), *247*

O

Oberembt, H., 204 (18), 213 (18), 215, 217 (18), *244*
Oberlin, M., 136, *144*
Offergeld, H., 190 (312), *198*
Ohashi, H., 128, *143*
Ohno, K., 321 (76), 322 (76), 323 (76), 325 (76), *332*
Ohta, T., 86 (141), *116*, 158 (73), *166*
Okami, T., 19, *21*
Olivier, M., 24 (62), 25 (62), *28*
Openshaw, H. T., 269, *273*
Oppensheim, P., 179 (73), *192*
Orekhov, A. P., 16, 17 (36), 18, *21*, 24 (56), *28*, 68 (110, 111), *75*, 83 (78, 82, 84), 84 (107–109), 85 (129), 93 (129), 95 (129), *114*, *115*, *116*, 120 (5), 130 (5), 141, *143*, *145*, 158 (68), 159 (68), *166*, 203, 204 (1, 2), *243*, 254 (15), 255 (15), *263*, 276 (3), 279 (3), 291 (3), 305 (3), 307 (3), 322 (3), 328 (3), *331*
Osada, S., 127, *143*
Ott, E., 183 (103), 190 (103), *192*

P

Packendorff, K., 183 (103), 190 (103), *192*
Palet, L. P. J., 228 (65), *245*
Paliatseas, P. G., 107 (261), *118*
Pallares, Sodi, E., 201, 211, *247*
Parabirsing, E. N., 86 (150), *116*
Paret, J., 57 (89), *74*
Parinaud, E., 184 (116), *193*
Paris, R., 266, *272*
Passl, J., 13, 14 (20), *20*, 24 (57), *28*
Paul, W., 184 (127), 186 (192), *193*, *195*
Pavesi, V., 83 (85, 86), *115*
Peachy, S. J., 34 (20), *72*
Pelletan, G., 84, 87 (177), *117*
Peplau, G., 261, *263*
Perkin, A. G., 85 (112), 87 (173), *115*, *117*
Perkin, W. H., Jr., 32 (13a, b), 33 (13a, b), 35 (13a, b), 40 (13b), 65 (105), 70 (13a), *72*, *73*, *75*, 83 (96), 84 (182), 87 (182, 204), 88, 89, 90, 91 (204, 215, 216, 217), 92 (221), 95 (221, 228), 98, 102, 106, *115*, *117*, *118*, 127 (33, 34), *143*, 149, 150 (14–16), 151, 154 (19), 156 (19), 157 (29, 30, 31), 158 (15, 16), 160, 161, 162 (15), *164–166*, 170 (6), 171 (16), 173 (28), 174 (44), 177 (65), 180 (79), 185 (80), *190*, *191*, *192*, 257 (30), *263*
Perrey, H., 42 (60), *73*
Perrins, J. D., 84 (167), 87 (167, 171), *116*, 186, *194*
Peschke, W., 35 (25), 41, 43, *72*
Petrie, J. M., 266 (7), *272*
Pfau, E., 184 (155), *194*
Pfohl, C. A., 45 (68), *73*
Pictet, A., 1, *6*, 7, *20*, 31 (6a), 35 (22a), 39 (50, 51a, b), 40 (22a), 51 (76), 55 (76), 56, 58 (22a), 60 (76), 63 (98a), 70 (114), *72*, *73*, *74*, *75*, 78 (2), 92, 98, 105 (249), *113*, *117*, 149, *164*
Pikl, J., 204 (15), 207 (15), 213 (15), 218 (15), *244*
Pillai, P. P., 86 (156), 87 (175), *116*, *117*
Pinder, A. R., 182 (85), 183 (85), 187 (85), 198, *192*, *195*
Pink, H. S., 157 (32), *165*

Piquet, J., 45 (66b), *73*
Plant, O. H., 189 (262), *197*
Platonova, T. F., 17, *21*
Plattner, P. A., 266, 270 (14), *272*
Plugge, P. C., 31 (3), 67, *71*, *75*, 184 (116), *193*
Polacci, G., 186 (170), *194*
Polex, 213 (10), *244*
Polgar, N., 38 (44), *73*, 85 (126), 93 (126), 95 (126), 107 (257), *116*, *118*
Pommerehne, H., 85 (113), *115*, 204 (13), 213 (13), 215 (13), *244*
Pope, W. J., 34 (20), *72*
Popovici, N., 189 (274), *197*
Portelance, V., 68 (111a), *75*
Posega, R., 103, *118*, 134, *144*
Power, F. B., 173, 186 (33), *191*, 266 (6), *272*
Prescott, A. B., 84 (167), *116*, 186 (193), *195*
Pringsheim, F., 58 (92), *74*
Probst, J. M., 120 (1), *143*, 254 (5), *262*
Proskurnina, N., 4 (21), *6*, 16, 17 (36), 20, *21*, 203, 204 (1, 2, 109), 209 (109), 210 (109), *243*, *246*
Pschorr, R., 36 (27a, b), 38 (27a, b), *72* 121, 122, 136, *143*, *144*, 182
Puckmer, W. A., 186 (195), *195*
Purfürst, C., 298 (46), *332*
Pyman, F. E., 204 (111), 218, 219, 221, 240, *247*
Pyman, F. L., 19, *21*, 34 (15–17, 21a), 36 (21a), 52 (80, 81a), 55 (17, 85), *72*, *74*, 84 (185), 87 (176), 91, 92, *117*, 151, 154, 155, 156 (18), 159, 160, *165*, *166*, 175 (53), 176 (60), 181, 182 (82), 185 (82), 186 (84), 187 (84), *191*, *192*

Q

Quevauviller, A., 48 (73a), *74*

R

Rabe, P., 83 (95), *115*, 179 (75, 76), 185 (75, 76), *192*
Rabinovich, M. S., 322 (80, 82), 325 (80), 326 (82), 328 (82), 330 (82), *332*
Rakshit, J. N., 83 (101), *115*, 170 (9), 183 (95), 184 (95, 148), *190*, *192*, *194*
Ramsay, D. A., 186 (177), *194*, 258 (34), *263*
Rankin, J., 92, 95 (221), *117*, 127 (33, 34), *143*
Raurich, F. E., 187 (205), *195*
Ravenna, C., 189 (276), *197*
Rây, J. N., 91, 102, 104 (238), *117*, *118*, 170 (10), *190*
Raymond-Hamet, M., 190 (297, 298, 302, 303), *198*, 261, *263*, 272 (35), *273*
Redemann, C. E., 159 (79), *166*
Reimers, F., 184 (144), *194*
Reitz, H. H., 14, *21*
Remfry, F. G. P., 19, *21*, 175 (53), 181 (84), 186 (84), 187 (84), *191*, *192*
Reti, L., 2 (11), *6*, 23, 24 (31, 34), 25, *26*, *27*
Reutter, L., 23, *27*
Reyes, F. R., 86 (144, 146), *116*, 130 (59), 142 (105), *144*, *145*
Reynolds, W. C., 34 (17), 55 (17), *72*, 186 (174), *194*
Rhode, 179 (77), *192*
Ri, T., 189 (251, 252, 268), 190 (251, 252), *196*, *197*
Rice, H. V., 190 (311), *198*
Richert, F., 85 (115), *115*
Richter, E., 84 (191), *117*
Riesenfeldt, Hermine, 41, *73*
Rigal, M., 266, *272*
Rigler, N. E., 85 (121), *115*, 215 (24), *244*, 261 (45, 46), *263*
Rikl, A., 189 (250), *196*
Ritchie, E., 224 (136), 227 (136), *247*
Robertson, Mary C., 174 (45), *191*
Robinson, G. M., 84 (186), *117*
Robinson, R., 2 (13), *6*, 35 (24), 37 (34, 35), 39, 40 (24), 52 (82), 53 (82), 54 (82), 70 (115), *72*, *73*, *74*, *75*, 83 (100), 84 (186), 89, 90, 91 (217), *115*, *117*, 157 (130), *165*, 169 (1), 170 (6), 171 (16), 174 (42, 44), 176 (42, 59), 180 (79), 181, 182 (82, 85), 183 (85, 86), 185 (80, 81, 82), 186 (84), 187 (84, 85,) *190*, *191*, *192*
Robiquet, M., 183, *192*
Roca, J., 25 (66), *28*
Rodionov, V. M., 19, *21*
Röder, H., 14, *20*, 24 (58), *28*
Rogers, E. F., 279 (14), 291 (14), 305 (14). *331*
Ronco, A., 268 (21), *273*
Rose, C. I., 217 (33), *244*

Rose, J. N., 15, 23, 24, 25, *27*
Rosendahl, H. V., 322 (83), 326 (83), *332*
Rosenkranz, J., 35 (22c), 58 (22c), *72*
Rosenmund, K. W., 41 (58), *73*
Rosenthaler, L., 87 (202, 203), *117*, 184 (145), *194*
Roser, W., 170 (5, 14), 171, 172, 174, 179 (70), *190*, 191, 192
Rothlin, E., 272 (35), *273*
Rüdel, C., 213 (12), 215 (12), *244*
Rumpf, F., 1 (6), *6*
Rupp, E., 186 (196), *195*
Ruzicka, L., 266, 267, 268 (20, 22), 269 (22), 270 (14, 25, 26), *272*, *273*
Rygh, A., 183 (106), 190 (106, 281), *193*, *197*
Rygh, O., 183 (105, 106), 190 (105, 106, 277–282), *193*, *197*

S

Safford, W. E., 23, *27*
Sakae, R., 86 (140), *116*, 128, *143*
Saksonov, P. P., 83 (83), *114*
Sakurai, S., 46 (71b), 57 (71b), *74*
Sakussov, V. V., 189 (269), *197*
Salomon, O., 173 (29), *191*
Salway, A. H., 172, *191*, 266 (6), *272*
Sanada, T., 205 (100, 102), 222 (99–102, 118), 223 (102, 118), *246*, *247*
Sandstede, G., 93, *118*
Santi, R., 272, *273*
Santos, A. C., 79 (11), 86 (134, 143, 144, 146, 152), 93 (134, 152), 95 (134, 152), *113*, *116*, 130 (59), 142 (105, 106), *144*, *145*, 157 (35), *165*, 204 (21), 205 (37, 38), 215, 220, *244*
Sargent, L. J., 86 (148), *116*, 132, 140, *144*
Sartoretto, P. A., 250 (3), *252*
Sas, F. E. R., 187 (202), *195*
Sato, H., 190 (306), *198*
Sato, Y., 318 (71), *332*
Satomi, M., 42 (61), *73*, 204 (23), 215 (23), 216 (23), *244*
Sawa, S., 223 (106), *246*
Saway, K., 108, *118*
Schales, O., 1 (7), *6*, 70, *75*
Schenck, G., 84 (111), *115*
Schilbach, C., 88, *117*
Schilhab, A., 186 (183), *195*
Schlemmer, F., 84 (111), *115*, 260 (40), *263*
Schlittler, E. 3 (19), *6*, 86 (147), *116*, 125, 126 (26), 127, 130 (60), 132, 136, 137 (92), 138 (92), 139, *143*, *144*, *145*, 266, 271 (13), *272*
Schlotterback, J. O., 79 (8, 14, 23), 102, *113*, *118*, 157 (37), 159 (37), *165*, 173 (37), 188, *191*, *196*, 253 (3), 254 (10), 255 (10), *262*, *263*
Schmid, L., 83 (90), *115*
Schmidt, E., 79 (18), 81 (57), 84 (110), 87 (169), 88, 91, *113–117*, 158 (72), *166*, 170 (13), 173 (35, 36), *191*, 253 (1), 254, 262 (11), *262*, *263*
Schneck, G., 260 (40), *263*
Schneider, W., 39 (49), *73*, 309 (64, 65), 311 (65), 316 (65), *332*
Schniderschitz, N., 183 (113), *193*
Schoeler, A., 136, *144*
Schoenheimer, R., 1 (2), *6*
Schöpf, C., 1 (9), *6*, 16, 18, *21*, 35, 36 (21b), 36 (21b, 30), 38 (30), 42 (60), 53 (30), 54 (84), 55 (30), 59 (84), 61 (84), 62 (84), 71, *72*, *73*, *74*, *75*
Scholtz, M., 184 (320), *198*, 205 (56), 227 (56, 59, 60, 62), 228 (56, 58), 229 (64), 230 (62), 231, *245*
Schoof, 184 (130), *193*
Schou, S. A., 186 (185, 186, 187), *195*
Schranzhofer, F., 32 (9), 34 (9), *72*
Schröder, H., 57 (91), *74*
Schröter, K., 39 (49), *73*
Schroff, v., 322 (83), 326 (83), *332*
Schulemann, W., 33 (14), *72*
Schultze, H., 85 (128), *116*, 213 (16), 218 (16), *244*
Schulze, H., 296 (35), 297 (39), 298 (39), 299 (39), 302 (39), 304 (58), 305 (58), 320 (73), 321 (73), 322 (73, 84), 323 (73), 325 (73), 326 (84), *331*, *332*
Schwarz, 256 (29), 257, 258, *263*
Schwarz, R., 200 (69), 203 (69), 227 (69), 229 (69), *245*
Scott, W. E., 268 (20), 270 (25, 26), *273*
Seel, H., 261, *263*
Seka, R., 60 (97), *75*
Selle, F., 79 (18), *113*, 158 (40), 159 (40), *165*, 253 (1), 254, *262*
Semonsky, M., 19, *21*
Sen, H. D., 184 (139), *193*
Sen, S. K., 64 (101), *75*, 85 (131), 86 (131), *116*
Seshacharyulu, E. V., 170 (12), *190*

Sharp, T. M., 296 (36), 303 (54), 307 (36, 54), 308 (36, 54), 309 (54), *331*, *332*
Shaw, G. L., 35 (26), 43, *72*
Shedden, F., 84 (183), *117*
Shimada, J., 190 (294), *198*
Shimanouti, F., 279 (5), 288 (5), 305 (5), *331*
Shinozaki, K., 86 (163), 87 (163), 93 (163), 95 (163), *116*
Shirai, H., 127 (31, 32), 129 (45–47), 130 (45), 141 (31, 32), *143*, *144*, 227 (121), *247*
Shishido, H., 128, 137 (91), *143*, *144*
Siddiqui, S., 87 (172), 112 (172), *116*
Siebeling, W., 175 (55), *191*
Sigmund, W., 189 (275), *197*
Silberg, F. D., 187 (206), *195*
Silberschmidt, R., 121 (10), 125, *143*
Simmer, A., 184 (117), *193*
Singh, H. D., 184 (139), *193*
Sisido, H., 137 (90), *144*
Slesser, A., 186 (180), *194*
Small, L. F., 31
Smiles, J., 83 (104), *115*, 149 (1), *164*
Smith, H., 83 (93), *115*, 184 (158), 185 (158), 186 (158), *194*
Smith, J. C., 83 (100), *115*
Smith, S., 190 (285), *197*
Smith, T., 83 (93), *115*, 184 (158), 185 (158), 186 (158), *194*
Snesarev, A. P., 184 (135), *193*
Sobel, P., 24 (59), *28*
Soine, T. O., 79 (10), *113*
Sonoda, J., 279 (6), 287, (6), 288 (6), 328 (89), 330 (89), *331*, *333*
Sorochinskaya, V. F., 184 (142), *193*
Sowa, F. J., 250 (3), *252*
Späth, E., 2 (10), *6*, 7 (2), 9, 10, 12, 13, 14 (13, 20), 15 (25), 17, 18, *20*, *21*, 23, 24, *26*, 34 (19), 35 (19), 36 (29), 37 (33, 42), 38 (44), 39 (53), 40 (19), 53 (29), 54 (33), 55 (29, 33, 86), 58 (86), 59 (96, 97), 60 (33), 61 (42), 62 (29, 33, 42), 70, *72*, *73*, *74*, *75*, 78 (1), 79 (21), 81 (58, 59), 83 (90), 84 (111), 85 (126, 127), 91 (56), 93 (126), 94 (225), 95 (126), 96 (58, 59, 230, 232), 97 (58), 98, 101, 102, 103 (56), 104 (247, 248), 105, 106 (250), 107 (257), 108 (247), 109, 110, 112 (227), *113*, *114*, *115*, *116*, *118*, 123 (19), 125, 126 (25), 131, 132, 134, *143*, *144*, 154 (21), *165*, 177 (66), *192*, 204 (14, 15), 205 (71), 207 (15), 213, 218 (15), 228 (72), 231, *244*, *245*, 257, 258, 260, 262 (39), *263*
Spengler, T., 7, *20*, 70 (114), *75*
Steiner, P., 184 (150, 151), *194*
Steiner-Bernier, M., 9, *20*, 26, *28*
Stenhauer, A. J., 187 (220), *196*
Stenhouse, J., 86 (151, 155), *116*
Sternberg, H., 83 (90), *115*
Stevens, T. S., 32 (13a), 33 (13a), 35 (13a), 70 (13a), *72*, 157 (31), *165*, 174 (40, 45), *191*
Stevenson, E. M., 45 (68), *73*
Stichel, A., 79 (19), 83 (19), *113*, 255 (19), 258, 259, 262 (25), *263*
Stieda, H., 261, *263*
Stippler, H., 106, *118*
Stoepel, P., 109, *118*
Stormont, M. F., 189 (248), *196*
Stoyle, F. W., 173 (28), *191*
Strache, H., 32 (9), 34 (9), *72*
Straub, W., 183 (96), *192*
Strauhal, F., 125, 126 (25), *143*
Strugatzki, M. K., 187 (206), *195*
Stuchlik, L., 32 (9), 34 (9), *72*
Sudzuki, H., 86 (161), 98, *116*
Sugasawa, S., 46 (71b–e), 52 (82), 53 (82), 54 (82), 57 (71b), *74*
Suginome, H., 279 (5, 6, 7, 33), 287 (6, 7, 28, 29), 288 (5, 6, 28), 292 (33), 297 (29, 41), 298 (41, 44), 301 (41), 303 (56), 305 (5, 29), 307 (41), 321 (76), 322 (76), 323 (76), 325 (28, 76), 328 (89), 330 (89), *331*, *332*, *333*
Sultan, F. W., 24 (65), *28*
Sumwalt, Margaret, 44, *73*
Suominen, E. E., 126, *143*
Swanezy, E. F., 45 (69), 47 (69), *74*

T

Takada, J., 87 (174), *117*
Takahashi, H., 216 (31), *244*
Takase, T., 128, *143*, 190 (306), *198*
Tamches, A., 45 (70), 46 (70), 47 (70), *74*
Tamura, K., 297 (49), 301 (49, 50), 302 (51), 303 (51), 304 (49, 50, 51), 307 (49), *332*
Tanaka, K., 205 (128), 222 (128, 129, 223 (128), *247*
Tanaka, Y., 19, *21*

Tani, C., 86 (154, 158), 93 (158), 95 (154, 158), *116*, 239, *247*
Tarbell, D. S., 34 (18), 41 (18), 55 (18), *72*
Tashijan, E., 45 (69), 47 (69), *74*
Taylor, E. P., 57 (90), *74*
Taylor, H. W., 45 (68), *74*
Tharrer, K., 123 (19), 126, *143*
Theissen, M., 256 (25), 259, 262 (25, 37), *263*
Thierfelder, K., 36 (30), 38 (30), 53 (30), 54 (84), 55 (30), 59 (84), 61 (84), 62 (84), *72*, *74*
Thimme, K., 187 (215), *196*
Thomas, F., 171 (16), *191*
Thoms, H., 175 (55), *191*
Tickle, T., 296 (38), 299 (38), *331*
Tietz, W., 84 (110), *115*, 158 (75), 160 (75), *166*, 254 (7), *262*
Tin, K., 189 (247), *196*
Tinkler, C. K., 90, *117*, 172 (19), 174 (41), *191*
Todd, A. R., 204 (108, 112), 205 (112), 206 (113), 217, 218 (108), 219, 221, 240, 241, 242, 243, *246*, *247*, 269, *273*
Tomaso, C., 9, *20*, 26, *28*
Tomita, M., 4 (22), *6*, 42 (61), *73*, 85 (116a, 117a, 123), 86 (135, 154, 158), 93 (123, 158), 95 (123, 154, 158), *115*, *116*, 127 (31), 129 (45, 46), 130 (45), 141 (31), *143*, *144*, 204 (22, 23, 41), 205 (40, 41, 55), 206 (88, 90, 107), 207 (96–98), 210 (110, 135), 214, 215 (22, 23), 216 (23, 127, 132), 217 (126, 127, 132, 133), 220 (133), 221 (41), 223 (45–47, 128), 227 (55, 121, 134), 235 (55, 107), 236, 238 (88, 90–92), 239, 242 (97, 98), *244*, *245*, *246*, *247*
Tondeur, R., 266, 269, 270 (24), *272*, *273*
Topchiev, K., 19, *21*, 170 (11), *190*
Topps, J. E. C., 280 (20), 281 (20), *331*
Torquati, T., 1 (3), *6*
Trabucchi, E., 272, *273*
Trendelenburg, P., 189 (263), *197*
Trier, G., 1 (5), *6*, 70, *75*
Trikojus, V. M., 177 (65), *192*
Trimurti, N., 142, *145*
Troeger, J., 84 (188), *117*
Tröthandl, O., 81 (58), 93 (58), 95, 96 (58), 97 (58), *114*
Troitskaya, N. A., 20 (62), *21*
Troller, A., 225 (50), *245*
Troshtzenko, A. T., 190 (293), *198*
Tsopelas, B., 45 (70), 46 (70), 47 (70), *74*
Tsuruta, S., 240 (89), *246*
Turner, R. B., *6*
Tweeden, M. E., 82 (75), *114*

U

Uhle, F. C., 272 (37), *273*
Uibrig, C., 175, *191*
Ulfert, F., 322 (84), 326 (84), *332*
Umezawa, S., 279 (6), 287 (6, 28), 288 (6, 28), 325 (28), *331*
Unger, H., 36 (28), 55 (28), *72*
Uyeo, S., 204 (8), 205 (55), 206 (107), 223 (106), 227 (55), 235 (55, 107), 236, *244*, *245*, *246*

V

Valenzuela, P., 86 (134), 93 (134), 95 (134), *116*
Vanag, G., 184 (125), *193*
van der Haar, A. W., 184 (131, 132), *193*
van Dorp, D. A., 37, *73*
van Duin, C. F., 83 (100), *115*
van Itallie, L., 187 (220), *196*
Varier, N. S., 86 (156), *116*
Vashistha, S. K., 87 (172), 112 (172), *116*
Verne, C., 123, *143*
Viehoever, A., 186 (184), *195*
Völker, O., 292 (32), 322 (32), *331*
Vongerichten, E., 135, 136, *144*
Vorozhtzov, N. N., 190 (293), *198*
Voss, A., 91 (218), *117*, 151 (17), *165*
Voynnet, R., 187 (217), *196*

W

Wackenroder, 103, *118*
Wagner, G., 138, 139 (93), *144*
Wagner, H., 81 (53), 108, *114*, 163, *166*
Wahl, H., 43, *72*
Waldo, J. H., 35 (26), 43, *72*
Wales, H., 186 (188), *195*
Walther, O., 41, *73*
Walz, T., 309 (67), *332*
Wangerin, A., 187 (223), *196*
Warnat, K., 121 (14, 15), 123, *143*
Wasicky, R. 84, (192), *117*, 186 (169), *194*
Wassmuth, H., 1 (8), *6*
Wastl, N., 20, *21*
Watkins, G. M., 85 (122), *115*

Watkins, H. C., 79 (8), 102, *113*, *118*, 173 (37), 188 (37), *191*, 253 (3), *262*
Wattiez, N., 187 (204), *195*
Wegscheider, H., 32 (9), 34 (9), *72*, 88
Weidemann, G., 322 (85), 326 (85), 327 (85), *332*
Weijlard, J., 45 (69), 47 (69), *74*
Weitnauer, G., 141, 142, *145*
Welch, A. D., 190 (310), *198*
Welti, H., 32 (12), *72*
Weltzien, W., 58 (92), *74*
Wertheim, T., 183, *192*
West, R., 231 (74, 78), 233 (74, 78), *245*
Wester, D. H., 184 (317), *198*
Whitmore, W. F., 184 (126), *193*
Wicke, H., 104, *118*
Wilhelm, F., 173 (35), 187 (212), *191*, *195*
Will, W., 87 (170), 88 (206), *116*, *117*, 173 (34), 174 (39), 175 (39), 186 (31), *191*
Willstaedt, H., 31 (7), *72*, 183 (111), *193*
Winchester, W. T., 271 (29, 30), *273*
Winterfeld, K., 79 (20), *113*, 255 (18), 256 (18, 23, 25), 259 (18), 261, 262 (18, 25), *263*
Winterstein, E., 1 (5), *6*
Wintersteiner, E., 70, *75*
Wintersteiner, O., 231, 232, 233 (81, 104), *246*
Wintgen, M., 254 (6), 260, 262 (38), *262*, *263*
Wisegarver, B. B., 159 (79), *166*
Wöhler, F., 169, *190*
Wolf, L., 187 (200), *195*
Wolfes, O., 46 (71g), 57 (71g), *74*
Wood, C. A., 184 (126), 184 (146), *193*, *194*
Wood, H. C., 189 (242), *196*
Woodward, R. B., *6*
Wotanabe, T., 222 (103), *246*
Wrann, S., 226 (53), *245*
Wrede, F., 83 (92), *115*, 185 (161), 187 (219), 190 (161), *194*, *196*

Y

Yamagata, M., 86 (135), *116*
Yamashita, Y., 205 (42), 223 (42), *245*
Yano, K., 204 (25, 26), 206 (83), 216 (25–28), 235, *244*, *246*
Yokoyama, H., 190 (305), *198*
Yoshikawa, H., 46 (71c), 57 (71c), *74*
Young, P. C., 35 (24), 40 (24), *72*
Yunosov, S., 68 (110, 111), *75*, 83 (78, 82), 84 (107–109), *114*, *115*, 120 (5), 130 (5), 141 (100, 102), *143*, *145*, 158 (68), 159 (68), *166*, 254 (15), 255 (15), *263*, 279 (9), 291 (9), 297 (9), 322 (87), 325 (87), 328 (93), *331*, *333*

Z

Zabrocky, R., 266, *272*
Zaĭtseva, O. A., 17, *21*
Zechmeister, L., 2 (11), *6*
Zeehuisen, H., 228 (66), *245*
Zerewitinoff, T., 63 (104), *75*
Ziegenbein, H., 81 (53), 108, *114*, 129, *144*, 162, 163, *166*
Zilva, S. S., 190 (285), *197*
Zitser, A. I., 32 (10), *72*
Zunz, E., 189 (272), *197*
Zweifel, B., 272, *273*
Zwerina, K., 225 (51), *245*
Zwikker, J. J. L., 187 (218), *196*

Subject Index*

*(Botanical names are printed in italics. Prefixes such as *nor-*, *iso-*, are printed in italics and disregarded for index purposes.)

A

Abuta candicans, 227
N-Acetylmescaline, 8
Aconine, 297, 300
Aconines, 276
Aconitine, 300
Aconitines, 292
Aconitinone, 302
Aconitoline, 302
Aconitum, spp., 275
Aconitum anthora, 279
Aconitum balfourii, 295, 307
Aconitum callianthum, 307
Aconitum chasmanthum, 295, 309
Aconitum deinorrhizum, 295, 307
Aconitum excelsum, 295, 297
Aconitum fauriei, 295, 297
Aconitum fischeri, 279, 287, 297, 305
Aconitum gigas, 322
Aconitum grossedantatum, 297, 305
Aconitum hakusanense, 297, 307
Aconitum heterophyllum, 279, 280, 284
Aconitum ibukiense, 295, 297, 305
Aconitum kamtschaticum, 279, 287, 297, 305
Aconitum lucidusculum, 279, 287, 328
Aconitum lycoctonum, 275, 320, 322
Aconitum majimai, 297
Aconitum manchurikum, 297
Aconitum miyabei, 279, 292
Aconitum mokchangense, 297
Aconitum napellus, 279, 295, 297
Aconitum sachalinense, 279, 297
Aconitum senanense, 305
Aconitum septentrionale, 275, 322, 326
Aconitum soongoricum, 279, 291
Aconitum spicatum, 295, 305
Aconitum subcuneatum, 295, 297
Aconitum talassicum, 275, 279, 291, 322, 326, 328
Aconitum tortuosum, 305
Aconitum yezoense, 279, 287, 295, 297
Aconitum zuccarini, 297
Actinodaphne hookeri, 127
Actinodaphne procera, 125
Actinodaphnine, 127
Adlumia cirrhosa, 79
Adlumia fungosa, 79, 157, 187, 188
Adlumidine, 168, 178, 188
Adlumine, 168, 176, 183, 188, 190
l-Adlumine, 100
Ajacine, 322
Ajacinine, 328
Ajacinoidine, 328
Ajaconine, 292, 293
Allocassaic acid, 267
Allocryptopine, 159
Anhalamine, 8, 10, 14
Anhalidine, 8, 10, 14
Anhalinine, 8, 10, 14
Anhalonidine, 8, 10, 13, 19
Anhalonine, 9, 12, 14, 19
Anhalonium fissuratum, 24
Anhalonium jourdanianum, 8
Anhalonium lewinii, 8, 24
Anhalonium williamsii, 8
Anhydroberberilic acid, 88
Anhydrocryptopine, 153, 257
Anolobine, 120, 139
Anomospermum grandifolium, 232
Anona muricata, 86, 142
Anona reticulata, 86, 142
Anona squamosa, 86, 142
Anonaine, 120, 142
Anthranilic acid, 325
Apocodeine, 120
Apomorphine, 120
Aporphine, 119
Archangelisia flava, 86, 93, 95
Argemone alba, 79
Argemone hispida, 79
Argemone mexicana, 79, 157
Ariocarpus fissuratus, 24
Ariocarpus retusus, 24
Armepavine, 68
Aromoline, 201, 211, 221

Artabotrinine, 120, 140
Artabotrys suaveolens, 86, 140
Asaronic acid, 250
Asimina triloba, 86, 139
Astrophytum myriostigma, 24
Atherosperma repandulum, 217
Atisine, 276, 280
Atisines, 277, 278
Aurotensine, 97
Aztequine, 203, 210

B

Bebeerine, 201, 212, 227
Bebirine, 227
Benzoylaconine, 297, 300
Benzoylheteratisine, 284
Benzoylmesaconine, 300
Benzylisoquinoline, 29
Berbamine, 201, 211, 213, 215
Berberal, 88
Berberilic acid, 88
Berberine, 78
  structure, 87
Berberis aetnensis, 85
Berberis aquifolium, 85, 213, 215
Berberis buxifolia, 85
Berberis darwinii, 85
Berberis fortunei, 85
Berberis heteropoda, 85, 95
Berberis insignis, 85
Berberis japonica, 85
Berberis laurina, 85, 186
Berberis nepalensis, 63, 64, 85, 111
Berberis nervosa, 85
Berberis swaseyi, 85, 215
Berberis thunbergii, 85, 93, 95, 213, 215
Berberis trifoliolata, 85
Berberis umbellata, 85, 111
Berberis vulgaris, 85, 93, 95, 213, 215
Bicucine, 178
Bicuculline, 168, 178, 182, 187, 190
Bikhaconine, 304
Bikhaconitine, 305
Bisbenzylisoquinoline, 199
Biscoclaurine, 199
Bocconia arborea, 79, 157, 159, 254, 256
Bocconia cordata, 79, 157, 159, 254, 255
Bocconia frutescens, 79, 157, 159
Bocconia pearcei, 79, 254
Boldea fragrans, 123
Boldine, 123
Bufo melanostictus, 125
Bulbocapnine, 132
Burane, 265
Buxus sempervirens, 227

Cactus alkaloids, 23
Canadine, 91
Capauridine, 100
Capaurimine, 102
Capaurine, 100
Capnoidine, 168, 178, 188
Carnegiea gigantea, 15, 24
Carnegine, 15, 20, 71
Casealutine, 96
Cassa, 265
Cassaic acid, 267, 270
Cassaidic acid, 269
Cassaidine, 266, 268
*nor*Cassaidine, 266
Cassaine, 266
Cassamic acid, 270
Cassamine, 269, 270
Cepharanthine, 201, 211, 223
Ceratocapnos spp., 157
Cereus pecten-aboriginum, 15, 24
Cereus peruvianus, 24
Challote, 8
Cheilanthifoline, 98
Chelerythrine, 254, 260
ψ-Chelerythrine, 255
Chelidonine, 5, 253, 257
Chelidonium majus, 79, 157, 159, 253, 254, 255, 256
Chondocurine, 201, 212, 233
Chondodendrine, 227
Chondodendron candicans, 227
Chondodendron microphyllum, 224, 227
Chondodendron platyphyllum, 224, 227, 230, 231
Chondodendron tomentosum, 224, 227, 231, 233
Chondrofoline, 201, 212, 230
Cinchomeronic acid, 172
Cissampelos insularis, 227
Cissampelos pareira, 227
Cocculus laurifolius, 65
Cocculus leaeba, 86, 93
Cocculus sarmentosus, 238, 242
Cocculus trilobus, 220, 238, 242
Coclaurine, 65

*nor*Coclaurine, 201
Codamine, 37, 53, 60, 61
Coelocline polycarpa, 86
Colchicine, 189
Columbamine, 95
Condelphine, 275, 322, 326
Consolidine, 328
Coptis japonica, 86, 95, 110
Coptis occidentalis, 87
Coptis orientalis, 86, 93
Coptis teeta, 87
Coptis trifolia, 87
Coptisine, 102
Coralydine, 39
*nor*Coralydine, 39, 94
Coralyn, 39
Cordrastine, 168, 178, 182
Coreximine, 112
Corlumidine, 168, 177, 189
Corlumine, 168, 176, 189, 190
Corpaverine, 4, 68
Corybulbine, 107
Corycavamine, 163
Corycavidine, 163
Corycavine, 162
Corydaldine, 104
Corydaline, 39, 103
Corydalis ambigua, 79, 93, 102, 103, 107, 158
Corydalis aurea, 8, 18, 68, 79, 93, 97, 100, 103, 158, 159, 178, 187
Corydalis bulbosa, 79, 133, 158
Corydalis caseana, 80, 93, 95, 96, 97, 158, 159, 187
Corydalis cava, 91, 95
Corydalis cheilantheifolia, 80, 91, 95, 98, 102, 158, 159
Corydalis claviculata, 80, 102, 158, 249, 252
Corydalis cornuta, 80, 102, 158
Corydalis crystallina, 80, 158, 187, 188
Corydalis decumbens, 80, 93, 103, 133, 158
Corydalis incisa, 158, 188
Corydalis lutea, 80, 93, 96, 102, 130, 158
Corydalis micrantha, 80, 93, 97, 100, 158
Corydalis montana, 80, 94, 97, 100, 102, 103, 158
Corydalis nobilis, 80, 94, 96, 102, 130, 149, 158, 187, 189
Corydalis ochotensis, 80, 97, 155, 158
Cordalis ochroleuca, 80, 94, 95, 96, 187
Corydalis ophiocarpa, 80, 91, 95, 99, 155, 158, 159, 189
Corydalis pallida, 8, 18, 81, 94, 100, 102, 158
Corydalis platycarpa, 81, 94, 96, 102, 103, 107, 130, 158, 187
Corydalis scouleri, 81, 97, 98, 149, 158, 159, 187, 188, 189
Corydalis sempervirens, 81, 149, 158, 187, 188, 189
Corydalis sibirica, 81, 97, 98, 149, 155, 158, 187, 189
Corydalis solida, 79
Corydalis ternata, 81, 91, 102, 120, 129, 130, 158
Corydalis thalictrifolia, 81, 95, 102, 108, 158, 188
Corydalis tuberosa, 8, 18, 81, 93, 97, 102, 103, 107, 108, 120, 129, 130, 132, 158, 162, 163
Corydalis vernyi, 103
Corydine, 129
Corypalline, 18
Corypalmine, 95
Corytuberine, 130
Coscinium blumeanum, 86, 93, 95
Coscinium fenestratum, 86
Cotarnic acid, 170
Cotarnine, 169, 170
Cotarnonitrile, 179
Coumingaine, 266
Coumingic acid, 270
Coumingidine, 266, 270
Coumingine, 266, 270
Crebanine, 129
Cryptocavine, 5, 155
Cryptopalmatine, 161
Cryptopine, 149, 150, 257
*iso*Cryptopine, 153
Cularidine, 252
Cularimine, 251
Cularine, 3, 249
Curine, 201, 212, 230
Cycleanine, 141, 227
Cynometra densiflora, 265
Cysticapnos vesicarius, 158

D

Dactylicapnos macrocapnos, 81, 102, 158, 159
Daphnandra aromatica, 221

Daphnandra micrantha, 218, 221, 240
Daphnandra repandula, 217
Daphnandrine, 201, 218, 240, 242
Daphnoline, 201, 218, 220, 240, 242
Dauricine, 201, 203, 207
Dauricine dimethiodide, 209
Dehydrocorydaline, 39
Delartine, 322, 325
Delatine, 292, 293
Delbine, 328
Delcosine, 328
Delphamine, 328
Delphatine, 328
Delpheline, 328
Delphinine, 309
Delphinium spp., 275
Delphinium ajacis, 279, 292, 322, 328
Delphinium barbeyi, 322
Delphinium biternatum, 328
Delphinium brownii, 322
Delphinium confusum, 275, 322, 326
Delphinium consolida, 322, 328
Delphinium elatum, 279, 292, 322, 328
Delphinium occidentale, 328
Delphinium oreophilum, 322
Delphinium semibarbatum, 322
Delphinium staphisagria, 279, 289, 295, 309, 328
Delphonine, 309
Delsemine, 322
Delsoline, 328
Delsonine, 328
Deltaline, 328
Dendromecon rigidum, 81
Dicentra canadensis, 82, 129, 130, 133, 158
Dicentra chrysantha, 82, 149, 155, 158, 187
Dicentra cucullaria, 82, 149, 158, 159, 161, 187, 189, 249, 252
Dicentra eximia, 82, 112, 120, 122, 127, 129, 158, 249, 251
Dicentra formosa, 82, 120, 122, 126, 129, 158, 249
Dicentra ochroleuca, 82, 149, 158, 187
Dicentra oregana, 82, 95, 120, 122, 127, 129, 158, 159, 249
Dicentra pusilla, 82, 126, 158
Dicentra spectabilis, 82, 148, 157, 158, 256
Dicentrine, 126
Dicranostigma franchetianum, 82, 102, 158, 253
Dicranostigma lactucoides, 82, 130, 158
Didehydrohydrastine, 181
Dihydroanhydroberberine, 176
Dihydroatisine, 281
Dihydroberberine, 90
Dihydrocassaidine, 269
Dihydromenisarine, 242
Dihydropapaverine, 35
3,4-Dihydroxyphenacetaldehyde, 1
3,4-Dihydroxyphenethylamine, 1
3,4-Dihydroxyphenylalanine, 1
Dimethylaminoethanol, 267, 270
1,7-Dimethylphenanthrene, 286
Dioxyberberine, 88
Dolichotele uberiformis, 24
Domesticine, 128

E

Echinocactus visnaga, 24
Echinocereus mamillosus, 24
Echinopsis eyriesii, 25
d-ψ-Ephedrine, 141
l-Ephedrine, 141
Epiphyllum ackermannii, 24
Epistephanine, 201, 211, 222
ψ-Epistephanine, 223
Erythrophlamic acid, 270
Erythrophlamine, 269
Erythrophleic acid, 269
Erythrophleine, 269
Erythrophleum, 265
pharmacology, 271
Erythrophleum chlorostachys, 266
Erythrophleum couminga, 265
Erythrophleum fordii, 265
Erythrophleum guineense, 265
Erythrophleum laboucherii, 266
Eschscholtzia californica, 82, 158, 159, 254, 256
6-Ethyl-1-methylphenanthrene, 282
Eupaverine, 46
Evodia meliaefolia, 87

F

Fagara coco, 148
α-Fagarine, 159
Fangchinoline, 201, 211, 219
Fibraurea chloroleuca, 86, 95
Fibraurea tinctoria, 86, 93, 95
Fumaria capreolata, 158
Fumaria officinalis, 82, 97, 98, 102, 155, 158

G

Glaucentrine, 122
Glaucine, 120
Glaucium corniculatum, 158
Glaucium fimbrilligerum, 83, 120, 130, 158, 159, 254, 255
Glaucium flavum, 83, 97, 120, 130, 158, 254
Glaucium luteum, 120
Glaucium serpieri, 83, 97, 120, 130, 158
Gnoscopine, 168, 180
α-Gnoscopine, 181, 184
β-Gnoscopine, 181, 185
Glymnocalycium gibbosum, 25
Gymnocalycium multiflorum, 25

H

Hang-fang-chi, 216, 219
Hemipinic acid, 172, 179
m-Hemipinic acid, 33
Heteratisine, 284
Hetisine, 284, 286
Homochelidonine, 254
Homophleine, 266
Hunnemanine, 160
Hunnemannia fumariaefolia, 83, 158, 160
Hydrastal, 175
Hydrastic acid, 174, 256
Hydrastine, 168, 173, 181, 185, 190
dl-α-Hydrastine, 186
dl-β-Hydrastine, 187
dl-Hydrastine-a, 181
dl-Hydrastine-b, 181
Hydrastinine, 173
Hydrastis canadensis, 87, 91, 173, 185, 186
Hydrocotarnine, 18, 169, 180
Hydrohydrastinine, 18, 174
β-Hydroxyisovaleric acid, 270
Hydroxylaudanosine, 52
Hydroxynarcotine, 169
Hypaconine, 304
Hypecoum leptocarpum, 158
Hypocoum procumbens, 158
Hypoepistephanine, 201, 211, 223

I

Illigera pulchra, 125
Indaconitine, 309
Insularine, 201, 212, 235
Insularinic acid, 235
Isoatisine, 281, 282
Isobebeerine, 224
Isochondodendrine, 201, 211, 224
Isocorybulbine, 108
Isocorydine, 130
Isocorypalmine, 95
Isoquinolines, biosynthesis, 1
Isotalatisidine, 275, 322, 326
Isotetrandrine, 201, 211, 215
Isothebaine, 3, 120, 135
Isotrilobine, 201, 237, 238

J

Jateorhiza columba, 86, 95
Jateorhiza palmata, 86, 92, 95
Jatrorrhizine, 95
Jesaconitine, 297, 298, 300

K

Kobusine, 276, 287
Koshiu-wyaku, 65

L

Lappaconine, 322, 326
Lappaconitine, 322, 326
Laudanidine, 59
Laudanine, 53, 57, 58
Laudanosine, 37, 48, 51, 55, 56, 60
*nor*Laudanosine, 1
Laudanosoline, 53
Laurelia novae-zelandae, 134, 137
Laureline, 2, 120, 137
Laurepukine, 3, 134
Laurotetanine, 125
Litsea chrysocoma, 125
Litsea citrata, 125, 126
Litsea cubeba, 125
Lodal, 176
Lophocereus schottii, 25
Lophophora williamsii, 8, 24
Lophophorine, 9, 12, 14, 19
Lucaconine, 328
Luciculine, 287
Lucidusculine, 287
Luteanine, 130
Lycaconitine, 322
Lycoctonine, 275, 320, 322

M

Magnolamic acid, 209
Magnolamine, 4, 201, 203, 209
Magnolia fuscata, 203, 209

Magnoline, 201, 203
Mahonia acanthifolia, 64, 85
Mahonia aquifolium, 85
Mahonia borealis, 64, 85
Mahonia fortunei, 85
Mahonia griffithii, 64, 85
Mahonia japonica, 85
Mahonia leschenaultii, 64, 85
Mahonia manipurensis, 64, 86
Mahonia napalensis, 85
Mahonia philippinensis, 86, 93, 95
Mahonia sikkimensis, 64, 86
Mahonia simonsii, 63, 64, 86
Mahonia swaseyi, 85, 215
Mahonia trifoliolata, 85
Mancone, 265
Meconin, 169, 173
Menisarine, 201, 237, 242
Menispermum acutum, 136
Menispermum canadense, 207
Menispermum dauricum, 207, 216
Mesaconine, 297, 300
Mesaconitine, 297, 300
Mescaline, 7, 8
p-Methoxybenzoylaconine, 300
Methoxychelidonine, 255
4-Methoxyphthalic acid, 250
Methylaminoethanol, 269
N-Methylanhalonidine, 10
O-Methyl-*d*-anhalonidine, 8, 12
N-Methyl-*l*-anhalonine, 12
Methylenepapaverine, 38
Methylisochondodendrine, 201, 212, 227
N-Methyllaurotetanine, 126
N-Methylmescaline, 8
l-Methylphenanthrene, 282
Michelia fuscata, 209
Micranthine, 201, 218, 237, 240, 242
Miyaconine, 294
Miyaconinone, 294
Miyaconitine, 292, 294
Miyaconitinone, 292, 294
Morphine, 190
Morphothebaine, 120
Mu-fang-chi, 216
Muricine, 142
Muricinine, 142

N

Nandina domestica, 86, 109, 128, 148, 158
Nandinine, 109
Nantenine, 128
Napelline, 291, 293
α-Naphthaphenanthridine, 253, 258
Narceine, 169, 179
*nor*Narceine, 169, 179
*pseudo*Narceine, 179
Narcotine, 168, 169, 180, 189
*iso*Narcotine, 180
l-α-Narcotine, 183
Narcotoline, 168, 173, 185, 190
Ncassa, 265
Nectandra, 227
Neocotarnine, 172
Neoline, 304
Neomamillaria magnimamma, 24
Neoprotocuridine, 201, 212, 234
Neprotine, 63, 111
Normenisarine, 201, 237, 242

O

Ophiocarpine, 5, 99, 156, 176
Opianic acid, 169, 172, 180
Opuntia vulgaris, 24
Oxodelphinine, 316
Oxoisoatisine, 282
Oxonitine, 297
Oxyacanthine, 201, 211, 213
Oxyberberine, 88, 90
Oxyhydrastinine, 174
Oxynarcotine, 179
Oxysanguinarine, 260

P

Pachycereus marginatus, 25
Pachycereus pecten-aboriginum, 24
Palmatine, 92
Palmatrubine, 97
Papaver armeniacum, 68, 83
Papaver bracteatum, 83
Papaver caucasicum, 68, 83
Papaver dubium, 83
Papaver fluoribundum, 68, 83
Papaver hybridum, 83
Papaver orientale, 83, 135, 158
Papaver rhoeas, 83
Papaver somniferum, 8, 83, 148, 183
Papaveraldine, 33, 40
Papaverine, 30, 44
  synthesis, 39
Papaverinic acid, 33
Papaverinium salts, 36

Papaverinol, 33
Paracyclea insularis, 235
Pavine, 34
Pellote, 8
Pellotine, 8, 10, 13, 14, 19
Petrocapnos spp., 158
Peumus boldus, 123
Peyote, 8
Peyotl, 8
Phanostenine, 129
Pheanthine, 201, 211, 220
Pheanthus ebracteolatus, 220
Phellodendron amurense, 87, 93
β-Phenylnaphthalene, 5
Phthalideisoquinoline, 167, 168
Phymatotrichum omnivorum, 261
Picraconitine, 297
Pilocereine, 25
Platycapnos spp., 158
Platycapnos spicatus, 158
Pleogyne cunninghamii, 224, 227
Pneumus, 123
Protoberberine, 77, 78
Protocuridine, 201, 212, 234
Protopapaverine, 37
Protopine, 5, 147, 148, 157
Pseudaconine, 304, 307
Pseudaconitine, 307
α-Pseudaconitine, 307
Pesudocodamine, 53, 62, 63
Pseudokobusine, 287
Pseudolaudanine, 53, 62
Pteridophyllum racemosum, 83, 158, 160
Pukateine, 2, 120, 138
Pyraconitine, 296
Pyridine-2,3,4-tricarboxylic acid, 33
Pyro-α-oxodelphinine, 317
Pyropseudaconine, 307
Pyropseudaconitine, 296

R

Radix pareira bravae, 224, 227
Repandine, 201, 211, 217
Rhipsalis teres, 24
Roemeria refracta, 84, 141
Roemerine, 120, 141

S

Salsamine, 16
Salsola arbuscula, 8, 16
Salsola richteri, 8, 16
Salsolidine, 16
Salsoline, 16, 20, 71
Sanguinaria canadensis, 84, 158, 160, 254, 255
Sanguinarine, 255, 261
Sarcocapnos spp., 158
Sassy, 265
Schlummbergera russeliana, 24
Scoulerine, 97
Selenicereus grandiflorus, 24
Septentrionaline, 322, 326
Shobakunine, 93
Sinactine, 98
dl-Sinactine, 154
Sinomenium acutum, 86, 98, 136
Songorine, 291, 293
Staphisine, 276, 289, 293
Stephania capitata, 127, 129, 141, 227
Stephania cepharantha, 215, 223, 227
Stephania japonica, 222, 223
Stephania sasakii, 129, 223
Stephania tetrandra, 216
Stephanine, 141
Stetsonia coryne, 24
Strychnine, 190
Stylophorum diphyllum, 84, 102, 158, 253, 256
Stylopine, 102
Suaveoline, 132
Sychnosepalum microphyllum, 224

T

Talatisamine, 328
Talatisidine, 328
Talatisine, 291, 291
Talauma, 210
Teli, 265
Tetrahydroberberine, 91
Tetrahydro-ψ-berberine, 95
Tetrahydroisoquinolines, 7
Tetrahydropalmatine, 93
Tetrahydropapaverine, 34
Tetrandrine, 201, 211, 216
Tetranthera citrata, 125
Thalictricavine, 108
Thalictrifoline, 108
Thalictrine, 112
Thalictrum foliolosum, 87, 112
Tinospora bakis, 86, 93
Toddalia aculeata, 87
Trichocereus candicans, 24

Trichocereus huascha, 25
Trichocereus lamprochlorus, 24
Trichocereus spachianus, 24
Trichocereus terscheckii, 24
Trichocereus thelegonoides, 25
Trichocereus thelegonus, 25
Trilobamine, 220
Trilobine, 201, 237, 238
1,2,8-Trimethylphenanthrene, 268, 269, 271
Tritopine, 59
Tropic acid, 5
Tubocurarine, 201, 212, 231
d-Tubocurarine, 66
Tuduranine, 120, 136

U

Umbellatine, 111
Unona discreta, 86

V

Veratric acid, 33

W

Worenine, 110

X

Xylopia discreta, 86
Xylopia polycarpa, 86

Z

Zanthoxylum brachyacanthum, 87, 148, 159
Zanthoxylum caribaeum, 87
Zanthoxylum clava-herculis, 87
Zanthoxylum coco, 148, 159
Zanthoxylum ochroxylum, 87